THE INTEL MICROPROCESSORS

8086/8088, 80186, 80286, 80386, and 80486 Architecture, Programming, and Interfacing

THE INTEL MICROPROCESSORS

8086/8088, 80186, 80286, 80386, and 80486 Architecture, Programming, and Interfacing

BARRY B. BREY
DeVry Institute of Technology

Merrill, an imprint of
Macmillan Publishing Company
New York

Collier Macmillan Canada, Inc.
Toronto

Maxwell Macmillan International Publishing Group
New York   Oxford   Singapore   Sydney

Macmillan Publishing Company
866 Third Avenue, New York, New York 10022

Collier Macmillan Canada, Inc.

Library of Congress Cataloging-in-Publication Data

Brey, Barry B.
   The Intel microprocessors: 8086/8088, 80186, 80286, 80386, and 80486: architecture,
   programming, and interfacing/Barry B. Brey. — 2nd ed.
   p.   cm.
   Includes index.
   1. Intel 8086 (Microprocessor)   2. Intel 8088 (Microprocessor)
   3. Intel 80xxx series microprocessors.   I. Title.
   QA76.8.1292B75 1991   90-20498
   004.165 — dc20   CIP
ISBN 0-675-21309-6   (Hardcover Edition)
ISBN 0-02-946322-X   (International Edition)

IE Printing: 1 2 3 4 5   Year: 1 2 3 4 5

ISBN 0-02-946322-X

This text is dedicated to my loving wife, Sheila,
whose patience and understanding have made this endeavor possible.

PREFACE

This second edition of a best-selling text book on the 8086/8088 and 80186/80188 microprocessors has been enhanced to incorporate the 80286, 80386, and 80486 microprocessors. In this rapidly evolving field, it is difficult to keep the text material relevant. I thank all of you who remained loyal to this text until this update. As with the first edition, this text is designed to be used in conjunction with a curriculum in engineering, computer science, and both computer and engineering technology. This edition is applicable as a reference text to those in the field who wish to update their expertise in microprocessors. The nonprofessional who is interested in the microprocessor and who owns a personal computer will also find it useful.

This edition begins with an overview of the 8086/8088 microprocessor family and coverage of the instruction set along with its diverse addressing modes. The 8086/8088 instructions set and hardware principles are upward compatible to the 80186/80188, 80286, 80386, and 80486 microprocessors.

The first five chapters of this text deal with the complexities of the instruction set and include illustrative examples of how to use the instructions along with several fairly complicated programs that illustrate the use of the assembler program and the DOS. A new Appendix is added that thoroughly covers the DOS function 21H, with example software, up through version 4.01 of DOS. It also contains additional information on other functions that are used to control the video display in a PC-type computer and on its memory allocations. The Appendix that covers each instruction is expanded to include the 80286, 80386, and 80486 microprocessors. A new Appendix illustrates which instructions change the flag bits and which flag bits change.

Chapters 6 through 10 deal with the architecture of the 8086/8088 microprocessors and also with applications of the hardware and software. Chapter 6 details the pinout of the 8086 and 8088 microprocessors and describes each pin connection. It illustrates the timing for these microprocessors and ancillary components required to buffer and operate them in a computer system. Chapter 7 continues with a discussion of memory interface using read-only memory, SRAM, and DRAM. Memory interfacing fixates on decoding. Chapter 8 fosters an understanding of I/O interface through the use of many examples of both the interface components and their applications. Chapter 9 extends I/O interface with a complete discussion of interrupt processed I/O including the interrupt structure of the microprocessor with both software and hardware examples. Chapter 10 explains Direct Memory Access (DMA) using a DMA controller and also using bus arbitration. Bus arbitration allows many microprocessors to coexist in the same system sharing memory and I/O while each retaining individual memory and I/O.

Chapter 11 describes the interface and operation of the Numeric Coprocessor (8087, 80287, and 80387). These coprocessors are essential to hundreds of software applications found in computer systems as diverse as CAD programs and spread sheet programs. The numeric coprocessor is also an integrated module in the 80486 microprocessor which means that software will become more reliant on this device. The numeric coprocessor's instruction set is covered along with its internal architecture. Several application programs are illustrated so that software can be developed and understood for this machine.

Chapters 12 and 13 acquaint the reader with the software and hardware changes of the 80186/80188, 80286, 80386, and 80486 microprocessors in contrast with the 8086/8088 microprocessor. The 80186/80188 microprocessor is a popular device in many control systems because of its high level of hardware integration and because of its software compatibility with the 8086/8088. This microprocessor finds applications in many control systems and also as a PC-type computer system and daughter boards such as LAN controllers. The 80286 microprocessor is popular in the AT type 80286 based computer system. Although this system is being replaced by the 80386SX and also the 80386 and 80486 microprocessor, it still finds widespread application. Most recently the powerful 80386 and its newer 80486 version have been appearing in a multitude of applications. These new machines extend the amount of memory available in a system and increase the flexibility of the software system with various additional addressing modes, registers, and also support features such as paging and protected mode operation. This text presents these updated microprocessors in a clear and concise manner so that they can be used as software and hardware engines as needed by the designer.

I am grateful to the following reviewers for their helpful suggestions for making this second edition as useful as possible for students and teachers alike: Gerald Cockrell (Indiana State University), Eric Jacobson (South Dakota School of Mines), Mike Chalupka (Texas State Tech Institute), Joseph Takacs (University of Akron), Ronald Ciminero (University of Cincinnati), Brad Howarth (Conestoge College), Jack Clark (El Camino College), Scott Moser (Capitol Tech), Ron Richolson (Kansas Tech) and Wayne Blinka (Texas State Tech Institute).

CONTENTS

12   THE 80186/80188 AND 80286 MICROPROCESSORS

377

13   THE 80386 AND 80486 MICROPROCESSORS

425

APPENDIXES

487

INDEX

632

THE INTEL MICROPROCESSORS

8086/8088, 80186, 80286, 80386, and 80486
Architecture, Programming, and Interfacing

CHAPTER 1

Introduction to the 8086/8088 Microprocessor

INTRODUCTION

The purpose of this chapter is to introduce the Intel 8086 and 8088 microprocessors. In it, we explain how the 16-bit microprocessors evolved from the early 4-bit and more recent 8-bit microprocessors, investigate the architecture of the basic 8086 and 8088 microprocessor, discuss the memory structures of the 8086 and 8088, and clarify the instruction set and data formats. We will treat the hardware and interfacing of the 8086 and 8088 somewhat differently, but their software is in all respects identical.

OBJECTIVES

Upon completion of this chapter, you will be able to:

1. Explain how the 8-bit microprocessor evolved into the 16-bit microprocessor.
2. Describe the operation of the execution unit (EU) and the bus interface unit (BIU) of the 8086 and the 8088 microprocessors.
3. Explain how the memory and internal register array are structured.
4. Define the terms **memory segment** and **offset address**.
5. Calculate the effective address for the next program step using the contents of the instruction pointer (IP) and code segment (CS) registers.
6. Show how data are stored in the memory for the following integer and unsigned data types: byte, word, and long word.
7. Provide an overview of the 8086/8088 instruction set.

1

1−1   THE EVOLUTION OF THE 16-BIT MICROPROCESSOR

Before we discuss the evolution of the 16-bit microprocessor, we must first understand what brought the 4- and 8-bit microprocessors onto the market. Let us take this opportunity, then, for a brief historical survey.

The 4-Bit Microprocessor

In 1971, Intel Corporation released the world's first microprocessor—the infamous *4004*, a 4-bit microprocessor. This integrated, programmable controller on a chip was meager by today's standards, addressing a mere 4096 4-bit memory locations. In addition, its instruction set contained only 45 different instructions. As a result, the 4004 could be used only in very limited applications such as early video games and small microprocessor-based controllers. When more sophisticated applications were required, the 4004 proved inadequate.

The 8-Bit Microprocessor

Later in 1971, realizing that the microprocessor was a commercially viable product, Intel Corporation released the *8008*—an 8-bit microprocessor. The expanded memory size (16K × 8) and the additional instructions (a total of 48) available in this new microprocessor provided the opportunity for many more advanced applications.

As engineers began developing more and more demanding uses for the microprocessor, however, the still relatively small memory and instruction set of the 8008 soon began to limit its usefulness. Thus, in 1973, Intel Corporation introduced the *8080*—the first of the modern 8-bit microprocessors. Soon other companies began releasing their own versions of the 4- and 8-bit microprocessors. The explosion had begun.

But what was special about the 8080? Not only could it address more memory and execute more instructions, but it executed instructions ten times faster than the 8008. An addition that took 20 μs on an 8008-based system took only 2.0 μs on an 8080-based system. Also, the 8080 was transistor–transistor logic (TTL) compatible. All these advantages ushered in the era of the 8080, and the era of the microprocessor.

A newer version of the 8080, the *8085*, was introduced by Intel Corporation in 1977. Only slightly more advanced than the 8080, the 8085 addresses the same amount of memory, executes about the same number of instructions, and adds in 1.3 μs instead of 2.0 μs. The main advantage of the 8085 is its built-in clock generator and system controller, which were external components in the 8080-based system.

The 16-Bit Microprocessor

In 1978, Intel Corporation released the *8086* microprocessor and a year later the *8088*. Both devices are 16-bit microprocessors that execute instructions in as little as 400 ns, a vast improvement over the execution speed of the 8085. In addition, the 8086 and 8088 are capable of addressing an astounding 1M byte or 512 K words (16 bits) of memory. These execution speeds and memory sizes allow the 8086 and 8088 to replace smaller minicomputers in many applications which limited memory and word size.

One important need that spurred the evolution of the 16-bit microprocessor was in the area of *hardware multiplication and division*. These functions are not available on most of the 8-bit microprocessors, with the exception of the Motorola MC6809, which can multiply, but not divide. But the 16-bit microprocessor evolved for other reasons, as well. It provides larger *addressable memory space* than the 8-bit microprocessors had, thus allowing some very sophisticated operating systems that just didn't fit into 64K bytes of memory. The 8086 and 8088 also have a large number of *internal registers*, which are accessible in 200 ns as opposed to the 800 ns it takes to reach a register on an 8-bit microprocessor. These registers thus allow software to be written far more efficiently. Finally, *software applications programs* (spreadsheets, word processors, and spelling checkers) began to require more than the 64K bytes of memory available on the 8-bit microprocessor. The time was ripe for the 16-bit microprocessor.

1-2   BASIC 8086 AND 8088 ARCHITECTURE

Efficient programming and interfacing depend upon a clear understanding of the basic architecture of the 8086 and 8088 microprocessors and microprocessor-based systems. This section provides a detailed description of the basic architecture of these microprocessors.

Basic Internal Architecture

Like the early microprocessors, the 8086 and 8088 fetch their instructions from the memory, but they do it in an entirely new way because their internal structure is distinctly different.

Figure 1-1(a) illustrates the normal operation of an 8085, which is typical of most 8-bit microprocessors. Notice that the instruction is fetched from the memory by a memory-read operation. Next, while the 8085 executes the instruction, the memory system is idle. The 8086 and 8088 make use of this idle memory time by prefetching the next instruction while executing the current one.

Figure 1-1(b) illustrates the sequence of events for the 8086 and 8088 microprocessor. Notice that the bus is almost always busy. (There are times when the bus is idle, but not often.) Notice also that the 8086 and 8088 contain two internal units, the *execution unit* (EU) and the *bus interface unit* (BIU). The BIU is responsible for fetching an instruction, the operand of an instruction or data from the memory, and the EU is responsible for executing the instructions. The 8086 and 8088 are able to utilize the bus with maximum efficiency because both contain internal memory in the form of a *queue* or *FIFO* (first-in, first-out) memory.

Figure 1-2 illustrates the EU and the BIU, in which the queue is located. The 8086 queue is 2 bytes wide and three locations deep. It is therefore able to hold three 16-bit numbers. The 8088 has a byte-wide queue that is 4 bytes deep. These queues allow the 8086/8088* to fetch instructions while the EU is busy executing them. This allows the 8086/8088 to use the memory system more effectively.

---

*From this point forward, whenever the 8086 and 8088 are listed as 8086/8088, the discussion addresses both microprocessors.

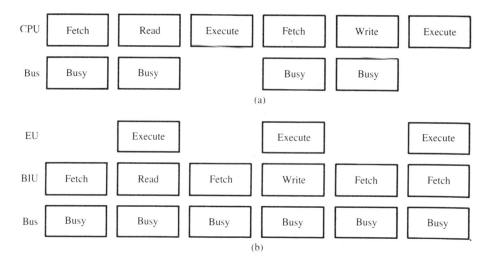

FIGURE 1–1 Bus timing. (a) The 8085A CPU and its bus timing, which indicates the activity level of the 8085A bus. (b) The 8086/8088 and its EU, BIU, and bus timing, which indicates the activity level of the 8086/8088 bus.

Bus Interface Unit (BIU).   The BIU contains a *prefetch queue*, a *bus controller*, *segment registers*, and the *instruction pointer* (IP). The main purposes of the BIU are to keep the prefetch queue filled with instructions, to generate and accept the system control signals, to provide the system with a memory address or input/output (I/O) port number, and to act as a window between the EU and memory for data. We explain the control signals in complete detail in Chapter 6 and the method used to form memory addresses in Section 1–3.

The BIU ensures that the queue is filled with instructions by fetching the next single byte of an instruction if the 8088 queue has space, and *two* bytes if the 8086 queue has space. Prefetching allows the execution unit to obtain the next instruction directly from the BIU instead of the memory as required by older, 8-bit microprocessors. Because the next instruction is already inside of the 8086/8088 when execution is imminent, the microprocessor executes software at a much higher speed than if every instruction were fetched directly from the memory.

Execution Unit (EU).   The purpose of the EU is to carry out instructions that are fetched from the prefetch queue. The execution unit contains an *arithmetic and logic unit* (ALU), an *instruction register*, and a *register array*. The ALU performs arithmetic and logic operations on memory or register data. The instruction register receives the instructions from the prefetch queue, at which time they are decoded to direct the operation of the execution unit. The register array, a scratchpad memory, holds information temporarily. It also contains pointers or index registers used to address operand data located in the memory. Operand data are also addressed and transferred through the BIU.

System Architecture

Figure 1–3 illustrates the system architectures of both the 8086 and 8088 microprocessors. In both cases, communication to the system occurs through three buses: *address*,

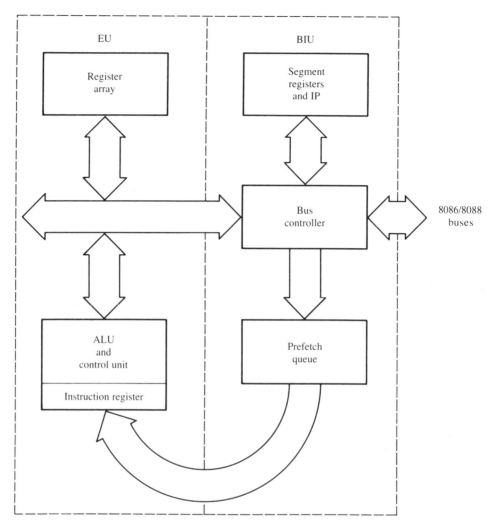

FIGURE 1–2 The Internal structure of the 8086/8088 microprocessor illustrating the EU (execution unit) and the BIU (bus interface unit).

data, and *control*. The address bus provides a memory address to the system memory and also I/O addresses to the system I/O devices. The data bus transfers data between the microprocessor and the memory and I/O attached to the system. The control bus provides control signals that cause the memory or I/O to perform a read ($\overline{RD}$) or a write ($\overline{WR}$) operation.

A close examination of Figure 1–3(a) and (b) will reveal that the data bus widths of the two processors are different. The 8086 system has a 16-bit data bus, and the 8088 has an 8-bit data bus. Additional differences do exist. The address bus of the 8086 contains a $\overline{BHE}$ (bus high enable) signal, and the address bus of the 8088 does not. $\overline{BHE}$ is used to select the upper part of the 16-bit data whenever a byte read or write occurs, and *address bit* (A_0) is used to select the lower byte for a byte read. The only other

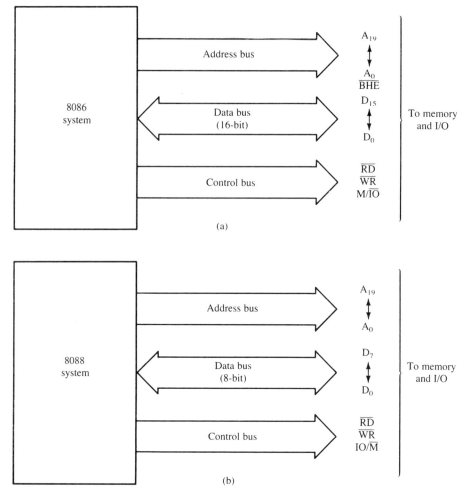

FIGURE 1–3   Basic 8086 and 8088 systems. (a) The 8086 system, illustrating the 16-bit data bus, the 20-bit address bus, and the control bus. (b) The 8088 system, illustrating the 8-bit data bus, the 20-bit address bus, and the control bus.

difference between the system interface of these two microprocessors is the IO/$\overline{\text{M}}$ signal on the 8088 and the M/$\overline{\text{IO}}$ signal on the 8086. The IO/$\overline{\text{M}}$ signal is used to select the I/O or memory in the system. If it is a logic 0, then memory is selected; if it is a logic 1, I/O is selected. The function of the M/$\overline{\text{IO}}$ pin is identical except that the logic levels are inverted.

The 16-bit data bus on the 8086 allows it to fetch instructions more quickly than the 8088 because it fetches them two bytes rather than one byte at a time. Both microprocessors address 1M byte of memory because they both contain a 20-bit address bus. The main advantage of the 16-bit data bus is that instructions are generally fetched at a faster rate, as are 16-bit data.

1-3   MEMORY AND THE 8086 AND 8088

Although both the 8086 and 8088 microprocessors address 1,048,576 (IM) bytes of memory, they differ in physical memory organization.

Logical Memory

The logical memory space is the same for both the 8086 and the 8088 microprocessors, as illustrated in the programmer's memory map of Figure 1–4. *Logical memory* is the name often given to the memory viewed by the programmer through the software. It may be different from the *physical memory* in the system, which is the actual organization of the memory that the hardware designer sees.

The logical memory of both the 8086 and the 8088 begins at memory location 00000H and extends to location FFFFFH. The logical memory is a byte (8 bits) wide, and this range of addresses specifies the 1M byte of memory available in the system. A 16-bit word of memory addressed by either microprocessor begins at any byte address and extends for two consecutive bytes. For example, the word at location 00122H is stored at bytes 00122H and 00123H with the least significant byte stored in location 00122H.

Physical Memory

The physical memories of the 8086 and 8088 differ in width. The 8086 memory is 16 bits wide, and the 8088 memory is 8 bits wide. For programming there is no difference— memory is always 8 bits wide—but there is a difference for the hardware designer.

8088 Physical Memory. Figure 1–5 illustrates the physical memory space of the 8088 microprocessor. Notice that this map is identical to the map of the logical memory

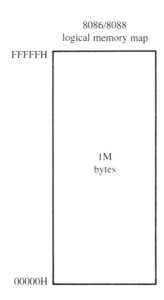

FIGURE 1–4 The logical memory map (programmers map) of both the 8086 and 8088 microprocessors, show-ing the 1M byte of memory addressed from memory lo-cations 00000H through FFFFFH.

8086/8088
logical memory map

FFFFFH

1M
bytes

00000H

FIGURE 1–5 The physical memory map (hardware map) of the 8088 microprocessor. Notice that it is identical to the logical memory map of Figure 1–4.

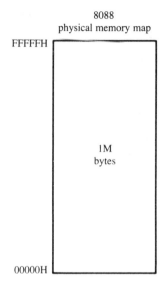

FIGURE 1–6 The physical memory map (hardware map) of the 8086 microprocessor. Notice that the memory is divided into two separate 8-bit banks of memory.

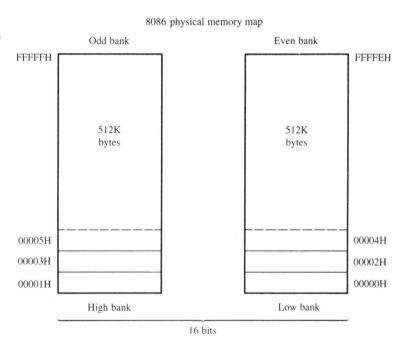

illustrated in Figure 1–4. If you are familiar with the 8085 or any other 8-bit microprocessor memory interfacing, then the 8088 memory interfacing should be easy to understand.

8086 Physical Memory. Figure 1–6 illustrates the physical memory space of the 8086 microprocessor. Unlike that of 8088, it contains two distinct banks of memory: the odd bank and the even bank. Because each 8086 bank of memory is 512K × 8, the total addressable memory space is still 1M byte. The advantage of this organization is that the 8086 can directly address any byte or word of data. It therefore reads or writes a 16-bit word in one operation (provided the address of the data is even), while the 8088 requires two reads or writes to transfer 16 bits of data. The 8086 software executes more efficiently because it accesses many instructions and 16-bit data at twice the speed of the 8088.

1-4   THE PROGRAMMING MODEL

All forms of programming depend upon a clear understanding of the internal register structure of the 8086/8088. This section illustrates the register structure of the 8086/8088 and explains how memory is addressed through the segment registers and an offset address.

Figure 1–7 illustrates the internal register array of both the 8086 and 8088 microprocessors. Again, as far as programming is concerned, these microprocessors are identical. The internal register array consists of three groups of registers: *general purpose*

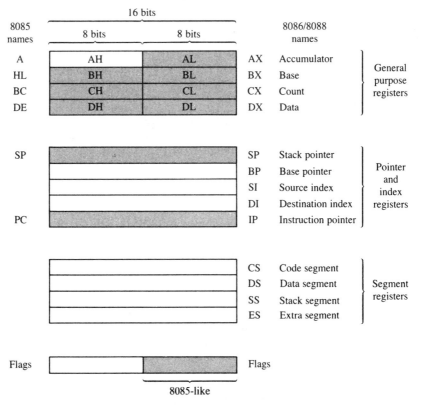

FIGURE 1–7 The programming model of the 8086 and 8088 microprocessors. Note that the shaded areas represent the 8085A register subset.

registers, pointer and index registers, and *segment registers.* In addition to these group-ings, there is also a *flag register* that indicates conditions about the operation of the arithmetic and logic unit (ALU).

General Purpose Registers

The general purpose registers are used in any manner that the programmer wishes. Each general purpose register is addressable as a 16-bit register (AX, BX, CX, and DX) or as two 8-bit registers (AH, AL, BH, BL, CH, CL, DH, and DL). Some of the instructions explained in later chapters also use the general purpose registers for specific tasks. For this reason, each is also given a name (*Accumulator, Base, Count,* and *Data*). In assembly language, the general purpose register is always referred to by the two-letter combination.

Notice in the illustration that these registers are also labeled for the 8085 micro-processor. This is done because the 8085 software can be translated into 8086/8088 software with the register designations illustrated.

The primary functions of the general purpose registers include:

AX   (*Accumulator*)—often used to hold the temporary result after an arithmetic and logic operation.

BX   (*Base*)—often used to hold the base address of data located in the memory and also the base address of a table of data referenced by the translate instruc-tion (XLAT).

CX   (*Count*)—the count for certain instructions such as shift count (CL) for shifts and rotates, the number of bytes (CX) operated upon by the repeated string operations, and a counter (CX) with the LOOP instruction.

DX   (*Data*)—a general purpose register that also holds the most significant part of the product after a 16-bit multiplication, the most significant part of the divi-dend before a division, and the I/O port number for a variable I/O instruction.

Pointer and Index Registers

Although the pointer and index registers are also general purpose in nature, they are more often used to index or point to the memory location holding the operand data for many instructions.

These registers include:

SP   (*Stack Pointer*)—used to address data in a LIFO (last-in, first-out) stack mem-ory. This occurs most often when the PUSH and POP instructions are exe-cuted or when a subroutine is CALLed or RETurned from in a program.

BP   (*Base Pointer*)—a general purpose pointer often used to address an array of data in the stack memory.

SI   (*Source Index*)—used to address source data indirectly for use with the string instructions.

DI   (*Destination Index*)—normally used to address destination data indirectly for use with the string instructions.

IP   (*Instruction Pointer*)—always used to address the next instruction executed by the 8086/8088. The actual location of the next instruction is formed by adding the contents of IP to CS × 10H, as described in the next section.

Data are often indirectly addressed through four of these five 16-bit registers, but never by an instruction pointer.

Segment Registers

Segment registers are unique to the 8086/8088 microprocessor and its advanced family members. They were designed to solve a problem peculiar to this family. Because all index and pointer registers are 16 bits wide, and the memory in the 8086/8088 is 1M byte, which requires a 20-bit address, the index and pointer registers are not wide enough to *directly* address any memory location. Intel devised the segment to circumvent this problem.

A segment of memory is a block of 64K bytes of memory addressed by a special register called a *segment register*. Figure 1–8 illustrates segments in the memory of the 8086/8088. Four separate segments can exist simultaneously in the memory space: the *code segment*, the *data segment*, the *stack segment*, and the *extra segment*. Data are indexed or pointed to in a segment by the *index registers*, *pointer registers*, *base register*, or *instruction pointer*.

Each segment register holds a 16-bit portion of the 20-bit starting address of a 64K byte segment of memory. The 20-bit address is formed by appending the segment register with a 0000_2 (0H) placed on the least significant end of the number in the segment register. Table 1–1 provides examples of the content of segment registers and the addresses indirectly addressed by them.

FIGURE 1–8 An example memory map illustrating the contents of each segment register and the location of the segments addressed by the segment registers in the memory.

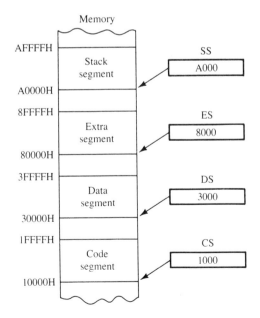

TABLE 1–1 The contents of the segment registers and the 64K-byte block of addresses indirectly addressed by the segment register

Segment Register	Memory Address Range
0100H	01000H–10FFFH
0101H	01010H–1100FH
1234H	12340H–2233FH
2000H	20000H–2FFFFH

Notice that segments may be spaced as closely as 16 bytes and that they may overlap. If an 8086/8088 system contains only 64K bytes of memory, then all four segment registers are loaded with 0000H, and all the segments overlap. The address range for each segment is then location X0000H–XFFFFH. (The X is a "don't care" and may be any hexadecimal digit.) The task of software conversion (8085 to 8086/8088) is simplified because the 8085 has a range of memory locations (0000H–FFFFH) that accommodates the "don't care" listed.

Each segment register has a special function and is normally associated with one or more of the index or pointer registers. To generate the memory location, the contents of a segment register, containing the segment address, are added to an index or pointer register, which contains the *offset address*.

Figure 1–9 shows how a memory address is generated within a segment by combining the contents of the segment register and the offset address in an index or pointer register to generate the *effective address*, or actual logical memory location addressed by an instruction. The effective address is the sum of the *segment address* and the *offset address*. In this example, the data segment register (DS) contains a 1000H, so the data

FIGURE 1–9 An example memory map depicting how address 10010H is referenced when DS = 1000H and BX contains an offset address of 0010H.

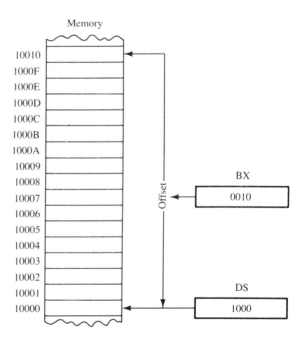

segment begins at memory location 10000H. Since the offset address (0010H) is contained in the base register (BX), the effective address is thus at memory location 10010H, or 1000H × 10H + 0010H.

Segment registers are normally used for a specific purpose, but they can be overridden, as discussed in Chapter 3. The normal or *default segment* register assignments are briefly described in the following list:

CS　(*Code Segment*)—a 64K-byte section of the memory that contains the program or code. This register is changed most often by a jump, call, or return instruction. The address of the next instruction executed by the 8086/8088 is generated by adding the contents of the instruction pointer (IP) offset address to the contents of CS × 10H.

DS　(*Data Segment*)—a 64K-byte section of the memory that contains data referenced by almost all instructions and many addressing modes. Data are almost always moved into or out of the memory via the data segment. The effective address of the data is generated by adding the contents of one of the index or pointer registers (BX, SI, or DI) to the contents of DS × 10H.

SS　(*Stack Segment*)—a 64K-byte section of the memory used for the LIFO stack. The effective stack address is a combination of the contents of the stack pointer (SP) plus SS × 10H. For example, if SS contains a 1000H and SP contains a 0000H, then the stack address is located at 10000H. 10000H is also written as 1000:0000 — that is, a segment address of 1000H and an offset address of 0000H. Data referenced with the base pointer (BP) are normally found in the stack segment.

ES　(*Extra Segment*)—a special segment register that is normally used only for string instructions. When a string instruction is executed, the destination location is addressed by the destination index register (DI) plus ES × 10H, and the source data are addressed by the source index register (SI) plus DS × 10H.

Table 1–2 illustrates the normal or default segment assignments, different types of memory references, and alternate assignments. More information on address generation is provided in Chapter 2.

Flag Register

The *Flag register*, also called a status register or program status word, is a 16-bit register that contains 8085-like flags and also four new 8086/8088 flags. The rightmost 8 bits contain flags (C, P, A, Z, and S) that are identical to the flag bits found in the 8085 microprocessor. The leftmost 8 bits contain flags (T, I, D, and O) that are unique to the 8086/8088 and its advanced family members.

Figure 1–10 illustrates the relative bit positions of each flag bit and the one-letter designation used to identify each flag bit. The flag bits include:

C　(*Carry*)—indicates carrying out or borrowing into the leftmost bit position following an arithmetic operation. *Carry* is also modified by some of the shift and rotate instructions.

TABLE 1–2   Default and alternate address sources

Type of Reference	Default Segment	Alternate Segment	Offset
Instruction fetch	CS	None	IP
Stack operation	SS	None	SP
Data (except for the following)	DS	CS, ES, or SS	various
String source	DS	CS, ES, or SS	SI
String destination	ES	None	DI
BP used as a base register	SS	CS, ES, or DS	BP

P   (*Parity*)—refers to the parity of the result of an arithmetic or logic operation. If the result contains an even number of 1s, the parity bit is set to indicate even parity; otherwise, it is cleared to indicate odd parity.

A   (*Auxiliary Carry*)—represents carrying or borrowing between half-bytes of an 8-bit arithmetic or logic operation using the AL register.

Z   (*Zero*)—indicates that the result of an arithmetic or logic operation is 0. If $Z = 1$, the result is 0.

S   (*Sign*)—indicates the sign of the result of an arithmetic or logic operation. A logic 1 in the sign flag bit indicates a negative result.

T   (*Trap*)—causes the 8086/8088 to enter into a single-step mode of operation. More detail on the operation of the trap flag is provided in Chapter 9.

I   (*Interrupt Enable*)—enables or disables the INTR (interrupt request) pin. If $I = 1$, then INTR is enabled.

D   (*Direction*)—selects the auto-increment or auto-decrement mode of operation for the destination index (DI) and the source index (SI) in string operations. If $D = 0$, then SI and DI are incremented during the execution of a string instruction.

O   (*Overflow*)—indicates an arithmetic overflow after an addition or subtraction. For example, if a 7FH (+ 127) and a 01H (+ 1) are added, and they are signed numbers, the result is 80H (− 128). Because − 128 is not the correct signed result, the O flag is set to indicate an overflow.

FIGURE 1–10   The 8086/8088 flag register.

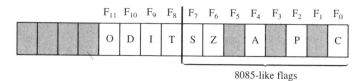

8085-like flags

1-5   DATA FORMATS

Successful programming also depends on a clear understanding of data formats. In this section, we describe the common data formats used with the 8086/8088 microprocessor. Data are presented as: ASCII, BCD, *8-bit (byte) signed and unsigned integers, 16-bit (word) signed and unsigned integers, 32-bit (double-word) signed and unsigned integers*, and both *short* and *long real numbers* (or floating-point numbers).

ASCII Data

ASCII data (see Table 1–3) are normally used to represent alphanumeric characters in the memory of a computer system. The ASCII code is a 7-bit code with the eighth and most significant bit used to hold parity in some systems. If the ASCII data are used with a printer, the most significant bit is a 0 for alphanumeric printing and a logic 1 for graphics character printing.

The ASCII control characters are also listed in Table 1–3 along with a brief description of the function of each code. If control codes are entered on the keyboard, the control key is held down, followed by an @ for a 00, an *a* for an 01, a *b* for an 02, and so forth.

BCD

Binary coded decimal (BCD) information is stored in either packed or unpacked forms in the memory. Packed BCD occurs when two BCD digits are stored per memory byte, unpacked BCD when one BCD digit is stored per byte. With BCD data, the valid 4-bit binary codes are 0000 (0)–1001 (9).

Byte

Byte data are stored in two forms: unsigned and signed integers. Figure 1–11 illustrates both the unsigned- and the signed-integer byte-wide formats. Notice that the only difference between the signed and unsigned forms is the weight of the leftmost bit position. In the signed form, the leftmost bit is negative, and in the unsigned form, it is positive or unsigned. For example, an 80H is equal to an unsigned value of 128 and a signed value of -128. An 81H is equal to an unsigned value of 129 or a signed value of -127—that is, $-128 + 1$.

Even though negative signed numbers are represented in this way, they are in *two's complement* form. This method of evaluating a signed number is much easier than the act of two's complementing the number to determine its value, especially in the world of calculators that are designed for programmers.

Word

A *word* (16 bits) is formed with 2 bytes of data. The least significant byte is always stored in the lowest numbered memory location, and the most significant byte in the highest. Figure 1–12(a) illustrates the weights of each bit position in a word of data, and Figure

TABLE 1–3 The ASCII code

Code	Hex	Comment	Code	Hex	Comment
NUL	00	Null character	SP	20	Space
SOH	01	Start of header	!	21	
STX	02	Start of text	"	22	
ETX	03	End of text	#	23	
EOT	04	End of transmission	$	24	
ENQ	05	Enquiry	%	25	
ACK	06	Acknowledge	&	26	
BELL	07	Bell or beeper	'	27	Apostrophe
BS	08	Back space	(	28	
HT	09	Horizontal tab	)	29	
LF	0A	Line feed	*	2A	
VT	0B	Vertical tab	+	2B	
FF	0C	Form feed	,	2C	Comma
CR	0D	Carriage return	–	2D	Minus
SO	0E	Shift output	.	2E	Period
SI	0F	Shift input	/	2F	
DLE	10	Data link escape	0	30	
DC1	11	Direct control 1	1	31	
DC2	12	Direct control 2	2	32	
DC3	13	Direct control 3	3	33	
DC4	14	Direct control 4	4	34	
NAK	15	Negative acknowledge	5	35	
SYN	16	Synchronous idle	6	36	
ETB	17	End of transmission block	7	37	
CAN	18	Cancel	8	38	
EM	19	End of medium	9	39	
SUB	1A	Substitute	:	3A	Colon
ESC	1B	Escape	;	3B	Semicolon
FS	1C	Form separator	<	3C	
GS	1D	General separator	=	3D	
RS	1E	Record separator	>	3E	
US	1F	Unit separator	?	3F	

TABLE 1-3 *continued*

Code	Hex	Comment	Code	Hex	Comment
@	40		`	60	Accent grave
A	41		a	61	
B	42		b	62	
C	43		c	63	
D	44		d	64	
E	45		e	65	
F	46		f	66	
G	47		g	67	
H	48		h	68	
I	49		i	69	
J	4A		j	6A	
K	4B		k	6B	
L	4C		l	6C	
M	4D		m	6D	
N	4E		n	6E	
O	4F		o	6F	
P	50		p	70	
Q	51		q	71	
R	52		r	72	
S	53		s	73	
T	54		t	74	
U	55		u	75	
V	56		v	76	
W	57		w	77	
X	58		x	78	
Y	59		y	79	
Z	5A		z	7A	
[	5B		{	7B	
\	5C		|	7C	
]	5D		}	7D	
^	5E		~	7E	Tilde
_	5F	Underscore		7F	

FIGURE 1–11   8-bit integers. (a) An unsigned 8-bit Integer. (b) A signed 8-bit Integer.

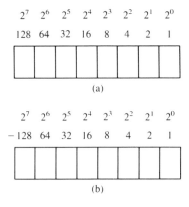

FIGURE 1–12   16-bit Integers. (a) The binary weights of each bit position in a 16-bit word of data. Recall that if the number is signed, the weight of the leftmost bit position is negative. (b) A 1234H stored in the memory beginning at location at 10000H.

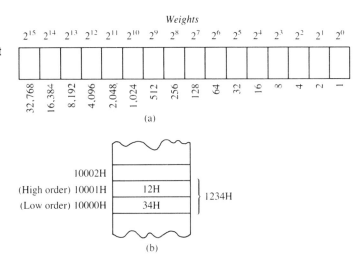

1–12(b) illustrates how a 1234H is stored in the memory. The only difference between a signed and an unsigned number is the leftmost bit position. In the signed number its weight is negative, and in the unsigned number it has no sign. Again, this leftmost bit is the same as for byte data except that its positional value is different.

Double Words

Double-word format is used to store 32-bit numbers (4 bytes) that are the product in a multiplication or the dividend in a division. Figure 1–13 illustrates the binary weights and memory storage formats for a double word. In addition to storing data, the double-word format is also used for storing addresses in the memory. Figure 1–14 illustrates the form used to store an address in a double word. Notice that the offset address is stored in the two lowest numbered memory locations with its least significant byte first, followed by the segment number in the two highest numbered memory locations. The segment number is also stored with its least significant byte first.

Real Numbers

Because the 8086/8088 is used with many high-level languages and also some very sophisticated control systems, real numbers are often encountered. A real number or, as it is often called, a *floating-point number*, is composed of two parts: a *mantissa* and an *exponent*. Figure 1–15 depicts both the 4- and 8-byte forms of the real number as it is stored in the 8086/8088 system. This is the same form specified by the IEEE standard, IEEE-754, version 10.0. Figure 1–15(a) illustrates the single-precision form that contains an 8-bit exponent, a 24-bit mantissa (fraction), and a sign bit.

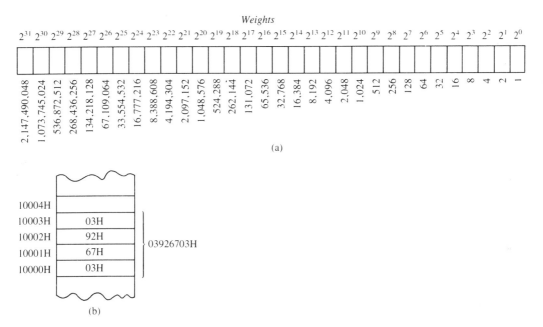

(a)

(b)

FIGURE 1–13 32-bit Integers. (a) The binary weights of each bit position in a 32-bit double word of data. (b) A 03926703H stored in the memory beginning at location 10000H.

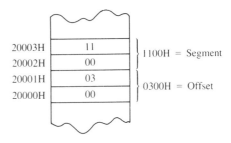

FIGURE 1–14 An example memory map illustrating how memory address 11300H is stored in the memory. The segment number is 1100H and the offset address is 0300H. Notice that the offset address is stored first, followed by the segment address.

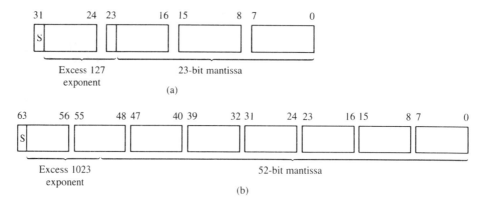

FIGURE 1–15   Real or floating-point data storage. (a) The 4-byte short form of a real number. (b) The 8-byte long form of a real number.

Simple arithmetic indicates that it should take a 33-bit number to store all these data. Not true—the 24-bit mantissa contains an implied (hidden) 1 bit that allows the mantissa to be stored in 23 bits. The *hidden bit* is the first bit of the normalized real number. When a number is normalized, it is adjusted so that its value is at least 1, but less than 2. For example, if a 12 is converted to binary (1100) and normalized, the result is a 1.1×2^3. Table 1–4 illustrates the short-form version of this number and other numbers.

The exponent is stored as a biased exponent. With the short-form real number, the bias is 127 (7FH); with the long-form real number, it is 1023 (3FFH). In the previous example, there is an exponent of 2^3, represented as a biased exponent of $127 + 3$ or 130 (82H) in short form and $1023 + 3$ or 1026 (402H) in long form. There are two exceptions to these rules: (1) if the number is 0.0, then the real number is stored with an exponent, sign, and mantissa of 0, and (2) if the number is too large to be held in the real number format, the exponent, sign, and mantissa are stored as ones.

TABLE 1–4   Short-form real number notation

Decimal	Binary	Normalized	Sign	Biased Exponent	Mantissa
+12	1100	1.1×2^3	0	10000010	1000000 00000000 00000000
−12	1100	-1.1×2^3	1	10000010	1000000 00000000 00000000
+100	1100100	1.1001×2^6	0	10000101	1001000 00000000 00000000
−1.75	1.11	-1.11×2^0	1	01111111	1100000 00000000 00000000
0.25	.01	1.0×2^{-2}	0	01111101	0000000 00000000 00000000
0.0	0	0	0	00000000	0000000 00000000 00000000

1-6   THE INSTRUCTION SET

The 8086/8088 *instruction set* includes equivalents to the instructions found in the 8085 or almost any 8-bit microprocessor plus some new operations. This section provides a brief overview of each general category of an instruction and the instructions themselves. Usage for the instructions is explained further in Chapters 2–5. The instruction categories described in this section include: *data transfer*, *arithmetic*, *bit manipulation*, *string*, *program transfer*, and *processor control*.

Data Transfer

The 8086/8088 instruction set includes 14 data transfer instructions that move bytes or words of data between memory and registers as well as between the accumulator and the I/O ports. Table 1–5 lists these instructions and also briefly notes the operating characteristics of each.

Arithmetic

The 8086/8088 is capable of adding, subtracting, multiplying, and dividing data as either bytes or words. The system adds and subtracts by using signed or unsigned bytes or words and BCD or ASCII data. It multiplies and divides by 8- or 16-bit operations performed on signed, unsigned, or ASCII numbers. Table 1–6 lists the arithmetic instructions found in the 8086/8088 microprocessor.

TABLE 1–5 The data transfer instructions

Opcode	Function
MOV	Moves byte or word
PUSH	Pushes word onto stack
PUSHF	Pushes flags onto stack
LAHF	Moves flags into AH
SHAF	Loads flags from AH
POP	Pops word from stack
POPF	Pops flags from stack
IN	Inputs data to accumulator from I/O device
OUT	Outputs data from accumulator to I/O device
XCHG	Exchanges bytes or words
XLAT	Translates table lookup instruction
LEA	Loads effective address
LDS	Loads DS and the operand with a 32-bit address
LES	Loads ES and the operand with a 32-bit address

TABLE 1–6 Arithmetic instructions

Opcode	Function
ADD	Adds bytes or words
ADC	Adds bytes or words plus carry flag
AAA	Adjusts ASCII after addition
DAA	Adjusts BCD after addition
INC	Adds 1 to byte or word
SUB	Subtracts bytes or words
SBB	Subtracts bytes or words minus carry flag
NEG	Changes sign of byte or word (two's complement)
CMP	Compares bytes or words
AAS	Adjusts ASCII after subtraction
DAS	Adjusts BCD after subtraction
DEC	Subtracts 1 from byte or word
MUL	Multiplies unsigned byte or word
IMUL	Multiplies signed byte or word
AAM	Adjusts ASCII after multiplication
DIV	Divides unsigned byte or word
IDIV	Divides signed byte or word
CBW	Converts byte to word
CWD	Converts word to double word
AAD	Adjusts ASCII before division

Bit Manipulation

Twelve instructions provide binary bit manipulation capabilities to the 8086/8088 microprocessor. These instructions include *logic operations*, *shifts*, and *rotates*. A brief description of each instruction and its symbolic opcode appears in Table 1–7.

String Instructions

The string instructions are used to manipulate strings of data in the memory. Each string is composed either of bytes or words and is up to 64K bytes in length. The string instructions use the SI and DI registers to address the data and the CX register to count the number of bytes or words operated upon. String instructions occur once unless they are prefixed with the REP, REPE/REPZ, or REPNE/REPNZ prefix. If a string instruction is thus prefixed, it is repeated up to the number of times contained in the count register—CX. Table 1–8 lists the string operations available in the 8086/8088 microprocessor.

TABLE 1-7 Bit manipulation instructions

Opcode	Function
AND	ANDs bytes or words
OR	ORs bytes or words
XOR	Exclusive-ORs bytes or words
NOT	Inverts bytes or words
TEST	Tests bytes or words (AND)
SHL/SAL	Shifts logical/arithmetic left
SHR	Shifts logical right
SAR	Shifts arithmetic right
ROL	Rotates byte or word left
RCL	Rotates byte or word left through carry
ROR	Rotates byte or word right
RCR	Rotates byte or word right through carry

TABLE 1-8 String instructions

Opcode	Function
MOVS	Moves bytes or words
CMPS	Compares bytes or words
SCAS	Scans for byte or word
LODS	Loads AL or AX with byte or word
STOS	Stores AL or AX in byte or word

Program Transfer

Program transfer instructions include *jump*, *call*, and *return*, instructions familiar in the 8085 as well as some additional instructions that form *loops*. Table 1-9 lists the program transfer instructions.

Processor Control

The processor control instructions enable and disable interrupts, modify the flag bits, and synchronize external events. The 8086/8088 contains 12 processor control instructions listed in Table 1-10.

TABLE 1-9   Program transfer instructions

Opcode	Function
CALL	Calls subroutine
RET	Returns from subroutine
JMP	Jumps to another part of program
INT 3	Type 3 interrupt
INTO	Interrupts on overflow
IRET	Interrupt return
JA/JNBE	Jumps above/jumps not below or equal to
JAE/JNB	Jumps above or equal to/jumps not below
JB/JNAE	Jumps below/jumps not above or equal to
JBE/JNA	Jumps below or equal to/jumps not above
JC	Jumps carry set
JE/JZ	Jumps equal/jumps 0
JG/JNLE	Jumps greater/jumps not less than or equal to
JGE/JNL	Jumps greater than or equal to/jumps not less than
JL/JNGE	Jumps less than/jumps not greater than or equal to
JLE/JNG	Jumps less than or equal to/jumps not greater than
JNC	Jumps no carry
JNE/JNZ	Jumps not equal to/jumps not 0
JNO	Jumps no overflow
JNP/JPO	Jumps no parity/jumps parity odd
JNS	Jumps no sign (positive)
JO	Jumps on overflow
JP/JPE	Jumps parity/jumps parity even
JS	Jumps sign (negative)
LOOP	Loops CX times
LOOPE/LOOPZ	Loops while equal to/loops while 0
LOOPNE/LOOPNZ	Loops while not equal to/loop while not 0
JCXZ	Jumps if CX = 0

1-7   SUMMARY

1. The life of the 4-bit microprocessor was limited because of its inferior speed, instruction set, and memory.
2. The 8-bit microprocessor solved many of the problems encountered with the 4-bit microprocessors until recent times. Recently, microprocessor-based systems have

TABLE 1-10 Processor control instructions

Opcode	Function
STC	Sets carry
CLC	Clears carry
CMC	Complements carry
STD	Selects auto-decrement mode
CLD	Selects auto-increment mode
STI	Enables interrupts
CLI	Disables interrupts
HLT	Halts until a reset or an interrupt
WAIT	Waits for $\overline{\text{TEST}}$ pin $= 0$
ESC	Provides escape to coprocessor
LOCK	Locks the bus during the next instruction
NOP	Performs no operation

begun replacing minicomputers in many applications that require 16-bit data widths, additional instructions, and much more memory than the 8-bit microprocessors provided.

3. The 16-bit microprocessor is becoming more popular because of its increased execution speed, enhanced instruction set, and vast amount of addressable memory.

4. A change in the internal organization of the 16-bit microprocessor has made its use of the buses connected to the memory more efficient. The prefetch queue, which prefetches instructions while the memory is idle, allows more efficient use of the memory system.

5. The execution unit (EU) and the bus interface unit (BIU) allow the 8086/8088 to execute software more efficiently than earlier 8-bit microprocessors.

6. Compared to that of the older 8-bit microprocessor, the system architecture of a 16-bit microprocessor differs only slightly. Both systems contain an address bus, a data bus, and a control bus. The main difference is the number of bus connections, which are greater on a 16-bit microprocessor.

7. Logical memory is the memory system viewed by the programmer; physical memory is the actual structure of the memory viewed by the hardware designer. The 8088 logical and physical memory maps are identical, while the 8086 logical and physical maps differ. The 8086 physical memory is constructed of two separate byte-wide banks of memory—an even and an odd bank.

8. The programming models of the 8086 and the 8088 microprocessors are identical. Both contain general purpose registers, index and pointer registers, segment registers, and a flag register.

9. The general purpose registers of the 8086/8088 are composed of four 16-bit registers (AX, BX, CX, and DX) that are used as 16-bit registers or as eight 8-bit registers (AH, AL, BH, BL, CH, CL, DH, and DL).

10. There are five 16-bit pointer and index registers (SP, BP, IP, SI, and DI) available to the programmer in the 8086/8088 microprocessor.
11. Segment registers hold the 16-bit segment number that is appended on the rightmost side by a 0000_2 to form a 20-bit address. This allows the 8086/8088 to address 64K bytes per segment of memory. The four memory segments available to the programmer are the code, data, stack, and extra segments.
12. A memory address is created (effective address) by using a segment register to address a 64K-byte segment of the memory plus an offset. The offset is a 16-bit number that is added to the segment address to form the actual memory address.
13. The flag or status word contains 8085-like flags (rightmost 8 bits) plus four new flags. The new flags are used to control the interrupts (I), select the direction (D) of the auto-increment/auto-decrement feature in string instructions, sense an overflow (O), and control the single-instruction mode of operation (T).
14. Data formats for the 8086/8088 consist of bytes (8 bits), words (16 bits), and double words (32 bits).
15. Real numbers are expressed in either 32-bit (short) or 64-bit (long) formats using the IEEE-754 standard.
16. The 8086/8088 instruction set includes instructions that allow data transfer, arithmetic, bit manipulation, string operations, program transfer, and processor control.

1–8   QUESTIONS AND PROBLEMS

1. What were some of the problems of the early 4-bit microprocessors?
2. List a few applications for the early 4-bit microprocessors.
3. What improvements in microprocessor technology led to the advent of the 8-bit microprocessor?
4. Compare the execution speeds of the 4-, 8-, and 16-bit microprocessors.
5. How much memory can the 8086 microprocessor address?
6. What is the EU? Explain its purpose.
7. What is the BIU? Explain its purpose.
8. What is the prefetch queue? Why does it allow the microprocessor to execute software more efficiently?
9. The 8086 has a _____ -byte prefetch queue, and the 8088 has a _____ -byte prefetch queue.
10. What three buses are connected to the memory and I/O of the 8086/8088 microprocessor?
11. Both the 8086 and 8088 microprocessors address _____ bytes of memory.
12. Logical memory in the 8086/8088 is numbered from _____ to _____ .
13. A word requires _____ bytes of memory.
14. What are the differences between the 8088 logical and physical memory maps?
15. What are the differences between the 8086 logical and physical memory maps?
16. A bank of memory is capable of storing _____ bytes in the 8086 memory system.

17. How many 8-bit general purpose registers are available in the 8086/8088? What are their names?
18. How many 16-bit general purpose registers are available in the 8086/8088? What are their names?
19. Why is the CX register called the count register?
20. Why is the DX register called the data register?
21. List the five pointer and index registers and explain their normal function.
22. Segment registers are used to address a 64K-byte block of memory. How is this possible when a segment register is only 16 bits wide and the memory address is 20 bits wide?
23. May memory segments overlap? If so, what is the minimum number of overlapped bytes other than 0?
24. If IP = 1000H and CS = 2000H, then the actual address of the next program instruction is at memory location _____ .
25. If SS = 1234H and SP = 0100H, the current address of the stack is

     _____ .

26. What two pointers use the stack segment register to address memory?
27. The string source (SI) is located in the _____ segment, and the string destination (DI) is located in the _____ segment.
28. How many of the 16 flag bits actually contain information?
29. List and describe the function of each of the 8085-like flag bits.
30. Explain where the D flag bit is used and what it is used for.
31. What is an overflow?
32. A byte = ___ bits, a word = ___ bits, and a double word = ___ bits.
33. Signed and unsigned numbers are bytes, words, and double words. (TRUE/FALSE)
34. Show how a 123H is stored in a word and a double word if both the word and double word begin at memory address 10000H.
35. Show how memory address 1000:1234 is stored in a double word that begins at address 04000H.
36. Convert the following decimal numbers to IEEE-754 short-form real numbers:
    a. 10
    b. − 11
    c. 101.125
    d. − 65.0625
    e. 300.09375

CHAPTER 2

Addressing Modes

INTRODUCTION

Efficient software development for the 8086/8088 requires complete familiarity with the addressing modes available to each instruction. In this chapter, we will use the MOV (move data) instruction to describe data-addressing modes. The MOV transfers bytes or words of data between registers or between registers and memory. In describing program memory–addressing modes, we will use call and jump instructions, which modify the flow of the program.

The data-addressing modes we will examine here include: register, immediate, direct, register indirect, base-plus-index, register relative, and base relative–plus–index addressing. The program memory–addressing modes include: program relative, direct, and indirect addressing.

OBJECTIVES

Upon completion of this chapter, you will be able to:

1. Explain the operation of each data-addressing mode.
2. Use the data-addressing modes to form assembly language statements.
3. Explain the operation of each program memory–addressing mode.
4. Use the program memory–addressing modes to form assembly language statements.
5. Select the appropriate addressing mode to accomplish a given task.

2–1   DATA-ADDRESSING MODES

Because the MOV instruction is one of the simplest and most flexible of the 8086/8088 instructions, it will provide the basis for the explanation of data-addressing modes throughout this chapter. Figure 2–1 illustrates the MOV instruction and defines the direction of the data flow. Notice that the source is far to the right and the destination is next to the opcode with source and destination separated by a comma. If you are familiar with the 8085 microprocessor, this is not new; but if you are familiar with another microprocessor, it may at first seem awkward. Some microprocessors move the data in the opposite direction.

The instruction MOV AX,BX transfers the contents of the source register (BX) into the destination register (AX). In other words, this instruction copies the contents of the BX register into the AX register. It is very important to note that the source *never* changes and the destination *almost always* changes. This is true regardless of the data-addressing mode or instruction.*

Figure 2–2 depicts the operations performed by each of the data-addressing modes for a MOV instruction. The data-addressing modes used with this instruction include:

1. *Register Addressing*—used to transfer a byte or word from the source register to the destination register. (That is, MOV AX,CX will copy the contents of register CX into register AX.)
2. *Immediate Addressing*—used to transfer the immediate byte or word of data to the destination register. (That is, MOV AX,1234H copies 1234H into register AX.) Note that when the letter H follows a number, it denotes a hexadecimal value.
3. *Direct Addressing*—transfers a byte or word between the memory and a register. The memory address of the data is stored with the instruction. (That is, MOV AX,LIST takes 16-bit contents of memory address LIST and moves them into register AX.)
4. *Register Indirect Addressing*—transfers a byte or word between a register and the memory location addressed by a register. (That is, MOV AX,[BX] moves the 16-bit contents of the memory location addressed by the BX register into register AX.)
5. *Base-Plus-Index Addressing*—used to transfer a byte or word between a register and the memory location indicated by the sum of a base register and an index register. (That is, MOV AX,[BX + SI] moves the 16-bit contents of the address indexed by the sum of BX + SI into register AX.)
6. *Register Relative Addressing*—transfers a byte or word between a register and the memory location addressed by a register and a displacement. (That is, MOV AX,[BX + 4] or MOV AX,ARRAY[SI]. The first instruction transfers the 16-bit contents of the memory location indexed by BX + 4 into the AX register. The second example transfers the contents of the memory location addressed by ARRAY + SI.)

FIGURE 2–1   The MOV AX,BX instruction illustrating how the source is copied into the destination.

MOV   destination, source

MOV   AX, BX

---

*The exceptions to this rule are the CMP and TEST instructions, to be discussed in later chapters.

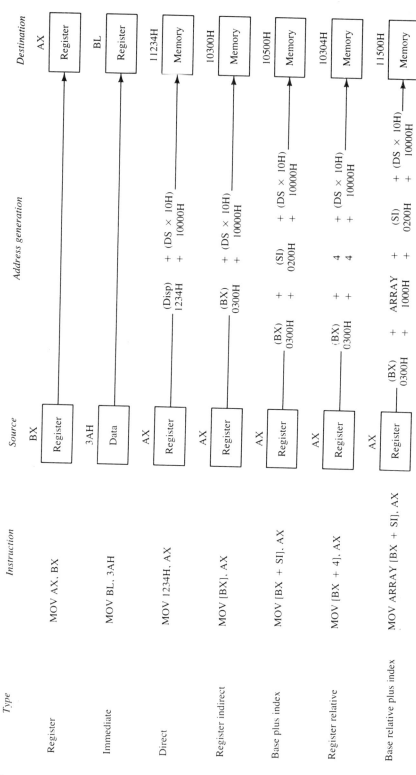

FIGURE 2–2 8086/8088 data-addressing modes.

(Notes: BX = 0300H, SI = 0200H, Array = 1000H and DS = 1000H)

Type	Instruction	Source	Address generation	Destination
Register	MOV AX. BX	BX Register		AX Register
Immediate	MOV BL. 3AH	3AH Data		BL Register
Direct	MOV [234H. AX	AX Register	(Disp) + (DS × 10H) 1234H + 10000H	11234H Memory
Register indirect	MOV [BX]. AX	AX Register	(BX) + (DS × 10H) 0300H + 10000H	10300H Memory
Base plus index	MOV [BX + SI]. AX	AX Register	(BX) + (SI) + (DS × 10H) 0300H + 0200H + 10000H	10500H Memory
Register relative	MOV [BX + 4]. AX	AX Register	(BX) + 4 + (DS × 10H) 0300H + 4 + 10000H	10304H Memory
Base relative plus index	MOV ARRAY [BX + SI]. AX	AX Register	(BX) + ARRAY + (SI) + (DS × 10H) 0300H + 1000H + 0200H + 10000H	11500H Memory

30

7. *Base Relative–Plus–Index Addressing*—used to transfer a byte or word between a register and the memory location addressed by a base register and an index register plus a displacement. (That is, MOV AX,ARRAY[BX + DI] or MOV AX,[BX + DI + 4]. The first example addresses the memory location indexed by ARRAY + BX + DI and transfers a 16-bit number from that memory location into register AX. The second example uses the address generated by the addition BX + DI + 4.)

2–2   REGISTER ADDRESSING

Register addressing is one of the easiest addressing modes to master once the numerous registers inside the 8086/8088 are known. The 8086/8088 contains the following 8-bit registers: AH,AL,BH,BL,CH,CL,DH, and DL and the following 16-bit registers: AX,BX,CX,DX,SP,BP,SI,DI,CS,DS,SS, and ES. In most instructions, one of these registers will be either the source or the destination—except for the segment registers, which are used with only a few types of instructions (MOV, PUSH, and POP). It is very important that the registers that are moved or operated upon be of a uniform size. Never mix 8- and 16-bit register types, because the assembler will issue an error for this disallowed operation.

Table 2–1 illustrates some of the many different versions of the register move instructions. It is virtually impossible to list them all because of the vast number of combinations available. For example, just the 8-bit subset of the MOV instructions comprises 256 different 8086/8088 instructions. The only form of MOV that is not allowed, besides one that would mix data sizes, is a MOV from one segment register to another.

Figure 2–3 illustrates the function of the MOV BX,CS instruction. Note that the source does not change, but the destination does. Here the 1234H is copied from the CX register into the BX register.

TABLE 2–1 Examples of register-addressed Instructions

Assembly Language	Operation
MOV AL,BL	BL → AL
MOV CH,CL	CL → CH
MOV AX,CX	CX → AX
MOV SP,BP	BP → SP
MOV DS,AX	AX → DS
MOV SI,DI	DI → SI
MOV DI,SI	SI → DI
MOV BX,ES	ES → BX
MOV CS,DS	Not allowed (segment-to-segment)
MOV BL,BX	Not allowed (mixed sizes)

FIGURE 2-3 The effect of executing the MOV BX,CX instruction at the point just before the BX register changes. Note that the 1234H is copied from the CX register and is about to enter the BX register. Once 1234H enters the BX register, the 76AFH currently in BX is lost.

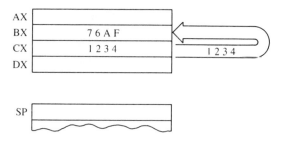

2-3   IMMEDIATE ADDRESSING

Another relatively simple data-addressing mode is immediate addressing, so called because the data are stored immediately after the hexadecimal opcode in the memory. Immediate addressing transfers the immediate byte or word of data from a program instruction into a register or memory location. Figure 2–4 depicts the operation of a MOV AX,3456H instruction. This instruction copies the 3456H from the instruction into the AX register.

In symbolic assembly language, the immediate data are preceded by the # symbol in a few, but not all, 8086/8088 assemblers—for example, MOV AX,#3456H. Some assemblers do not require the #, but represent the immediate data as MOV AX,3456H. This text does not use the # symbol to indicate immediate data. We represent the data as *hexadecimal* by appending the letter H, or as *decimal* by representing the data without any special character. (The MOV AL,33 instruction moves a 33 decimal into the 8-bit AL register.) Table 2–2 illustrates several MOV instructions with immediate data.

FIGURE 2-4 The effect of executing a MOV AX,3456H instruction. Here the data, which follow the opcode B8, are moved from the memory into the AX register. The operation is shown at the point just before register AX changes.

TABLE 2-2 Examples of immediate addressing with the MOV instruction

Assembly Language	Operation
MOV BL,44	2CH → BL
MOV AX,44H	0044H → AX
MOV SI,0	0000H → SI
MOV CH,100	64H → CH
MOV SP,3000H	3000H → SP

2-4   DIRECT DATA ADDRESSING

Direct data addressing is used not only with most commands but also for many instructions in a typical program. It has two basic forms: *direct addressing*, which applies only to the MOV instruction and, in particular, to a MOV between memory and AX or AL; and *displacement addressing*, which is used with almost any instruction in the 8086/8088 instructions set.

Direct Addressing

Direct addressing is included in the instruction set so that the 8085 instructions LDA and STA can easily be converted to 8086/8088 instructions. This mode is used whenever data are transferred between AL and memory or AX and memory. (When we cover machine language in Chapter 3, the reason will become apparent.) This instruction is 3 bytes long.

A MOV AL,DATA instruction, as it is represented in many 8086/8088 assemblers, transfers a copy of the byte of data stored at memory location DATA (1234H here) in the data segment to the AL register. (Some assemblers represent this instruction as a MOV AL, [1234H].) Figure 2-5 shows how this instruction is executed. Here DS = 1000H, so that the actual memory address referenced by the instruction is 11234H—the sum of 1234H + 10000H (1000H × 10H).

Table 2-3 lists for four possible forms of this direct-addressed instruction. Again, only the AX and AL registers may be moved to and from the memory with this type of instruction.

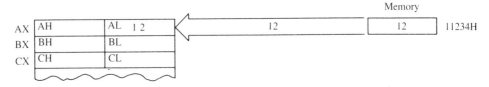

FIGURE 2-5   The effect of executing the MOV AL,[1234H] instruction if DS = 1000H. Here the AL register is shown after the data (12) have destroyed the previous contents of register AL.

TABLE 2-3   The four possible forms of direct-addressing

Assembly Language	Operation
MOV AL,NUMBER	A byte is copied from the data segment plus offset NUMBER into AL
MOV AX,COW	A word is copied from the data segment plus offset COW into AX
MOV NEWS,AL	AL is stored at a location in the data segment plus offset NEWS
MOV THERE,AX	AX is stored at a location in the data segment plus offset THERE

Displacement Addressing

Displacement addressing is almost identical to direct addressing except that the instruction is often 4 bytes wide instead of 3. This type of direct data addressing is also much more flexible because most of the 8086/8088 instructions can use it.

Figure 2–6 illustrates the operation of the MOV CL,[2000H] instruction. Notice that this instruction operates in the same manner as the MOV AL,[1234H] instruction of Figure 2–5. The difference only becomes apparent upon examination of the assembled versions of these instructions: MOV AL,[1234H] is a 3-byte instruction, and MOV CL,[2000H] is a 4-byte instruction, as shown in Example 2–1.

EXAMPLE 2–1

```
0000 A0 1234                 MOV   AL,[1234H]
0003 8A 0E 2000              MOV   CL,[2000H]
```

Table 2–4 lists some of the many MOV displacement forms of direct data addressing. Not all the forms are listed because there are 512 different MOV instructions of this type.

Register Indirect Addressing

Register indirect addressing allows data to be addressed at the memory location pointed to by any of the following registers: BX, BP, SI, and DI. For example, if register BX contains a 1000H and the MOV AX,[BX] instruction is executed, the data at memory location 1000H in the data segment are copied into the AX register. Assuming that DS = 0100H, this instruction then copies the word of data from memory location 2000H into the AX register (see Figure 2–7). Note that the [] symbols specify indirect addressing in 8086/8088 assembly language. Some typical instructions using indirect register addressing are illustrated in Table 2–5.

BX, BP, SI, and DI.   When using register indirect addressing or any of the other addressing modes that follow, it is important to remember that the BX, SI, and DI registers normally address memory in the data segment (DS), and BP normally addresses memory in the stack segment (SS).

Indirect addressing is often used to refer to tabular data in the memory. For example, suppose you must create a table of information that will hold 50 samples taken from a

FIGURE 2–6   The effect of executing the MOV CL,[2000H] instruction if DS = 1000H. Here the CL register is shown after the data (8A) have destroyed the previous contents of CL.

TABLE 2-4   Examples of direct data addressing using a displacement

Assembly Language	Operation
MOV CH,DOG	The contents of memory location DOG in the data segment are copied into CH. The actual value of DOG is calculated by the assembler
MOV CH,[1000H]	The contents of the memory location addressed by offset 1000H in the data segment are copied into CH
MOV DATA,BP	BP is copied into memory location DATA and DATA + 1 in the data segment
MOV NUMBER,SP	SP is copied into memory location NUMBER and NUMBER + 1 in the data segment

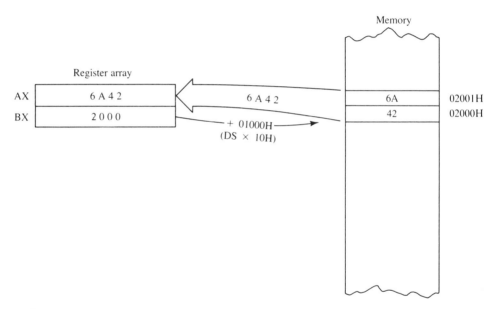

FIGURE 2-7   The effect of executing the MOV AX,[BX] instruction if DS = 0100H and BX = 1000H. Here the AX register is shown after the data (6A42H) have destroyed the previous contents of AX.

digital voltmeter. Figure 2–8 illustrates the table and also the BX register used to address each location in the table sequentially. In order to accomplish this, you would need to load the location of the table into the BX register with a MOV immediate instruction. After initializing the starting address of the table, you would then use the indirect-addressing mode to store the data sequentially.

The sequence shown in Example 2–2 loads BX with the address of the table and initializes the count located in register CX to a 50. The OFFSET directive tells the

TABLE 2–5   Examples of instructions using register indirect addressing

Assembly Language	Operation
MOV CX,[BX]	A word from the location addressed by the BX register within the data segment is copied into CX
MOV [BP],DL	A byte is copied into the stack segment at the location addressed by BP
MOV [DI],BH	A byte is copied into the data segment at the location addressed by DI
MOV [DI],[BX]	Memory-to-memory moves are not allowed except for string instructions

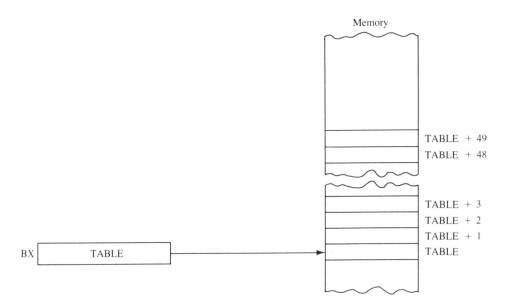

FIGURE 2–8   An array of data (TABLE) containing 50 bytes that are indirectly addressed through the BX register.

assembler to load BX with the offset address of TABLE and not the contents of TABLE. Once the counter and pointer are initialized, a repeat-until-CX-0 loop is entered. Here data are input (IN) from the voltmeter and then stored in the memory location indirectly addressed by BX. BX is next incremented so that the following iteration of the loop will store the voltmeter data at the next sequential memory location, TABLE + 1. Finally, the LOOP instruction decrements the CX register and checks to see if CX is a 0. If CX is not a 0, the program continues at memory location AGAIN, and, if CX is a 0, it ends or continues with another sequential instruction.

EXAMPLE 2-2

```
        ;instructions that read 50 bytes of data from DATA_PORT
        ;and stores them in a TABLE.
        ;

0000 BB 0000 R    MOV    BX BX,OFFSET TABLE    ;address TABLE
0003 B9 0032      MOV    CX,50                 ;load counter

0006              AGAIN:

0006 E4 2A        IN     AL,DATA_PORT          ;read data
0008 88 07        MOV    [BX],AL               ;save data
000A 43           INC    BX                    ;address next
000B E2 F9        LOOP   AGAIN
```

2-5   BASE-PLUS-INDEX ADDRESSING

Base-plus-index addressing is similar to register indirect addressing because it indirectly addresses memory data using one of the base registers BP or BX plus an index register (DI or SI). 'In many cases, the base register holds the beginning address of a memory array, and the index register holds the relative position of the data in the array. Remember that BX addresses data in the data segment and BP addresses data in the stack segment.

Addressing Data

Figure 2-9 illustrates how the data are addressed for the MOV DX,[BX + DI] instruction. Here BX = 1000H, DI = 0010H, and DS = 0100H, which translates to memory address 02010H for this data transfer. This instruction copies the data from memory location 02010H into the DX register. Table 2-6 lists some of the instructions found for base-plus-index addressing.

Addressing Arrays

A major use for base-plus-index addressing is to address elements in an array of data. Suppose that it is desirable to address the elements in an array of data located in the data segment at location ARRAY. To accomplish this, you would need to load the BX register (base) with address ARRAY and the DI (the index register) with the element number of the array to be accessed. Figure 2-10 illustrates the use of BX and DI to access an element in an array of data.

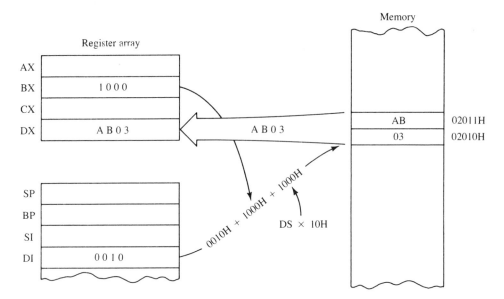

FIGURE 2-9 An example showing how the base-plus-index mode of addressing functions for the MOV DX, [BX + DI] instruction. Notice that memory address 02010H is referenced by this instruction because DS (0100H), BX (1000H), and DI (0010H) are summed to generate this address.

TABLE 2-6 Examples of base-plus-index addressing

Assembly Language	Operation
MOV CX,[BX + DI]	CX is loaded from a location in the data segment addressed by the sum of BX and DI
MOV CH,[BP + SI]	CH is loaded from a location in the stack segment addressed by the sum of BP and SI
MOV [BX + SI],SP	The SP register is stored in the data segment at the location addressed by the sum of BX and SI
MOV [BP + DI],CS	The CS register is stored in the stack segment at the location addressed by the sum of BP and DI

A short program listed in Example 2–3 moves array element 10H into array element

EXAMPLE 2–3

```
     ;using the base plus index addressing mode

0000 BB 0032 R     MOV     BX,OFFSET ARRAY ;address ARRAY
```

```
0003 BF 0010        MOV    DI,10H         ;address element 10H
0006 8A 01          MOV    AL,[BX+DI]     ;get data
0008 BF 0020        MOV    DI,20H         ;address element
000B 88 01          MOV    [BX+DI],AL     ;save data
```

20H. Notice that the array element number is loaded into the DI register in order to transfer the byte of data from one array element to another.

2–6   REGISTER RELATIVE ADDRESSING

Register relative addressing is similar to base-plus-index addressing and displacement addressing (discussed under direct data addressing). In register relative addressing, the data in a segment of memory are addressed by adding the displacement to the contents of a base or index register (BP, BX, DI, or SI). Figure 2–11 illustrates the operation of the MOV AX,[BX + 1000H] instruction. Here BX = 0100H and DS = 0200H, so that the address generated is the sum of DS × 10H, BX, and the displacement of 1000H for a total of 03100H. Remember that if you use BP to address memory with this mode, the address is located in the stack segment. Table 2–7 lists a few instructions that use register relative addressing.

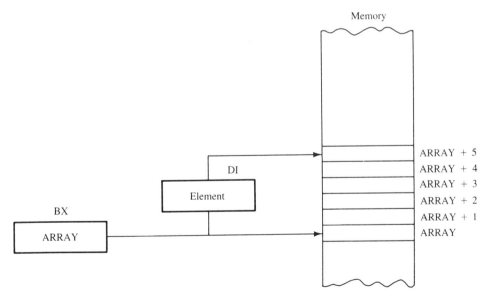

FIGURE 2–10   An example showing base-plus-index addressing. Here an element (DI) of an array of data (BX) is accessed.

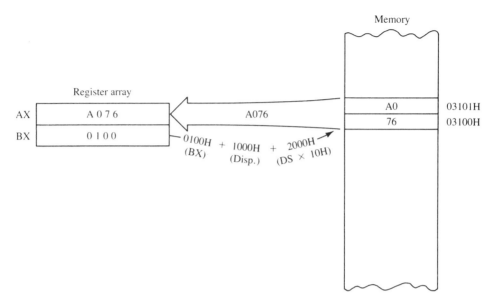

FIGURE 2–11   The effect of executing the MOV AX, [BX + 1000H] instruction if BX = 0100H and DS = 0200H.

TABLE 2–7 Examples of register relative addressing

Assembly Language	Operation
MOV AX,[DI + 100H]	Data are transferred from the data segment location addressed by the sum of 100H and the contents of DI
MOV ARRAY[SI],BL	BL is stored in the data segment at memory array address ARRAY, element SI
MOV LIST[BP],CL	CL is stored in the stack segment at memory array address LIST, element BP
MOV DI,SET[BX]	DI is loaded from the data segment at array SET, element BX

Addressing Array Data

It is possible to address array data with register relative addressing much as one does with base-plus-index addressing. (Refer to Section 2–5 for base-plus-index addressing techniques.) In Figure 2–12, we illustrate register relative addressing with the same example we used to illustrate base-plus-index addressing to show how the displacement ARRAY is added to index register DI to generate a reference to an array element.

Example 2–4 shows how this new addressing technique can transfer the contents of array element 10H to array element 20H. Notice the similarity between this program and the base-plus-index addressing program.

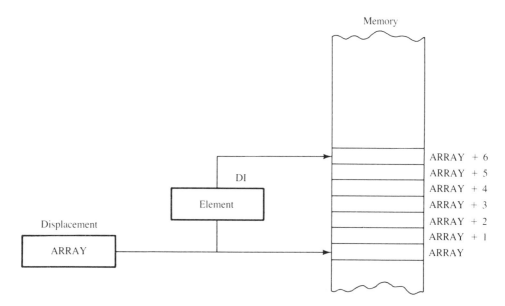

FIGURE 2-12 Register relative addressing used to address an element of ARRAY. The displacement addresses the start of the array, and the contents of DI (the element) selects an element of the array.

2-7 BASE RELATIVE-PLUS-INDEX ADDRESSING

The final data-addressing mode available in the 8086/8088 is base relative–plus–index addressing. This mode is similar to base-plus-index addressing, but besides adding the contents of a base register and an index register, it also adds a displacement to generate the address. This type of addressing is often used to address two-dimensional arrays of memory data.

Addressing Data

Base relative–plus–index addressing is the least-used addressing mode. Figure 2–13 shows how data are referenced if the instruction executed by the 8086/8088 is a MOV AX,[BX + SI + 100H]. Here the displacement 100H, BX = 0020H, SI = 0010H, and DS = 1000H, so that the effective address for this instruction is memory location 10130H—the sum of the displacement, BX, SI, and DS × 10H. Clearly, this mode is too complex to be used frequently. Some typical instructions for base relative–plus–index addressing are listed in Table 2–8.

EXAMPLE 2–4

```
     ;using register relative addressing

0000 BF 0010          MOV  DI,10H          ;address element 10H
0003 8A 85 0300 R     MOV  AI,ARRAY[DI]    ;get data
0007 BF 0020          MOV  DI,20H          ;address element 20H
000A 88 85 0300 R     MOV  ARRAY[DI],AL    ;save data
```

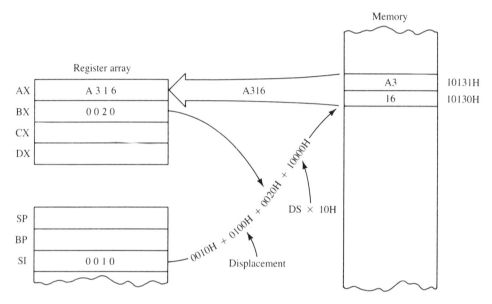

FIGURE 2–13 An example of base relative–plus–index addressing is illustrated with the MOV,100H[BX + SI] instruction. This instruction moves data from memory to the AX register. The memory address is the sum of DS × 10H, 100H, BX, and SI.

TABLE 2–8 Examples of base relative–plus–index instructions

Assembly Language	Operation
MOV DH,[BX + DI + 20H]	DH is loaded from the data segment memory location addressed by the sum of BX, DI, and the displacement of 20H
MOV AX,FILE[BX + DI]	AX is loaded from the data segment location addressed by the sum of BX, DI, and the offset FILE
MOV LIST[BP + DI],CL	CL is stored at the location in the stack segment addressed by the sum of BP, DI, and the offset address LIST

Addressing Arrays

Suppose that a file of many records exists in the memory and each record contains many elements. The displacement addresses the file, the base register addresses a record in the file, and the index register addresses an element in the record. This very complex form of addressing is illustrated in Figure 2–14.

Example 2–5 provides a program that will copy element 0 of record A into element 2 of record C, using base relative–plus–index addressing.

2-8   PROGRAM MEMORY-ADDRESSING MODES

Program memory–addressing modes are used with the JMP and CALL instructions and consist of three different forms: *direct, relative,* and *indirect.* This section presents all three forms of program memory addressing, using the JMP instruction.

Direct Program Memory Addressing

Direct program memory addressing is what the 8085 microprocessor used for all its jumps and calls. (Other 8-bit microprocessors have made less use of this mode.) The 8086/8088 are also able to use this form of addressing, but do not use it nearly as much as relative and indirect program addressing.

The instructions for direct program memory addressing store the address with the opcode. For example, if a program is to jump to memory location 10000H for the next instruction in a program, the address 10000H is stored with the opcode. Figure 2–15 shows the direct *intersegment* JMP instruction and the 4 bytes required to store the next segment and offset addresses. A JMP 10000H stores a segment number of 1000H, which is loaded into CS, and an offset of 0000H, which is loaded into IP.

The only other instruction for direct program addressing is the intersegment CALL instruction. In most cases, the name of a label refers to a memory address rather than a hexadecimal address. When using the name of a label, most assemblers select the best form of addressing for the JMP instruction or CALL instruction.

Relative Program Memory Addressing

Relative program memory addressing is not available on the 8085 microprocessor, but it is available on most other 8-bit microprocessors, as well as 8086/8088. The term *relative*

EXAMPLE 2–5

```
        ;using the base plus indexed addressing mode

0009 BB 0364 R      MOV  BX,OFFSET RECA    ;address record A
0003 BF 0000        MOV  DI,0              ;address element 0
0006 8A 81 04F4 R   MOV  L,FILE[BX+DI]     ;get data
000A BB 042C R      MOV  BX,OFFSET RECC    ;address record C
000D BF 0002        MOV  DI,2              ;address element 2
0010 88 81 04F4 R   MOV  FILE[BX+DI],AL    ;save data
```

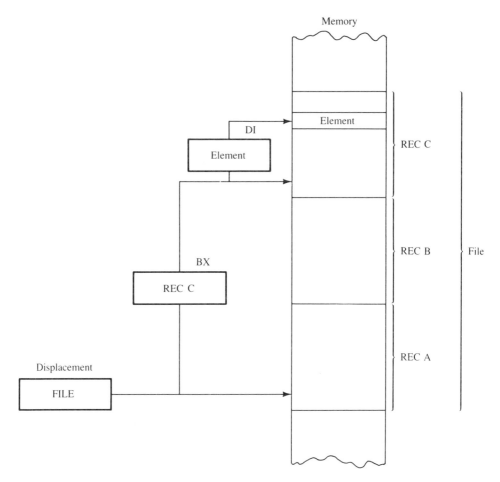

FIGURE 2–14 Base relative–plus–index addressing used to address a FILE that contains multiple records (REC); each record contains many elements.

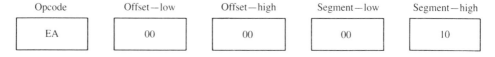

FIGURE 2–15 The 5-byte machine language instruction for a JMP [10000H] instruction. The opcode is followed by the offset address (0000H) and then the code segment address (1000H).

actually means "relative to the *instruction pointer* (IP)." For example, if a JMP instruction is to skip the next two bytes of the program, then, *relative to the instruction pointer,* which always points to the next instruction, a 2 is added to skip 2 bytes. This example of relative JMP is illustrated in Figure 2–16. Notice that the JMP instruction is a 1-byte instruction, and the displacement, the number added to the instruction pointer, is also a 1-byte number.

FIGURE 2–16 A JMP [2] instruction, which will skip over the next two bytes in the program. In this example, the program continues at location 10004H.

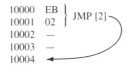

Relative instructions occur as JMP and CALLS, and contain either an 8- or 16-bit displacement. All assemblers determine how far the JMP instruction is required to go and then automatically select the proper displacement. If the distance is too great, many assemblers use the direct JMP.

An 8-bit displacement allows forward and reverse referencing with displacement values of − 128 to + 127, and the 16-bit displacement allows displacement values of ± 32K.

Indirect Addressing

The 8086/8088 allows several forms of program indirect addressing for the JMP and CALL instructions. Table 2–9 illustrates some of the acceptable program indirect jump instructions, which can use any 16-bit register (AX,BX,CX,DX,SP,BP,SI, or DI), any relative register ([BX], [BP], [SI], or [DI]), and any relative register with a displacement.

Figure 2–17 shows a jump table that is stored beginning at memory address TABLE. This table is referenced by the short program illustrated in Example 2–6. In this

TABLE 2–9 Examples of program indirect addressing

Assembly Language	Operation
JMP AX	Jump to the intrasegment memory location addressed by AX
JMP CX	Jump to the intrasegment memory location addressed by CX
JMP NEAR PTR [BX]	Jump to the intrasegment memory location stored at the location addressed by BX in the data segment
JMP NEAR PTR [DI]	Jump to the intrasegment memory location stored at the location addressed by DI in the data segment
JMP TABLE[BX]	Jump to the intrasegment memory location stored at the location addressed by BX plus the displacement TABLE in the data segment

FIGURE 2–17 A jump table that is used to allow the program to select different jump addresses for different values in the BX register.

```
TABLE   DW   L0C0 ⎫   Addresses of four
        DW   L0C1 ⎪   different programs.
        DW   L0C2 ⎪ (Each address is a 2-byte
        DW   L0C3 ⎭       offset.)
```

example, the BX register is loaded with a 4 so that, when it is combined in the JMP TABLE[BX] instruction with TABLE, the effective jump address is the contents of the second entry in the table—LOC2.

2–9   STACK MEMORY ADDRESSING

The stack is an important portion of the memory system in all microprocessors. It holds data temporarily and stores return addresses from subroutines. The stack memory is a LIFO (last-in, first-out) memory in the 8086/8088 microprocessor. Data are placed onto the stack with a PUSH instruction, or a CALL instruction in the case of the subroutine return address. Data are removed from the stack via the POP instruction, or a RET instruction in the case of subroutine return addresses.

EXAMPLE 2–6

```
          ;using indirect addressing for a jump

0000 BB 0004          MOV   BX,4              ;address LOC2
0003 FF A7 0000 R     JMP   TABLE[BX]         ;jump to LOC2
```

8086/8088 Stack

The stack memory in the 8086/8088 is maintained by two registers: the *stack pointer* (SP) and the *stack segment register* (SS). Whenever a word of data is pushed onto the stack (see Figure 2–18(a)), the high-order 8 bits are placed in the location addressed by $SP - 1$, and the low-order 8 bits are placed in the location addressed by $SP - 2$. The SP is then decremented by 2 so that the next word of data is stored in the next available memory location. The SP register always points to the area of memory located in the stack segment. SP is always added to $SS \times 10H$ to form the stack memory address.

Whenever data are popped from the stack (see Figure 2–18(b)), the low-order 8 bits are removed from the location addressed by SP and the high-order 8 bits are removed from the location addressed by $SP + 1$. SP is then incremented by a 2. Table 2–10 lists some of the PUSH and POP instructions available in the 8086/8088 instruction set. Note that PUSH and POP always store or retrieve *words* of data—never bytes.

2–10   SUMMARY

1. The data-addressing modes include *register, immediate, direct, register indirect, base-plus-index, register relative,* and *base relative–plus–index addressing.*
2. The program memory–addressing modes include *direct, relative,* and *indirect addressing.*

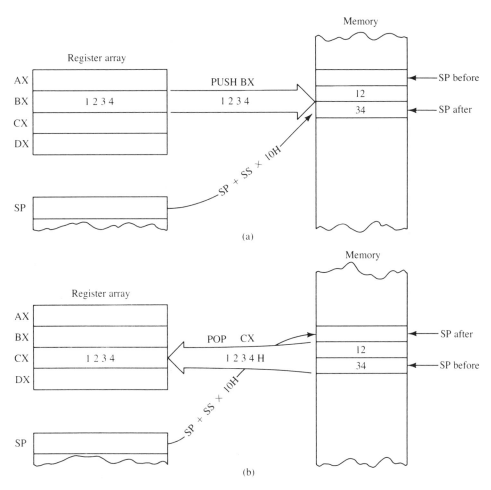

FIGURE 2-18 The PUSH and POP instructions. (a) PUSH BX places the contents of the BX register onto the stack addressed by the SP + SS × 10H. (b) POP CX removes data from the stack at the location addressed by SP + SS × 10H and places the data into the CX register.

TABLE 2-10 Examples of PUSH and POP instructions

Assembly Language	Operation
POPF	Pop flag word from stack
PUSHF	Push flag word onto stack
PUSH AX	Push AX onto stack
POP BX	Pop data from stack into BX
PUSH DS	Push DS onto stack
POP CS	Illegal instruction
PUSH [BX]	Push word stored at location addressed by BX onto stack

TABLE 2-11   8086/8088 addressing modes

Instruction	Address Generation
MOV AL,BL	Register addressing
MOV AL,LIST	(DS × 10H) + LIST
MOV AL,12	Immediate data of 12 decimal
MOV AL,[BP]	(SS × 10H) + BP
MOV AL,[BX]	(DS × 10H) + BX
MOV AL,[DI]	(DS × 10H) + DI
MOV AL,[SI]	(DS × 10H) + SI
MOV AL,[BP + 3]	(SS × 10H) + BP + 3
MOV AL,[BX − 10]	(DS × 10H) + BX − 10
MOV AL,[DI + 100H]	(DS × 10H) + DI + 100H
MOV AL,[SI + 300H]	(DS × 10H) + SI + 300H
MOV AL,LIST[BP]	(SS × 10H) + BP + LIST
MOV AL,LIST[BX]	(DS × 10H) + BX + LIST
MOV AL,LIST[DI]	(DS × 10H) + DI + LIST
MOV AL,LIST[SI]	(DS × 10H) + SI + LIST
MOV AL,LIST[BP + 2]	(SS × 10H) + BP + LIST + 2
MOV AL,LIST[BX + 20H]	(DS × 10H) + BX + LIST + 20H
MOV AL,LIST[DI − 6]	(DS × 10H) + DI + LIST − 6
MOV AL,LIST[SI + 1]	(DS × 10H) + SI + LIST + 1
MOV AL,[BP + DI]	(SS × 10H) + BP + DI
MOV AL,[BP + SI]	(SS × 10H) + BP + SI
MOV AL,[BX + DI]	(DS × 10H) + BX + DI
MOV AL,[BX + SI]	(DS × 10H) + BX + SI
MOV AL,[BP + DI + 2]	(SS × 10H) + BP + DI + 2
MOV AL,[BP + SI − 2]	(SS × 10H) + BP + SI − 2
MOV AL,[BX + DI + 10]	(DS × 10H) + BX + DI + 10
MOV AL,[BX + SI + 200H]	(DS × 10H) + BX + SI + 200H
MOV AL,LIST[BP + DI]	(SS × 10H) + BP + DI + LIST
MOV AL,LIST[BP + SI]	(SS × 10H) + BP + SI + LIST
MOV AL,LIST[BX + DI]	(DS × 10H) + BX + DI + LIST
MOV AL,LIST[BX + SI]	(DS × 10H) + BX + SI + LIST
MOV AL,LIST[BP + DI + 2]	(SS × 10H) + BP + DI + LIST + 2
MOV AL,LIST[BP + SI − 3]	(SS × 10H) + BP + SI + LIST − 3
MOV AL,LIST[BX + DI + 100H]	(DS × 10H) + BX + DI + LIST + 100H
MOV AL,LIST[BX + SI + 2AFH]	(DS × 10H) + BX + SI + LIST + 2AFH

3. Table 2-11 lists all the data-addressing modes available in the 8086/8088 microprocessor.

4. The MOV instruction copies the contents of the source into the destination, and the
source does not change.

5. Register addressing specifies any 8-bit register (AH, AL, BH, BL, CH, CL, DH, or
DL) or any 16-bit register (AX, BX, CX, DX, SP, BP, SI, or DI). In addition to the
registers mentioned, certain instructions also allow the segment registers (CS, DS,
SS, or ES) to be addressed.

6. Immediate addressing requires that 8 or 16 bits of data immediately follow the opcode
in the memory. This type of addressing is generally used to manipulate constant data.

7. Direct data addressing is used by two special MOV instructions in order to translate
8085 code into 8086/8088 code. A modified form called displacement addressing also
directly addresses data in the memory and is used by most of the instructions in the
instruction set.

8. Register indirect addressing allows data to be addressed at the memory location
pointed to by either an index or base register. This type of addressing is very useful
for accessing lists of data.

9. Base-plus-index addressing is often used to address data in an array. The memory
address is formed by adding a base register, index register, and segment register times
10H.

10. Register relative addressing uses either a base or index register plus a displacement
to access memory data. This type of addressing also lends itself well to addressing
data in an array.

11. Base relative–plus–index addressing is useful for addressing data in a two-
dimensional array. The address is formed by adding a base register, index register,
displacement, and segment register times 10H.

12. Three program memory–addressing modes exist in the 8086/8088 microprocessor:
the *direct, relative,* and *indirect modes.*

13. Direct program memory addressing is allowed only with the JMP and CALL instructions. In direct program memory addressing, the offset and segment address of the
next instruction to be executed are stored after the opcode.

14. Relative program memory addressing allows a JMP or CALL instruction to branch
forward or backward in the current code segment by up to $\pm$ 32K.

15. Indirect program memory addressing allows the JMP and CALL instructions to
address another portion of the program or a subroutine indirectly through a register
or a memory location.

16. The PUSH and POP instructions always transfer words of data between the operand
and the stack.

2-11 QUESTIONS AND PROBLEMS

1. What do the following MOV instructions accomplish?
   a. MOV AX,BX
   b. MOV BX,AX

    c. MOV BL,CH

    d. MOV SP,DI

    e. MOV CS,AX

2. List the 8-bit registers that can be specified in instructions.

3. List the 16-bit registers that can be specified in instructions.

4. List the 16-bit registers that are addressed by only a few of the instructions.

5. What is wrong with the MOV BL,CX instruction?

6. What is wrong with the MOV CS,SS instruction?

7. Form an instruction that will place a 12H into the BL register.

8. What special symbol is occasionally found in immediate data addressing?

9. What 8086/8088 instruction is used to replace the 8085 LDA instruction?

10. What is a displacement? How does it determine the memory address in a MOV [2000H],AX instruction?

11. What do the symbols [ ] indicate?

12. Suppose that DS = 0200H, BX = 0200H, and DI = 0300H. Determine the data memory address accessed by each of the following instructions.

    a. MOV AL,[2000H]

    b. MOV AL,[BX]

    c. MOV [DI],AL

13. What is wrong with the MOV [BX],[DI] instruction?

14. Explain the difference between a MOV BX,DATA instruction and a MOV BX,OFF-SET DATA instruction.

15. Given that DS = 1000H, SS = 2000H, BP = 1000H, and DI = 0100H, determine the data memory addresses for each of the following instructions.

    a. MOV AL,[BP + DI]

    b. MOV CX,[DI]

    c. MOV DX,[BP]

16. Given that DS = 1200H, BX = 0100H, and SI = 0250H, determine the data memory addresses for each of the following instructions

    a. MOV [100H],DL

    b. MOV [SI + 100H],AL

    c. MOV BL,[BX + 100H]

17. Given that DS = 1100H, BX = 0200H, LIST = 0250H, and SI = 0500H, determine the data memory addresses for each of the following instructions.

    a. MOV LIST[SI],DX

    b. MOV BL,LIST[BX + SI]

    c. MOV BH,[BX + SI]

18. What 8086/8088 base register addresses data in the stack segment?

19. List all three program memory–addressing modes.

20. How many bytes of memory are required to store a direct intersegment JMP instruction? What is stored in each of the bytes?

21. Indicate which JMP instruction (direct, long displacement, or short displacement) assembles if the JMP THERE instruction is stored at memory address 10000H and label THERE is located at the following memory addresses.

    a. 10020H

    b. 11000H

     c. 0FFFEH

     d. 20000H

22. Form a JMP instruction that will jump to the address pointed to by the BX register.

23. Select a JMP instruction that will jump to the location stored at memory address TABLE.

24. How many bytes of data are placed on the stack by the PUSH instruction?

25. Explain how the PUSH [DI] instruction functions.

CHAPTER 3

Data Movement Instructions

INTRODUCTION

In this chapter, we cover all the 8086/8088 data movement instructions. These include: MOV, PUSH, POP, XCHG, XLAT, IN, OUT, LEA, LDS, LES, LAHF, SAHF, and the string MOVS, LODS, and STOS instructions. We present data movement instructions first because they are probably the most often used and the easiest to understand and master.

We will also take a detailed look at some of the assembly language pseudo-operations. The 8086/8088 microprocessor almost always requires some type of assembler because the machine language instructions are so complex to form. (This text assumes that the user is developing assembly language software on an IBM personal computer with the MACRO assembler or a similar software system. An appendix briefly explains the assembler and provides some detail on the linker.)

Finally, we explain the format required to generate machine language instructions, because there are times when it is necessary to interpret a hexadecimal dump of machine code.

OBJECTIVES

Upon completion of this chapter, you will be able to:

1. Explain the operation of each data movement instruction with any applicable addressing mode.
2. Explain the purposes of some assembly language pseudo-operations and key words such as EQU, DB, DW, DD, ALIGN, OFFSET, ASSUME, ORG.
3. Given a specific data movement task, select the appropriate 8086/8088 assembly language instruction to accomplish it.
4. Given a hexadecimal machine language instruction, determine the symbolic opcode, source, destination, and addressing mode.

3-1 MOV REVISITED

We used the MOV instruction in Chapter 2 to explain the 8086/8088 addressing modes. In this chapter, we will use it to explain the machine language forms available to the programmer for various addressing modes. We introduce machine code here because at times it will be necessary to interpret when a program generated by an assembler requires *debugging* or *modification*. It is also used to convert between machine and assembly language instructions in Appendix A.

Machine Language

Machine language instructions for the 8086/8088 vary in length from 1 to 6 bytes. Although this seems an almost unmanageable arrangement, there is some order to this microprocessor's machine language.

First, byte 1 of any machine language instruction is the *opcode,* which indicates the operation (addition, subtraction, etc.) the microprocessor is to perform. Figure 3-1 illustrates the general form of the opcode for many of the 8086/8088 machine language instructions. Here the first 6 bits of byte 1 are the opcode, and the remaining 2 bits indicate the direction (D) of the data flow and whether the data are a byte or a word (W). If $D = 1$, the data flow to the register (REG) specified in byte 2, and if $D = 0$, the data flow from the register (REG) specified in byte 2. If $W = 0$, the opcode performs the operation on a byte, and if $W = 1$, the opcode operates on a word.

Figure 3-2 illustrates byte 2, which is used to specify the *mode* of operation (MOD), the *register* (REG), and the *register* or *memory location* (R/M) operated upon.

MOD Field. The MOD field selects one of the various forms of addressing and displacement or the operation for the instruction. These forms are listed in Table 3-1. If the MOD field contains an 11, the R/M field of byte 2 addresses a register, and if the MOD field contains 00, 01, or 10, R/M refers to one of the memory-addressing modes of operation. When MOD selects a mode of memory addressing, it indicates that the addressing mode contains no displacement (00), an 8-bit sign-extended displacement (01), or a 16-bit displacement (10).

FIGURE 3-1 Byte 1 of many machine language instructions, illustrating the position of the opcode, D, and W.

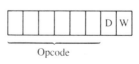

Opcode

FIGURE 3-2 Byte 2 of many machine language instructions, illustrating the position of the MOD, REG, and R/M fields.

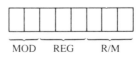

MOD   REG   R/M

TABLE 3–1 MOD field specifications

MOD	OPERATION
00	No displacement
01	8-bit sign-extended displacement
10	16-bit displacement
11	A register

All 8-bit displacements are sign-extended into 16-bit displacements within the 8086/8088 microprocessor. If the 8-bit displacement is 00H–7FH (positive), it is sign-extended to 0000H–007FH, and if it is 80H–FFH (negative), it is sign-extended to an FF80H–FFFFH. In other words, whenever a number is sign-extended, the sign bit is copied into the next higher order byte.

Register Assignments. Table 3–2 lists the register assignments for both the REG field and the R/M field when MOD = 11. Notice that this table contains two lists of register assignments: one is used when W = 1 for words, and the other is used when W = 0 for bytes.

Suppose that a 2-byte instruction, 8BECH, is found in a machine language program. This instruction is converted into binary and placed in the instruction format for bytes 1 and 2 as illustrated in Figure 3–3. The opcode is a 100010. If you refer to Appendix A, which lists machine language instructions, you will see that this is the opcode for a MOV instruction. Also notice that both the D and W bits are 1, which means that a word is moved into the register specified in the REG field. REG contains a 101, indicating register BP, so that the MOV instruction moves data into BP. Because the MOD field contains 11, the R/M field also indicates a register. R/M = 100 (SP), so that this instruction moves the data from SP and BP and is written in symbolic form as an MOV BP, SP.

R/M Memory Addressing. If the MOD field contains a 00, 01, or a 10, then the R/M field takes on a new meaning. Table 3–3 lists the memory-addressing modes for the R/M field.

Notice that all the addressing modes represented in Chapter 2 are listed in this table. The displacement discussed in Chapter 2 is determined by the MOD field. If MOD = 00

TABLE 3–2 REG and R/M (when MOD = 11) assignments

Code	W = 0 (Byte)	W = 1 (Word)
000	AL	AX
001	CL	CX
010	DL	DX
011	BL	BX
100	AH	SP
101	CH	BP
110	DH	SI
111	BH	DI

FIGURE 3–3 The 8BEC instruction placed in the byte 1 and 2 formats of Figures 3–1 and 3–2. This machine language instruction is de- coded as the symbolic in- struction MOV BP,SP.

Opcode	D	W	MOD	REG	R/M

1	0	0	0	1	0	1	1		1	1	1	0	1	1	0	0

Opcode = MOV
D = To register (REG)
W = Word
MOD = R/M is register
REG = BP
R/M = SP

TABLE 3–3 R/M memory- addressing modes

Code	Function
000	[BX + SI]
001	[BX + DI]
010	[BP + SI]
011	[BP + DI]
100	[SI]
101	[DI]
110	[BP]*
111	[BX]

*See text under Special Addressing Mode.

and R/M = 101, the addressing mode is [DI], but, if MOD = 01 or 10, then the addressing mode is, for example, displacement[DI] or DATA[DI].

Figure 3–4 illustrates the machine language version of a MOV DL,[DI] instruction. This instruction is 2 bytes long and has an opcode 100010, D = 1 (to register from R/M), W = 0 (byte), MOD = 00 (no displacement), REG = 010 (DL), and R/M = 101 ([DI]).

Special Addressing Mode. There is a special addressing mode that does not appear in Tables 3–1, 3–2, or 3–3, which is used whenever memory data are referenced by only the displacement—for example, the MOV [1000H], DL or the MOV DATA, DL instruc- tions. The instruction in the first example moves the contents of DL into the memory location addressed by the sum of the displacement 1000H and DS × 10H. Whenever an instruction has only a displacement, the MOD field is always a 00 and the R/M field is always a 110. This combination is supposed to indicate that the instruction has no dis- placement and uses addressing mode [BP], but you cannot actually use addressing mode [BP] without a displacement. The assembler takes care of this by automatically using an 8-bit displacement (MOD = 01) of 00H whenever the [BP] form of addressing is used — [BP + 0].

Figure 3–5 illustrates the binary bit pattern required to encode the MOV [1000H], DL instruction into machine language. If the individual does not know this special form of addressing, this instruction is incorrectly assumed to be a MOV [BP],DL.

FIGURE 3–4   A MOV
DL,[DI] instruction coded into
binary machine language.

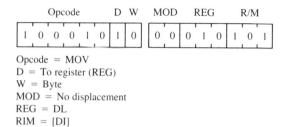

Opcode = MOV
D = To register (REG)
W = Byte
MOD = No displacement
REG = DL
RIM = [DI]

FIGURE 3–5   A
MOV[1000H],DL instruction
coded into binary machine
language. Note that two additional bytes are required for
the displacement of 1000H.

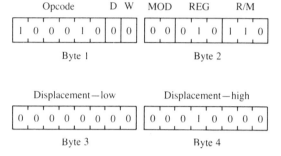

Figure 3–6 shows what form the assembler generates for a MOV [BP],DL instruction. This is a 3-byte instruction with the third byte used as a displacement of 00H.

An Immediate Instruction.   Suppose that a MOV WORD PTR[BX + 1000H], 1234H instruction is coded into machine language. This instruction moves a 1234H into the word
of memory addressed by the sum of 1000H, BX, and DS × 10H. This 6-byte instruction
uses 2 bytes to specify the opcode, D, W, MOD, REG, and R/M; 2 bytes for the data value
of 1234H; and 2 bytes for the displacement value of 1000H. Figure 3–7 illustrates the bit
pattern assigned to each of the 6 bytes of this instruction.

Segment MOV Instructions.   If the contents of a segment register is moved by the MOV,
PUSH, or POP instruction, a special set of register bits (REG field) selects the proper
segment register (see Table 3–4).

FIGURE 3–6   The MOV
[BP],DL instruction coded into
binary machine language requires a 1-byte displacement
of 00H in order for the
8086/8088 to execute this
instruction.

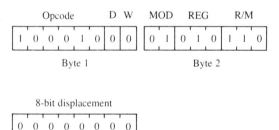

FIGURE 3–7 A MOV word PTR[BX + 1000H], 1234H instruction converted into binary machine language requires 6 bytes of memory: 2 for the instruction, 2 for the displacement of 1000H, and 2 for the immediate data of 1234H.

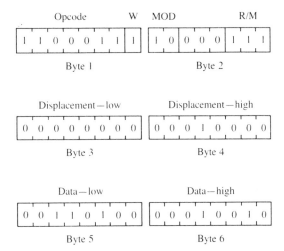

Opcode	W	MOD	R/M
1 1 0 0 0 1 1	1	1 0 0 0 0	1 1 1

Byte 1   Byte 2

Displacement—low	Displacement—high
0 0 0 0 0 0 0 0	0 0 0 1 0 0 0 0

Byte 3   Byte 4

Data—low	Data—high
0 0 1 1 0 1 0 0	0 0 0 1 0 0 1 0

Byte 5   Byte 6

Note: D and REG are not used in immediate memory addressing.

TABLE 3–4 Segment register selection bits

Code	Segment Register
000	ES
001	CS*
010	SS
011	DS

*MOV CS,XX and POP CS are not allowed.

Figure 3–8 illustrates a MOV BX,CS instruction. Notice that the opcode for this type of MOV is different from the other MOV instructions presented thus far.

Although this has not been a complete coverage of machine language coding, it should give you a good start in machine language programming. Remember, the program is always written in *symbolic machine language* (assembly language) and translated by a program called an *assembler* or, on very rare occasions, by hand to *binary machine language*. With the 8086/8088, let us hope that an assembler is available for the conversion because the process is very time-consuming.

FIGURE 3–8 A MOV BX,CS instruction converted into binary machine language. Here the REG is encoded as the CS register and R/M is encoded as the BX register.

Opcode	MOD	REG	R/M
1 0 0 0 1 1 0 0	1 1	0 0 1	0 1 1

Note: W and D are not present in this instruction.

3-2   PUSH/POP

PUSH and POP are important instructions used to store and retrieve data from the LIFO stack memory. The 8086/8088 microprocessor has four forms of PUSH and POP instructions: *register, register/memory, segment register,* and *flags.*

Register addressing allows the contents of any 16-bit register to be transferred to or from the stack. Register/memory addressing stores either the contents of a 16-bit register or memory location on the stack. Segment register addressing allows any segment register to be pushed onto the stack and all but the code segment register (CS) to be retrieved from the stack. The final form, *flag addressing,* allows the flag or status register to be transferred between the flag register and the stack.

PUSH

The PUSH instruction always transfers 2 bytes of data onto the stack. The source of the data may be the flag register, any internal 16-bit register, any segment register, or any 2 bytes of memory data.

Whenever data are pushed onto the stack, the first (most significant) data byte is stored in the stack segment at the location addressed by $SP - 1$.

The second (least significant) data byte is stored in the stack segment at the location addressed by $SP - 2$. After the data are stored by a PUSH, the SP register is decremented by a 2. Figure 3–9 illustrates the operation of the PUSH AX instruction, which transfers a copy of the contents of the AX register onto the stack ([SP − 1] = AH, [SP − 2] = AL, and SP = SP − 2).

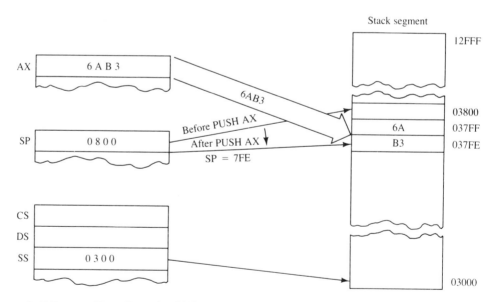

FIGURE 3–9 The effect of a PUSH AX instruction on the SP register and stack memory locations 037FFH and 037FEH.

Table 3–5 lists the four forms of PUSH instructions available in the 8086/8088 microprocessor as well as the binary bit pattern of each byte in each command.

PUSHF

The PUSHF instruction copies the contents of the flag register onto the stack. Like the PUSH instructions, PUSHF stores the most significant portion of the flags onto the stack at location SP − 1 and the least significant portion at SP − 2. After storing the flag register, the SP register is decremented by a 2.

POP

The POP instruction performs the inverse operation of a PUSH instruction. POP removes data from the stack and places it into the target register, flags, or word memory location. Like the PUSH instruction, POP is available in four forms: *register, register/memory, segment register,* and *flags*.

Suppose that a POP BX instruction is executed. The first byte of data is removed from the stack (memory location addressed by SP) and placed in the BL register. The second byte is removed from location SP + 1 and placed in the BH register. After both bytes are removed from the stack, the stack pointer is incremented by a 2. Figure 3–10 graphically depicts the operation of the POP BX instruction.

Table 3–6 lists opcodes, composition, and an example of each type of POP instruction. Note that the POP CS instruction is not allowed.

Initializing the Stack

When the stack area is initialized, both the stack segment register (SS) and the stack pointer (SP) are loaded. In most cases, it is normal to designate an area of memory as the stack segment by loading SS with the bottom location of the stack segment.

For example, if the stack segment is to reside in memory locations 10000H–1FFFFH, then the SS register is loaded with a 1000H. (Remember that the microprocessor multiplies the contents of the segment register by a 10H to obtain the actual segment's memory address.) To start the stack at the top of the stack segment, the stack pointer (SP) is loaded with a 0000H. Figure 3–11 illustrates how this value causes data to be pushed onto the top of the stack segment with a PUSH CX instruction. Remember that all the segments are cyclic in nature—that is, the top location of a segment is contiguous with the bottom location of a segment.

TABLE 3–5 The PUSH instructions

Symbolic	Byte 1	Byte 2	Example
PUSH reg	0101 0rrr		PUSH BX
PUSH mem	1111 1111	mm11 0aaa	PUSH [BX]
PUSH seg	000s s110		PUSH DS
PUSHF	1001 1100		PUSHF

Notes: aaa = any memory addressing mode, mm = MOD code, rrr = any 16-bit register, and ss = any segment register.

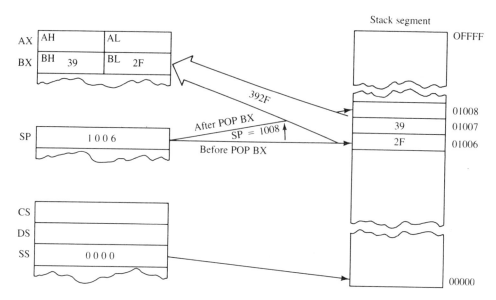

FIGURE 3–10   POP BX removes 2 bytes of data from the stack segment and places them into the BX register.

TABLE 3–6   The POP instructions

Symbolic	Byte 1	Byte 2	Example
POP reg	0101 1rrr		POP DI
POP mem	1000 1111	mm00 0aaa	POP [DI + 2]
POP seg	000s s111		POP ES
POPF	1001 1101		POPF

Notes: aaa = any memory addressing mode, mm = MOD code, rrr = any 16-bit register, and ss = any segment register.

3–3   LOAD-EFFECTIVE ADDRESS

There are three load-effective address instructions used to load a register or a register and a segment register with an address. Note that an address is loaded into a register with these instructions, not the data from the address. Table 3–7 lists the three forms of load-effective address instructions available in the 8086/8088.

LEA

The LEA instruction is used to load a register with the address of the data specified by the operand. As the first example in Table 3–7 shows, the operand address DATA is loaded into register AX, not the contents of address DATA.

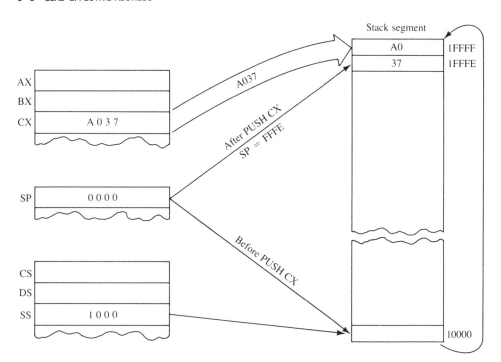

FIGURE 3-11 PUSH CX illustrating the cyclic nature of the stack segment. Notice that SP starts at 0000H and, after being decremented, ends up at FFFEH.

TABLE 3-7 Load-effective address instructions

Symbolic	Function
LEA AX,DATA	AX is loaded with the address at DATA
LDS DI,LIST	DI and DS are loaded with the address at LIST
LES BX,CAT	BX and ES are loaded with the address at CAT

By comparing an LEA with a MOV, we can observe the following effect: LEA BX,[DI] loads the address specified by [DI] (contents of DI) into the BX register; MOV BX,[DI] loads the data stored at the memory location addressed by [DI] into register BX.

Earlier in the text, we considered several examples involving the OFFSET pseudo-operation, which performs essentially the same function as the LEA instruction for simpler operand addresses. For example, MOV BX,OFFSET LIST performs the same function as LEA BX,LIST. Both instructions load the offset address of memory location LIST into the BX register.

But why is the OFFSET pseudo-operation available if the LEA instruction accomplishes the same task? First, OFFSET can be used only for simple operands such as LIST, DATA, and the like. It may not be used for an operand such as [DI], LIST[SI]. The OFFSET pseudo-operation is more efficient than the LEA instruction for simple operands. It takes the 8086/8088 microprocessor longer to execute an LEA BX,LIST instruction than it takes to execute a MOV BX,OFFSET LIST. (LEA BX,LIST takes eight clocks and MOV BX,OFFSET LIST takes four clocks.) The MOV BX,OFFSET LIST instruction executes twice as fast as the LEA BX, LIST instruction because the assembler calculates the offset address and uses the MOV immediate instruction to load BX instead of having the microprocessor calculate the offset address as it executes the LEA instruction.

Suppose that the 8086/8088 executes an LEA BX,[DI] instruction and DI contains a 1000H. Because the offset address is stored in DI, the microprocessor transfers a copy of DI into BX. This is accomplished with a MOV BX,DI instruction if efficiency is strived for in a program.

Another example is LEA CX,[BX + DI]. Here the offset address is the sum of BX and DI. The execution of this instruction loads CX with the modulo-64K sum of BX + DI. If BX = 1000H and DI = 2000H, the offset address loaded into CX is 3000H, and, if BX = 1000H and DI = FF00H, the offset address loaded into CX is 0F00H. Notice that the result here is modulo-64K. (Any carry-out of the 16-bit result is dropped.)

LDS and LES

The LDS and LES instructions load a 16-bit register with an offset address and either the DS or ES segment register with a new segment address. These instructions use any of the valid memory-addressing modes to select the location of the new offset address and segment number. They may not use a register (MOD = 11).

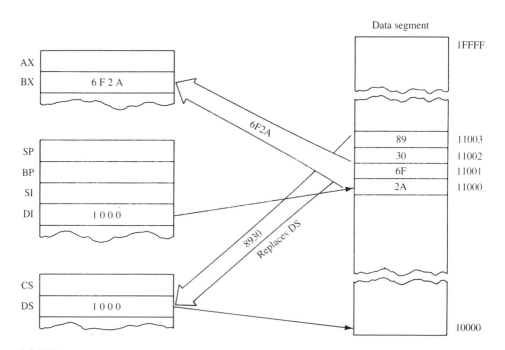

FIGURE 3–12 LDS BX,[DI] loads the BX register from locations 11000H and 11001H and the DS register from locations 11002H and 11003H. This instruction will change the data segment from 10000H–1FFFFH to 89300H–992FFH.

For example, as Figure 3–12 shows, the LDS BX,[DI] instruction will transfer the 32-bit number addressed by the DI register into the BX register and the DS register. The LDS and LES instructions point to a new data segment or extra segment and also load the specified register with a new offset address. We illustrate these instructions later in this chapter using string manipulation instructions. Note that the address loaded into the registers must be stored in the memory before the LDS or LES instruction can be used to load the address from the memory.

3-4   STRING DATA TRANSFERS

There are three string data transfer instructions—LODS, STOS, and MOVS—each of which allows data to be transferred as a block or group or as a single byte or word. Before we discuss these instructions, however, let us first examine the functions of the direction flag (D) and the segment registers as they apply to the DI and SI registers for string operations.

Direction Flag (D)

The direction flag (D) selects the auto-increment (D = 0) or the auto-decrement (D = 1) mode of operation for DI and SI during the string operations. The D flag is cleared with the CLD instruction and set with the STD instruction. Therefore CLD selects auto-increment and STD selects auto-decrement.

The transferral of a byte with the string instruction causes the addition (auto-increment) or subtraction (auto-decrement) of a 1 from DI and/or SI. The transferral of a word causes the addition or subtraction of a 2. Only the registers used for the string instructions are incremented or decremented. If DI is used but SI is not, then only DI is incremented or decremented when a string instruction is executed.

DI and SI

During the execution of a string instruction, it is possible to access memory through either the DI or SI registers or both. The DI offset address is normally located in the extra segment (ES), and the SI offset address in the data segment (DS). The segment assignment of the SI register may be changed by the segment override prefix, discussed in a later section of this chapter. DI is *always* located in the extra segment and cannot be changed to another segment.

LODS

The LODS instruction loads AL with a byte of data from the memory location addressed by SI or AX with a word of data addressed by SI. Table 3–8 lists the permissible forms of the LODS instruction. LODSB and LODSW cause a byte or word transfer; LODS followed by an operand selects a byte or word transfer. Operands are often defined as bytes with a DB and as words with a DW. DB is the pseudo-operation that *defines bytes*, and DW is the pseudo-operation that *defines words*.

TABLE 3-8 Forms of the LODS instruction

Symbolic	Function
LODSB	AL = [SI], byte transfer
LODSW	AX = [SI], word transfer
LODS BYTE	AL = [SI], if BYTE is defined as a byte
LODS WORD	AX = [SI], if WORD is defined as a word

Figure 3-13 illustrates the effect of executing the LODSW instruction if the D flag = 0, SI = 1000H, and DS = 1000H. Here the 16-bit number stored at memory locations 11000H and 11001H is loaded into the AX register. Because the D flag is equal to 0 and this is a *word* transfer, the contents of SI are automatically incremented by 2 after AX is loaded with memory data.

STOS

The STOS instruction stores AL or AX at the memory location addressed by DI in the extra segment. Table 3-9 lists the permissible forms of the STOS instruction. As with LODS, a B or W may be used to indicate a byte or a word transfer, or an operand address defined as a byte or a word may be included.

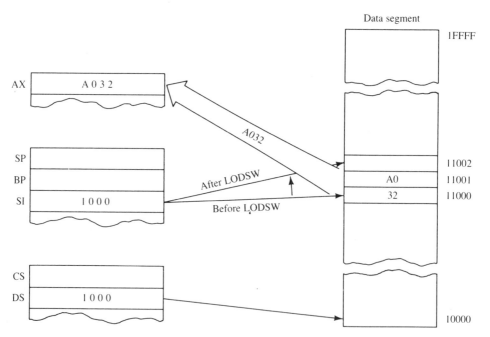

FIGURE 3-13   The effect of executing the LODSW instruction if DS = 1000H, SI = 1000H, D = 0, 11000H = 32, and 11001H = A0.

TABLE 3–9 Forms of the STOS instruction

Symbolic	Function
STOSB	[DI] = AL, byte transfer
STOSW	[DI] = AX, word transfer
STOS BYTE	[DI] = AL, if BYTE is defined as a byte
STOS WORD	[DI] = AX, if WORD is defined as a word

STOS with a REP. The *repeat prefix* (REP) may be added to any string instruction. REP causes CX to be decremented by a 1 each time that the string instruction that it prefixes is executed. This causes the string operation to repeat until the value of CX (count) is a 0.

Suppose that 10 bytes of data in an area of memory (BUFFER) must be cleared to 0. This can be accomplished with a series of STOS instructions (10 of them) or with one STOS prefixed by a REP. The program listed in Example 3–1 uses the LES instruction, which loads an address from the memory, to initialize both the ES and DI registers prior to loading the counter and clearing the direction flag.

EXAMPLE 3–1

```
;clearing a block of memory using STOS

0000 C4 3E 05BC R    LES  DI,BUFFER    ;get buffer address
0004 B9 000A         MOV  CX,10        ;load counter
0007 FC              CLD               ;select auto-increment
0008 B0 00           MOV  AL,0         ;clear AL
000A F3/ AA          REP  STOSB        ;clear buffer
```

The address that the LES loads must be defined by the assembler in some manner. The DD (define-double-word) pseudo-operation is often used to define the contents of a 32-bit memory pointer. Next AL is cleared to 00H and the STOSB instruction, prefixed by a REP, is executed. This instruction will store the contents of AL in 10 consecutive bytes of the memory array BUFFER. After each 0 is stored in the buffer, the STOSB instruction automatically advances the memory pointer in DI by a 1.

A much faster way of clearing the buffer is to use the REP STOSW instruction with a count of 5, as listed in Example 3–2. Here 5 words of 0000H are stored in the buffer, clearing 10 bytes of memory. The programmer is free to decide if the REP prefix will be on the same line as the STOS or on the preceding line in the assembly language program.

EXAMPLE 3–2

```
;using STOSW to clear a buffer

0000 C4 3E 05BC R    LES  DI,BUFFER    ;get buffer address
0004 B9 0005         MOV  CX,5         ;load counter
0007 FC              CLD               ;select auto-increment
0008 B8 0000         MOV  AX,0         ;clear AL
000B F3/ AB          REP  STOSW        ;clear buffer
```

MOVS

The most powerful string data transfer instruction is the MOVS because it transfers a byte or word from one area of the memory to another—in other words, it is a *memory-to-memory transfer*. An MOVS transfers the data from the location addressed by the SI register in the data segment to the location addressed by the DI register in the extra segment. Table 3–10 lists the permissible forms of the MOVS instruction. Notice that only the source operand address located in DS may be overridden with the override prefix.

Suppose that the contents of a 100-byte array of data must be transferred to another 100-byte array. The repeated MOVSB instruction is ideal for this operation, as the program listing of Example 3–3 illustrates.

EXAMPLE 3–3

```
        ;using the MOVS instruction

0000 C4 3E 05C0 R    LES  DI,LIST1    ;addressLIST1
0004 C5 36 05C4 R    LDS  SI,LIST2    ;address LIST2
0008 FC              CLD              ;clear direction
0009 B9 0064         MOV  CX,100      ;load counter
000C F3/ A4          REP  MOVSB       ;transfer 100 bytes
```

LES and LDS are used to load the segment registers and DI and SI with the addresses of LIST1 and LIST2. If the DS and ES registers are already loaded with the proper segments, then the MOV instruction is substituted for LES and LDS. Once the pointers are initialized, the counter is loaded, and the data are transferred by the repeated MOVSB instruction.

TABLE 3–10   Forms of the MOVS instruction

Symbolic	Function
MOVSB	[DI] = [SI], byte transfer
MOVSW	[DI] = [SI], word transfer
MOVS BYTE1,BYTE2	[DI] = [SI], if BYTE1 and BYTE2 are bytes
MOVS WORD1,WORD2	[DI] = [SI], if WORD1 and WORD2 are words

3–5   MISCELLANEOUS DATA TRANSFER INSTRUCTIONS

Do not be fooled by the word "miscellaneous." The data transfer instructions detailed in this section—XCHG, LAHF, SAHF, XLAT, IN, and OUT—are extremely important ones, but, because they are used less than the others, they are grouped together in this section of the text.

XCHG

The XCHG instruction exchanges the contents of any register with the contents of any register or memory location, not including the segment registers or memory-to-memory exchanges. It uses any of the addressing modes discussed in Chapter 2. Table 3–11 lists the forms of the XCHG instruction, along with the binary bit pattern required for each type. As this table illustrates, an XCHG between AX and another 16-bit register is the most efficient operation because it takes only 1 byte of memory to store the instruction.

LAHF and SAHF

LAHF and SAHF are used in the translation of 8085 software to 8086/8088 software. Otherwise, they have very little application in the programming of the 8086/8088. Specifically, LAHF and SAHF transfer the least significant (8085-like) flag byte to and from the AH register. This operation, in conjunction with a PUSH AX or POP AX, emulates the 8086 PUSH PSW and POP PSW instructions as long as the relative positions of A and F are not important. The sequence of instructions in Example 3–4 shows how to emulate an 8086 PUSH PSW so that the positions of A and F are correct.

EXAMPLE 3–4

```
        ;emulating the 8085 PUSH PSW instruction

000E 9F            LAHF                ;transfer flags
000F 86 C4         XCHG AL,AH          ;position A and F
0011 50            PUSH AX             ;save them
```

XLAT

The XLAT (translate) instruction converts the contents of the AL register into a number stored in a table. This instruction is used to perform the direct table lookup technique that converts from one code to another. An XLAT instruction first adds the contents of AL to the contents of the BX register to form a memory address in the data segment. It then loads the data stored at this address into the AL register.

Suppose that a 7-segment LED display lookup table is stored at location TABLE and the translate instruction is used to convert the contents of the accumulator from BCD into 7-segment code. Example 3–5 provides a short program to accomplish this. Figure 3–14

TABLE 3–11 XCHG instructions

Symbolic	Byte 1	Byte 2
XCHG AX,reg	1001 0rrr	
XCHG reg,reg	1000 011w	11rr raaa
XCHG reg,mem	1000 011w	mmrr raaa

Notes: aaa = any memory addressing mode, mm = mode mode (MOD), rrr = any register except a segment regregister, and w = word/byte.

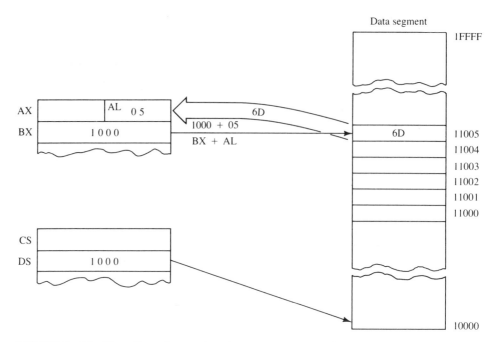

FIGURE 3–14   The effect of executing the XLAT instruction at the point just before the 6DH from memory location 11005H is gated into the AL register.

illustrates the operation of this sequence of instructions if TABLE = 1000H, DS = 4000H, and the initial value of AL = 05H (a 5 BCD).

EXAMPLE 3–5

```
          ;using XLAT to convert from BCD to 7-segment code

0012 BB 000 R    MOV   BX,OFFSET TABLE    ;address lookup table
0015 D7          XLAT
```

IN and OUT

Table 3–12 lists the forms of the IN and OUT instructions. Notice that the contents of AX or AL *only* are transferred between the I/O device and the microprocessor. IN transfers data from an I/O device into the AL or AX register, and OUT transfers data from AL or AX to an I/O device.

   Two forms or port-addressing modes are available with the IN and OUT instructions: *fixed port* and *variable port*. Fixed-port addressing allows data transfers between either AL or AX and an 8-bit I/O port address. It is called "fixed-port addressing" because the port number is stored with the instruction, usually in a ROM, where the port number is fixed.

Variable-port addressing allows data transfers between either AL or AX and a 16-bit I/O port address. It is called ''variable-port addressing'' because the port number is stored in the DX register, which is changed at will by the programmer.

If, for example, an OUT 19H,AL instruction is executed, it transfers the contents of AL out of the microprocessor to an I/O device with the address 19H. Figure 3–15 illustrates how this information appears on the external pin connections of an 8088 microprocessor-based system.

TABLE 3–12 IN and OUT instructions

Symbolic	Function
IN AL,pp	8-bit data from port pp are input to AL
IN AX,pp	16-bit data from port pp are input to AX
IN AL,DX	8-bit data from port DX are input to AL
IN AX,DX	16-bit data from port DX are input to AX
OUT pp,AL	8-bit data from AL are sent to port pp
OUT pp,AX	16-bit data from AX are sent to port pp
OUT DX,AL	8-bit data from AL are sent to port DX
OUT DX,AX	16-bit data from AX are sent to port DX

Notes: pp = an 8-bit I/O port address and DX = the 16-bit I/O port port address held in register DX.

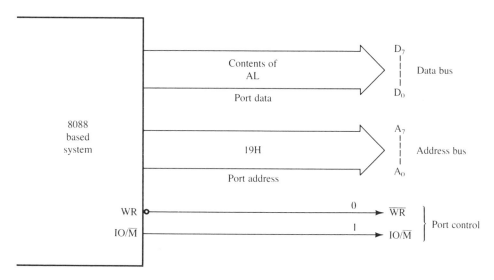

FIGURE 3–15 The location of the port number or port address, the data, and the control signals on the 8088 buses for an OUT 19H,AL.

3–6   SEGMENT OVERRIDE PREFIX

The segment override prefix, which may be added to almost any 8086/8088 instruction in any memory-addressing mode, allows the programmer to change the default segment for any instruction by adding an extra byte (the segment override prefix) to the beginning of an instruction in machine code.

For example, MOV AX,[DI], which normally addresses data in the data segment, can be modified to the MOV AX,ES:[DI] instruction, which will then address data in the extra segment.

Table 3–13 lists some instructions that have been altered by the segment override prefix. Notice that most of these instructions allow data to be accessed in any segment. Because the segment override prefix adds an extra byte to an instruction, it is wise to use this feature as little as possible to maximize the efficiency of the software.

3–7   ASSEMBLER DIRECTIVES

Assembler directives are commands to the assembler that direct the assembly process. This section of the text shows how to use assembler directives and how to write an assembly language program.

Directives

The 8086/8088 assembler recognizes many assembler directives (see Table 3–14) that indicate how an operand is treated by the assembler or how the assembler handles a program.

Storing Data in a Memory Segment

The DB, DW, or DD directives (also DQ and DT) store bytes, words, or double words of data in the memory. Example 3–6 illustrates how various data can be stored.

Memory can be reserved for future data by using the DB, DW, or DD directives followed by the duplicate (DUP) directive. DUP itself indicates to the assembler that a character surrounded by ( ) is to be duplicated; the digit before it specifies the number of duplications. If a question mark appears inside the parentheses, then no character is

TABLE 3–13 Instructions that include the segment override prefix

Symbolic	Segment Accessed	Normal Segment
MOV AX,DS:[BP]	Data segment	Stack segment
MOV AX,ES:[BP]	Extra segment	Stack segment
MOV AX,SS:[DI]	Stack segment	Data segment
MOV AX,CS:[SI]	Code segment	Data segment
MOV AX,ES:LIST	Extra segment	Data Segment

TABLE 3-14 8086/8088
assembler directives

Word	Function
ALIGN	Starts at an even memory address
ASSUME	Indicates where the segments are located
AT	Stores the segment in the memory
BYTE	Acts as a byte operand
DB	Defines a byte (8 bits)
DD	Defines a double word (32 bits)
DQ	Defines quad word (64 bits)
DT	Defines 10 bytes (80 bits)
DUP	Duplicates the following character
DW	Defines word (16 bits)
END	Indicates end of listing
ENDP	Indicates end of procedure
ENDS	Indicates end of segment
EQU	Equates
FAR	Acts as far memory pointer (intersegment pointer)
NEAR	Acts as near memory pointer (intrasegment pointer)
OFFSET	Specifies the offset address
ORG	Sets origin within segment
PROC	Defines beginning of procedure
PTR	Acts as memory pointer
SEGMENT	Designates start of segment
STACK	Indicates stack segment
THIS	Used as THIS BYTE or THIS WORD
WORD	Acts as a word operand

Note: Most of these key words are accepted by most versions of the 8086/8088 assembler.

duplicated and the memory is left unchanged. Example 3-7 illustrates some examples of the DUP directive.

EXAMPLE 3-6

```
;using the DB, DW, and DD directives

05C8 01 02 03   DATA_ONE   DB    1,2,3        ;3 bytes defined
05CB 45                    DB    45H          ;byte defined
05CC 41                    DB    'A'          ;byte defined
05CD F0                    DB    11110000B    ;a binary 11110000
05CE 000C 000D             DW    12,13        ;words defined
05D2 05C0 R     DATA_TWO   DW    LIST1        ;word defined as LIST1
05D4 2345                  DW    2345H        ;word defined as 2345H
05D6 0000FFFF              DD    0FFFFH       ;double-word defined
```

EXAMPLE 3-7

```
                             ;using the duplicate (DUP) directive

05C8 00                      LIST_A    DB   ?                      ;reserve one byte
05C9 000A[                   LIST_B    DB   10 DUP(?)    ;reserve 10 bytes
        ??
                             ]

05D3 00                      ALIGN
05D4 000A[                   LIST_C    DW   10 DUP(?)    ;reserve 10 words
        ????
                             ]

05E8 0016[                   LIST_D    DD   22 DUP(?)    ;reserve double-words
        ????????
                             ]

0640 0064[                   ZEROS     DB   100 DUP(0)   ;store 100 zeros
        00
                             ]
```

EQU and THIS

The equate statement (EQU) is used to equate a numeric, ASCII, or label to another label. Equates are used to make an assembly language program clearer to facilitate debugging at a later date. Example 3–8 provides several different examples of the EQU statement.

EXAMPLE 3-8

```
               ;using the equate statement

= 000A         TEN           EQU 10
= 0041         LETTER_A      EQU 'A'
= 0063         COUNT         EQU 99
= 000A         NUMB_10       EQU 10
```

The THIS directive indicates a label name without specifying a new memory location. For example, when the stack is initialized, the stack pointer (SP) is placed at the top of the stack with the THIS and EQU directives. Example 3–9 shows how the term WORD is used with THIS and EQU to indicate the top of the stack.

EXAMPLE 3-9

```
           ;using the THIS, WORD, and BYTE directives

05C8[ 0032[              STACK_MEM DW    50 DUP (?)      ;reserve 50 bytes
        ???
                         ]

= 062C                   STACK_TOP EQU   THIS WORD       ;this is the top
062C 0A                            DB    10              ;store a 10
= 062D        DATA                 EQU   THIS BYTE       ;DATA is a byte
```

Memory Organization

The assembler uses special directives to inform the assembler of different memory segments. The SEGMENT directive names the beginning of a segment, and the ENDS indicates the end. Once the SEGMENT and ENDS directives have created a segment, the ASSUME statement informs the assembler which segments to use for data, extra, stack, and code segments.

Example 3–10 shows how to use these directives. Notice how the SEGMENT and ENDS indicate the boundaries and name of each segment and how the ASSUME statement indicates the segments used with CS, DS, SS, and ES.

EXAMPLE 3–10

```
0000                    DATA_SEG        SEGMENT

0000 000A[              LIST_A          DB   10 DUP (?)
            ??
                        ]

000A 000C[              LIST_B          DW   12 DUP (6)

            0006
                        ] ,

0022                    DATA_SEG        ENDS

0000                    EXTRA_SEG       SEGMENT

0000 48454C4C4F         STRING          DB   'HELLO'

0005                    EXTRA_SEG       ENDS

0000                    STACK_SEG       SEGMENT   STACK

0000 0032[                              DW   50 DUP (?)
            ????
                        ]

= 0064                  STACK_TOP       EQU THIS WORD

0064                    STACK_SEG       ENDS

0000                    CODE_SEG        SEGMENT

                        ASSUME      CS:CODE_SEG,SS:STACK_SEG
                        ASSUME      DS:DATA_SEG,ES:EXTRA_SEG

0000                    BEGIN           PROC      FAR
0000 BC 0064 R                          MOV       SP,OFFSET STACK_TOP
0003 B8 --- R                           MOV       AX,DATA_SEG
0006 8E D8                              MOV       DS,AX
0008 B8 --- R                           MOV       AX,EXTRA_SEG
000B 8E C0                              MOV       ES,AX
```

```
                         ;program here

000D                 BEGIN              ENDP

000D                 CODE_SEG           ENDS

                                        END BEGIN
```

The operating system normally loads the code segment register, but not the data, stack, and extra segment registers, which must be loaded by the start of any program. In this case, the AX register is loaded with the address of the data segment and then moved into DS. Note that the OFFSET directive is not used here: the assembler automatically inserts the OFFSET for any label defined as a segment name. The ES register is loaded in the same manner.

If you look closely at Example 3–10, you will notice that this example has been assembled so that an assembled program can be viewed. Notice how the four segments have been set up for this example. The data segment, called DATA–SEG, contains two variables. LIST–A is defined as 10 bytes of memory, and LIST–B is defined as 12 words of memory with each word containing a 0006. The extra segment, called EXTRA–SEG, contains an ASCII character string dubbed STRING. The stack segment, called STACK– SEG contains an area of memory that is 50 words in length for the system stack. Notice that the pseudo-opcode, STACK is listed beside SEGMENT to identify this as the stack segment for the assembler. Finally, the code segment, called CODE–SEG, contains AS- SUME statements that are used to identify the actual names of the segments and a few instructions that initialize the stack pointer, data segment, and extra segment registers. Notice that the assembler lists address 0064 as 0064. This is not an error, but the way that the assembler lists 16-bit data. When the program is linked for use in the computer the linker reverses this and produces a 6400, which is in the correct form for 8086/8088 machine language.

If a segment must be placed at a particular memory location, the AT directive originates it. Example 3–11 shows how the AT statement places the DATA segment at 0100H by loading the 0100H into the segment register so that the segment actually begins at memory location 01000H.

Not only are the data in this example stored at segment address 0100H, but LIST–A also starts at offset address 0100H within the data segment and is stored in the memory beginning at memory location 01100H. In most programs, the AT and ORG statements are not used.

EXAMPLE 3–11

```
0000                 DATA_SEG       SEGMENT AT 0100H

0100                                ORG      100H

0100 000A[           LIST_A         DW       10 DUP (?)
           ???
                     ]

010A                 DATA_SEG       ENDS
```

Subroutines/Procedures

Subroutines or procedures are indicated by the PROC and ENDP directives. PROC indicates the name and start of a procedure as well as its type (NEAR or FAR). ENDP indicates the end of a procedure.

For example, suppose that the contents of registers BX, CX, and DX must be added and the result stored in register AX. The listing of procedure ADDEM provided in Example 3-12 shows how this is accomplished.

EXAMPLE 3-12

```
0000                    ADDEM     PROC     FAR

0000 8B C3                        MOV      AX,BX
0002 03 C1                        ADD      AX,CX
0004 03 C2                        ADD      AX,DX
0006 CB                           RET

0007                    ADDEM     ENDP
```

The ADDEM procedure is defined with the PROC directive as a FAR procedure or label, which can exist at any memory location in the machine because it is composed of an offset address and a segment address. A NEAR procedure or label, on the other hand, must appear in the current code segment because its address is composed of only an offset address. If a label is followed by a colon (:), it is a NEAR label (LABEL:). If not, it is a FAR label (LABEL). Most labels should be followed by a colon because it is rare for a JMP or a CALL to occur outside of the current code segment.

OFFSET and PTR

The OFFSET directive indicates an offset address to the assembler, and the PTR or pointer directive indicates the type of data (byte or word).

For example, the address DATA can be loaded into the SI register by the MOV SI,OFFSET DATA instruction. A MOV SI,DATA instruction loads the contents of address DATA into SI. An OFFSET loads the address of DATA.

PTR is used when the type of data is not clear to the assembler. For example, suppose that the following instruction appears in a program: MOV [BX],2. Does this instruction move an 8- or 16-bit number 2 into the memory? The PTR directive with the word BYTE or WORD will make this clear to the assembler. Thus, the MOV BYTE PTR[BX],2 instruction moves a 2 into the 8-bit memory location addressed by BX, and the MOV WORD PTR[BX],2 instruction moves a 2 into the 16-bit memory location.

A Sample Program

Example 3-13 provides a sample program that transfers the contents of BLOCK1 into BLOCK2. Notice that the REP MOVSB instruction accomplishes the data transfer.

This example illustrates many of the directives discussed in this section of the text. Notice that COUNT is equated to a 100 so that the MOV CX,COUNT instruction loads the counter for the repeated MOVSB instruction. Also notice that the last instruction is an INT 21H, which returns control of the computer to the DOS (disk operating system) in a personal computer if AH = 4CH. We provide more detail for the assembler in later sections of the text and also in an appendix.

EXAMPLE 3–13

```
                ;example program that moves 100 bytes from BLOCK1 to BLOCK2


0000                    DATA_SEG    SEGMENT
0000 0064[              BLOCK1      DB      100 DUP (?)
        ??

        ]

0064                    DATA_SEG    ENDS

0000                    EXTRA_SEG   SEGMENT

0000 0064[              BLOCK2      DB      100 DUP (?)
        ??

        ]

0064                    EXTRA_SEG   ENDS

0000                    CODE_SEG    SEGMENT

                        ASSUME  CS:CODE_SEG,DS:DATA_SEG,ES:EXTRA_SEG

0000            BEGIN           PROC    FAR

0000 B8 --- R                   MOV     AX,DATA_SEG
0003 8E D8                      MOV     DS,AX
0005 B8 --- R                   MOV     AX,EXTRA_SEG
0008 8E C0                      MOV     ES,AX

000A BE 0000 R                  MOV     SI,OFFSET BLOCK1
000D BF 0000 R                  MOV     DI,OFFSET BLOCK2
0010 FC                         CLD
0011 B9 0064                    MOV     CX,100
0014 F3/ A4                     REP     MOVSB

0016 B4 4C                      MOV     AH,4CH
0018 CD 21                      INT     21H

001A            BEGIN           ENDP

001A            CODE_SEG        ENDS

                                END BEGIN
```

3-8   SUMMARY

1. Data movement instructions transfer data between registers, registers and memory, registers and the stack, memory and the stack, the I/O and the accumulator, and the flags and the stack.

2. Data movement instructions include: MOV, PUSH, POP, XCHG, XLAT, IN, OUT, LEA, LDS, LES, LAHF, SAHF, and the string instructions: LODS, STOS, and MOVS.

3. The first byte of all 8086/8088 instructions contains the opcode, which specifies the operation to be performed by the microprocessor for the current instruction.

4. The D bit in an opcode indicates the direction of the data flow. If D = 0, the data flow from the register specified in REG, and if D = 1, the data flow to the register specified in the REG field of an instruction.

5. The W bit of an instruction indicates whether the instruction is to operate upon a word or a byte. If W = 1, a word is operated upon, and if W = 0, a byte is operated upon.

6. MOD selects the operational mode of the machine language instruction. A MOD = 00 selects no displacement; MOD = 01 selects an 8-bit sign-extended displacement; MOD = 10 selects a 16-bit displacement; and MOD = 11 indicates that the R/M field contains a register.

7. A 3-bit binary code specifies the REG and R/M fields when MOD = 11. The 8-bit registers are AL, CL, DL, BL, AH, CH, DH, and BH, and the 16-bit registers are AX, CX, DX, BX, SP, BP, SI, and DI.

8. When the R/M field contains a memory-addressing mode, the 3-bit code in R/M indicates one of the following addressing modes: [BX + SI], [BX + DI], [BP + SI], [BP + DI], [SI], [DI], [BP], or [BX].

9. All data are addressed in the data segment unless the SP or BP registers are used to hold the offset address. In these two cases, the data are addressed in the stack segment.

10. The segment registers may be addressed only by the MOV, PUSH, or POP instructions. MOV CS,XX and POP CS are not allowed, but any other segment register may use these two instruction forms.

11. PUSH and POP instructions always transfer 2 bytes of data between the stack and another register or memory location. When data are pushed onto the stack, the most significant byte is stored first, followed by the least significant byte. The stack pointer is then decremented by a 2. A POP works in the reverse order, with the stack pointer incremented by a 2 after 2 bytes are removed from the stack.

12. PUSHF and POPF transfer data between the stack memory and the flag register.

13. LEA, LDS, and LES load a register or a register and a segment register with the address of memory data. LEA loads the offset address of memory data into a targeted 16-bit register. LDS and LES load an offset address into a 16-bit pointer and also a new segment address into either DS or ES.

14. String data transfer instructions use either the DI or SI registers or both to address data in the memory. The DI offset address is located in the extra segment, the SI offset address in the data segment for string operations.

15. The direction flag bit (D) specifies whether DI and/or SI are incremented or decremented after a string transfer. If D = 0, auto-increment is selected, and if D = 1,
auto-decrement is selected. These registers are incremented by a 1 for byte transfers
and a 2 for word transfers.

16. LODS loads AL or AX from the memory addressed by the SI register; STOS stores
AL or AX into the memory location addressed by DI; and MOVS transfers a byte or
word from the memory location addressed by SI into that addressed by DI.

17. The REP (repeat) prefix causes any of the string data transfer instructions to repeat the
number of times contained in CX. For each repeat, CX is decremented by a 1 so that,
if CX becomes a 0, then the next sequential instruction is executed, and, if not, the
string instruction is repeated.

18. The XLAT instruction converts the data in register AL into a number that is stored at
the location addressed by the sum of BX and AL.

19. IN and OUT are used to transfer data between the AL register and I/O or the AX
register and I/O. Two types of IN and OUT instructions are available: fixed port and
variable port.

20. The segment override prefix allows data to be addressed by almost any instruction in
any segment. For example, MOV AX,[BX] addresses data within the data segment
by default. It can address data in the extra segment by the segment override prefix,
ES: in this example—MOV AX,ES:[BX].

21. Assembler directives DB (define byte), DW (define word), DD (define double word),
and DUP (duplicate) store data directly in the 8086/8088 memory.

22. EQU equates values or labels to labels.

23. SEGMENT indicates the start and name of a segment; ENDS indicates the end.

24. ASSUME directs the assembler to the label used for the segment in a program.

25. PROC indicates the start and name of a procedure; ENDP indicates its end.

3-9   QUESTIONS AND PROBLEMS

1. The first byte of any 8086/8088 instruction is always the _____ .

2. Describe the purpose of the D and W bits in a machine language instruction.

3. The MOD field in a machine language instruction specifies what information?

4. If the register field (REG) of an instruction contains a 010 and W = 0, what register
does the instruction select?

5. What memory-addressing mode is specified when R/M = 001 and the MOD
bits = 00?

6. Identify the default segment register assigned for:
   a. SP
   b. BX
   c. DI
   d. BP
   e. SI

7. Convert an 8B07H instruction from machine language into assembly language.

8. Convert an 8B1E004CH instruction from machine language into assembly language.
9. If a MOV SI,[BX + 2] instruction appears in an assembly language program, what is its machine language equivalent?
10. Is a MOV CS,AX instruction a valid 8086/8088 instruction? Explain your answer.
11. What type of MOV instruction might be 6 bytes long?
12. PUSH and POP always transfer a _____-bit number between a register or memory and the stack.
13. What segment register may not be popped from the stack?
14. Describe the function of each of the following instructions:
    a. PUSH AX
    b. POP SI
    c. PUSH [BX]
    d. PUSHF
    e. POP DS
15. Explain what happens when the PUSH BX instruction is executed, showing which locations receive the contents of BH and BL. (Assume that SP = 0100H and SS = 0200H.)
16. The POP instruction always increments SP by a _____.
17. What values are loaded into the SP and SS registers so that the stack segment begins at location 02200H and the stack pointer addresses the top of the stack segment?
18. Compare the operation of a MOV BX,DATA instruction with an LEA BX,DATA instruction.
19. What is the difference between an LEA BX,DATA instruction and a MOV BX,OFFSET DATA instruction?
20. In general, which is more efficient, a MOV with an OFFSET or an LEA instruction?
21. Describe how the LDS BX,DATA instruction operates.
22. What is the difference between the LDS and the LES instructions?
23. Develop a sequence of instructions that moves the contents of data segment memory locations DATA and DATA + 1 into BX, DX, and SI.
24. What is the purpose of the direction flag bit?
25. Which instructions are used to set and clear the direction flag bit?
26. The string instructions use the SI and DI registers to address data in which of the memory segments?
27. Explain the operation of the LODSB instruction.
28. Explain the operation of the STOSW instruction.
29. What does the repeat prefix (REP) accomplish, and what type of instruction may it be used with?
30. Develop a sequence of instructions that copies 12 bytes of data from an area of memory addressed by SOURCE into an area of memory addressed by DEST. (Both SOURCE and DEST contain 32-bit addresses.)
31. Repeat Question 30 using offset addresses for both SOURCE and DEST.
32. Select an assembly language instruction that exchanges the contents of the BX register with the contents of the SI register.
33. Would LAHF and SAHF be used during normal 8086/8088 operation? Explain your answer.
34. Explain how XLAT transforms the contents of the accumulator (AL).

35. Explain what the IN AL,12H instruction accomplishes.
36. What is a segment override prefix?
37. Select an instruction that moves bytes of data from the memory location addressed by the BX register in the extra segment into the AH register.
38. What do assembler language directives accomplish in general?
39. Describe the purpose of the following assembly language directives: DB, DW, and DD.
40. Select an assembly language directive that reserves 30 bytes of memory for LIST1.
41. Describe the purpose of the EQU directive.
42. SEGMENT and ENDS are used to set the boundaries of a segment in the 8086/8088 assembly language program. How can a segment be assigned to an actual memory location?
43. Procedures must be preceded and followed by which two assembly language directives?
44. Explain why PTR is necessary in the following assembly language instruction: MOV WORD PTR [DI],3
45. What does the INT 21H preceded by a MOV AH,4CH accomplish in the personal computer?

CHAPTER 4

Arithmetic and Logic Instructions

INTRODUCTION

In this chapter, we will examine the arithmetic and logic instructions available in the 8086/8088 instruction set. Arithmetic instructions include addition, subtraction, multiplication, division, comparison, negation, incrementation, and decrementation. Logic instructions include AND, OR, Exclusive-OR, NOT, shifts, rotates, and logical comparison (TEST).

If you are already familiar with an 8-bit microprocessor, you will recognize that the 8086/8088 instruction set is much superior. And even if you have nothing to compare it to, you will quickly notice that the 8086/8088 possesses a powerful subset of arithmetic and logic instructions.

We will also introduce the **string comparison instructions,** which are very useful for scanning tabular data for a particular coincidence of information and for comparing two areas of memory for a match or no-match condition.

OBJECTIVES

Upon completion of this chapter, you will be able to:

1. Use the 8086/8088 arithmetic instructions to accomplish simple binary, BCD, and ASCII arithmetic.
2. Use AND, OR, and Exclusive-OR to accomplish binary bit manipulation.
3. Use the shift and rotate instructions.
4. Check the contents of a table for a match with the string instructions.

4–1   ADDITION, SUBTRACTION, AND COMPARISON

The core grouping of instructions in the arithmetic instruction set of any microprocessor always includes addition, subtraction, and comparison. The 8086/8088 microprocessor is no different. In this section, we will define these instructions, illustrate their use in manipulating register and memory data, and present some variations on them.

Addition

Addition takes many forms in the 8086/8088. In this section, we detail the use of ADD for both 8- and 16-bit binary addition and the *increment instruction,* which adds 1 to the contents of a register or a memory location. In Section 4–3, we will examine some other forms, such as the addition of BCD and ASCII numbers.

Table 4–1 illustrates the addressing modes allowed for the ADD instruction. (Addressing modes include all those mentioned in Chapter 2 of this text.) Since there are well over 1,000 possible 8086/8088 addition instructions, it is quite impossible to include them all in this table. About the only things that *cannot* be added are the contents of any segment register or the contents of one memory location to another. As we pointed out previously, the contents of the segment registers may only be moved, pushed, or popped.

Register Addition.   Example 4–1 provides a simple program illustrating the use of some of the register addition instructions. Notice in this example that the 16-bit contents of registers BX, CX, and DX are added to the contents of the AX register. Also note that after each addition, the microprocessor modifies the contents of the flag register. It is very important to remember that arithmetic and logic instructions always modify the contents

TABLE 4–1   Addition instructions

Instruction	Comment
ADD AL,BL	AL becomes the sum of AL + BL
ADD CX, DI	CX becomes the sum of CX + DI
ADD BL,44H	BL becomes the sum of BL + 44H
ADD BX,35AFH	BX becomes the sum of BX + 35AFH
ADD [BX],AL	The data segment memory byte addressed by BX becomes the sum of the data segment memory byte addressed by BX + AL
ADD CL,[BP]	CL becomes the sum of the stack segment memory byte addressed by BP + CL
ADD BX,[SI + 2]	BX becomes the sum of the data segment word addressed by SI + 2, plus the contents of BX
ADD CL,TEMP	CL becomes the sum of CL plus the data segment byte TEMP
ADD BX,TEMP[DI]	BX becomes the sum of BX plus the contents of the data segment array TEMP plus offset DI
ADD [BX + DI],DL	The data segment memory byte addressed by BX + DI becomes the sum of that byte plus DL

of the flag register. An ADD of any type affects the sign, zero, carry, auxiliary carry, parity, and overflow flags.

EXAMPLE 4-1

```
0000  03 C3              ADD     AX,BX
0002  03 C1              ADD     AX,CX
0004  03 C2              ADD     AX,DX
```

Immediate Addition.   In Example 4-2, which illustrates an 8-bit immediate addition, the flag bits are depicted along with their results. Here a 12H is first moved into register DL with an immediate move: then a 33H is added to it with an immediate addition. After the addition, the sum (45H) is placed in the DL register. As in all additions, the flags change, and in this example they change as follows:

$$Z = 0 \text{ result not } 0$$
$$C = 0 \text{ no carry}$$
$$A = 0 \text{ no half-carry}$$
$$S = 0 \text{ result positive}$$
$$P = 0 \text{ odd parity}$$
$$O = 0 \text{ no overflow}$$

EXAMPLE 4-2

```
0006  B2 12             MOV     DL,12H
0008  80 C2 33          ADD     DL,33H
```

Memory-to-Register Addition.   Suppose that a particular application requires the addition of memory data to the AL register. Example 4-3 provides an example of just such a situation, in which data stored in the data segment at consecutive memory byte locations DATA and DATA + 1 are added to register AL.

EXAMPLE 4-3

```
000B  BF 0064 R         MOV     DI,OFFSET DATA
000E  B0 00             MOV     AL,0
0010  02 05             ADD     AL,[DI]
0012  02 45 01          ADD     AL,[DI+1]
```

The operation proceeds as follows. First, the DI register is loaded with the offset address of DATA by the special pseudo-operation OFFSET, which loads an offset address into a register. DATA is located in the data segment in this example because the DI register is used to address memory data: All memory data reside in the data segment unless the BP or SP pointers are used to address memory or an override prefix is used before the instruction. If BP is used, then the stack segment contains the data. However, if an override prefix is used, the data may reside in any segment.

The instruction ADD AL,[DI] addresses the data at memory location DATA and adds it to the contents of the AL register. This occurs because DI is loaded with address DATA before the ADD instruction is executed. Next ADD AL,[DI + 1] adds the contents of memory address DATA + 1 to the AL register, leaving the sum of both DATA and DATA + 1 in register AL.

Array Addition.   Suppose that an array of data (ARRAY) contained in the memory has 10 bytes of data numbered element 0 through element 9. Example 4−4 illustrates a program that will add the contents of elements 3, 5, and 7. (This is not necessarily the best choice, but it is a convenient way to illustrate this type of addressing.)

EXAMPLE 4−4

```
0015 B0 00              MOV   AL,0
0017 BE 0003            MOV   SI,3
001A 02 84 00C8 R       ADD   AL,ARRAY[SI]
001E 02 84 00CA R       ADD   AL,ARRAY[SI+2]
0022 02 84 00CC R       ADD   AL,ARRAY[SI+4]
```

In this example, the AL register is cleared to 0 after a 3 is placed in register SI, which initially addresses the third element in the array. Next ADD AL,ARRAY[SI] adds array element 3 to the AL register, because SI contains a 3 that is added to address ARRAY. Next, elements 5 and 7 are added to element 3 in the AL register by the same addressing technique, except that a 2 is added to SI for element 5 and a 4 for element 7.

Increment Addition.   Increment addition (INC) is the addition of 1. In this operation, any addressing mode is allowed except for segment register addressing. Table 4−2 illustrates many of the forms of increment addition available in the 8086/8088 instruction set. Again, it is impossible to list them all because of the large number available.

Example 4−5 illustrates how Example 4−3 can be modified to use an INC instruction. Here INC DI modifies the contents of DI so that it points to address DATA + 1. If you compare Examples 4−3 and 4−5, you will notice that both add the contents of memory location DATA to DATA + 1. The only difference is that each does it in a slightly different way. The increment instruction affects the same flags as addition, except for the carry flag, which is not affected.

EXAMPLE 4−5

```
0026 BF 0064 R          MOV   DI,OFFEST DATA
0029 B0 00              MOV   AL,0
002B 02 05              ADD   AL,[DI]
002D 47                 INC   DI
002E 02 05              ADD   AL,[DI]
```

Subtraction

In this section we detail the many forms of subtraction (SUB) available for both 8- and 16-bit binary subtraction. We also include the decrement instruction, which is used to

TABLE 4-2 Increment instructions

Instruction	Comment
INC BL	Add 1 to register BL
INC SP	Add 1 to register SP
INC BYTE PTR[BX]	Add 1 to the byte of data segment memory addressed by pointer BX
INC WORD PTR[SI]	Add 1 to the 16-bit word of data segment memory addressed by pointer SI

TABLE 4-3 Subtraction instructions

Instruction	Comment
SUB CL,BL	CL becomes the difference of CL − BL
SUB AX,SP	AX becomes the difference of AX − SP
SUB DH,6FH	DH becomes the difference of DH − 6FH
SUB AX,0CCCCH	AX becomes the difference of AX − CCCCH
SUB [DI],CH	The data segment memory byte addressed by DI becomes the difference of the data segment memory byte addressed by DI − CH
SUB CH,[BP]	CH becomes the difference of the stack segment memory byte addressed by BP − CH
SUB AH,TEMP	AH becomes the difference of AH minus the contents of memory byte TEMP located in the data segment
SUB DI,TEMP[BX]	DI becomes the difference of DI minus the contents of data segment array TEMP plus offset BX

subtract a 1 from a register or memory location. Section 4-4 illustrates the subtraction of BCD and ASCII numbers.

Table 4-3 provides a list of the addressing modes allowed for the SUB instruction. These modes include all those mentioned in Chapter 2. In addition, there are well over 1,000 possible instructions. About the only things that cannot be subtracted are the contents of any segment register or the contents of one memory location from another. Like addition, subtraction also affects all the flag bits, and recall that the contents of the segment registers may only be moved, pushed, or popped.

Register Subtraction. Example 4-6 provides a simple program illustrating the use of some of the register subtraction instructions. Note in this example that the 16-bit contents of registers CX and DX are subtracted from the contents of the BX register. Also note that, after each subtraction the microprocessor modifies the contents of the flag register, as does every arithmetic and logic instruction.

EXAMPLE 4-6

```
0030 2B D9          SUB    BX,CX
0032 2B DA          SUB    BX,DX
```

Immediate Subtraction.   In Example 4–7, which illustrates an 8-bit immediate subtraction, the flag bits are depicted along with their results. Here a 22H is first moved into
register CH with an immediate move; then a 44H is subtracted from it with an immediate
subtraction. After the subtraction, the difference (DEH) is placed in the CH register. As
with all subtractions, the flags change, and in this example they change as follows:

$$Z = 0 \text{ result not } 0$$
$$C = 1 \text{ borrow}$$
$$A = 1 \text{ half-borrow}$$
$$S = 1 \text{ result negative}$$
$$P = 1 \text{ even parity}$$
$$O = 0 \text{ no overflow}$$

EXAMPLE 4-7

```
0034 B5 22          MOV    CH,22H
0036 80 ED 44       SUB    CH,44H
```

Notice how the carry flags (C and A) both hold borrows rather than carries, as after
an addition. Also notice that there is no overflow condition. In this example, a 44H was
subtracted from a 22H with a result of DEH or a $-$ 34. Because the quantity $-$ 34 fits
into an 8-bit number, there is no overflow in this example. An 8-bit overflow will occur
only if the result is outside the range $+$ 127 to $-$ 128.

Decrement Subtraction.   Decrement subtraction (DEC) is the subtraction of 1. Table 4–4
illustrates many of the forms of decrement instruction available in the 8086/8088 instruction set. Again, it is impossible to list all the forms because of the large number available.

TABLE 4-4   Decrement instructions

Instruction	Comment
DEC BH	Subtract 1 from register BH
DEC BP	Subtract 1 from register BP
DEC WORD PTR[DI]	Subtract 1 from the 16-bit word of data segment memory addressed by pointer DI
DEC WORD PTR[SI + 2]	Subtract 1 from the 16-bit word of data segment memory addressed by pointer SI + 2

Addition with Carry

An addition-with-carry instruction adds the bit in the carry flag (C) along with the operand data. It is useful in the addition of numbers wider than 16 bits.

Table 4–5 illustrates a number of add-with-carry (ADC) instructions along with a comment explaining the operation of each instruction. Like ADD, ADC also affects all the flags.

Suppose that the 32-bit number held in the AX and BX registers is added to the 32-bit number held in the CX and DX registers. This cannot be accomplished without adding a carry, and it is here that an ADC instruction becomes useful. In Example 4–8, notice that the least significant numbers in BX and DX are added with a normal ADD command. Of course, the ADD command affects the carry flag, which holds the carry if it occurs. Next, the most significant words are added, along with the carry produced from the prior addition. This leaves 32-bit sum in registers AX and BX.

EXAMPLE 4–8

```
0039 03 DA              ADD     BX,DX
003B 13 C1              ADC     AX,CX
```

Subtraction with Borrow

A subtraction-with-borrow instruction allows the bit in the carry flag (C), which holds a borrow for subtraction, to be subtracted along with the operand data. This type of instruction is useful in subtracting numbers wider than 16 bits.

Table 4–6 illustrates a number of subtract-with-borrow (SBB) instructions along with a comment explaining the operation of each instruction. Like SUB, SBB also affects all the flags.

If the 32-bit number held in the AX and BX registers is subtracted from the 32-bit number held in DI and SI, there must be some method of subtracting a borrow. This is where the SBB instruction enters in. In Example 4–9, notice that the contents of BX are subtracted from the least significant number in SI by the SUB instruction. This subtraction naturally affects the carry flag, which holds a borrow if it occurs in the SUB instruction. Next, the most significant words are subtracted, along with the borrow (SBB) produced from the prior subtraction. This leaves a 32-bit difference in registers AX and BX.

TABLE 4–5 Add-with-carry instructions

Instruction	Comment
ADC AL,AH	AL becomes the sum of AL + AH + carry
ADC CX,BX	CX becomes the sum of CX + BX + carry
ADC [BX],AL	The data segment byte addressed by BX becomes the sum of that byte plus AL + carry
ADC BX,[BP + 2]	BX becomes the sum of the stack segment word addressed by BP + 2 and the contents of both the BX register and carry

TABLE 4−6   Subtract-with-borrow instructions.

Instruction	Comment
SBB AH,AL	AH becomes the difference of AH − AL − carry
SBB AX,BX	AX becomes the difference of AX − BX − carry
SBB CL,3	CL becomes the difference of CL − 3 − carry
SBB[DI],AL	The data segment byte addressed by DI becomes the difference of that byte minus AL − carry
SBB DI,[BP + 2]	DI becomes the difference of the stack segment word addressed by BP + 2 and the contents of both the DI register and carry

EXAMPLE 4−9

```
003D  2B  DE           SUB    BX,SI
003F  1B  C7           SBB    AX,DI
```

Comparison

The comparison instruction (CMP) is actually a subtraction that does not change anything but the flag bits. It is useful for checking the contents of a register or a memory location for a particular value. This instruction is almost always followed by a conditional jump instruction, which tests the flag bits that are changed by CMP.

Table 4−7 illustrates a variety of comparison instructions that have the same addressing modes as subtraction and addition. Similarly, the only disallowed addressing modes are memory-to-memory and segment addressing.

Example 4−10 shows how the comparison instruction can determine whether the AL register contains a 10H. The CMP is followed by a new instruction that will not be covered until Chapter 5, but since it will help illustrate the comparison instruction, it is presented here. The CMP subtracts a 10H from AL, but does not change AL, because the difference is not returned to the destination register or memory location. The only things changed by this instruction are the flags.

EXAMPLE 4−10

```
0041  3C  10           CMP    AL,10H
0043  EB  44  90        JMP    ONTEN
```

If AL contains a 10H before the CMP in this example, then the zero flag is set; if it doesn't contain a 10H before the CMP, then the zero flag is cleared. The JZ (jump-on-zero) instruction tests the zero flag after the comparison instruction. If the zero flag is true, a jump to address ONTEN occurs. If the zero flag is false, no jump occurs.

TABLE 4–7 Comparison instructions

Instruction	Comment
CMP CL,BL	Subtracts BL from CL; neither BL nor CL change
CMP AX,SP	Subtracts SP from AX; neither AX nor SP change
CMP AX,0CCCCH	Subtracts CCCCH from AX; AX does not change
CMP [DI],CH	Subtracts CH from the data segment memory byte addressed by DI; neither byte changes
CMP CH,[BP]	Subtracts the stack segment memory byte addressed by BP from CH; neither byte changes
CMP AH,TEMP	Subtracts the contents of memory byte TEMP, which is located in the data segment, from AH; neither byte changes
CMP DI,TEMP[BX]	Subtracts the 16-bit contents of data segment array TEMP and offset BX from DI; neither word changes

Note: In all the CMP instructions, the only things that may change are the flags, which reflect the condition of the difference.

4-2   MULTIPLICATION AND DIVISION

Only the more modern 16-bit microprocessors contain the multiplication and division operations. Earlier 8-bit microprocessors were not able to multiply or divide directly. These operations required a specially written program. Because the manufacturers of microprocessors were aware of this inadequacy, they incorporated the multiplication and division instructions into their newer microprocessors.

The 8086/8088 is capable of performing both 8- and 16-bit multiplication and division on either signed or unsigned numbers. Because the instructions for these operations are already implemented, programs that require them are physically shorter and execute at higher rates of speed.

Multiplication

Multiplication, whether 8- or 16-bit, can be either signed (IMUL) or unsigned (MUL). Multiplication always results in a double-width product. For example, if two 8-bit numbers are multiplied, then the product is always 16 bits. Likewise, if two 16-bit numbers are multiplied, then the product is 32 bits.

Some of the flags (O and C) are affected by the multiplication instruction; the remaining flags are changed, but their state is not predictable. In 8-bit multiplication, if the 8 most significant bits of the result are 0, then both O and C are cleared; otherwise, they are both set. In 16-bit multiplication, if the 16 most significant bits of the result are 0, then both O and C are cleared; otherwise, they are set.

The addressing modes allowed for multiplication include everything allowed for addition and subtraction except for immediate addressing. There are no immediate multiplication instructions in the 8086/8088.

8-Bit Multiplication.   In 8-bit multiplication, whether signed or unsigned, the multiplicand is always in the AL register. Because the programmer can choose only the multiplier, the symbolic coded version of this instruction specifies only one operand. For example, MUL BL will multiply AL by BL and leave the 16-bit product in AX. Table 4–8 illustrates some of the allowable 8-bit multiplication instructions.

Suppose that BL and CL each contain two unsigned numbers that are multiplied to produce a 16-bit result in DX. Of course, this operation cannot be accomplished with a single instruction. In fact, it will take several instructions to complete. Example 4–11 illustrates a program that performs just such a multifaceted task. In addition, the example also loads both BL and CL with the initial data. Here a 5 is multiplied by a 10 and the result, 50, is moved into DX from AX after the multiplication.

In signed multiplication, the product is in true form if positive and in two's complement form if negative. The same is true of all positive and negative numbers used with the 8086/8088 microprocessor. In fact, if the program illustrated in Example 4–11 multiplied two signed numbers, only the opcode of the multiplication instruction would change—that is, MUL would be changed to IMUL.

EXAMPLE 4–11

```
0046 B3 05          MOV     BL,5
0048 B1 0A          MOV     CL,10
004A 8A C1          MOV     AL,CL
004C F6 E3          MUL     BL
004E 8B D0          MOV     DX,AX
```

16-Bit Multiplication.   Word multiplication is very similar to byte multiplication. The AX register always contains the 16-bit multiplicand, and the DX and AX registers contain the 32-bit product. DX will always contain the most significant 16 bits of the product, and AX the least significant 16 bits. As in 8-bit multiplication, the location and choice of the operand is left to the programmer. Table 4–9 depicts some 16-bit multiplication instructions.

TABLE 4–8   8-bit multiplication instructions

Instruction	Comment
MUL CL	The unsigned number in AL is multiplied by CL; the product is found in AX
IMUL DH	The signed number in AL is multiplied by DH; the product is found in AX
IMUL BYTE PTR[BX]	The signed number in AL is multiplied by the byte stored in the data segment at the address indexed by BX; the product is found in AX
MUL TEMP	The unsigned number in AL is multiplied by the 8-bit number at memory location TEMP; the product is found in AX. (Note that here the memory location TEMP is defined as an 8-bit location.)

TABLE 4-9 16-bit multiplication instructions

Instruction	Comment
MUL CX	The unsigned number in AX is multiplied by CX; the product is found in DX and AX
IMUL DI	The signed number in AX is multiplied by DI; the product is found in DX and AX
MUL WORD PTR[SI]	The unsigned number in AX is multiplied by the 16-bit number in the data segment at the memory address pointed to by SI; the product is found in DX and AX

Division

Like multiplication, division in the 8086/8088 can also occur on 8-bit or 16-bit numbers that are either signed (IDIV) or unsigned (DIV). Numbers are always divided into a double-width dividend. For example, an 8-bit division always divides the 8-bit divisor into a 16-bit dividend. Likewise, in 16-bit division, the 16-bit divisor is always divided into a 32-bit dividend. As in multiplication, there is no immediate division instruction.

None of the flags are defined for a division. An error can occur if the quotient is too large or there is an attempt to divide by 0; here a divide-by-zero interrupt occurs. More detail on interrupts is contained in later chapters on the 8086/8088 hardware.

8-Bit Division. As we have mentioned, the dividend for an 8-bit division is located in the AX register and the divisor is the operand selected for the instruction. The results of an 8-bit division are two 8-bit numbers: the quotient (AL) and the remainder (AH). (In signed division, the sign of the remainder is always the same as the sign of the quotient.) Table 4-10 illustrates some of the 8-bit division instructions.

In 8-bit division, the numbers to be divided are usually 8 bits wide. To use the DIV or IDIV instruction, however, one of them must be converted to 16 bits. A new instruction called *convert byte to word* (CBW) will accomplish this. CBW converts the signed 8-bit number in AL to a 16-bit signed number in AX. This instruction is often used before an 8-bit signed division.

Example 4-12 illustrates a program to divide an unsigned 12H by a 3H. Notice that the CBW instruction is not used here. In its place is the MOV AH,0, which places a 00H into the AH register. If an 8-bit unsigned number is to be converted to a 16-bit unsigned number, a 00H is placed in AH. After the division, the AL register contains a 04H and the AH register contains a 00H; that is, the quotient is 4 and the remainder is 0.

EXAMPLE 4-12

```
0050 B0 12        MOV    AL,12H
0052 B1 03        MOV    CL,3
0054 B4 00        MOV    AH,0
0056 F6 F1        DIV    CL
```

TABLE 4–10   8-bit division instructions

Instruction	Comment
DIV CL	The unsigned number in AX is divided by CL; the quotient is in AL, and the remainder is in AH
IDIV BL	The signed number in AX is divided by BL; the quotient is in AL, and the remainder is in AH
DIV BYTE PTR[BP]	The unsigned number in AX is divided by the byte in the stack segment stored at the address located by BP; the quotient is in AL, and the remainder is in AH

TABLE 4–11   16-bit division instructions

Instruction	Comment
DIV CX	The unsigned number in DX and AX is divided by CX; the quotient is found in AX and the remainder in DX
IDIV SI	The signed number in DX and AX is divided by SI; the quotient is found in AX and the remainder in DX
DIV DATA	The unsigned number in DX and AX is divided by the word stored in the data segment at memory location DATA (a word of information)

16-Bit Division.   Sixteen-bit division is nearly the same as 8-bit division except that the dividend is 32 rather than 16 bits wide. The DX register contains the most significant part of the dividend and the AX register the least significant part. After the division, the quotient is found in AX and the remainder in DX. Table 4–11 depicts some of the many 16-bit division instructions.

As in 8-bit signed division, the dividend must often be converted into a 32-bit number. This is accomplished by a special instruction called *convert word to double word* (CWD). The CWD instruction converts the signed 16-bit number in AX into a signed 32-bit number in DX and AX.

Example 4–13 illustrates the division of two 16-bit signed numbers. Here a − 100 is placed in AX and a + 9 in CX. The CWD instruction, placed before the IDIV instruction, then converts the 16-bit signed number in AX into a 32-bit signed number in both DX and AX. The quotient (− 11) is found in AX and the remainder (− 1) in DX. Notice that the signs of both remainder and quotient are the same.

EXAMPLE 4–13

```
0058                    MOV    AX-100
005B B9 0009            MOV    CX,9
005E 99                 CWD
005F F7 F9              IDIV   CX
```

4-3   BCD AND ASCII ARITHMETIC

The 8086/8088 allows arithmetic manipulation of both binary coded decimal (BCD) and American Standard Code for Information Interchange (ASCII) data through the regular arithmetic instructions and a group of instructions that adjust the results to BCD or ASCII codes.

BCD operations are used in applications that require little arithmetic, such as *point of sales terminal* (POS). ASCII operations are used in systems that employ ASCII-coded data to store numbers. ASCII numeric data are typically stored in spreadsheet programs and in higher level languages.

BCD Arithmetic

Four instructions are used for BCD arithmetic: *decimal adjust after addition* (DAA), *decimal adjust after subtraction* (DAS), *adjust result of BCD multiplication* (AAM), and *adjust before BCD division* (AAD). The DAA, DAS, and AAM instructions are used after adding, subtracting, or multiplying BCD numbers with the ADD, SUB, or MUL instructions. The AAD instruction is used before a division to preadjust the numbers before using the DIV instruction.

In addition and subtraction, the numbers to be added or subtracted are stored 2 digits per byte in the AL register. This is called a *packed BCD format*. For example, if a byte contains a 34H—and it represents BCD—then the number is a 34 in BCD code. Notice that the byte contains 2 BCD digits: 3 and 4.

In multiplication and division, the numbers are stored 1 digit per byte, as unpacked BCD numbers. If AL equals a 01, then it is a 1 BCD.

DAA.   Suppose that DX and BX both contain 4-digit BCD numbers. Example 4-14 provides a sample program that will add them and store the 4-digit sum in CX. This program is much longer than one might expect because the DAA instruction will correct only the number found in register AL. Consequently, for the DAA to correct the result, all the additions must add to AL. In this example, a 99 and a 34 are first added to produce CDH—certainly not BCD. The DAA instruction corrects this to a 33 with a carry of 1 in C. Next the ADC instruction adds the 30 and the 12 plus carry, which produces a 43H. After correction, the result is still 43H because this is already a valid BCD number. After these instructions are executed, the CX register will contain a 4333H or 4,333 in BCD code, which is the correct sum of 1,234 plus 3,099.

EXAMPLE 4-14

```
0061 BA 1234          MOV    DX,1234H
0064 BB 3099          MOV    BX,3099H
0067 8A C3            MOV AL,BL
0069 02 C2            ADD    AL,DL
006B 27               DAA
006C 8A C8            MOV    CL,AL
006E 8A C7            MOV    AL,BH
0070 12 C6            ADC    AL,DH
0072 27               DAA
0073 8A E8            MOV    CH,AL
```

DAS.   DAS works like DAA because it adjusts only AL and follows the subtraction just as DAA followed the addition. Example 4–15 is actually Example 4–14 reworked so that it does a BCD subtraction rather than a BCD addition. If you compare these two programs, you will note that ADD and ADC in Example 4–14 are changed to SUB and SBB in Example 4–15 and that DAA is replaced with DAS. If this program is executed, the difference is 1,865 BCD—found in the CX register.

EXAMPLE 4–15

```
0075 BA 1234          MOV    DX,1234H
0078 BB 3099          MOV    BX,3099H
007B 8A C3            MOV    AL,BL
007D 2A C2            SUB    AL,DL
007F 2F               DAS
0080 8A C8            MOV    CL,AL
0082 8A C7            MOV    AL,BH
0084 1A C6            SBB    AL,DH
0086 2F               DAS
0087 8A E8            MOV    CH,AL
```

AAM Instruction.   The AAM instruction is used after the multiplication of two single-digit BCD unpacked numbers. As Example 4–16 shows, if AL contains a 05 and CL contains a 05 before multiplication, the AX register will contain a 0018H after multiplication, which is not the correct product in BCD. If the multiplication is followed by an AAM instruction, the AX register will be corrected to a 0205H or a 2-digit unpacked BCD result of 25.

EXAMPLE 4–16

```
0000 B0 05            MOV    AL,5
0002 B1 05            MOV    CL,5
0004 F6 E1            MUL    CL
0006 D4 0A            AAM
```

AAD.   The AAD instruction is used before a division, while all the other adjustment instructions are used after the arithmetic operation. The AAD instruction requires AX to contain a 2-digit unpacked BCD number, in which AH holds the most significant digit and AL the least. Before this 2-digit BCD number can be divided by a single-digit BCD number, it must be adjusted with the AAD instruction. The division will then produce a single-digit result in AL with any remainder in AH.

Example 4–17 illustrates how 72 in BCD is divided by 9 to produce the correct result of 8. Here the 72 is loaded into AX so it can be divided by the 9 in BL. The AAD instruction will then adjust the 0702H in AX to produce a 0048H in AX. (Notice that this instruction converts the unpacked BCD number into binary.) Once AAD has converted 72 in BCD to 48H, the DIV instruction will produce the correct result of 08H in AL and 00H in AH—a quotient of 8 with no remainder.

EXAMPLE 4–17

```
0008 B8 0702          MOV    AX,0702H
000B B3 09            MOV    BL,9
000D D5 0A            AAD
000F F6 F3            DIV    BL
```

ASCII Arithmetic

The ASCII arithmetic instructions are used with ASCII-coded numbers. These range from 30H through 39H and represent the numbers 0 through 9. There are two instructions that apply to ASCII-coded numbers: (1) *adjust for ASCII addition* (AAA) and (2) *adjust for ASCII subtraction* (AAS). These instructions always use register AX as the source before adjustment and as the destination after.

AAA. The addition of two 1-digit ASCII numbers will not result in ASCII code or any other useful code. For example, if a 31H is added to a 39H, the result is a 6AH. The addition of an ASCII 31H and a 39H should produce a 2-digit ASCII result of 10 decimal (10 base ten) or a 31H and a 30H. Care must be taken with this instruction, because it will clear AH to 0 if the sum is less than 10 decimal and add a 01H to AH if the result is larger than 9.

    If the AAA instruction follows the addition as previously outlined, the contents of AX will be adjusted so that AH contains a 01H and AL contains a 00H. Although this in not an ASCII result, it can easily be converted to ASCII by adding a 3030H to the AX register. This procedure is illustrated in the program listed in Example 4–18. Notice that the numbers must be summed in AL for AAA to correct the result. After AAA, the AX register is equal to a 0100H, which contains the 2-digit answer, but not in ASCII code. To complete the process, an ADD AX,3030H instruction makes AX equal a 3130H. The answer in AX is a 2-digit ASCII result of 10 decimal.

EXAMPLE 4–18

```
0011 B8 0031          MOV    AX,31H
0014 04 39            ADD    AL,39H
0016 37               AAA
0017 05 3030          ADD    AX,3030H
```

AAS. Like the AAA, the AAS adjusts the AX register after an ASCII subtraction. For example, suppose that ACSII 35H is subtracted from 39H. The result will be a 4, which requires no correction. In this case, AAS will modify neither AH nor AL. For this reason, you must be careful with the number in AH. On the other hand, if 38H is subtracted from 37H, then AL will equal 09H and the number in AH will be decremented by 1. This decrement allows multiple-digit ASCII numbers to be subtracted from each other.

4-4   BASIC LOGIC OPERATIONS

The basic logic operations include AND, OR, Exclusive-OR, and NOT. In addition, this section covers the TEST instruction, a special AND operation, and the NEG instruction, which is really an arithmetic operation that is similar to NOT.

Logic operations are generally used for binary bit control in *low-level software*, which controls I/O devices in most systems. All the logic instructions affect the flag bits: the carry and overflow flags are always cleared, and the remaining flags are modified to indicate the outcome of the logical operation.

AND

The AND operation performs logical multiplication, as illustrated in the truth table in Figure 4-1. Here two bits—A and B—are ANDed to produce the result, X. As the truth table indicates, X is a logic 1 only when both A and B are logic 1s. It is important to remember that a 0 AND anything is always a 0.

The AND operation is often used to replace discrete logic AND gates if the speed required is not too great. This results in a tremendous savings, often of 200,000 percent or more, because the cost of a 7408 (AND gate) is approximately 10 cents and the cost of the memory used to store the AND instruction is approximately 1/20 of a cent.

AND is also used to clear bits of a binary number selectively (often called *masking*). The process of masking is illustrated in Figure 4-2. Notice from this illustration that the leftmost four bits are cleared to 0, since 0 ANDed with anything is always 0. Also notice that the Xs (*don't cares*) are passed through the AND operation without a change in the rightmost four bit positions. This occurs because any number (X) ANDed with a 1 will not

FIGURE 4-1 The truth table demonstrating the AND operation (logical multiplication).

A	·	B	=	X
0		0		0
0		1		0
1		0		0
1		1		1

FIGURE 4-2 Here a mask (0000 1111) is ANDed with an unknown number. Notice how the leftmost 4 bits are masked off (cleared) to 0.

	XXXX	XXXX	(Unknown pattern)
·	0000	1111	(Mask pattern)
	0000	XXXX	(Result)

change the original number (X). Also notice how the number is ANDed bit position by bit position.

Any addressing modes for the AND instruction are allowed except memory-to-memory operations. Also, the segment registers may not be used as operands. Refer to Table 4-12 for a sampling of various AND instructions.

An ASCII-coded number can be easily converted into a BCD number by using the AND instruction to mask off the four most significant bit positions of the ASCII-coded character. In Example 4-19, the contents of the BX register are the 2-digit ASCII number 3135H (15) that is converted to a 2-digit unpacked BCD number in AX (0105H). It is important to notice how the AND instruction masks both ASCII digits simultaneously.

EXAMPLE 4-19

```
001A BB 3155          MOV     BX,3155H
001D 8B C3            MOV     AX,BX
001F 25 0F0F          AND     AX,0F0FH
```

OR

The OR operation performs logical addition, which is slightly different from arithmetic addition. In logical addition, the sum is only a 0 when both numbers are 0; otherwise the sum is a 1. The truth table of the OR operation is depicted in Figure 4-3. Here the inputs — A and B — are ORed to produce the output, X. It is important to remember that a 1 ORed with anything yields a 1.

The OR operation is often used to replace discrete logic OR gates if the speed required is not too great. This results in a tremendous savings, often of 200,000 percent or more. The OR operation also selectively sets bits of a binary number, as illustrated in Figure 4-4. Notice from the illustration that the rightmost 4 bits are set to 1, since a 1 ORed with anything is 1. Also notice that the Xs *(don't cares)* have passed through the OR operation without a change in the leftmost 4 bit positions. This occurs because any number (X) ORed with a 0 will not change the original number (X). Also notice how the number is ORed bit position by bit position.

TABLE 4-12 AND instructions.

Instruction	Comment
AND AL,BL	AL is the logical product of AL AND BL
AND CX,DX	CX is the logical product of CX AND DX
AND CL,33H	CL is the logical product of CL AND 33H
AND DI,4FFFH	DI is the logical product of DI AND 4FFFH
AND AX,[DI]	AX is the logical product of AX AND the contents of the word stored in the data segment at the address pointed to by DI
AND ARRAY[SI],AL	The data segment location ARRAY + SI is the logical product of that byte of memory AND AL

FIGURE 4–3 The truth table illustrating the OR operation (logical addition). Note that a + sign is used to indicate the OR operation.

A	+	B	=	X
0		0		0
0		1		1
1		0		1
1		1		1

FIGURE 4–4 A test pattern (0000 1111) is ORed with an unknown number to illustrate how the OR operation is used to selectively set bits.

```
  XXXX   XXXX    (Unknown pattern)
+ 0000   1111    (Test pattern)
  XXXX   1111    (Result)
```

Any addressing modes for the OR instruction are allowed except memory-to-memory operations. Also, the segment registers may not be used as operands. Table 4–13 lists a variety of OR instructions.

Suppose that two BCD numbers are multiplied and adjusted with the AAM instruction. The result appears in AX as a 2-digit unpacked BCD number. Example 4–20 illustrates this multiplication and shows how to change the product into a 2-digit ASCII-coded number with an OR instruction. Notice how the OR instruction converts the 0305H found in the AX register into a 3335H by ORing AX with a 3030H. (The OR operation can, of course, be replaced with an ADD; it is used here only as a·convenient illustration.)

TABLE 4–13 OR instructions

Instruction	Comment
OR AH,BL	AH is the logical sum of AH OR BL
OR SI,DX	SI is the logical sum of SI OR DX
OR DH,A3H	DH is the logical sum of DH OR A3H
OR SP,990DH	SP is the logical sum of SP OR 990DH
OR DX,[BX]	DX is the logical sum of DX OR the contents of the word stored in the data segment at the address pointed to by BX
OR DATE[DI + 2],AL	The data segment location DATE + DI + 2 is the logical sum of that byte of memory OR AL

EXAMPLE 4–20

```
0022 B0 05          MOV    AL,5
0024 B3 07          MOV    BL,7
0026 F6 E3          MUL    BL
0028 D4 0A          AAM
002A 0D 3030        OR     AX,3030H
```

The Exclusive-OR

The Exclusive-OR operation (XOR) differs from the Inclusive-OR (OR) mainly in that the 1,1 condition of the OR function produces a 1 while the 1,1 condition of the Exclusive-OR operation produces a 0. In other words, the Exclusive-OR *excludes* the latter condition while the Inclusive-OR *includes* it.

Figure 4–5 illustrates the truth table for the Exclusive-OR gate. (Compare with Figure 4–3 to appreciate the difference between these two OR functions.) If the inputs of the Exclusive-OR function are both 0 or both 1, the output is 0. If the inputs are different, then the output is 1.

Any addressing modes are allowed in the XOR instruction except for memory-to-memory operations. Also, the segment registers may not be used as operands. Table 4–14 illustrates various types of XOR instructions.

The Exclusive-OR operation is often used to replace discrete logic Exclusive-OR gates if the speed required is not too great. In replacing logic gates with the Exclusive-OR instructions, it is possible to realize a savings often of 200,000 percent or more. The Exclusive-OR operation also selectively inverts bits of a binary number, as illustrated in Figure 4–6. Notice that the rightmost four bits are inverted in this illustration. This happens because a 1 Exclusive-ORed with anything inverts the bit position. In addition, the Xs *(don't cares)* have passed through the Exclusive-OR operation without a change in the leftmost four bit positions, because any number (X) Exclusive-ORed with a 0 will not change the original number (X). It is also important to note that the number is Exclusive-ORed bit position by bit position.

FIGURE 4–5 The truth table for the Exclusive-OR function. Notice that the ⊕ sign is used to indicate an Exclusive-OR operation.

A ⊕ B		= X
0	0	0
0	1	1
1	0	1
1	1	0

TABLE 4–14   XOR instruction

Instruction	Comment
XOR CH,DL	CH is the Exclusive-OR of CH and DL
XOR SI,BP	SI is the Exclusive-OR of SI and BP
XOR AH,0EEH	AH is the Exclusive-OR of AH and EEH
XOR SI,00DDH	SI is the Exclusive-OR of SI and 00DDH
XOR BX,[SI]	BX is the Exclusive-OR of BX and the contents of the word stored in the data segment at the address pointed to by SI
XOR DATE[DI + 2],AL	The data segment location DATE + DI + 2 is the Exclusive-OR of that byte of memory and AL

FIGURE 4–6   A test pattern (0000 1111) Exclusive-ORed with an unknown quantity produces inversion in the bit positions where the test pattern contains logic 1.

```
   XXXX    XXXX    (Unknown pattern)
+  0000    1111    (Test pattern)
  ─────────────
   XXXX    X̄X̄X̄X̄    (Result)
```

Suppose that the first 10 bits of the AX register must be inverted while the remaining bits are unchanged. An XOR AX,03FFH instruction will invert the rightmost 10 bits without affecting the remaining bits of AX.

Test

The TEST instruction performs the AND operation, but, unlike the AND instruction, it affects only the flag register and not the source or destination operands of the instruction. TEST is similar to AND in that a segment register cannot be an operand. Also, TEST and AND use the same addressing modes.

TEST is often used in the same manner as CMP, but to test a single bit rather than an entire number. For example, TEST is the logical choice to check the rightmost bit position of AX for a 1 or 0, because it can test the rightmost bit by itself without changing it. TEST AX,1 will indicate whether the rightmost bit is a 0 or 1 in Z. If the Z flag is true (indicates 0), then the rightmost bit of AX is a 0; otherwise it is a 1.

NOT and NEG

Logical inversion or *one's complement* (NOT) and arithmetic sign inversion or *two's complement* (NEG) are the last two logic functions available except for shifts and rotates. Each has only one operand, as illustrated in Table 4–15. Unlike the other logic instructions, NOT or NEG will affect the flag bits.

The NOT instruction, or one's complement, inverts each bit position of a number. Thus a 00H becomes an FFH. The NEG instruction or two's complement is merely the one's complement plus 1. It will negate (NEG) an 88H to yield a 77H (one's complement) plus 1, or a 78H.

TABLE 4–15 NOT and NEG instructions

Instruction	Comment
NOT CH	CH is one's complemented
NEG CH	CH is two's complemented
NEG AX	AX is two's complemented
NOT TEMP	Memory location TEMP within the data segment is one's complemented. The size of TEMP is determined by how TEMP is defined
NOT BYTE PTR[BX]	The memory location in the data segment addressed by BX is one's complemented

4–5 SHIFTS AND ROTATES

Shift and rotate instructions manipulate numbers at the binary bit level. They find their widest application in low-level I/O control software in many systems. The 8086/8088 microprocessor contains a complete set of shift and rotate instructions used to shift or rotate any memory data or the data in any register.

Shifts

Shift instructions position or move numbers in a register or memory location. They also perform simple arithmetic such as multiplication by powers of 2^n *(left shift)* and division by powers of 2^{-n} *(right shift)*. The 8086/8088 instruction set contains four different shift instructions: two are *logical shifts,* and two are *arithmetic shifts.* All four are depicted graphically in Figure 4–7.

Notice that in Figure 4–7 there are two different right shifts and two different left shifts. The logical shifts move a 0 into the right-hand bit position for a logical left shift and a 0 into the left-hand bit position for a logical right shift. There are also two arithmetic shifts. Like the logical left shift, the arithmetic left shift moves a 0 into the right-hand bit position. The arithmetic right shift, on the other hand, shifts a 1 or 0 into the left-hand bit position: if the number is positive, it shifts a 0 in; if negative, a 1. It is important to notice how the sign bit is copied back into the sign bit for an arithmetic right shift.

The arithmetic right shift thus differs from the logical in that it will always divide a *signed* number by 2; a logical right shift will always divide an *unsigned* number by a 2, and a left shift will always multiply a number by a 2.

Table 4–16 illustrates some of the addressing modes allowed in the shift instructions. Notice that a register or memory can be shifted one place or many places if CL is used to hold a shift count. Example 4–21 shows how the contents of the DX register are shifted 14 places to the left. If the CL register were not used to hold a shift count, this operation would take 14 SHL instructions. With CL as a counter, it takes only two instructions. Therefore, CL must *always* hold the shift count—this is not an option.

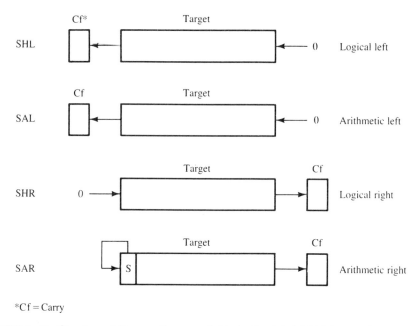

*Cf = Carry

FIGURE 4–7   The four shift operations available in the 8086/8088 instruction set. Note that the target is any 8- or 16-bit register or memory location except the segment regis-ters.

TABLE 4–16   Shift instructions

Instruction	Comment
SHL BL,1	Logically shifts BL left 1 place
SHR AX,1	Logically shifts AX right 1 place
SAL BYTE PTR[BX],CL	Arithmetically shifts the 8-bit contents in the data segment location addressed by BX left the number of places con-tained in CL
SAR SI,CL	Arithmetically shifts SI right the number of places contained in CL

EXAMPLE 4–21

```
002D B1 0E          MOV    CL,14
002F D3 E2          SHL    DX,CL
```

Suppose that the contents of AX are multiplied by 10, as in Example 4–22. This can be done in two different ways: by MUL instruction or by shifts and additions. A number that is shifted one time to the left is doubled. When the original number is doubled and added to the original number times 8, the result is a new number equal to 10 times the original. This same principle can be used to multiply any number by any constant.

EXAMPLE 4-22

```
0031 D1 E0          SHL     AX,1            ;2  x  AX
0033 8B D8          MOV     BX,AX
0035 D1 E0          SHL     AX,1            ;4  x  AX
0037 D1 E0          SHL     AX,1            ;8  x  AX
0039 03 C3          ADD     AX,BX           ;10  x  AX
```

Rotates

Rotate instructions position data by rotating the information in a register or memory location either from one end to the other or through the carry flag. They are most often used to shift or position numbers wider than 16 bits in the 8086/8088 microprocessor. The four rotate operations are illustrated in Figure 4-8.

Numbers can be rotated either through the register or memory location and C or through the register or memory location only. With either type of rotate instruction, the programmer can use either a left or a right rotate. Addressing modes for the rotates are the same as for the shifts. CL is used as a counter for multiple-bit rotates. Some of the possible rotate instructions are listed in Table 4-17.

A rotate is often used to shift a very wide number to the left or right. The program in Example 4-23 will shift the 48-bit number in DX, BX, and AX left one bit position. Notice that the least significant 16-bit portion (AX) is first shifted to the left. This moves the leftmost bit of AX into C. Next the RCL BX,1 instruction moves C into the rightmost bit of BX, and the leftmost bit of BX is moved into C. Finally, the last instruction, RCL DX,1 places C in the rightmost bit of DX and rotates it left.

FIGURE 4-8 The four rotate operations available in the 8086/8088 instruction set. Note that both the RCL and RCR instructions have data rotated through C (carry) and ROL and ROR rotate data only through the target.

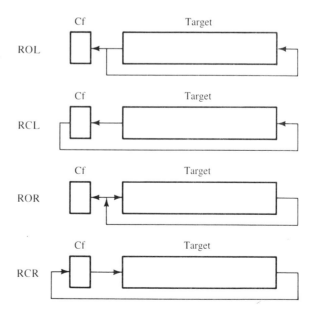

TABLE 4–17   Rotate instructions

Instruction	Comment
ROL SI,1	Rotates SI left 1 place
RCL BL,1	Rotates Bl through carry left 1 place
RCR AH,CL	Rotates AH through carry right the number of places contained in CL
ROR WORD PTR[BP]	Rotates the stack segment word at the memory location addressed by BP right 1 place

EXAMPLE 4–23

```
003B  D1 E0        SHL     AX,1
003D  D1 D3        RCL     BX,1
003F  D1 D2        RCL     DX,1
```

4–6   STRING COMPARISONS

As we have seen in Chapter 3, the string instructions in the 8086/8088 microprocessor are very powerful because they allow the programmer to move á large block of data from one part of memory to another or store the same byte or word in a large block of memory with only a few instructions.

In this section, we will discuss additional string operations that allow a section of memory to be compared for a particular value or two sections of memory to be compared for a match or no-match condition.

SCAS

The scan string instruction (SCAS) compares either the AL register with a byte block of memory or the AX register with a word block of memory. That is, it subtracts the AL register without affecting AL or memory and subtracts the AX register without affecting AX or memory. The opcode for byte comparison is SCASB and for word comparison, SCASW.

Like the MOVS, LODS, and STOS string instructions presented in Chapter 3, the SCAS instructions also use the direction flag (D) to select either auto-increment or auto-decrement for SI and/or DI. They can also be repeated if they have a conditional repeat prefix. It is important to remember that DI always addresses data in the extra segment (ES), SI in the data segment (DS).

Suppose a section of the memory (100H bytes beginning at address BLOCK) must be tested to see if it contains a 00H. The program in Example 4–24 shows how to search this part of the memory using the SCASB instruction. Note that the repeat causes memory area BLOCK to be scanned until either CX reaches 0 (100H iterations) or until the 00H is found in the memory. Another conditional repeat prefix, *repeat while equal* (REPE), is also available.

EXAMPLE 4-24

```
0041 BF 0000 R        MOV    DI,OFFSET BLOCK      ;address block
0044 FC               CLD                         ;clear direction
0045 B9 0100          MOV    CX,100H              ;load counter
0048 B0 00            MOV    AL,0                 ;clear AL
004A F2/ AE           REPNE  SCASB                ;test memory
```

In both conditional repeats, the string operation repeats while the condition is true and while the counter (CX) is not 0. The repeat is exited when the counter reaches 0 or when the condition is no longer true. Each iteration causes the counter to be decremented, but the act of decrementing the counter *does not* affect the flags. The SCASB instruction *does,* however, affect the flags as it compares the AL register with the contents of the memory addressed by DI.

REPE can be replaced by REPZ, and *repeat, not equal while* (REPNE) can be replaced by REPNZ. This would not normally be done because it would never be necessary to compare for a 0 or not 0 condition, only an equal or not-equal condition. It is essential to remember that REPE repeats while equal and REPNE repeats while not equal—that is, as long as the counter (CX) has not reached 0.

The program of Example 4-24 exits the REPNE SCASB instruction if CX becomes 0 or if the condition is equal. How then can you tell if the 00H has been found? One easy way is to look at the zero flag (Z). If it indicates a 0 or equal condition, then the 00H is in memory area BLOCK. If it indicates a non-0 or not-equal condition, then memory area BLOCK did not contain a 00H. Be aware that DI will point to the memory location after the 00H in this example.

CMPS

The *compare strings instruction* (CMPS) always compares two pieces of memory data—either a byte (CMPSB) or a word (CMPSW)—for a match or a no-match condition. The contents of the location addressed by DI in the extra segment are subtracted from the contents of the location addressed by SI in the data segment without changing anything in memory or any register other than the flags. Unlike SCAS, it uses the automatic increment or decrement mode for both SI and DI after a comparison. But, like SCAS, it takes a conditional repeat prefix.

Example 4-25 illustrates a short sequence of instructions that compare two sections of the memory for a match. The CMPSB instruction is prefixed with REPE so that the operation can be repeated while each byte of the 10-byte area of memory is compared.

In this example, a line of unknown data is compared against a table containing known data. If the line has the correct information, then the sequence will end with an equal condition and a count in CX of 0. If there is no match, then the CX register will not be 0, and the sequence will end with a not-equal condition. This operation can be very useful in sorting ASCII character strings or searching ASCII data.

EXAMPLE 4-25

```
004C BE 01C8 R      MOV   SI,OFFSET LINE   ;address LINE
004F BF 03C8 R      MOV   DI,OFFSET TABLE  ;address TABLE
0052 B9 000A        MOV   CX,10            ;load counter
0055 FC             CLD                    ;clear direction
0056 F3/ A6         REPE CMPSB
```

4-7   SUMMARY

1. Addition (ADD) can be either 8- or 16-bit. The allowable addressing modes include any register except a segment register, immediate data, or any memory-addressing method. All flag register bits are affected by ADD. The add-with-carry instruction (ADC) adds the contents of the carry flag (C).

2. The increment instruction (INC) adds a 1 to the contents of any memory location or any register except the segment registers. All flag bits except C are affected by an INC instruction.

3. Subtraction (SUB) can be either 8- or 16-bit. The allowable addressing modes include any register except a segment register, immediate data, or any of the memory-addressing modes. All flag register bits are affected by SUB. The subtract-with-borrow (SBB) instruction subtracts the contents of the carry flag (C).

4. The decrement (DEC) instruction subtracts a 1 from the contents of any memory location or any register except the segment registers. All flag bits except C are affected by a DEC instruction.

5. The compare instruction (CMP) is a special form of subtraction that does not store the difference; instead, the flag bits change to reflect it.

6. Multiplication can be 8- or 16-bit, signed (IMUL) or signed (MUL). In 8-bit multiplication, the AL register is multiplied by the operand and the product is always found in AX. In 16-bit multiplication, the AX register is multiplied by the operand and the 32-bit product is always found in DX and AX.

7. Division can be 8- or 16-bit, signed (IDIV) or unsigned (DIV). In 8-bit division, AX is divided by the operand to produce a quotient in AL and a remainder in AH. In 16-bit division, the 32-bit number contained in AX and DX is divided by the operand to produce a quotient in AX and a remainder in DX.

8. BCD data are added and subtracted in packed form (two digits per byte) and multiplied and divided in unpacked form (one digit per byte). DAA and DAS adjust BCD addition and subtraction after an ADD and a SUB. AAM is used after a MUL to adjust the results of BCD multiplication, and AAD is used before a DIV to preadjust the results of BCD division.

9. ASCII data are added or subtracted using the ASCII adjust-after-addition instructions (AAA) or the ASCII adjust-after-subtraction instructions (AAS).

10. AND, OR, and Exclusive-OR operations are performed on 8- or 16-bit data with any addressing mode except segment register addressing. All flags are affected except for the carry (C) and overflow (O) flags, which are cleared.

11. The TEST instruction is a special AND instruction that affects only the flags.

12. The instruction NOT performs the one's complement, and the NEG instruction per-forms the two's complement.
13. There are eight different shift and rotate instructions. There are both logical and arithmetic shift operations, which include both right and left shifts. Rotate opera-tions, both left and right, are either through the carry or not through the carry.
14. The scan string instruction (SCAS) compares AL or AX with a section of memory addressed by the DI register within the extra segment.
15. The compare strings instruction (CMPS) compares memory data with memory data. The data are addressed by DI in the extra segment and SI in the data segment.
16. Conditional repeat prefixes can be placed in front of SCAS or CMPS to make these instructions automatically repeat while a condition is true and while CX is not 0. The repeat-while-equal instruction (REPE) causes the string operation to repeat until CX is 0 or until a not-equal condition exists. The repeat-while-not-equal instruction (REPNE) causes the operation to repeat until an equal condition occurs or until CX is 0.

4-8   QUESTIONS AND PROBLEMS

1. Select an ADD instruction that will:
   a. add BX to AX
   b. add 12H to AL
   c. add DI to BP
   d. add 22H to CX
   e. add the data addressed by SI to AL
   f. add the data stored 2 bytes after the location addressed by BX to CL
   g. add CX to the data at location FROG
2. What is wrong with an ADD CL,AX instruction?
3. Is it possible to add CX to DS?
4. If AX = 1001H and DX = 20FFH, list the sum of the contents of each flag bit after an ADD AX,DX instruction is executed.
5. Develop a short sequence of instructions that will add the contents of AL, BL, CL, DL, and AH and save the result in DH.
6. Develop a short sequence of instructions that will add the contents of AX, BX, CX, DX, and SP and save the result in DI.
7. Select an instruction that will add BX to DX and also add the contents of C (carry) to the sum.
8. Select an instruction that will add 1 to the contents of the SP.
9. What is wrong with the INC [BX] instruction?
10. Select a SUB instruction that will:
    a. subtract BX from CX
    b. subtract EEH from DH
    c. subtract DI from SI
    d. subtract 3322H from SP
    e. subtract the data addressed by SI from CH

f. subtract the data stored 10 words after the location addressed by SI from DX

g. subtract AL from memory location FROG

11. If DL = F3H and BH = 72H, list the difference after BH is subtracted from DL and show the contents of the flag bits.

12. Write a short sequence of instructions that will subtract the numbers in DI, SI, and BP from the AX register and store the difference in BX.

13. Choose an instruction that will subtract 1 from the BL register.

14. Explain what the SBB [DI + 4],DX instruction accomplishes.

15. Explain the difference between a SUB and a CMP instruction.

16. When two 8-bit numbers are multiplied, in which register is the product found?

17. When two 16-bit numbers are multiplied, in which two registers is the product found? Indicate which register contains the most and least significant portions of the product.

18. When numbers are multiplied, what happens to the O and the C flags?

19. What is the difference between the IMUL and the MUL instructions?

20. Write a sequence of instructions that will cube the 8-bit number found in DL, assuming that DL contains a 5 initially. Make sure your result is a 16-bit number.

21. When 8-bit numbers are divided, in which register is the dividend found?

22. When 16-bit numbers are divided, in which registers is the dividend found?

23. What types of errors are detected during division by the 8086/8088 microprocessor?

24. Explain the difference between the IDIV and the DIV instructions.

25. Where is the quotient found after a 16-bit division?

26. Write a short sequence of instructions that will divide the number in BL by the number in CL and then multiply the result by 2.

27. What instructions are used for correcting BCD arithmetic?

28. What instructions are used for correcting ASCII arithmetic?

29. Explain how the AAM instruction is used to correct a BCD multiplication.

30. Develop the sequence of instructions required to add the 4-digit BCD number in AX and BX to the 4-digit BCD number in CX and DX. (AX and CX are the most significant registers.)

31. Select an AND instruction that will:

    a. AND BX with DX and save the result at BX

    b. AND EAH with DH

    c. AND DI with BP and save the result at DI

    d. AND 1122H with AX

    e. AND the data addressed by BP with CX and save the result in memory

    f. AND the data stored four words before the location addressed by SI with DX and save the result in DX

    g. AND AL with memory location WHAT and save the result in WHAT

32. Develop a short sequence of instructions that will clear the three leftmost bits of DH without changing DH and save the result in BH.

33. Select an OR instruction that will:

    a. OR BL with AH and save the result at AH

    b. OR 88H with CX

    c. OR DX with SI and save result at SI

    d. OR 1122H with BP

    e. OR the data addressed by BX with CX and save the result in memory

    f. OR the data stored 40 bytes after the location addressed by BP with AL and save the result in AL

    g. OR AH with memory location WHEN and save the result in WHEN

34. Develop a short sequence of instructions that will set the rightmost five bits of DI without changing DI. Save the result in SI.

35. Select an XOR instruction that will:

    a. XOR BH with AH and save result in AH

    b. XOR 99H with CL

    c. XOR DX with DI and save result at DX

    d. XOR A122H with SP

    e. XOR the data addressed by BX and DX and save the result in memory

    f. XOR the data stored 30 words after the location addressed by BP with DX and save the result in DX

    g. XOR DI with memory location WELL and save the result in WELL

36. Develop a sequence of instructions that will set the rightmost four bits of AX, clear the leftmost three bits of AX, and invert bit positions 7, 8, and 9 of AX.

37. Describe the difference between the AND and TEST instructions.

38. What is the difference between a NOT and a NEG?

39. Select the correct instruction to perform each of the following tasks:

    a. shift DI right one place with a 0 moved into the leftmost bit position

    b. move all the bits in AL left one place making sure a 0 moves into the rightmost bit position

    c. rotate the bits left one place in SI

    d. rotate carry through DX one place to the right

    e. move the DH register right one place with the sign bit shifted through DH

40. Describe what a SCASW instruction will accomplish.

41. For string instructions, DI is always in which segment of memory?

42. What is the purpose of the D flag bit?

43. Explain what the REPE instruction does.

44. What condition or conditions will terminate the repeated string operation REPNE SCASB?

45. Describe what the CMPSB instruction accomplishes.

46. Develop a sequence of instructions that will scan through a section of byte memory called LIST for a 66H.

CHAPTER 5

Program Control Instructions

I

INTRODUCTION

A computer is not worth much without the program control instructions that guide it through its operations. Without these, a computer would need to be led step by step through a program. With them, it will automatically move from one sequence of a program to another without operator intervention.

    This chapter covers all the program control instructions, including jumps, calls, returns, interrupts, and machine control instructions, as well as relevant programming techniques.

OBJECTIVES

Upon completion of this chapter, you will be able to:

1. Use both conditional and unconditional jump instructions to control the flow of a program.
2. Use the call and return instructions to include procedures in the program structure.
3. Explain the operation of the interrupts and interrupt control instructions.
4. Program with the machine control instructions to modify some of the flag bits.
5. Understand how programs function in the 8086/8088 microprocessor.

5-1   THE JUMP GROUP

The main type of program control instruction, the jump (JMP), allows the programmer to skip over sections of a program to any part of the memory. The conditional jump instructions allow the programmer to make decisions based upon numerical tests using the conditions indicated by the 8086/8088 flag bits.

In this section of the text, we cover all jump instructions and illustrate their use with sample programs. We also revisit LOOP instructions, first presented in Chapter 3, and conditional LOOP instructions.

Unconditional Jump (JMP)

Three types of unconditional jump instructions (refer to Figure 5-1) are available in the 8086/8088: short jump, near jump, and far jump. The *short jump* is a 2-byte instruction that allows jumps or branches to memory locations within +127 and -128 bytes from the memory location following the jump. The 3-byte *near jump* allows a jump or branch to any memory location in the current code segment. And, finally, the 5-byte *far jump* allows a jump to any memory location in the microprocessor. The short and near jumps are often called *intrasegment jumps* and the far jump is often called an *intersegment jump*.

Short JMP.   Short jumps are called *relative jumps* because they can be moved anywhere in the memory without a change. This is because an address is *not* stored with the opcode; instead a *displacement*, or distance, is stored. The short jump displacement or distance is a 1-byte signed number whose value can range between +127 and -128. This function is clearly illustrated in Figure 5-2. When the 8086/8088 executes a short jump, the displacement is added to the value in the instruction pointer (IP) to generate a new address. This new address is the jump address, at which program execution continues after the jump. Example 5-1 shows how a short jump can be used to move from one section of memory to another. It also illustrates the use of the near label (see below) with this jump instruction.

EXAMPLE 5-1

```
0000 B8 0001          START:    MOV    AX,1
0003 03 C3                      ADD    AX,BX
0005 E9 0200 R                  JMP    NEXT

0200 8B D8            NEXT:     MOV    BX,AX
0202 E9 0000 R                  JMP    START
```

In assembly language programming, a label is used in place of an absolute memory address. There are two ways to specify a label in the 8086/8088: (1) LABEL: indicates that the label is near, (2) LABEL indicates that the label is far. A near label is used for both the short and near jumps (intrasegment jumps), and a far label is used with the far jump (intersegment jumps). Notice that the near label ends with a colon (:) and the far label does not. This is how the assembler distinguishes them. It is important to remember

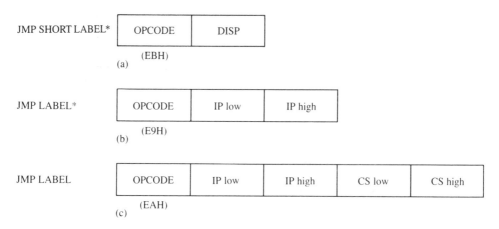

FIGURE 5–1   The types of jump instructions. (a) Short JMP (2 bytes), (b) near JMP (3 bytes), and (c) far JMP (5 bytes).

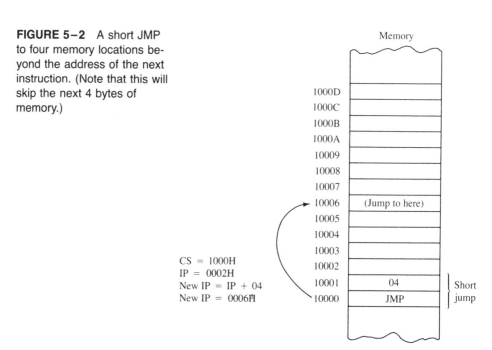

FIGURE 5–2   A short JMP to four memory locations beyond the address of the next instruction. (Note that this will skip the next 4 bytes of memory.)

that the colon follows the label only when used as an address and not when it is an operand. JMP LABEL: will produce an error because here LABEL is an operand.

Near JMP.   The near jump is similar in function to the short jump except the distance of the jump is farther. A near jump is able to move to any location within the current code

segment for the next instruction because the second and third bytes of this 3-byte instruction are moved into the IP register when the jump is executed. Figure 5–3 illustrates the
operation of the near jump instruction.

This instruction can also be relocated because the relative location of the instruction
in the code segment remains the same even if the code segment location is changed.
However, the *entire* code segment must be relocated, not just the jump instruction within
it. The short jump, in contrast, may be relocated anywhere within the code segment.

Far JMP.   Far jumps (see Figure 5–4) are used to obtain a new segment number and a new
offset address in that segment. Bytes 2 and 3 of the 5-byte far jump hold the new
instruction pointer register (IP) data, and bytes 4 and 5 hold the new code segment register
(CS) data. Unlike the short and near jumps, the far jump is used with a label that does not
have a colon.

Jumps with Register Operands.   The jump instruction can also be used to specify a 16-bit
register as an operand. This automatically sets up the instruction as an indirect near jump.
The address of the jump is in the register specified by the jump instruction. The contents
of the register specified are moved into IP so that an intrasegment jump occurs to the
location addressed by the register. This type of jump is very useful when referencing a
jump table. A JMP NEAR PTR AX may also be used to specify a near indirect jump.

Example 5–2 illustrates a jump table and the sequence that is used to access an entry
in the table. Suppose that the number in BX comes from some form of menu-driven
software. The operator types the number 2 on the keyboard, and the software used to read
the key converts it to binary and places it in BX. Example 5–2 takes the number 2, typed
in this example, and decrements it. Next the 1 is added twice to memory address TABLE,
which is loaded into the SI register. After the addition, SI equals memory address

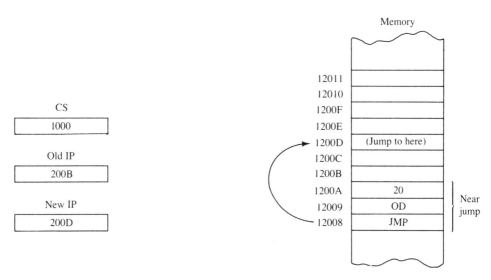

FIGURE 5–3   A near JMP that replaces the contents of the IP register with the 2 bytes
(offset address) that follow the opcode.

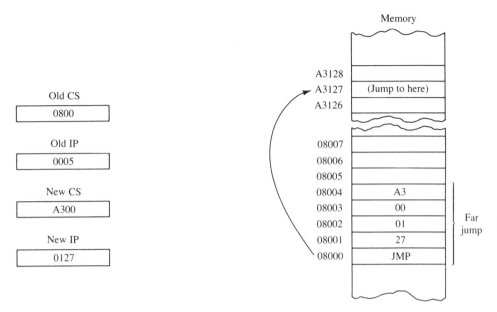

FIGURE 5–4   A far JMP that replaces the contents of both the CS and IP registers with the 4 bytes that follow the opcode.

TABLE + 2. Next the MOV AX,[SI] instruction retrieves the address stored at TABLE + 2 into AX (address TWO in this example). When the JMP AX instruction is executed, the address in AX (TWO) is transferred into IP. This example causes the program to continue executing software at memory address TWO just as if the program contained a JMP TWO. If a 1 is typed, then this same sequence of instructions will jump to memory location ONE to continue the software.

EXAMPLE 5–2

```
0205 BE 0600 R              MOV     SI,OFFSET TABLE
0208 4B                     DEC     BX
0209 03 F3                  ADD     SI,BX
020B 03 F3                  ADD     SI,BX
020D 8B 04                  MOC     AX,[SI]
020F FF E0                  JMP     AX

0600 1000       TABLE:      DW      ONE
0602 2000                   DW      TWO
0604 3000                   DW      THREE
```

Jumps with Memory Indirect Operands.   When an indirect jump instruction is used in a program, its type must be specified with NEAR PTR or FAR PTR. Example 5–3 illustrates how these designations can alter what appears to be the same jump instruction. The first jump (intrasegment) references memory location ADDR1 for a 4-byte double word that holds the next IP and CS location. The second jump (intersegment) references a 2-byte word that holds the next IP.

EXAMPLE 5-3

```
0606 FF 2E 07CA R              JMP     ADDR1

060A BF 07C8 R                 MOV     DI,OFFSET ADDR2
060D FF 25                     JMP     [DI]
```

Conditional Jumps

Conditional jumps are short jumps; that is, the range of the jump is always within + 127 to − 128 bytes from the address of the next instruction. All conditional jump instructions are listed in Table 5-1 along with the condition tested by each.

The conditional jumps test the following flag bits: sign (S), zero (Z), carry (C), parity (P), and overflow (O). If the condition that is tested for is true, a jump to the label occurs, and if the condition is false, no jump occurs and the next sequential instruction is executed.

TABLE 5-1 Conditional jump instructions

Instruction	Condition Tested	Comment
JA	C = 0 and Z ≠ 0	Jump above
JAE	C = 0	Jump above or equal to
JB	C = 1	Jump below
JBE	C = 1 or Z = 1	Jump below or equal to
JC	C = 1	Jump carry set
JE or JZ	Z = 1	Jump equal to or jump 0
JG	Z = 0 and S = O	Jump greater than
JGE	S = O	Jump greater than or equal to
JL	S ≠ O	Jump less than
JLE	Z = 1 or S ≠ O	Jump less than or equal to
JNC	C = 0	Jump carry cleared
JNE or JNZ	Z = 0	Jump not equal to or jump not 0
JNO	O = 0	Jump no overflow
JNS	S = 0	Jump no sign
JNP	P = 0	Jump no parity
JO	O = 1	Jump on overflow
JP	P = 1	Jump on parity
JS	S = 1	Jump on sign
JCXZ	CX = 0	Jump if register CX is 0

Most of the conditional jumps are fairly straightforward and test just one of the flag bits, but some are more complicated. The more complicated ones are used for magnitude comparisons. JA, JAE, JE, JNE, JB, and JBE check the relative magnitudes of *unsigned numbers*. JG, JGE, JE, JNE, JL, and JLE check the relative magnitudes of *signed numbers*.

The remaining conditional jumps test individual flag bits such as overflow and parity. Notice that JE has an alternate opcode JZ. All the instructions have alternates, but they really don't make much sense except for JE/JZ and JNE/JNZ. For example, JA/JBE means jump above/jump below or equal. It makes little sense to say jump below or equal when jump above is much clearer. JBE is an alternate of JA that is seldom used. Likewise most conditional jumps have alternates that are seldom used. These test for a 0 or an equal condition and not-0 or a not-equal condition.

The most radical conditional jump instruction is the JCXZ instruction, which tests not the flag bits but the contents of the CX register. If CX is a 0, a jump to the label occurs, and if CX is not 0, the next sequential instruction is executed.

Suppose that the string instruction SCASB is used to search a table for a 0AH. (Refer to Example 5–4.) At the end of the search, the 0AH may have been found, or it may not have been found. In this case, the JCXZ instruction proves very useful in checking for the not-found condition. If the entire table is checked and no 0AH is found, then the counter (CX) will reach a 0. If the 0AH is found, then CX will not be a 0.

EXAMPLE 5–4

```
                        ;scan a table of 100 bytes for a 0AH
                        ;
                        ;byte 100 = 00H to indicate the end of the table

060F BF 0600 R   SCAN:  MOV    DI,OFFSET TABLE    ;address table
0612 B9 0064             MOV    CX,100             ;load counter
0615 B0 0A               MOV    AL,0AH             ;load AL
0617 FC                  CLD
0618 F2/ AE              REPNE  SCASB              ;scan for 0AH
061A E3 00               JCXZ   NOT_FOUND
```

LOOPs

The LOOP instruction is a combination of the conditional jump and the decrement CX instructions. It will decrement the contents of register CX and, if CX is not 0, jump to the label associated with LOOP. If CX becomes a 0, then the next sequential instruction in the program is executed.

Example 5–5 shows how data in one block of memory (BLOCK1) are added to data in a second block of memory (BLOCK2) using the LOOP instruction to control the numbers added. Notice how LODSW and STOSW are used in this example. Also notice that the segment override prefix (SEG ES:) selects the extra segment for the ADD instruction. This is done because the DI register points to data in the extra segment for the string operations.

EXAMPLE 5-5

```
              ;adds the words in BLOCK1 to BLOCK2

061C B9 0064            MOV   CX,100
061F BE 03C8 R          MOV   SI,OFFSET BLOCK1
0622 BF 05C8 R          MOV   DI,OFFSET BLOCK2

0625        AGAIN:

0625 AD                 LODSW
0626 26: 03 05          ADD   AX,ES:[DI]
0629 AB                 STOSW
062A E2 F9              LOOP AGAIN
```

Conditional LOOPs. As with REP, the LOOP instruction also has some conditional forms: LOOPE and LOOPNE. LOOPE (LOOP *while* equal) will jump to the address pointed to by the label if CX is not a 0 and an equal condition exists. It will exit the loop whenever CX becomes a 0 or whenever an unequal condition is indicated by the flag bits. The LOOPNE (LOOP *while* not equal) instruction functions in the opposite manner. LOOPNE remains in the loop as long as CX is not a 0 and while an unequal condition exists. LOOPNE exits the loop when CX becomes a 0 or whenever an equal condition exists. Both are LOOP *while* instructions: LOOPE is a loop *while* equal, and LOOPNE is a loop *while* not equal.

As with conditional repeats, the conditional loop instructions have alternates: LOOPZ is the same as LOOPE, and LOOPNZ is the same LOOPNE. These alternates may be used at any time, but it is important for documentation to use the opcode that fits a particular application.

5-2 **SUBROUTINES**

The subroutine is a very important part of any computer's software architecture. It is a group of instructions that usually performs one given task and is important because it is used many times by a program but need only be stored once in the memory. This saves memory space and also makes the task of programming much simpler because it takes less time to code a program that contains subroutines. The only disadvantage of a subroutine is that it takes the computer a small amount of additional time to link to the subroutine (CALL) and return from it (RET). The stack is used to store the return address so that the subroutine may return to the program at the point after the CALL instruction in the program.

In the 8086/8088 microprocessor's assembler, there are some definite rules for the storage of subroutines. First, the subroutine is called a *procedure* as it would be in a higher level language such as Pascal. Example 5-6 shows how both a near (intrasegment) and far (intersegment) procedure is specified for the assembler.

EXAMPLE 5-6

```
062                     NAME     PROC        FAR

062C 8B C3                MOV    AX,BX
062E 03 C1                ADD    AX,CX
0630 CB                   RET

0631                     NAME     ENDP

0631                    LABEL PROC NEAR

0631 F7 E3                MUL    BX
0633 F7 E1                MUL    CX
0635 F7 E2                MUL    DX
0637 C3                   RET

0638                    LABEL ENDP
```

Notice from this example that two new pseudo-opcodes appear in the listing: PROC and ENDP. PROC is used to indicate the start of a procedure (subroutine), the name of the procedure, and the type of CALL and RET instructions used by the assembler. The name of the subroutine can be any valid assembly language name. The type can be near or far, depending on whether the programmer expects the procedure to be located within the code segment or some distance from it. Two procedures have been illustrated here: one a near type and the other a far type. The second new pseudo-opcode, ENDP, tells the assembler that it has reached the end of a procedure and also the name of procedure.

Most procedures that are to be part of a system library should be written as far procedures. In addition, any jumps within the procedure should be short so that they can be relocated easily. Because the short jump is completely relocatable, procedures using it can be added to any program without special preparation. In a universal procedure, all registers used must be stored on the stack and then retrieved before the return. Also all jumps within the procedure must be short.

CALLs

The CALL instruction transfers the flow of a program to a procedure. CALLs differ from jumps because they save the contents of IP on the stack if the CALL is near or IP and CS on the stack if it is far.

Near CALL.   The near CALL instruction is 3 bytes long and its second and third bytes contain the offset location of the near procedure. Therefore the CALL saves the IP on the stack and jumps to the procedure. But why save the IP register? IP contains the address of the next sequential instruction in the memory—the one following the CALL. When IP is pushed onto the stack, the stack contains the return address—the address of the next instruction. Figure 5–5 shows the return address being stored on the stack and also the jump to the procedure.

Far CALL.   The far CALL instruction is like the far jump because it allows a CALL to any location in the memory. The far CALL is a 5-byte instruction in which bytes 2 and 3

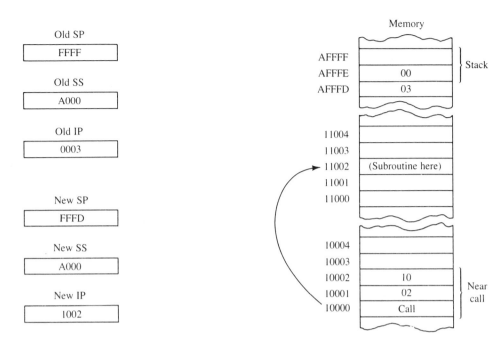

FIGURE 5-5 The effect of a near call instruction on the stack and the SP, SS, and IP registers. Notice how the old IP is stored on the stack.

contain the IP of the procedure and bytes 4 and 5 contain the new code segment value (CS) for the procedure. In addition to jumping to the procedure, the far CALL instruction pushes both the IP and the CS registers onto the stack. Because the IP and CS registers contain the address of the next instruction to be executed, the return address is pushed onto the stack. This process is illustrated in Figure 5-6.

CALLs with Register Operands. Like jumps of this type, CALLs may also have a register operand, making an indirect CALL possible. This type of CALL is used in much the same manner as the JMP register call. The register specified in the indirect CALL contains the 16-bit offset address of the subroutine. It is important to note that the CALL register instruction may only be an intrasegment CALL because the register contains only a 16-bit offset address.

Example 5-7 illustrates the use of the CALL register instruction to call the subroutine that begins at offset address COMPUTE.

EXAMPLE 5-7

```
0000 BE 0005 R              MOV        SI,OFFSET COMPUTE
0003 FF D6                  CALL       SI

0005                COMPUTE PROC NEAR

0005 52                     PUSH       DX
0006 8B D0                  MOV        DX,AX
```

```
0008 E5 33                  IN          AX,DATA
000A E7 AA                  OUT         PORT,AX
000C 8B C2                  MOV         AX,DX
000E 5A                     POP         DX
000F C3                     RET

0010              COMPUTE ENDP
```

CALLs with Indirect Memory Addressing.   The CALL with indirect memory addressing is
particularly useful whenever a computed GOTO (BASIC language) statement is required
in assembly language programs. Indirect memory calls are either of the near or far type,
depending on how the memory data are organized and how the subroutine is defined with
the PROC pseudo-opcode.

Example 5–8 shows how a computed goto is used to reference various procedures
in the memory. Here DI contains the number 1, 2, or 3. This number is modified to a 0,
2, or 4 and added to SI, which generates the lookup table address. The lookup table
(TABLE) contains the correct addresses of procedures ONE, TWO, and THREE.

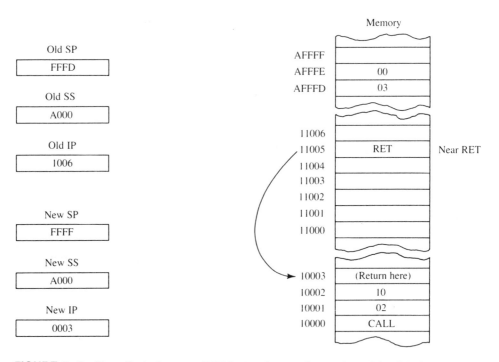

FIGURE 5–6   The effect of a near RET instruction on the stack and the SP, SS, and IP
registers.

EXAMPLE 5-8

```
                 ;lookup table in data segment

0764 0008 R      TABLE        DW      ONE
0766 0018 R                   DW      TWO
0768 0028 R                   DW      THREE

                 ;calling sequence for computer CALL
                 ;to a near subroutine
                 ;
                 ;assumes that DI is a number between one and three
                 ;
0000 4F                       DEC     DI
0001 BB 0764 R                MOV     BX,OFFSET TABLE
0004 03 FF                    ADD     DI,DI
0006 FF 11                    CALL    [BX+DI]

0008             ONE          PROC    NEAR
                              . . .
                              . . .
0008             ONE          ENDP

0018             TWO          PROC    NEAR
                              . . .
                              . . .
0018             TWO          ENDP ,

0028             THREE        PROC    NEAR
                              . . .
                              . . .
0028             THREE        ENDP
```

RETs

The return instruction (RET) removes either a 16-bit number (near return) from the stack and places it in the IP or a 32-bit number (far return) and places it in IP and CS. The near and far return instructions are both defined in the procedure's PROC statement and automatically selected by the assembler.

When IP or IP and CS are changed, the address of the next instruction is at a new location. This new location is the address of the instruction that immediately follows the most recent CALL to a procedure. Figure 5-7 illustrates how CALL links to a procedure and how RET returns from a procedure.

There is one other form of the return instruction. This form allows a number to be added to the contents of the stack pointer (SP) before the return. If the pushes must be deleted before a return, a 16-bit displacement is added to the SP before the RET retrieves the return address from the stack and returns.

Example 5-9 shows how this type of return dumps (erases) the data placed on the stack by a few pushes. The RET 4 in this example adds a 4 to the SP before removing

FIGURE 5–7 A short program and subroutine that illustrates the linkage between the program and the subroutine with the CALL and RET instructions.

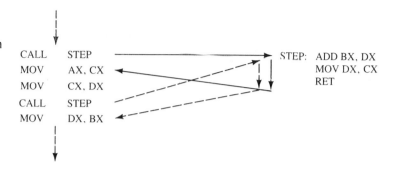

```
CALL    STEP
MOV     AX, CX
MOV     CX, DX
CALL    STEP
MOV     DX, BX
```

```
STEP:   ADD BX, DX
        MOV DX, CX
        RET
```

the IP from the stack. Since PUSH AX and PUSH BX together place 4 bytes of data on the stack, this return effectively deletes AX and BX data from the stack. This example is used only in special cases and is not the normal type of return.

EXAMPLE 5–9

```
0000                    TEST_RIG    PROC    NEAR

0000 50                             PUSH    AX
0001 53                             PUSH    BX
                                    . . .
                                    . . .
0002 C2 0004                        RET     4

000                     TEST_RIG    END_P
```

5–3   INTERRUPTS

An *interrupt* is either a hardware-generated subroutine call (externally derived) or a software-generated subroutine call (internally derived). It will interrupt the program that is currently executing by calling the *interrupt service subroutine*.

Hardware interrupts are covered in Chapter 9. This section deals with *software interrupts,* which are special types of CALL instructions in the 8086/8088 microprocessor. In it, we cover the three types of interrupt instructions (INT, INTO, and INT 3), provide a map of all of the available interrupt vector locations, and explain the purpose of the special interrupt return instruction (IRET).

Interrupt Vectors

An *interrupt vector* is a 4-byte number stored in the first 1,024 bytes of the memory (00000H–003FFH). There are 256 such interrupt vectors, of which some are used for hardware and some for software. Each vector contains the address of the interrupt service subroutine—the subroutine called by an interrupt. These vectors and their functions are listed in Table 5-2 along with each of their memory locations. Each vector location in the table is 4 bytes in length and contains the address of the interrupt service subroutine. The first 2 bytes of the vector contain the number that is loaded into IP register (IP low followed by IP high), and the next two bytes contain the number that is loaded into the CS register (CS low followed by CS high) in response to an interrupt.

Interrupt Instructions

The 8086/8088 has three different interrupt instructions available to the programmer: INT, INTO, and INT 3. Each of these instructions fetches a vector from the interrupt vector table and then calls the subroutine at the location addressed by the vector entry. In addition to calling the subroutine, these instructions also push the flags onto the stack.

INTs. There are 256 different software interrupt instructions available to the programmer. Each INT instruction has a numeric operand whose value ranges from 0 to 255 (00H–FFH). For example, an INT 100 will use interrupt vector 100. Each of these instructions are 2 bytes long, except for INT3, which is a special 1-byte software interrupt instruction.

Whenever a software interrupt instruction is executed, it (1) pushes the flags onto the stack, (2) clears the I and T flags, (3) pushes CS onto the stack, (4) fetches the new CS location from the vector table, (5) pushes IP onto the stack, (6) fetches the new IP location from the vector table, and (7) jumps to this new location. The INT is thus very similar to a far CALL except that it not only pushes both CS and IP onto the stack but also pushes a copy of the flag register onto the stack. Indeed, it could be called a combination PUSHF and CALL instruction.

Notice that when the INT software instruction is accepted, it clears the interrupt flag (I) bit, which controls the external hardware interrupt pin interrupt request (INTR). When I is a logic 0, the INTR pin is turned off or disabled. When I is a logic 1, the INTR pin is turned on or enabled. The purpose of the T flag will be discussed in Chapter 9 on interrupts.

Software interrupts are most commonly used in systems subroutines, which are common to all or most programs that use a system and control such things as a printer, CRT, and display. The far CALL, which is normally used for these functions, is 5 bytes

TABLE 5-2 Interrupt vector map		
Number	Address	Function
0	0H–3H	Divide error
1	4H–7H	Single step
2	8H–BH	NMI (hardware interrupt)
3	CH–FH	Breakpoint
4	10H–13H	Interrupt on overflow
5–31	14H–7FH	Reserved for future use*
32–255	80H–3FFH	User interrupts

*These interrupts are used on some of the newer versions of the 8086/8088 such as the 80186/80188, 80286, and 80386.

in length, and the INT instruction is only 2 bytes in length. The INT, used in place of a far CALL, thus saves 3 bytes of memory each time a subroutine is called. This can add up to a very sizable savings of memory space in many programs.

When using software interrupts, you may need to insert an instruction that enables interrupts in the middle of the subroutine called by the INT instruction. This is further detailed and explained in Chapter 9.

IRET.   The interrupt return instruction (IRET) is used only with the software or hardware interrupts. Unlike a simple return instruction, the IRET will (1) pop stack data back into IP, (2) pop stack data back into CS, and (3) pop stack data back into the flags. A close examination reveals that the IRET instruction is, in fact, a combination of the RET and POPF instructions.

Whenever the IRET pops the flags back into the flag register, the prior contents of I and T, which are cleared after the push flags portion of the INT instruction, are restored. This means that if interrupts are enabled prior to a software interrupt (they are always disabled during the interrupt service subroutine), they are automatically reenabled by the IRET instruction.

INT 3.   The INT 3 instruction acts like any other software interrupt except that it is only 1 byte long, while all other software interrupt instructions are 2 bytes long. Vector number 3 (see Table 5–2) is even given a special name, *breakpoint interrupt,* because it is fairly easy for the programmer to insert a 1-byte instruction at any point in the software.

Once inserted, the INT 3 instruction will call the subroutine pointed at by vector 3 at the point in the software where the INT 3 is stored, breaking away from the software at this point. If the software at the INT 3 interrupt service subroutine displays all the registers and waits, it is fairly easy to use this interrupt to debug a faulty program.

INTO.   Interrupt on overflow (INTO) is a conditional interrupt instruction. If the overflow flag (O) is set and the INTO instruction is encountered in a program, the subroutine whose address is stored at vector 4 will be called. On the other hand, if the O bit is cleared and the INTO instruction is encountered, no interrupt will be called. This instruction is similar to the JO instruction except that it will interrupt rather than jump on an overflow.

The INTO instruction is most widely used following signed arithmetic to detect an overflow error condition. In this type of program, an INTO appears after every addition and subtraction.

INT 50

Suppose that, in a particular system, it is often necessary to add the contents of DI, SI, BP, and BX and save the result in AX. Because this is a common task, it is worthwhile writing as an interrupt rather than as a subroutine. Example 5–10 illustrates this interrupt and shows how the interrupt vector is defined in an assembly language program. Each time this function is required, an INT 50 instruction is used to call it.

EXAMPLE 5–10

```
                    ;interrupt service subroutine

0000 03 C3      ADDM:   ADD     AX,BX
0002 03 C6              ADD     AX,SI
```

```
0004 03 C7              ADD    AX,DI
0006 03 C5              ADD    AX,BP
0008 CF                 IRET
```

Interrupt Control

Although this section does not cover hardware interrupts, it is necessary at this time to introduce two instructions used to control the hardware interrupt structure: set interrupt flag (STI) and clear interrupt flag (CLI). These instructions are used to set and clear the I flag bit. Since, when the I flag is cleared the INTR pin is disabled, and when the I flag is set INTR is enabled, STI will enable interrupts and CLI will disable them.

5-4 MACHINE CONTROL AND MISCELLANEOUS INSTRUCTIONS

The last category of instructions available in the 8086/8088 instruction set is the machine control and miscellaneous group. These instructions provide control of the carry bit, sample the $\overline{\text{TEST}}$ pin, and perform various other functions. Because most of these instructions are used in hardware control, they need only be mentioned here. We cover them in complete detail in the chapters that deal with the hardware application of these features.

Controlling the Carry Flag Bit (C)

The carry flag is used during multiple-word addition and subtraction and indicates error conditions within subroutines. There are three instructions that allow the programmer to select the condition of the carry flag (C) bit: set carry (STC), clear carry (CLC), and complement carry (CMC).

WAIT

The WAIT instruction tests the hardware pin $\overline{\text{TEST}}$, which is used to test a variety of external hardware events. If the $\overline{\text{TEST}}$ pin is a logic 1, the 8086/8088 will become idle and wait for the $\overline{\text{TEST}}$ pin to become a logic 0. (Note that an interrupt will also exit the wait or idle condition.) $\overline{\text{TEST}}$ is often used with the 8087 coprocessor to test the BUSY output pin of that circuit. We discuss this instruction in more detail in the hardware chapters.

HLT

The halt instruction (HLT) stops the execution of software. There are only two ways to exit a halt: by an interrupt or by a hardware system reset. This instruction is normally used only in special cases.

NOP

When the microprocessor encounters a NOP, it takes three clocking periods to execute. Yet, the NOP performs no operation. Why would a NOP ever be used in software? NOP finds application in time delay software. In machine language programs, it is advisable for the programmer to leave patch areas every 50 bytes or so in case the program needs modification at some future date. These patch areas normally contain NOP instructions so that the program's operation will not be affected by these patch areas.

LOCK Prefix

The LOCK prefix is a byte placed before any 8086/8088 instruction to inhibit the external coprocessor in the system from gaining access to system buses. More detail on LOCK is provided later, in the chapters on coprocessors.

ESC

The escape instruction (ESC) passes information to the 8087 arithmetic coprocessor. Whenever the escape instruction is executed, the 8086/8088 performs an NOP, and the external coprocessor receives a 6-bit opcode encoded in the ESC instruction. In addition, the ESC instruction also accesses a memory location so that the coprocessor can read or write data if necessary. ESC is an opcode for an external coprocessor. More detail is provided in the chapter on the 8087 arithmetic processor.

5-5   SAMPLE PROGRAMS

This section provides some sample programs that illustrate how to organize a program for use with the IBM-PC macroassembler (MASM) or assembler (ASM). It also demonstrates some common programming techniques that are useful in many applications.

Setting up the Program for an EXE File

An execute (EXE) file is actually a new command for the DOS *(disk operating system)*. For example, if you create an EXE file named DOG.EXE, then all you need to type to execute this program is DOG. It is not as easy to set up the program for the IBM-PC assembler as an execute file, however, as it is for some other machines. Each segment must be defined and many other small details attended to or the assembler will not accept the program. Example 5–11 shows a template used for most assembly language programs when the program and all its subroutines exist together.

EXAMPLE 5–11

```
;;;;;;;;;;;;;;;;;;;;;;;;;;;;;;;;;;;;;;;;;;;;;;;;;;
;                                               ;
;Example program that will display a few;
;messages in the video screen.          ;
;                                               ;
;;;;;;;;;;;;;;;;;;;;;;;;;;;;;;;;;;;;;;;;;;;;;;;;;;
```

```
                                   ;
= 0024                             MES_END        EQU        '$'
= 000D                             CR             EQU        13
= 000A                             LF             EQU        10
= 0009                             NINE           EQU        9
                                   ;
                                   ;;;;;;;;;;;;;;;;;;;;;;;;;;;;;;;;;;;;;;;;;;;;;
                                   ;                                          ;
                                   ;         Stack segment                   ;
                                   ;                                          ;
                                   ;;;;;;;;;;;;;;;;;;;;;;;;;;;;;;;;;;;;;;;;;;;;;
                                   ;
0000                               STACK_SEG      SEGMENT    STACK

0000 0100[                                        DW         256 DUP (?)
        ????
              ]
= 0200                             STACK_TOP      EQU        THISWORD

0200                               STACK_SEG      ENDS
                                   ;
                                   ;;;;;;;;;;;;;;;;;;;;;;;;;;;;;;;;;;;;;;;;;;;;;
                                   ;                                          ;
                                   ;         Data segment                    ;
                                   ;                                          ;
                                   ;;;;;;;;;;;;;;;;;;;;;;;;;;;;;;;;;;;;;;;;;;;;;
                                   ;
0000                               DATA_SEG       SEGMENT

0000 0D                            MESSAGE_1      DB         CR
0001 0005[                                        DB         5 DUP (OAH)
      OA
          ]
0006 42 41 52 52 59 20                            DB         'BARRY B. BREY'
     42 2E 20 42 52 45
     59
0013 0D                                           DB         CR
0014 OA                                           DB         LF
0015 24                                           DB         MES_END
0016 77 61 73 20 68 65     MESSAGE_2              DB         'was here!!'
     72 65 21 21
0020 24                                           DB         MES_end

0021                               DATA_SEG       ENDS
                                   ;
                                   ;;;;;;;;;;;;;;;;;;;;;;;;;;;;;;;;;;;;;;;;;;;;;
                                   ;                                          ;
                                   ;         Code segment                    ;
                                   ;                                          ;
                                   ;;;;;;;;;;;;;;;;;;;;;;;;;;;;;;;;;;;;;;;;;;;;;
                                   ;
0000                               CODE_SEG        SEGMENT

                      ASSUME       CS:SEG,SS:STACK_SEG
                      ASSUME       DS:DATA_SEG

0000                  MAIN                         PROC    FAR
```

```
0000 BC 0200 R      MAIN                      MOV      SP,OFFSET STACK_TOP
0003 B8 ---T                                  MOV      AX,DATA_SEG
0006 8E D8                                     MOV      DS,AX

0008 BA 0000 R                                MOV      DX,OFFSET MESSAGE_1
0006 8E 0018 R                                MOV      AX,DATA_SEG

000E BA 0016 R                                MOV      DX,OFFSET MESSAGE_2
0011 E8 0018 R                                CALL     DISPLAY

0014 B4 4C                                    MOV      AH,4CH
0016 CD 21                                    INT      21H

0018                 MAIN                      ENDP

0018                 DISPLAY                   PROC     NEAR

0018 B4 09                                    MOV      AH,NINE
001A CD 21                                    INT      21H
001C C3                                        RET

001D                 DISPLAY                   ENDP

001D          CODE_SEG    ENDS

                     END    MAIN
```

Once the program, called *name* (NAME.ASM) in this example, is entered into a disk file with the editor, it can then be assembled by the following steps:

1. Type a MASM NAME; or ASM NAME; (depending on which you own) to assemble the program. This creates a new file called NAME.OBJ, which cannot be executed.
2. Type a LINK NAME; to link the program with other modules if they exist and convert it into an execute file, NAME.EXE.
3. Type a NAME to execute this program. What you should see on the screen after 5 line feeds is:

BARRY B. BREY
was here!!

The same procedure will assemble, link, and execute any edited XXXXXXXX. ASM program file that you create with whatever editor you happen to have at your disposal. Editors range from a simple systems, such as EDLIN, to complicated word processors, such as WORDSTAR®* used in the nondocument mode of operation. Once you use a word processor to create and edit programs, you will never again use an editor such as EDLIN. Word processors are much easier to use and they allow the information in a program to be moved about with ease.

*WORDSTAR® is a registered trademark of Wordstar, Inc.

Program Equates. The first section of a program listing is called *program equates*. This section is used to equate (EQU) labels to various values used throughout the program. EQUs clarify the instructions that are used in the main program and also in procedures and the data definition section of the program listing. Program equates are optional, but they make the program more readable and therefore more self-documenting. Notice how much more readable MESSAGE _ END is than just the '$'. MESSAGE _ END means something to the average reader; '$' is meaningful only to the reader who is intimately familiar with the computer and operating system. Please refer to Appendix A, which deals with DOS, for more detail.

Stack Segment. The next portion of a program listing is the stack segment. Here the stack area is set up to allow the program to use the CALL and return (RET) instructions and any other stack operations (PUSH and POP) that might be necessary for operation.

The first statement in the stack segment is the SEGMENT pseudo-operation (a statement that generates no machine code, but instructs the assembler or linker). The SEGMENT pseudo-operation identifies the start of a segment for the assembler and indicates that it is to begin at a *paragraph boundary* (PARA), which occurs at every 16 bytes throughout the 8086/8088 memory.

The SEGMENT statement also indicates to the linker that the segment called STACK _ SEG is PUBLIC—that is, it can be combined with other segments of the same name. Although this is not a feature of this program, a segment made·public allows this program to be added to or concatenated with other segments of the same name if they are joined to this one by the linker program.

The next statement is DB 256 DUP (?), which defines bytes of memory. In this example, 256 bytes of memory have been reserved for the stack segment and the stack. The 256 DUP (?) portion of the DB statement tells the assembler to reserve 256 locations of any value for this statement. The ? used for the duplicate statement (DUP) indicates that the assembler shall not fill these bytes with any data; instead, they remain unchanged.

When the linker converts the file to an EXE, it automatically sets up the stack segment register (SS) to point to this segment and the program initializes the stack pointer (SP), which is always initialized to the location of the area reserved for the stack in the stack segment. The name STACK–SEG is often used to define the stack segment as illustrated.

The last statement in the stack segment, end segment (ENDS), identifies the end of the segment. It must be used to end each segment identified in a program, and it must have the same label as the preceding SEGMENT statement used to open the segment.

Data Segment. The data segment in this example is called DATA _ SEG, but it can be called anything the programmer wishes. As in the stack segment, the first statement must be SEGMENT, and the last statement must be ENDS.

The data segment sets up all the data segment variables used with the program. In this example, the data segment contains a number of DB statements that store string or ASCII data in the data segment.

This sample program does not contain an extra segment. If it did, it too would begin with the SEGMENT statement and end with ENDS. The programmer is also free to choose the name of the extra segment.

Code Segment. The code segment contains the program. The choice of its name is optional. Notice that the code segment also begins with a SEGMENT statement and ends with the ENDS statement.

The second statement in the code segment ASSUME, tells the assembler that the name you have selected for the code segment (CS) is CODE_SEG and the name for the data segment (DS) is DATA_SEG. It also informs the assembler the (SS) is STACK_SEG. If this program had included an extra segment (ES), it too would be declared to the assembler at this point with the ASSUME statement.

The first real software in the code segment is the procedure main program, which is identified as a far procedure called MAIN. (The main procedure is normally identified as far.)

The first statement initializes the stack pointer. The next two statements set up the DS register. (The only segment registers that are automatically loaded by DOS are CS and SS.) In this example, the DS register is loaded with DATA_SEG, the start of the data segment. If the extra segment is in a program, it must be loaded in the same fashion.

Finally, the real program emerges. Two messages are displayed by this program: MESSAGE_ONE and MESSAGE_TWO.

The next procedure is called DISPLAY_MESSAGE. It is set up as a near procedure, and in this example it is very short.

Here the PC–DOS function 9 is used to display the character string on the CRT screen. Built-in functions are called with the INT 21H instruction, with the function number placed in AH before the call. In this case, the built-in function 9 displays the character string addressed by the DX register. If you go back to MAIN, you will notice that the address of the message is loaded into DX before a call to this procedure occurs.

The last statement of the file is the END statement. This tells the assembler that the end of the file has arrived, and it also tells the linker where the first statement of the program is located.

Sample Input/Output Program

This first sample program (see Example 5–12) makes the IBM-PC look like a typewriter. This is a very simple program, but it does illustrate how the template first presented in Example 5–11 is used, with a slight modification.

Here the equates section contains only three statements. In a very large program, it could contain hundreds of equates.

It is interesting to note that this program contains no data segment. In this case, it is not needed because the program stores no data in the memory, nor does it read data from the memory. It simply continues to read a key from the keyboard until a dollar sign is typed, returning the computer to the DOS so that another program may be executed.

The basic assembly language program illustrated here calls a read key subroutine that uses one of the built-in PC-DOS functions–number 6, the keyboard input function. Function number 6 waits for a key to be typed, reads the key from the keyboard, and returns with the typed character in register AL. It also displays whatever character has been typed.

EXAMPLE 5-12

```
                         ;;;;;;;;;;;;;;;;;;;;;;;;;;;;;;;;;;;;;;;;;;
                         ;                                        ;
                         ;Example program that will accept data  ;
                         ;from the keyboard and display them on  ;
                         ;the monitor until a $ is typed.        ;
                         ;                                        ;
                         ;;;;;;;;;;;;;;;;;;;;;;;;;;;;;;;;;;;;;;;;;;
                         ;
= 0006                   SIX            EQU        6
= 0024                   DOLLAR         EQU        '$'
                         ;
                         ;;;;;;;;;;;;;;;;;;;;;;;;;;;;;;;;;;;;;;;;;;
                         ;                                        ;
                         ;      Stack segment                     ;
                         ;                                        ;
                         ;;;;;;;;;;;;;;;;;;;;;;;;;;;;;;;;;;;;;;;;;;
                         ;
0000                     STACK_SEG      SEGMENT    STACK
0000 0100[
        ????
                  ]
                         STACK_TOP      EQU        THIS WORD

0200                     STACK_SEG      ENDS
                         ;
                         ;;;;;;;;;;;;;;;;;;;;;;;;;;;;;;;;;;;;;;;;;;
                         ;                                        ;
                         ;      Code segment                      ;
                         ;                                        ;
                         ;;;;;;;;;;;;;;;;;;;;;;;;;;;;;;;;;;;;;;;;;;
                         ;
0000                     CODE_SEG       SEGMENT
                         ASSUME CS:CODE_SEG,SS:STACK_SEG

0000                     MAIN           PROC       FAR

0000 BC 0200 R                          MOV        SP,OFFSET STACK_TOP

0003                     AGAIN:

0003 E8 000E R                          CALL       READ_KEY
0006 3C 24                              CMP        AL,DOLLAR_SIGN
0008 75 F9                              JNE        AGAIN

000A B4 4C                              MOV        AH,4CH
000C CD 21                              INT        21H

000E                     MAIN           ENDP

000E                     READ_KEY       PROC       NEAR
```

```
000E B4 06                                      MOV      AH,SIX
0010 B2 FF                                       MOV      DI,OFFH
0012 CD 21                                       INT      21H
0014 74 F8                                       JZ       READ_KEY
0016 8A D0                                       MOV      DL,AL
0018 CD 21                                       RET

001B                          READ_KEY          ENDP

001B                          CODE_SEG          ENDS

                              END               MAIN
```

When a key is typed, the MAIN program calls the read key procedure and checks to see if it is a dollar sign. If a dollar sign has been typed, it returns to DOS; if not, it reads another key from the keyboard.

Sample Two-Number Addition Program

This sample program (see Example 5–13) accepts two numbers from the keyboard, adds them, and displays the results on the CRT screen. This is a more complex program than the previous one.

EXAMPLE 5–13

```
                    ;;;;;;;;;;;;;;;;;;;;;;;;;;;;;;;;;;;;;;;;;;;;;;;
                    ;                                            ;
                    ;Example program that will add two numbers   ;
                    ;that are entered through the keyboard and    ;
                    ;then display the result on the CRT screen    ;
                    ;The maximum size of the number is 2 digits.;
                    ;                                            ;
                    ;;;;;;;;;;;;;;;;;;;;;;;;;;;;;;;;;;;;;;;;;;;;;;;
                    ;
= 0006              SIX             EQU     6
= 0009              NINE            EQU     9
= 0002              TWO             EQU     2
= 000D              CR              EQU     13
= 000A              LF              EQU     10
= 0024              EOM             EQU     '$'
= 0021              DOS_FUNC        EQU     21H
= 004E              NO              EQU     'N'
= 0059              YES             EQU     'Y'
= 002B              PLUS            EQU     '+'
= 003D              EQUAL           EQU     '='
= 0030              ZERO_ASCII      EQU     '0'
= 0039              NINE_ASCII      EQU     '9'
                    ;
                    ;;;;;;;;;;;;;;;;;;;;;;;;;;;;;;;;;;;;;;;;;;;;;;
                    ;                                           ;
                    ;           Stack segment                   ;
                    ;                                           ;
                    ;;;;;;;;;;;;;;;;;;;;;;;;;;;;;;;;;;;;;;;;;;;;;;
                    ;
0000                STACK_SEG       SEGMENT STACK

0000 0100[                          DW      256 DUP (?)
```

```
                         ????
                         ]
 = 0200                               STACK_TOP       EQU        THISWORD

 0200                                 STACK_SEG       ENDS
                         ;
                         ;;;;;;;;;;;;;;;;;;;;;;;;;;;;;;;;;;;;;;;;;;
                         ;              Data segment                 ;
                         ;                                           ;
                         ;;;;;;;;;;;;;;;;;;;;;;;;;;;;;;;;;;;;;;;;;;
                         ;
 0000                    DATA_SEG SEGMENT

 0000 0D 0A 0A    SIGN_ON   DB     CR,LF,LF
 0003 41 64 64 20 74 77    DB     'Add two numbers(Y/N)?',0
      6F 20 6E 75 6D 62
      65 72 73 20 28 59
      2F 4E 29 3F 20 00
 001B 24                   DB     EOM
 001C 0D 0A 0A 24 NEXT_MES DB     CR,LF,LF,EOM
 0020 0002[       NUMB1     DB     2 DUP (?)
         ??
              ]
 0022 0002[       NUMB2     DB     2 DUP (?)
         ??
              ]
 0024                    DATA_SEG ENDS
                         ;
                         ;;;;;;;;;;;;;;;;;;;;;;;;;;;;;;;;;;;;;;;;;;
                         ;                                           ;
                         ;              Code segment                 ;
                         ;                                           ;
                         ;;;;;;;;;;;;;;;;;;;;;;;;;;;;;;;;;;;;;;;;;;
                         ;
 0000                    CODE_SEG SEGMENT

                         ASSUME CS:CODE_SEG,SS:STACK_SEG
                         ASSUME DS:DATA_SEG

 0000            MAIN            PROC    FAR
 0000 BC 0200 R                  MOV     SP,OFFSET STACK_TOP
 0003 B8 --- R                   MOV     AX,DATA_SEG
 0006 8E D8                      MOV     DS,AX
 0008 8E C0                      MOV     ES,AX

 000A                    TOP:

 000A BA 0000 R                  MOV     DX,OFFSET SIGN_ON
 000D E8 00A4 R                  CALL    DISP_MES

 0010                    AGAIN:

 0010 E8 00B0 R                  CALL READ_KEY

 00A9 8A D0                      MOV     DL,AL
 00AB B4 06                      MOV     AH,SIX
 00AD CD 21                      INT     DOS_FUNC
 00AF C3                         RET

 00B0            OUT_CHAR ENDP

 00B0            READ_KEY PROC  NEAR
```

```
00B0 B4 06                          MOV       AH,SIX
00B2 B2 FF                          MOV       DL,OFFH
00B4 CD 21                          INT       DOS_FUNC
00B6 74 F8                          JZ        READ_KEY
00B8 C3                             RET

00B9            READ_KEY            ENDP

00B9            CODE_SEG            ENDS

                                    END       MAIN

                NEXT1:
0077

0077 58                             POP       AX
0078 E8 00A9 R                      CALL      OUT_CHAR
007B FE C9                          DEC       CL
007D 75 F8                          JNE       NEXT1
007F EB 89                          JMP       TOP

0081                MAIN_END:

0081 B4 4C                          MOV       AH,4CH
0083 CD 21                          INT       DOS_FUNC

0085            MAIN                ENDP

0085            READ_NUMB           PROC      NEAR

0085 B5 02                          MOV       CH,TWO

0087                        READ_NUMB1:

0087 E8 00B0 R                      CALL      READ_KEY
008A 2C 30                          SUB       AL,ZERO_ASCII
008C 8C 8C 72 F9                    JB        READ_NUMB1
008E 3C 39                          CMP       AL,NINE ASCII
0090 7.7 F5                         JA        READ_NUMB1
0092 88 05                          MOV       [DI],AL
0094 04 30                          ADD       AL,ZERO_ASCII
009A FE CD                          DEC       CH
09C 75 E9                           JNE       READ_NUMB1
009E 8A C3                          MOV       AL,BL
00A0 E8 00A9 R                      CALL      OUT_CHAR
00A3 C3                             RET

00A4            READ_NUMB           ENDP

00A4            DISP_MES PROC       NEAR

00A4 B4 09                          MOV       AH,NINE
00A6 CD 21                          INT       DOS_FUNC
00A8 C3                             RET

00A9            DISP_MES ENDP
00A9            OUT_CHAR PROC       NEAR

0013 24 DF                          AND       AL,0DFH
0015 3C 4E                          CMP       AL,NO
0017 74 68                          JE        MAIN_END
```

```
0019 3C 59                              CMP        AL,YES
001B 75 F3                              JNE        AGAIN
001D E8 00A9 R                          CALL       OUT_CHAR

0020 BA 001C R                          MOV        DX,OFFSET NEXT_MES
0023 E8 00A4 R                          CALL       DISP_MES

0026 32 C0                              XOR        AL,AL
028 A2 0020 R                           MOV        NUMB1,AL
002B A2 0021 R                          MOV        NUMB1+1,AL
002E A2 0022 R                          MOV        NUMB2,AL
0031 A2 0023 R                          MOV        NUMB2+1,AL

0034 B3 2B                              MOV        BI,PLUS
0036 BF 0200 R                          MOV        DI,OFFSET NUMB1
0039 E8 0085 R                          CALL       READ_NUMB

003C B3 3D                              MOV        CL,2
003E BF 0022 R                          MOV        BL,O
0041 E8 0085 R                          CALL       READ_NUMB
0044 B1 02                              MOV        CL,2
0046 B3 00                              MOV        BL,0
0048 A0 0021 R                          MOV        AL,NUMB1+1
004B 02 06 0023 R                       ADD        AL,NUMB2+1
004F 27                                 DAA
0050 8A F8                              MOV        BH,AL
0052 OC 30                              OR         AL,ZERO_ASCII
0054 50                                 PUSH AX
0055 8A C7                              MOV        AL,BH
0059 3C 0A                              CMP        AL,10
005B B3 01                              MOV        BL,1

005D                    NEXT:

005D A0 0020 R                          MOV        AL,NUMB1
0060 02 06 0022 R                       ADD        AL,NUMB2
0064 02 C3                              ADD        AL,BL
0066 27                                 DAA
0067 8A D8                              MOV        BL,AL
0069 OC 30                              OR         AL,ZERO_ASCII
006B 50                                 PUSH       AX
006C 8A C3                              MOV        AL,BL
006E 3C 0A                              CMP        AL,10
0070 72 05                              JB         NEXT1
0072 B0 31                              MOV AL,'1'
0074 50                                 PUSH AX
0075 FE C1                              INC        CL
```

In this example, notice that both ES and DS are assumed to be the DATA _ SEG and are also both loaded with the DATA _ SEG location. This is done because string operations are used in the program, and it would be inconvenient to create a separate segment for both DS and ES.

The program itself accepts two numbers, up to 40 digits long, from the keyboard. The first number is accepted until the plus (+) sign is typed; the second number is accepted until an equal (=) sign is typed. Once the equal sign is typed, the program adds both numbers using ASCII addition. The result is placed in a buffer called ANSWER and displayed on the monitor. The form of the data entered into the program is

$$23 + 33 = 56$$

Creating Library Modules

One main advantage of a computer with disk drives, an assembler, and linker is that library modules can be set up and permanently stored on the disk. Then, at a later date, these modules can be used to form many sections of the program. The library module is the most convenient way to store all commonly used procedures.

Example 5–14 illustrates a library module of a procedure that displays a message on the CRT screen. This procedure uses the PC-DOS function number 9, which displays the message addressed by the DX register.

The first statement, PUBLIC, indicates to the linker that this module may be used by other modules as they are linked. Therefore, this procedure may be used henceforward by any other program once it has been debugged and stored on the disk. Also notice that the LIB _ SEG statement is PUBLIC and is also called 'CODE'. When this procedure is linked, it will load only into a PUBLIC segment called 'CODE'. Also notice that the END statement does not have the start label as the programs did.

EXAMPLE 5–14

```
;;;;;;;;;;;;;;;;;;;;;;;;;;;;;;;;;;;;;;;;;;;;;
;                                            ;
;Library Module                              ;
;DISPLAY message addressed by DX             ;
;                                            ;
;;;;;;;;;;;;;;;;;;;;;;;;;;;;;;;;;;;;;;;;;;;;;
;

                              PUBLIC    DISPLAY
= 0009          NINE          EQU       9

0000            LIB_SEG       SEGMENT

                      ASSUME CS:LIB_SEG

0000            DISPLAY       PROC      FAR

0000 53                       PUSH      BX
0001 51                       PUSH      CX
0002 52                       PUSH      DX
0003 55                       PUSH      BP
0004 56                       PUSH      SI
0005 57                       PUSH      DI
0006 B4 09                    MOV       AH,NINE
0008 CD 21                    INT       21H
000A 5F                       POP       DI
000B 5E                       POP       SI
000C 5D                       POP       BP
000D 5A                       POP       DX
```

```
000E 59                              POP       CX
000F 5B                              POP       BX
0010 CB                              RET

0011                DISPLAY  ENDP

0011                LIB_SEG  ENDS

                                     END
```

Sample Library Module Program.   The library module (DISPLAY_MESSAGE procedure) that is created and stored on the disk in Example 5-14 is used by the short program
in Example 5-15. This example introduces a new statement, EXTRN, or external.

EXAMPLE 5-15

```
                    ;;;;;;;;;;;;;;;;;;;;;;;;;;;;;;;;;;;;;;;;;;;;;;;;;;
                    ;                                               ;
                    ;PROGRAM to display HELLO on the CRT            ;
                    ;uses DISPLAY                                   ;
                    ;                                               ;
                    ;;;;;;;;;;;;;;;;;;;;;;;;;;;;;;;;;;;;;;;;;;;;;;;;;;
                    ;
= 0024              EOM             EQU       '$'
= 0000              ZERO            EQU       0
                    ;
0000                DATA_SEG  SEGMENT

0000 48 45 4C 4C 4F     MESSAGE          DB          DB    'HELLO'
0005 24                          DB          EOM

0006                DATA_SEG  ENDS

0000                CODE_SEG  SEGMENT

                    ASSUME    CS:CODE_SEG,DS:DATA_SEG

                    EXTRNDISPLAY:FAR

0000                PROGRAM   PROC  FAR

0000 B8 --- R                   MOV   AX,DATA_SEG
0003 8E D8                      MOV   DS,AX

0005 BA 0000 R                  MOV   DX,OFFSET MESSAGE
0008 9A 0000 --- E              CALL       DISPLAY

000D B4 4C                      INT   21H

0011                PROGRAM   ENDP

0011                CODE_SEG  ENDS

                    END PROGRAM
```

The EXTRN statement declares external procedures—procedures found in library files. It appears inside a segment called LIB _ SEG, which has the same name as the one in the library segment. When the linker joins the modules, the code from the library module with DISPLAY_MESSAGE will be loaded. It will then be moved into the segment called CODE–SEG because both are PUBLIC and both are tagged 'CODE'.

Linkage.   For the library module to link with the program module, both must receive names from the editor. Suppose you have created the library module containing DISPLAY_MESSAGE and named it LIBRARY.ASM. This is assembled with MASM LIBRARY; to convert it into an object file named LIBRARY.OBJ. Next, the program is stored on the disk with the editor and called PROGRAM.ASM. After MASM PROGRAM; is typed, the program file is changed to an object file, PROGRAM.OBJ.

The following line will link these object files into one main file:

LINK PROGRAM + $LIBRARY;

This generates an execute file called PROGRAM.EXE. To run this, type PROGRAM, and the word hello will appear on the display. You may link as many library files as you wish to a program file.

5–6   SUMMARY

1. There are three types of unconditional jump instruction: short, near, and far. The short jump allows a branch to within $+127$ and -128 bytes, a near jump to anywhere within a segment (intrasegment), and a far jump to anywhere in the memory (intersegment).

2. Near labels end with a colon (LABEL:). No colon follows a far label (LABEL).

3. The displacement that follows a short jump is the distance from the next instruction to the location of the jump.

4. Indirect jumps are available in two forms: (1) jump to the location stored in a register (intrasegment only), and (2) jump to the location stored in a memory word or double word (intrasegment or intersegment).

5. Conditional jumps are all short jumps that test one or more of the flag bits: C, Z, O, P, and S. If the condition is true, a jump occurs, and if the condition is false, the next sequential instruction is executed.

6. A special conditional jump instruction (LOOP) will decrement the CX register and jump to the label when CX is not 0. Other forms of loop includes LOOPE, LOOPNE, LOOPZ, and LOOPNZ. LOOPE is a loop while the flags indicate an equal condition and the CX register is not 0.

7. Subroutines or procedures are groups of instructions that perform one task and are used from any point in a program many times. The CALL instruction is used to link to a subroutine and the return (RET) instruction is used to return from a subroutine. In assembly language, the name of the procedure is declared with a PROC pseudo-opcode, and the end of the procedure is declared with an ENDP pseudo-opcode.

8. The CALL instruction, which calls a subroutine, is actually a combination of two instructions: a PUSH and a JMP. CALL pushes the address of the next instruction—

the return address—onto the stack and then jumps to the subroutine. A near CALL places IP on the stack, and a far CALL places both IP and CS on the stack.

9. The return (RET) instruction is used to return from a subroutine. It accomplishes this by retrieving the return address from the stack and placing it back into IP (near RET) or IP and CS (far RET). RET is also able to modify the stack pointer by adding a signed 16-bit number to it. This procedure is often used to delete stack data before returning to the calling program.

10. Interrupts are either software instructions similar to CALL or hardware signals used to call subroutines. This process interrupts the currently executing program whenever a hardware signal demands attention.

11. Interrupt vectors are 4-byte areas of memory that contain the address (IP and CS) of the interrupt service subroutine. The 8086/8088 has 256 such interrupt vectors of which 32 are reserved for built-in or future functions and the remaining are available to the user.

12. Whenever an interrupt takes effect, the microprocessor pushes the flag register onto the stack, pushes the return address (IP and CS) onto the stack, clears T and I, and fetches the interrupt vector so that it can jump to the interrupt service subroutine.

13. Software interrupt instructions (INT), which are often used to replace system calls, are 2 bytes long, whereas the CALL instructions they replace are 5 bytes long. Thus software interrupts save 3 bytes of memory space.

14. A special return instruction (IRET) must be used to return from interrupts in order to remove the contents of the flag register from the stack before the return address.

15. Interrupt on an overflow (INTO) is a conditional interrupt that calls an interrupt service subroutine if the overflow flag (O) is set and does nothing if it is cleared.

16. The clear interrupt flag (CLI) and set interrupt flag (STI) instructions are used, respectively, to disable and enable the INTR pin on the 8086/8088. The INTR pin is one of two hardware interrupt inputs to the microprocessor. The other input, non-maskable interrupt (NMI), is not affected by CLI or STI.

17. The carry flag (C) is cleared, set, and complemented with the CLC, STC, and CMC instructions.

18. The WAIT instruction tests the condition of the $\overline{\text{TEST}}$ pin. If the WAIT instruction is encountered in a program, and $\overline{\text{TEST}}$ is a logic 1, the 8086/8088 waits for $\overline{\text{TEST}}$ to become a logic 0.

19. LOCK and ESC are used primarily with the external coprocessors.

20. An execute (EXE) file is created by the linker after the assembler has generated an object (OJB) file. Once an EXE file is created, the user can execute it by typing the name of the file.

21. When setting up an 8086/8088 assembly language program it is necessary to divide the programs into distinct areas: equates, stack segment, data segment, and code segment. If an extra segment is needed, it is also included, as are additional data, code, and any additional segments.

22. The SEGMENT pseudo-opcode defines the beginning of a segment and the ENDS pseudo-opcode indicates its ending.

23. The ASSUME pseudo-opcode tells the assembler what segment name has been selected for each segment except the stack segment.

24. Library modules are a very important part of assembly language program development because commonly used procedures are stored in the library on disk. The user

can CALL one of these subroutines by linking the library to the program and declaring the procedure's name external (EXTRN).

25. The first statement of a library file is the PUBLIC pseudo-opcode. PUBLIC notifies the linker that a procedure or procedures contained in the library can be linked to other programs.

5–7   QUESTIONS AND PROBLEMS

1. What is a short JMP?
2. What type of JMP is used when jumping anywhere within a segment?
3. Which jump instruction allows the program to continue execution at any memory location in the system memory?
4. What jump instruction is 5 bytes long?
5. Identify the following labels as near or far:
   a. WELL _ WATER:
   b. SEND _ DATA
   c. OUTPUT
   d. SEND _ STRING:
   e. SANTA _ CLAUS
   f. WINTER _ SPRING:
6. The near jump modifies the program address by changing which register or registers?
7. The far jump modifies the program address by changing which register or registers?
8. Explain what the JMP AX instruction will accomplish. Also identify it as near or far and indicate which register or registers change.
9. Contrast the operation of a JMP DI and a JMP[DI].
10. List the five flag bits that are tested by conditional jump instructions.
11. All conditional jumps are _____ jumps.
12. Explain when the JA instruction jumps.
13. Explain when the JO instruction will not jump.
14. Which conditional jump instructions test both the Z and C flag bits?
15. When will the JCXZ instruction jump?
16. LOOP will always decrement _____ and test it for 0 to determine if a jump occurs.
17. Explain how the LOOPE instruction functions.
18. Develop a short sequence of instructions that will store a 00H into 150H bytes of memory beginning at extra segment memory location DATA.
19. Develop a sequence of instructions that tests the number in the CX register to determine whether its unsigned value is above 0400H. If the value is above 0400H, then jump to label NEXT; if not, continue with the next sequential instruction.
20. What is a procedure?
21. Explain how the far CALL instruction functions.
22. How does the near RET instruction function?
23. All procedures must end with what opcode?
24. All procedures must end with what pseudo-opcode?

25. All procedures must begin with what pseudo-opcode?
26. How is a procedure identified as near or far?
27. Explain what the RET 6 instruction accomplishes.
28. Write a procedure that cubes the value in the CX register. This procedure may not affect any other register or any of the flag bits.
29. Write a procedure that multiplies DI by SI and then divides the result by 100H. Make sure that the result is left in AX upon returning from the procedure, and also make sure that none of the other registers or flags change.
30. What is an interrupt?
31. What software instructions are used to call interrupt service subroutines?
32. How many interrupt vectors are available in the 8086/8088?
33. What is the purpose of interrupt vector 0?
34. Illustrate the contents of an interrupt vector, making sure to identify each byte.
35. Explain what an INT 40H instruction does, making sure to indicate the memory location of the vector.
36. How does the IRET instruction differ from RET?
37. INTO will interrupt when what condition is present?
38. What instructions are used to control the INTR pin?
39. What instruction is used to check the TEST pin?
40. What is an EXE file?
41. What is an OBJ file?
42. What does the acronym DOS indicate?
43. Detail the steps required to convert an assembly language file into an execute file.
44. Why are equates used in an assembly language program?
45. What is the purpose of the SEGMENT pseudo-opcode?
46. What does the pseudo-opcode PUBLIC mean?
47. How is the end of a segment indicated in assembly language?
48. If the code segment is labeled PROGRAM, the data segment is labeled DATA, and the extra segment is labeled DATA_OLD, set up an ASSUME statement to tell the assembler the names of these segments.
49. How is the return address for DOS set up in the code segment?
50. What is a library module?
51. What changes a file into a library module?
52. How is a library procedure specified in a program?
53. What role does the linker play in using library modules?
54. If a program is called MINE and two libraries (LIB 1 and LIB 2) are to be used with it, set up the correct linker statement to join them.

CHAPTER 6

8086/8088 HARDWARE SPECIFICATIONS

INTRODUCTION

In this chapter, we describe the pin functions of both the 8086 and 8088 microprocessors and provide details on the following hardware topics: clock generation, bus buffering, bus latching, timing, wait states, and minimum mode operation versus maximum mode operation.

Before it is possible to connect or interface anything to the microprocessor, it is necessary to understand the pin functions and timing. Thus the information in this chapter is essential to a complete understanding of memory and I/O interfacing, which we cover in the remainder of the text.

OBJECTIVES

Upon completion of this chapter, you will be able to:

1. Describe the function of each 8086 and 8088 pin.
2. Understand the DC characteristics and indicate the fanout to common logic families.
3. Use the clock generator chip (8284A) to provide the clock.
4. Connect buffers and latches to the buses.
5. Interpret the timing diagrams.
6. Describe wait states and connect the circuitry required to cause various amounts of waits.
7. Explain the difference between minimum and maximum mode operation.

6-1 PINOUTS AND THE PIN FUNCTIONS

In this section we explain the function, and in some cases the multiple functions, of each of the pins. In addition, we discuss the DC characteristics to provide a basis for understanding the later sections on buffering and latching.

The Pinout

Figure 6-1 illustrates the pinouts of the 8086 and 8088 microprocessors. As a close comparison reveals, there is virtually no difference between these two microprocessors: both are packaged in 40-pin dual in-line packages (DIPs).

As we mentioned in Chapter 1, the 8086 is a 16-bit microprocessor with a 16-bit data bus, and the 8088 is a 16-bit microprocessor with an 8-bit data bus. (As the pinouts show, the 8086 has pin connections AD_0–AD_{15}, and the 8088 has pin connections AD_0–AD_7). Data bus width is therefore the only major difference between these microprocessors.

There is, however, a minor difference in one of the control signals. The 8086 has an $M/\overline{IO}$ pin, and the 8088 has an $IO/\overline{M}$ pin. The only other hardware difference appears on pin 34 of both chips: on the 8088, it is an $\overline{SS0}$ pin, while on the 8086, it is a $\overline{BHE}/S_7$ pin.

Power Supply Requirements

Both the 8086 and 8088 microprocessors require +5V with a supply voltage tolerance of ±10 percent. The 8086 draws a maximum supply current of 360 mA, and the 8088 draws a maximum of 340 mA. Both microprocessors operate in ambient temperature of between 32° F and about 180° F. This range is not wide enough to be used outdoors in the winter

FIGURE 6-1 (a) The pinout of the 8086 microprocessor; (b) the pinout of the 8088 microprocessor.

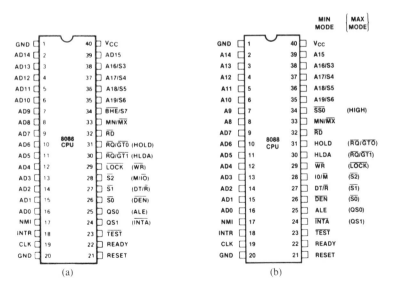

or even in the summer, but extended temperature–range versions of the 8086 and 8088 microprocessors are available. There is even a CMOS version, which requires a very low supply current and also has an extended temperature range. The 80C88 and 80C86 are CMOS versions that require only 10 mA of power supply current.

DC Characteristics

It is impossible to connect anything to the pins of the microprocessor without knowing the input current requirement for an input pin and the output current drive capability for an output pin. This knowledge allows the hardware designer to select the proper interface components for use with the microprocessor without the fear of damaging it.

Input Characteristics.   The input characteristics of these microprocessors are compatible with all the standard logic components available today. Table 6–1 depicts the input voltage levels and also the input current requirements for any input pin on either micro- processor. The input current levels are very small because the inputs are the gates of MOSFETs and represent only leakage currents.

Output Characteristics.   Table 6–2 illustrates the output characteristics of all the output pins on these microprocessors. The logic 1 voltage level of the 8086/8088 is compatible with that of most standard logic families, but the logic 0 level is not. Standard logic circuits have a maximum logic 0 output voltage of 0.4 V, and the 8086/8088 has a maximum of 0.45 V. Thus there is a difference of 0.05 V.

   This difference reduces the noise immunity from a standard level of 400 mV (0.8V– 0.45 V) to 350 mV. (The noise immunity is the difference between the logic 0 output voltage and the logic 0 input voltage levels.) This reduced noise immunity may result in problems with long connections and too many loads on a connection. It is therefore recommended that no more than 10 loads of any type or combination be connected to an output pin without buffers. If this loading is exceeded, noise will begin to take its toll in timing problems.

   Table 6–3 lists some common logic families and the recommended fanout from the 8086/8088. The best choice of component types for the connection to an 8086/8088 output pin is a 74LS, 74ALS, or 74HC logic component.

TABLE 6–1 Input charac- teristics of the 8086 and 8088 microprocessors

Logic Level*	Voltage	Current
0	0.8 V max	10 μA max
1	2.0 V min	10 μA max

*The input capacitance is typically 10 pF.

TABLE 6–2 Output charac- teristics of the 8086 and 8088 microprocessors

Logic Level	Voltage	Current
0	0.45 V max	2.0 mA max
1	2.4 V min	-400 μA max

TABLE 6-3 Recommended fanout from any 8086/8088 output pin connection

Family	Fanout	Sink Current	Source Current
TTL (74)	1	-1.6 mA	40 μA
TTL (74LS)	5	-0.4 mA	20 μA
TTL (74S)	1	-2.0 mA	50 μA
TTL (74ALS)	10	-0.2 mA	20 μA
CMOS (74HC)	10	-1 μA	1 μA
CMOS (CD)	10	-1 μA	1 μA
NMOS	10	-10 μA	10 μA

Pin Functions

The following list specifies the function and purpose of each of the 8086/8088 pin connections:

1. AD_7-AD_0 (8088)—Address/Data Bus: lines that compose the multiplexed address data bus of the 8088 and contain the rightmost 8 bits of the memory address or I/O port number whenever ALE is active (1) or data when ALE is inactive (0). These pins are at their high-impedance state during a hold acknowledge.
2. $A_{15}-A_8$ (8088)—Address Bus: bits where the address ($A_{15}-A_8$) appears throughout the entire bus cycle. $A_{15}-A_8$ go to their high-impedance state whenever a hold acknowledge occurs.
3. $AD_{15}-AD_8$ (8086)—Address/Data Bus: lines that compose the multiplexed address data bus of the 8086 and contain address information or I/O port numbers during ALE (1) or data when ALE is inactive (0). These pins go to their high-impedance state during a hold acknowledge.
4. A_{19}/S_6, A_{18}/S_5, A_{17}/S_4, and A_{16}/S_3—Address/Status: multiplexed pins that contain address bus bits $A_{19}-A_{16}$ during ALE and, for the remainder of the bus cycle, contain status bits S_6-S_3. These pins go to their high-impedance state during a hold acknowledge.

   Status bit S_6 always remains a logic 0, bit S_5 indicates the condition of the I flag bit, and bits S_4 and S_3 indicate which segment is accessed during the current bus cycles. Refer to Table 6-4 for the coding of S_4 and S_3.

TABLE 6-4 Truth table illustrating the function of status bits S_4 and S_3

S_4*	S_3*	Function
0	0	Extra segment
0	1	Stack segment
1	0	Code segment or no segment
1	1	Data segment

*These bits could be used to select a different 1M-byte bank of memory for each segment.

5. $\overline{\text{RD}}$—Read: a strobe that becomes a logic 0 whenever the data bus is receptive to either memory or I/O data. This pin floats during a hold acknowledge.

6. READY—Ready: a pin that is at a logic 1 level for the 8086/8088 to execute instructions without wait states. If this pin is held low, then wait states will be inserted. READY is used to interface slower memory and peripheral components to the 8086/8088.

7. INTR—Interrupt Request: one of two pins (NMI is the other) used to request a hardware interrupt. If INTR is held high when I is set, the 8086/8088 enters into an interrupt acknowledge cycle ($\overline{\text{INTA}}$ becomes active) after the current instruction has completed execution.

8. $\overline{\text{TEST}}$—Test: a pin that is checked by the WAIT instruction. If $\overline{\text{TEST}}$ is a logic 0, then the WAIT instruction continues execution with the next sequential instruction in the program, and if $\overline{\text{TEST}}$ is a logic 1, WAIT will wait for $\overline{\text{TEST}}$ to become a logic 0.

9. NMI—Nonmaskable Interrupt: the input that causes a type 2 interrupt vector call at the end of the current instruction whenever it becomes active. This input is positive-edge (a 0 to 1 transaction) triggered and is not affected by the I flag bit.

10. RESET—Reset: a pin that, if held high for a minimum of four clocks, will reset the 8086/8088. Whenever the 8086/8088 is reset, it begins executing instructions at memory location FFFF0H and disables future interrupts by clearing the I status bit.

11. CLK—Clock: an input that provides the basic timing for the 8086/8088. It has a 33 percent duty cycle (high one third of the clocking period and low for two thirds) to provide proper internal timing for the 8086/8088.

12. V_{cc}—V_{cc}: the +5 V, ±10% power supply pin.

13. GND—Ground: the ground connection; two pins, which must both be connected.

14. MN/$\overline{\text{MX}}$—Minimum/Maximum Mode: a pin used to select minimum mode operation when tied directly to +5 V and maximum mode operation when tied directly to ground.

15. $\overline{\text{BHE}}$/S_7—Bus High Enable/Status: used to activate the most significant data bus during a read or write.

Minimum Mode Pins.   Minimum mode operation of the 8086/8088 is obtained by connecting the MN/$\overline{\text{MX}}$ pin connection directly to +5 V. Do not connect this pin to +5 V through a pullup resistor, or it will not work.

1. IO/$\overline{\text{M}}$ (8088), M/$\overline{\text{IO}}$ (8086)—Memory or Input/Output: a pin that indicates when the address bus contains memory-addressing information or I/O-addressing information. This output floats to its high-impedance state during a hold acknowledge.

2. $\overline{\text{WR}}$—Write: a strobe used to indicate that the 8086/8088 data bus contains valid data to be written into the memory or I/O. This pin floats to its high-impedance state during a hold acknowledge.

3. $\overline{\text{INTA}}$—Interrupt Acknowledge: the response to an INTR. During an interrupt request, the $\overline{\text{INTA}}$ pin becomes a logic 0, indicating that the 8086/8088 bus is waiting for a vector number to be applied to its data bus connections.

4. ALE—Address Latch Enable: a pin used to indicate that the address data bus connections contain either a valid memory address or a valid I/O port address. ALE never floats to the high-impedance state.

5. DT/$\overline{R}$—Data Transmit/$\overline{Receive}$: a pin used to control the direction of data flow through externally connected data bus buffers. This pin floats to its high-impedance state during a hold acknowledge.
6. $\overline{DEN}$—Data Bus Enable: a signal that indicates that the address/data bus contains valid data. This pin floats to its high-impedance state during a hold acknowledge.
7. HOLD—Hold: an input used to request a direct memory access (DMA). When HOLD is active, the 8086/8088 will float its address, data, and control buses so that an external DMA controller may gain access to the memory and I/O space.
8. HLDA—Hold Acknowledge: an indication that the HOLD pin has gone high and that the buses are floated to their high-impedance states.
9. $\overline{SS0}$ (8088)—Status Line: a line that is equivalent to the $\overline{S0}$ line in maximum mode for both the 8086 and 8088. If this signal is combined with IO/$\overline{M}$ and DT/$\overline{R}$, it is possible to decode the current bus cycle (refer to Table 6–5).

Maximum Mode Pins. In order to achieve maximum mode operation for use with external coprocessors, connect the MN/$\overline{MX}$ pin to ground.

1. $\overline{S}_2$, $\overline{S}_1$, and $\overline{S}_0$—Status: bits used in maximum mode to generate the major system control signals through the 8288 bus controller (see Table 6–6). These pins float to their high-impedance state during a bus request.

TABLE 6–5 Bus cycle status (8088 only)

IO/$\overline{M}$	DT/$\overline{R}$	$\overline{SS0}$	Function
0	0	0	Indicates an interrupt acknowledge
0	0	1	Indicates a memory read
0	1	0	Indicates a memory write
0	1	1	Indicates a halt
1	0	0	Indicates a code access
1	0	1	Indicates an I/O read
1	1	0	Indicates an I/O write
1	1	1	Remains passive

TABLE 6–6 Bus control functions generated by an 8228 bus controller when $\overline{S}_2$, $\overline{S}_1$, and $\overline{S}_0$ are decoded

$\overline{S}_2$	$\overline{S}_1$	$\overline{S}_0$	Control Function
0	0	0	Indicates an interrupt acknowledge
0	0	1	Indicates an I/O read
0	1	0	Indicates an I/O write
0	1	1	Indicates a halt
1	0	0	Indicates a code access
1	0	1	Indicates a memory read
1	1	0	Indicates a memory write
1	1	1	Remains passive

TABLE 6–7   Queue status—
tracking bits QS_1 and QS_0

QS_1	QS_0	Queue Function
0	0	Indicates no operation
0	1	Indicates first byte of opcode from queue
1	0	Indicates queue is empty
1	1	Indicates subsequent byte from queue

2. $\overline{RQ/GT_0}$ and $\overline{RQ/GT_1}$—Request/Grant: pins used to request bus arbitration by external coprocessors. Each of these lines is a bidirectional connection that allows the coprocessor to request a DMA, the 8086/8088 to acknowledge a DMA, and the coprocessor to release the DMA.

3. $\overline{LOCK}$—Lock: an output that becomes a logic 0 for an entire instruction that is prefixed with LOCK. This is generally used to prevent an external coprocessor from gaining access to the 8086/8088 bus during the locked instruction.

4. QS_1 and QS_0—Queue Status: bits that provide a method for keeping track of the internal prefetch queue. The queue is 4 bytes long in the 8088 and 6 bytes long in the 8086. Table 6–7 illustrates the queue function for various logic levels on these two pins.

The queue status bits are used with the 8087 arithmetic coprocessor and synchronize the 8086/8088 with the 8087. Table 6–7 illustrates the queue function for various logic levels on these two pins.

6–2   ## CLOCK GENERATOR (8284A)

This section introduces the clock generator (8284A), the RESET signal, and—briefly— the READY signal for the 8086/8088 microprocessor. The READY signal and its associated circuitry are treated in detail in Section 6–5.

The 8284A Clock Generator

The 8284A is an ancillary component to the 8086/8088 microprocessor. Without the clock generator, many additional circuits are required to generate the clock (CLK) in an 8086/8088-based system. The 8284A provides the following basic functions or signals: clock generation, RESET synchronization, READY synchronization, and a TTL level peripheral clock signal. Figure 6–2 illustrates the pinout of the 8284A clock generator.

Pin Functions.   The 8284A is an 18-pin integrated circuit designed specifically for use with the 8086/8088 microprocessor. The following is a list of each pin and its function:

1. $\overline{AEN_1}$ and $\overline{AEN_2}$—Address Enable: pins provided to qualify the bus ready signals, RDY_1 and RDY_2, respectively. Section 6–5 illustrates the use of these two pins,

FIGURE 6−2 The pinout of
the 8284A clock generator.

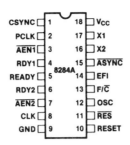

which are used to cause wait states, along with the RDY_1 and RDY_2 inputs. Wait
states are generated by the READY pin of the 8086/8088 microprocessor, which is
controlled by these two inputs.

2. RDY_1 and RDY_2—Bus Ready: inputs provided in conjunction with the $\overline{AEN}_1$ and
$\overline{AEN}_2$ pins to cause wait states in an 8086/8088-based system.

3. $\overline{ASYNC}$—Ready Synchronization Select: an input used to select either one or two
stages of synchronization for the RDY_1 and RDY_2 inputs.

4. READY—Ready: the output pin that connects to the 8086/8088 READY input. This
signal is synchronized with the RDY_1 and RDY_2 inputs.

5. X_1 and X_2—Crystal Inputs: pins connected to an external crystal used as the timing
source for the clock generator and all its functions.

6. $F/\overline{C}$—Frequency/Crystal: a pin used to select the clocking source for the 8284A. If
this pin is held high, an external clock is provided to the EFI input pin, and if it is
held low, the internal crystal oscillator provides the timing signal.

7. EFI—External Frequency Input: an input used when the $F/\overline{C}$ pin is pulled high. EFI
supplies the timing whenever the $F/\overline{C}$ pin is high.

8. CLK—Clock: the pin that provides the CLK input signal to the 8086/8088 and other
components in the system. The CLK pin has an output signal that is one third of the
crystal or EFI input frequency and has a 33 percent duty cycle, which is required by
the 8086/8088.

9. PCLK—Peripheral Clock: a signal that is one sixth the crystal or EFI input frequency
and has a 50 percent duty cycle. PCLK provides a clock signal to the peripheral
equipment in the system.

10. OSC—Oscillator Output: a TTL level signal that is at the same frequency as the
crystal or EFI input. OSC provides an EFI input to other 8284A clock generators in
some multiple-processor systems.

11. $\overline{RES}$—Reset Input: the active-low reset input to the 8284A. $\overline{RES}$ is often connected
to an RC network that provides power-on resetting.

12. RESET—Reset Output: the signal connected to the 8086/8088 RESET input pin.

13. CSYNC—Clock Synchronization: a pin used whenever the EFI input provides synchronization in systems with multiple processors. If the internal crystal oscillator is
used, this pin must be grounded.

14. GND—Ground: a pin connected to ground.

15. V_{cc}—Power Supply Input: a pin connected to +5 V with a tolerance of ±10 percent.

Operation of the 8284A

The 8284A is a relatively easy component to understand. Figure 6–3 illustrates the internal logic diagram of the clock generator.

Operation of the Clock Section.   The top half of the logic diagram represents the clock and reset synchronization section of the 8284A clock generator. As the diagram shows, the crystal oscillator has two inputs: X_1 and X_2. If a crystal is attached to X_1 and X_2, the oscillator will generate a square-wave signal of the same frequency as the crystal. The square wave is fed to an AND gate and also an inverting buffer that provides the OSC output signal. OSC can be used as an EFI input to other 8284As.

A close inspection of the AND gate reveals that when $F/\overline{C}$ is a logic 0, the *oscillator output* is steered through to the divide-by-3 counter. If $F/\overline{C}$ is a logic 1, then EFI is steered through to the counter.

The output of the divide-by-3 counter generates the timing for ready synchronization, a signal for another counter (divide-by-2), and the CLK signal to the 8086/8088 microprocessor. The CLK signal is also buffered before it reaches the outside world. Notice that the output of the first counter feeds the second. These two cascaded counters provide the divide-by-6 output at PCLK, the peripheral clock output.

Figure 6–4 shows how 8284A is connected to the 8086/8088. Notice (1) that $F/\overline{C}$ and CSYNC are grounded to select the crystal oscillator, and (2) that a 15-MHz crystal provides the normal 5-MHz clock signal to the 8086/8088 as well as a 2.5-MHz peripheral clock signal.

Operation of the Reset Section.   The reset section of the 8284A is very simple. It consists of a Schmitt trigger buffer and a single D-type flip-flop circuit. The D-type flip-flop

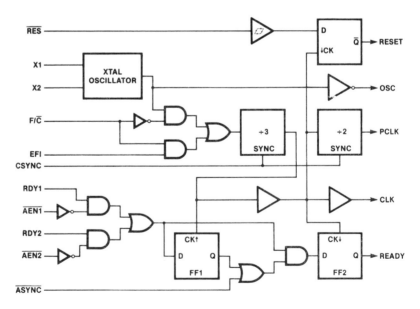

FIGURE 6–3   The internal block diagram of the 8284A clock generator.

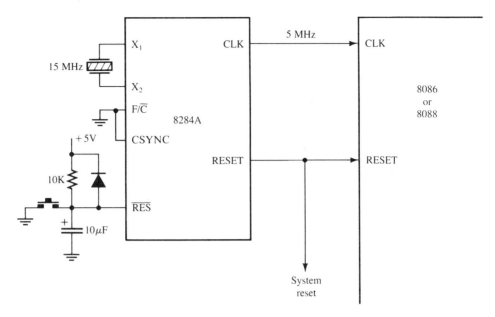

FIGURE 6-4 The clock generator (8284A) and the 8086 or 8088 microprocessor illustrating the connection for the clock and reset signals. A 15-MHz crystal provides the 5-MHz clock for the microprocessor.

ensures that the timing requirements of the 8086/8088 RESET input are met. This circuit applies the RESET signal to the microprocessor on the negative edge (1–0 transition) of each clock. The 8086/8088 samples RESET at the positive edge (0–1 transition) of the clock; therefore, this circuit meets the timing requirements of the 8086/8088.

Refer again to Figure 6–4. Notice that an RC circuit provides a logic 0 to the $\overline{RES}$ input pin when power is first applied to the system. After a short period of time, the $\overline{RES}$ input becomes a logic 1 because the capacitor charges toward +5 V through the resistor. A pushbutton switch allows the microprocessor to be reset by the operator. Correct reset timing requires the RESET input to become a logic 1 no later than four clocks after system power is applied and to be held high for at least 50 μs. The flip-flop makes certain that RESET goes high in four clocks, and the RC time constant ensures that it stays high for at least 50 μs.

6-3   BUS BUFFERING AND LATCHING

Before the 8086/8088 can be used with memory or I/O interfaces, its multiplexed buses must be demultiplexed. This section provides the detail required to demultiplex the buses and illustrates how the buses are buffered for very large systems. (Because the maximum fanout is 10, the system must be buffered if it contains more than 10 other components.)

Demultiplexing the Buses

The address/data bus on the 8086/8088 is multiplexed to save the number of pins required for the 8086/8088 microprocessor integrated circuit. Unfortunately, this burdens the hardware designer with the task of extracting or demultiplexing information from these multiplexed pins.

Why not leave the buses multiplexed? Memory and I/O require that the address remain valid and stable throughout a read or a write. If the buses are not demultiplexed, the address changes at the memory and I/O, which causes them to read or write data in the wrong locations.

All computer systems have three buses: (1) an address bus that provides the memory and I/O with the memory address or I/O port number, (2) a data bus that transfers data to and from the memory and I/O in the system, and (3) a control bus that provides control information to the memory and I/O. These buses must be present in order to interface memory and I/O.

Demultiplexing the 8088.   Figure 6–5 illustrates the 8088 microprocessor and the components required to demultiplex its buses. In this case, two 74LS373 transparent latches are used to demultiplex the address/data bus connections AD_7–AD_0 and the multiplexed address/status connections A_{19}/S_6–A_{16}/S_3.

These transparent latches, which are like wires whenever the address latch enable pin (ALE) becomes a logic 1, pass the inputs to the outputs. After a short time, ALE returns to its logic 0 condition, which causes the latches to remember the inputs at the time of the change to a logic 0. In this case, A_7–A_0 are remembered in the bottom latch and A_{19}–A_{16} in the top latch. This yields a separate address bus with connections A_{19}–A_0. These address connections allow the 8088 to address 1M bytes of memory address space. The fact that the data bus is separate allows it to be connected to any 8-bit peripheral device or memory component.

Demultiplexing the 8086.   Like the 8088, the 8086 system requires separate address, data, and control buses. It differs primarily in the number of multiplexed pins. In the 8088, only AD_7–AD_0 and A_{19}/S_6–A_{16}/S_3 are multiplexed. In the 8086, on the other hand, multiplexed pins include AD_{15}–AD_0, A_{19}/S_6–A_{16}/S_3, and $\overline{BHE}/S_7$. All these must be demultiplexed.

Figure 6–6 illustrates a demultiplexed 8086 with all three buses: address (A_{19}–A_0 and $\overline{BHE}$), data (D_{15}–D_0), and control ($M/\overline{IO}$, $\overline{RD}$, and $\overline{WR}$).

This circuit is almost identical to the one pictured in Figure 6–5, except that an additional 74LS373 latch has been added to demultiplex the address/data bus pins AD_{15}–AD_8 and a $\overline{BHE}/S_7$ input has been added to the top 74LS373 to select the high-order memory bank in the 16-bit memory system of the 8086. Here the memory and I/O system see the 8086 as a device with a 20-bit address bus (A_{19}–A_0), a 16-bit data bus (D_{15}–D_0), and a 3-line control bus ($M/\overline{IO}$, $\overline{RD}$, and $\overline{WR}$).

The Buffered System

If more than 10 unit loads are attached to any bus pin, the entire 8086 or 8088 system must be buffered. The demultiplexed pins are already buffered by the 74LS373 latches, which have been designed to drive the high-capacitance buses encountered in microcomputer

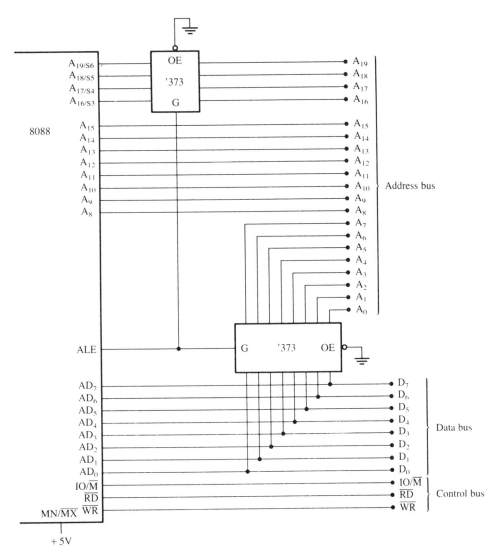

FIGURE 6-5 The 8088 microprocessor shown with a demultiplexed address bus. This is the model used to build many 8088-based systems.

systems. The output currents have also been increased so that more TTL unit loads may be driven: a logic 0 output provides up to 32 mA of current, and a logic 1 output provides 5.2 mA.

A fully buffered signal will introduce a timing delay to the system. This causes no difficulty unless memory or I/O devices are used which function at near the maximum speed of the bus. Section 6-4 treats this problem and the time delays involved in more detail.

The Fully Buffered 8088. Figure 6-7 depicts a fully buffered 8088 microprocessor. Notice that the remaining eight address pins, A_{15}-A_8, use a 74LS244 octal buffer; the

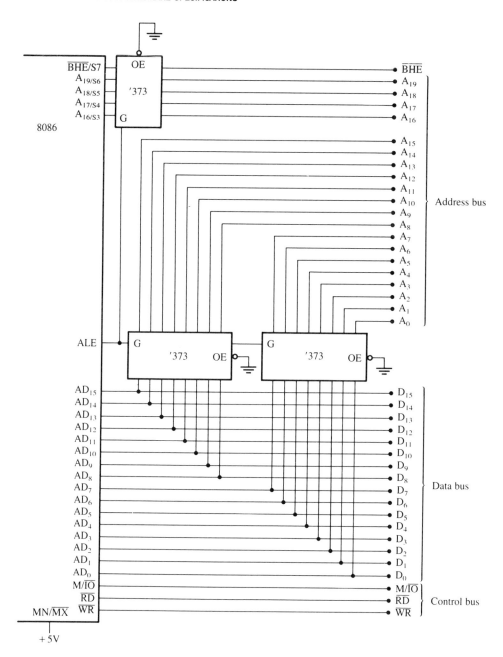

FIGURE 6–6 The 8086 microprocessor shown with a demultiplexed address bus. This is the model used to build many 8086-based systems.

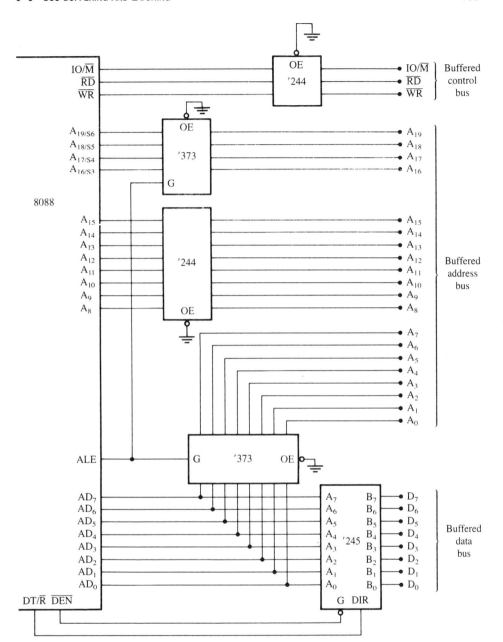

FIGURE 6-7   A fully buffered 8088 microprocessor.

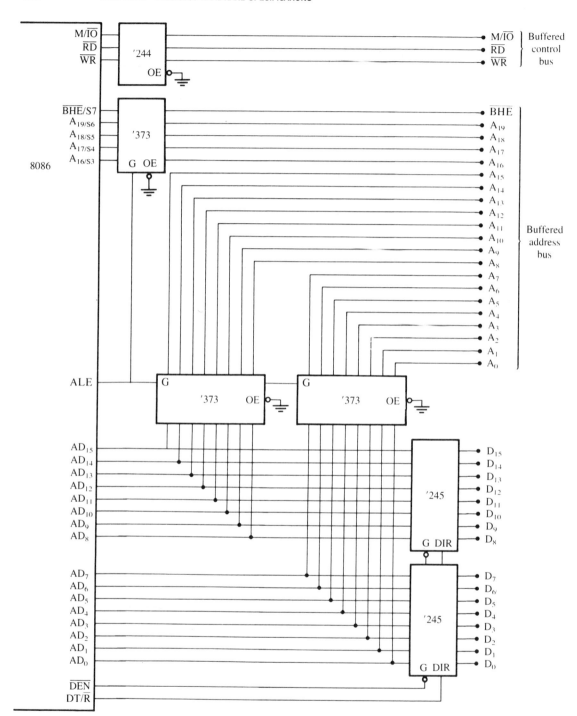

FIGURE 6–8 A fully buffered 8086 microprocessor.

eight data bus pins, D_7-D_0, use a 74LS245 octal bidirectional bus buffer; and the control bus signals, IO/$\overline{M}$, $\overline{RD}$, and $\overline{WR}$, use a 74LS244 buffer. A fully buffered 8088 system requires two 74LS244s, one 74LS245, and two 74LS373s. The direction of the 74LS245 is controlled by the DT/$\overline{R}$ signal and is enabled and disabled by the $\overline{DEN}$ signal.

The Fully Buffered 8086. Figure 6-8 illustrates a fully buffered 8086 microprocessor. Its address pins are already buffered by the 74LS373 address latches; its data bus employs two 74LS245 octal bidirectional bus buffers; and the control bus signals, M/$\overline{IO}$, $\overline{RD}$, and $\overline{WR}$, use a 74LS244 buffer. A fully buffered 8086 system requires one 74LS244, two 74LS245s, and three 74LS373s. The 8086 requires one more buffer than the 8088 because of the extra eight data bus connections $D_{15}-D_0$. It also has a $\overline{BHE}$ signal that is buffered for memory-bank selection.

6-4 BUS TIMING

It is essential to understand system bus timing before choosing a memory or I/O device for interfacing to the 8086 or 8088 microprocessor. This section provides insight into the operation of the bus signals and the basic read and write timing of the 8086/8088. It is important to note that we discuss *only* the times that affect memory and I/O interfacing in this section.

Basic Bus Operation

The three buses of the 8086 and 8088 —address, data, and control—function in exactly the same manner as those of any other microprocessor. If data are written to the memory (see the simplified timing for write in Figure 6-9), the microprocessor outputs the mem-

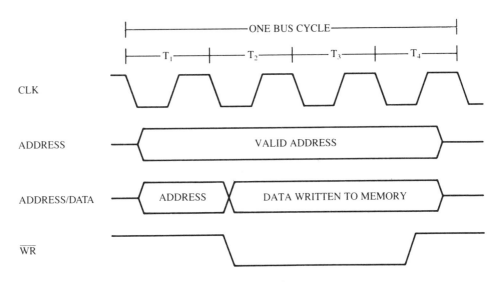

FIGURE 6-9 Simplified 8086/8088 write bus cycle.

ory address on the address bus, outputs the data to be written into memory on the data bus, and issues a write ($\overline{WR}$) to memory and IO/$\overline{M}$ = 0 for the 8088 and M/$\overline{IO}$ /= 1 for the 8086. If data are read from the memory (see the simplified timing for read in Figure 6–10), the microprocessor outputs the memory address on the address bus, issues a read ($\overline{RD}$) memory signal, and accepts the data via the data bus.

Timing in General

The 8086/8088 uses the memory and I/O in periods of time called *bus cycles,* which equal four system-clocking periods (T states). If the clock is operated at 5 MHz (the basic operating frequency for these two microprocessors), then one 8086/8088 bus cycle is completed in 800 ns. This means that the microprocessor reads or writes data between itself and memory or I/O at the rate of 1.25 million times a second. (Because of the internal queue, the 8086/8088 can execute 2.5 million instructions per second (MIPS) in bursts.) Other available versions of these microprocessors operate at much higher transfer rates due to higher clock frequencies.

T_1.   During the first clocking period in a bus cycle, which is called T_1, many things happen. The address of the memory or I/O location is sent out via the address bus and the address/data bus connections. (The address/data bus is multiplexed and at times contains memory-addressing information and at other times data.) Also output during T_1 are the control signals: ALE, DT/$\overline{R}$, and IO/$\overline{M}$ (8088) or M/$\overline{IO}$ (8086). IO/$\overline{M}$ or M/$\overline{IO}$ indicates whether the address bus contains a memory address or an I/O device (port) number.

T_2.   During T_2, the 8086/8088 issues the $\overline{RD}$ or $\overline{WR}$ signal, $\overline{DEN}$, and, in the case of a write, the data to be written. These events cause the memory or I/O device to begin to perform a read or a write. The $\overline{DEN}$ signal turns on the data bus buffers, if they are present in the system, so that the memory or I/O can receive data to be written or so the microprocessor can accept the data read from the memory or I/O for a read operation. If

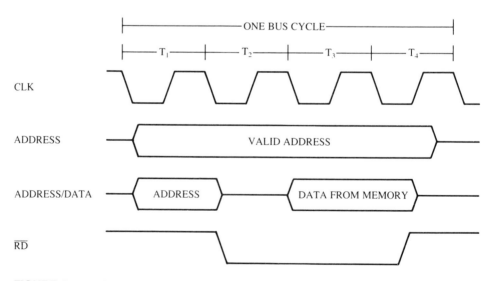

FIGURE 6–10   Simplified 8086/8088 read bus cycle.

this happens to be a write bus cycle, then the data are sent out to the memory or I/O through the data bus.

READY is sampled at the end of T_2, as illustrated in Figure 6–11. If READY is low at this time, T_3 becomes a wait state (T_w). More detail is provided in Section 6–5.

T_3. This clocking period is provided to allow the memory time to access data. If the bus cycle happens to be a read bus cycle, the data bus is sampled at the end of T_3.

T_4. In T_4, all bus signals are deactivated in preparation for the next bus cycle. This is also the time when the 8086/8088 samples the data bus connections for data that are read from memory or I/O. In addition, at this point, the trailing edge of the $\overline{\text{WR}}$ signal transfers data to the memory or I/O, which activate and write when the $\overline{\text{WR}}$ signal returns to a logic 1 level.

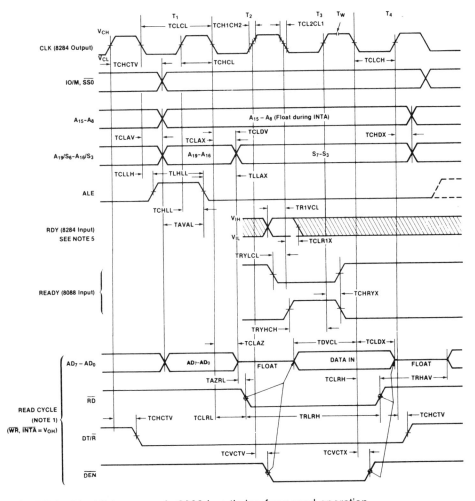

FIGURE 6–11 Minimum mode 8088 bus timing for a read operation.

Read Timing.   Figure 6–11 also depicts the read timing for the 8088 microprocessor. The 8086 read timing is identical except that the 8086 has 16 rather than 8 data bus bits. A close look at this timing diagram should allow you to identify all the main events described for each T state.

The most important item contained in the read timing diagram is the amount of time allowed the memory or I/O to read the data. Memory is chosen by its access time, which is the fixed amount of time the microprocessor allows it to access data for the read operation. It is therefore extremely important that the memory you choose comply with the limitations of the system.

Timing diagrams do not, however, provide straightforward memory access times. Instead it is necessary to combine several times to arrive at the access time. To find memory access time in this diagram, we must first locate the point in T_3 when data are sampled. If you examine the timing diagram closely, you will notice a line that extends from the end of T_3 down to the data bus. The end of T_3 is where the microprocessor samples the data bus.

Memory access time starts when the address appears on the memory address bus and continues until the microprocessor samples the memory data at T_3. Approximately three T states elapse between these times, but not exactly. (Refer to Figure 6–12 for the following times.) The address does not appear until T_{CLAV} time (110 ns if the clock is 5 MHz) after the start of T_1. This means that T_{CLAV} time must be subtracted from the three clocking states (600 ns) that separate the appearance of the address (T_1) and the sampling of the data (T_3). One other time must also be subtracted: the data setup time (T_{DVCL}), which occurs before T_3. Memory access time is thus three clocking states minus the sum of T_{CLAV} and T_{DVCL}. Because T_{DVCL} is 30 ns with a 5-MHz clock, the allowed memory access time is only 460 ns (access time = 600 ns − 110 ns − 30 ns).

Actually, the memory devices chosen for connection to the 8086/8088 operated at 5 MHz must be able to access data in *less* than 460 ns, because of the time delay introduced by the address decoders and buffers in the system. At least a 30- or 40- ns margin should exist for the operation of these circuits. Therefore, the memory speed should be no slower than about 420 ns to operate correctly with the 8086/8088 microprocessor.

The only other timing factor that may affect memory operation is the width of the $\overline{RD}$ strobe. On the timing diagram, the read strobe width is given as T_{RLRH}. The time for this strobe is 325 ns (5-MHz clock rate), which is wide enough for almost all memory devices manufactured with an access time of 400 ns or less.

Write Timing.   Figure 6–13 illustrates the write timing diagram for the 8088 microprocessor. Again, the 8086 is so nearly identical that it need not be presented here.

The main differences between read and write timing are minimal. The $\overline{RD}$ strobe is replaced by the $\overline{WR}$ strobe, the data bus contains information *for* the memory rather than information *from* the memory, and DT/$\overline{R}$ remains a logic 1 rather than a logic 0 throughout the bus cycle.

When interfacing some memory devices, timing may be especially critical between the point at which $\overline{WR}$ becomes a logic 1 and the time when the data are removed from the data bus. This is the case because, as you will recall, memory data are written at the trailing edge of the $\overline{WR}$ strobe. According to the timing diagram, this critical period is

FIGURE 6-12 8088 AC characteristics.

A.C. CHARACTERISTICS (8088: T_A = 0°C to 70°C, V_{CC} = 5V ±10%)*
(8088-2: T_A = 0°C to 70°C, V_{CC} = 5V ±5%)

MINIMUM COMPLEXITY SYSTEM TIMING REQUIREMENTS

Symbol	Parameter	8088		8088-2		Units	Test Conditions
		Min.	Max.	Min.	Max.		
TCLCL	CLK Cycle Period	200	500	125	500	ns	
TCLCH	CLK Low Time	118		68		ns	
TCHCL	CLK High Time	69		44		ns	
TCH1CH2	CLK Rise Time		10		10	ns	From 1.0V to 3.5V
TCL2CL1	CLK Fall Time		10		10	ns	From 3.5V to 1.0V
TDVCL	Data in Setup Time	30		20		ns	
TCLDX	Data in Hold Time	10		10		ns	
TR1VCL	RDY Setup Time into 8284 (See Notes 1, 2)	35		35		ns	
TCLR1X	RDY Hold Time into 8284 (See Notes 1, 2)	0		0		ns	
TRYHCH	READY Setup Time into 8088	118		68		ns	
TCHRYX	READY Hold Time into 8088	30		20		ns	
TRYLCL	READY Inactive to CLK (See Note 3)	-8		-8		ns	
THVCH	HOLD Setup Time	35		20		ns	
TINVCH	INTR, NMI, TEST Setup Time (See Note 2)	30		15		ns	
TILIH	Input Rise Time (Except CLK)		20		20	ns	From 0.8V to 2.0V
TIHIL	Input Fall Time (Except CLK)		12		12	ns	From 2.0V to 0.8V

A.C. CHARACTERISTICS (Continued)

TIMING RESPONSES

Symbol	Parameter	8088		8088-2		Units	Test Conditions
		Min.	Max.	Min.	Max.		
TCLAV	Address Valid Delay	10	110	10	60	ns	
TCLAX	Address Hold Time	10		10		ns	
TCLAZ	Address Float Delay	TCLAX	80	TCLAX	50	ns	
TLHLL	ALE Width	TCLCH-20		TCLCH-10		ns	
TCLLH	ALE Active Delay		80		50	ns	
TCHLL	ALE Inactive Delay		85		55	ns	
TLLAX	Address Hold Time to ALE Inactive	TCHCL-10		TCHCL-10		ns	
TCLDV	Data Valid Delay	10	110	10	60	ns	C_L = 20-100 pF for all 8088 Outputs in addition to internal loads
TCHDX	Data Hold Time	10		10		ns	
TWHDX	Data Hold Time After $\overline{WR}$	TCLCH-30		TCLCH-30		ns	
TCVCTV	Control Active Delay 1	10	110	10	70	ns	
TCHCTV	Control Active Delay 2	10	110	10	60	ns	
TCVCTX	Control Inactive Delay	10	110	10	70	ns	
TAZRL	Address Float to READ Active	0		0		ns	
TCLRL	$\overline{RD}$ Active Delay	10	165	10	100	ns	
TCLRH	$\overline{RD}$ Inactive Delay	10	150	10	80	ns	
TRHAV	$\overline{RD}$ Inactive to Next Address Active	TCLCL-45		TCLCL-40		ns	
TCLHAV	HLDA Valid Delay	10	160	10	100	ns	
TRLRH	$\overline{RD}$ Width	2TCLCL-75		2TCLCL-50		ns	
TWLWH	$\overline{WR}$ Width	2TCLCL-60		2TCLCL-40		ns	
TAVAL	Address Valid to ALE Low	TCLCH-60		TCLCH-40		ns	
TOLOH	Output Rise Time		20		20	ns	From 0.8V to 2.0V
TOHOL	Output Fall Time		12		12	ns	From 2.0V to 0.8V

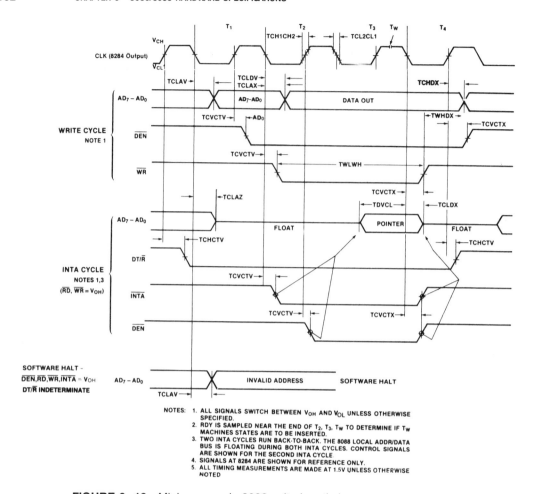

NOTES: 1. ALL SIGNALS SWITCH BETWEEN V$_{OH}$ AND V$_{OL}$ UNLESS OTHERWISE
          SPECIFIED.
        2. RDY IS SAMPLED NEAR THE END OF T$_2$, T$_3$, T$_W$ TO DETERMINE IF T$_W$
          MACHINES STATES ARE TO BE INSERTED.
        3. TWO INTA CYCLES RUN BACK-TO-BACK. THE 8088 LOCAL ADDR/DATA
          BUS IS FLOATING DURING BOTH INTA CYCLES. CONTROL SIGNALS
          ARE SHOWN FOR THE SECOND INTA CYCLE
        4. SIGNALS AT 8284 ARE SHOWN FOR REFERENCE ONLY.
        5. ALL TIMING MEASUREMENTS ARE MADE AT 1.5V UNLESS OTHERWISE
          NOTED

FIGURE 6–13   Minimum mode 8088 write bus timing.

T$_{WHDX}$ or 88 ns when the 8088 is operated with a 5-MHz clock. Hold time is often much less than this, and is in fact often 0 ns for memory devices. The width of the $\overline{WR}$ strobe is T$_{WLWH}$ or 340 ns at a 5-MHz clock rate. This rate, too, is compatible with most memory devices that have an access time of 400 ns or less.

6–5   READY AND THE WAIT STATE

As we mentioned earlier in this chapter, the READY input causes wait states for slower memory and I/O components. A *wait state* (T$_W$) is an extra clocking period inserted between T$_2$ and T$_3$ to stretch the bus cycle. If one wait state is inserted, then the memory access time, normally 460 ns with a 5-MHz clock, is stretched by one clocking period to 660 ns.

In this section, we discuss the READY synchronization circuitry inside the 8284A clock generator, show how to insert one or more wait states selectively into the bus cycle, and examine the READY input and the synchronization times it requires.

The READY Input

The READY input is sampled at the end of T_2 and again, if applicable, in the middle of T_w. If READY is a logic 0 at the end of T_2, then T_3 is delayed and T_w is inserted between T_2 and T_3. READY is next sampled at the middle of T_w to determine if the next state is T_w or T_3. It is tested for a logic 0 on the 1-0 transition of the clock at the end of T_2 and for a 1 on the 0-1 transition of the clock in the middle of T_w.

The READY input to the 8086/8088 has some stringent timing requirements. The timing diagram in Figure 6-14 shows READY causing one wait state (T_w) along with the required setup and hold times from the system clock. The timing requirement for this operation is met by the internal READY synchronization circuitry of the 8284A clock generator. When the 8284A is used for READY, the RDY (ready input to the 8284A) input occurs at the end of each T state.

RDY and the 8284A

RDY is the synchronized ready input to the 8284A clock generator. The timing diagram for this input is provided in Figure 6-15. Although it differs from the timing for the READY input to the 8086/8088, the internal 8284A circuitry guarantees the accuracy of the READY synchronization provided to the 8086/8088.

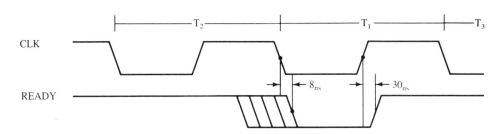

FIGURE 6-14 8086/8088 READY input timing.

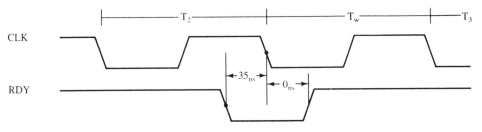

FIGURE 6-15 8284A RDY input timing.

Figure 6–16 again depicts the internal structure of the 8284A. The bottom half of this diagram is the READY synchronization circuitry. At the leftmost side, the RDY$_1$ and $\overline{\text{AEN}}_1$ inputs are ANDed, as are the RDY$_2$ and $\overline{\text{AEN}}_2$ inputs. The outputs of the AND gates are then ORed to generate the input to the one or two stages of synchronization. In order to obtain a logic 1 at the inputs to the flip-flops, RDY$_1$ AND $\overline{\text{AEN}}_1$ must be active or RDY$_2$ AND $\overline{\text{AEN}}_2$ must be active.

The $\overline{\text{ASYNC}}$ input selects one stage of synchronization when it is a logic 1 and two stages when a logic 0. If one stage is selected, then the RDY signal is kept from reaching the 8086/8088 READY pin until the next negative edge of the clock. If two stages are selected, the first positive edge of the clock captures RDY in the first flip-flop. The output of this flip-flop is fed to the second flip-flop so that on the next negative edge of the clock, the second flip-flop captures RDY.

Figure 6–17 illustrates a circuit used to introduce almost any number of wait states for the 8086/8088 microprocessor. Here an 8-bit serial shift register (74LS164) shifts a logic 0 for one or more clock periods from one of its Q outputs through to the RDY$_1$ input of the 8284A. With appropriate strapping, this circuit can provide various numbers of wait states. Notice also how the shift register is cleared back to its starting point. The output of the register is forced high when the $\overline{\text{RD}}$, $\overline{\text{WR}}$, and $\overline{\text{INTA}}$ pins are all logic 1s. These three signals are high until state T$_2$, so that the shift register shifts for the first time when the positive edge of the T$_2$ arrives. If one wait is desired, then output Q$_B$ is connected to the OR gate. If two waits are desired, output Q$_C$ is connected, and so forth.

Also notice in Figure 6–17 that this circuit does not always generate wait states. It is enabled from the memory only for memory devices that require the insertion of waits.

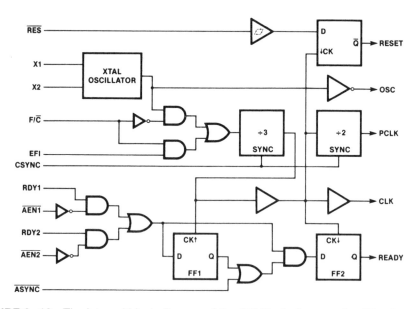

FIGURE 6–16 The internal block diagram of the 8284A clock generator. (Courtesy of Intel Corporation)

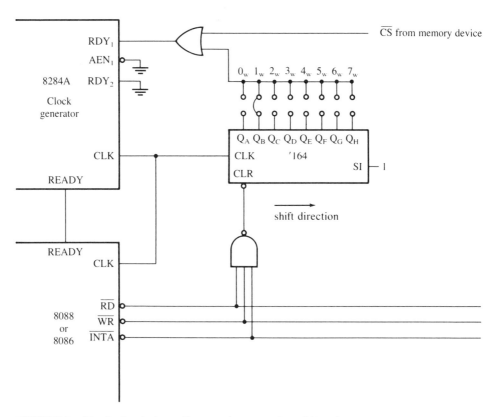

FIGURE 6-17 A circuit that will cause between 0 and 7 wait states.

If the selection signal from a memory device is a logic 0, the device is selected; then this circuit will generate a wait state.

Figure 6–18 illustrates the timing diagram for this shift register wait state generator when it is wired to insert one wait state. The timing diagram also illustrates the internal contents of the shift register's flip-flops to present a more detailed view of its operation. In this example, one wait state is generated.

6-6   MINIMUM MODE VERSUS MAXIMUM MODE

There are two available modes of operation for the 8086/8088 microprocessor: minimum mode and maximum mode. Minimum mode operation is obtained by connecting the mode selection pin MN/$\overline{\text{MX}}$ to +5 V, and maximum mode is selected by grounding this pin. Both modes enable different control structures for the 8086/8088 microprocessor. The mode of operation provided by minimum mode is similar to that of the 8085A, the most recent Intel 8-bit microprocessor, whereas maximum mode is new and unique and designed to be used whenever a coprocessor exists in a system.

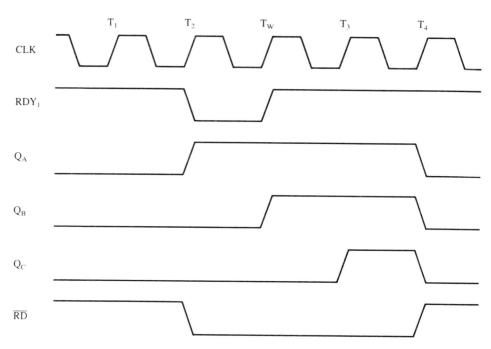

FIGURE 6–18   Wait state generation timing of the circuit of Figure 6–17.

Minimum Mode Operation

Minimum mode operation is the least expensive way to operate the 8086/8088 microprocessor (see Figure 6–19 for the minimum mode 8088 system). It costs less because all the control signals for the memory and I/O are generated inside the microprocessor. Its control signals are identical to those of the Intel 8085A, an earlier 8-bit microprocessor. This configuration allows 8085A peripherals to be used with the 8086/8088 without any special considerations.

Maximum Mode Operation

Maximum mode operation differs from minimum mode in that some of the control signals must be externally generated. This requires the addition of an external bus controller—the 8288 bus controller (see Figure 6–20 for the maximum mode 8088 system). There are not enough pins on the 8086/8088 for bus control during maximum mode because new pins and new features have replaced some of them. Maximum mode is used only when the system contains external coprocessors such as the 8087 arithmetic coprocessor.

The 8288 Bus Controller

An 8086/8088 system that is operated in maximum mode must have an 8288 bus controller to provide the signals that are eliminated from the 8086/8088 by the maximum mode operation. Figure 6–21 illustrates the block diagram and pinout of the 8288 bus controller circuit.

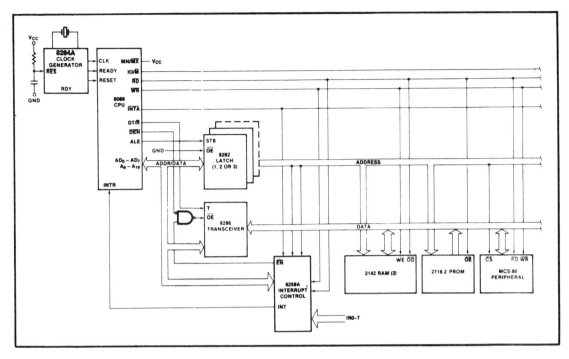

FIGURE 6-19   Minimum mode 8088 system.

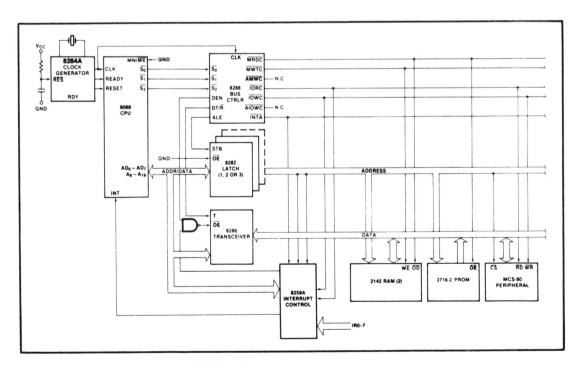

FIGURE 6-20   Maximum mode 8088 system.

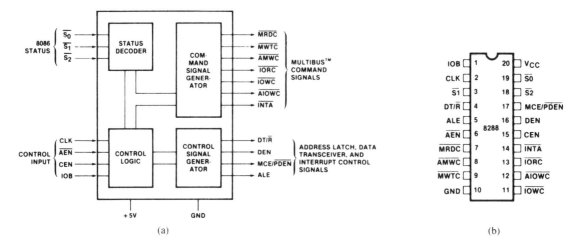

FIGURE 6–21   The 8288 bus controller. (a) Block diagram. (b) Pinout.

Notice that the control bus developed by this circuit contains separate signals for I/O (IORC and IOWC) and memory (MRDC and MWTC). It also contains advanced memory (AMWC) and I/O (AIOWC) write strobes and the INTA signal. These signals replace ALE, WR, IO/M, DT/R, DEN, and INTA, which are lost when the 8086/8088 is switched from the minimum mode to the maximum mode.

Pin Functions.   The following list provides a description of each pin of the 8288 bus controller.

1. $\overline{S}_2$, $\overline{S}_1$, and $\overline{S}_0$—Status Inputs: pins to the 8086/8088 status output bits $\overline{S}_2$, $\overline{S}_1$, and $\overline{S}_0$, which are decoded to generate the bus control signals.
2. CLK—Clock: an input connected to the 8284A CLK output pin. It helps generate the bus control signals.
3. ALE—Address Latch Enable: an output signal used to demultiplex the address information from the address/data bus and the address/status bus.
4. DEN—Data Enable: a pin that enables bidirectional data bus transceivers that are present in the system. Note that this is active high.
5. DT/R—Data Transmit/Receive: a signal that controls the direction of the bidirectional data bus transceivers in the system.
6. AEN—Address Enable: an input to enable the memory control signals.
7. CEN—Command Enable: an input to enable the command output pins.
8. IOB—I/O Bus Mode: an input used to select either the I/O bus mode or the system bus mode.
9. AIOWC—Advanced I/O Write Command: a command used to provide I/O with an advanced I/O write strobe.
10. IOWC—I/O Write Command: a command used to write data into an external I/O device.
11. IORC—I/O Read Command: a command used to read data from an external I/O device.

12. $\overline{\text{AMWC}}$—Advanced Memory Write Command: a command used to provide the memory with an early indication of a memory write operation.
13. $\overline{\text{MWTC}}$—Memory Write Command: the normal write signal that causes the memory to do a write operation.
14. $\overline{\text{MRDC}}$—Memory Read Command: the normal read signal that causes the memory to do a read operation.
15. $\overline{\text{INTA}}$—Interrupt Acknowledge: an output used to gate the interrupt vector number onto the data bus during an interrupt acknowledge.
16. MCE/$\overline{\text{PDEN}}$—Master Cascade Enable/Peripheral Data Enable: a pin that selects a cascade operation for an interrupt controller if IOB is grounded, and enables the I/O bus transceivers if IOB is tied high.

6-7   SUMMARY

1. The main differences between the 8086 and the 8088 are (a) an 8-bit data bus on the 8088 and a 16-bit data bus on the 8086, (b) an $\overline{\text{SS0}}$ pin on the 8088 in place of $\overline{\text{BHE}}/S_7$ on the 8086, and (c) an IO/$\overline{\text{M}}$ on the 8088 instead of an M/$\overline{\text{IO}}$ on the 8086.
2. Both the 8086 and the 8088 require a single +5-V power supply with a tolerance of ± 10 percent.
3. The 8086/8088 is TTL compatible if the noise immunity figure is derated to 350 mV from the customary 400 mV.
4. The 8086/8088 can drive one 74XXX, five 74LSXXX, one 74SXXX, ten 74ALSXXX, and ten 74HCXXX unit loads.
5. The 8284A clock generator provides the system clock (CLK), READY synchronization, and RESET synchronization.
6. The standard 5-MHz 8086/8088 operating frequency is obtained by attaching a 15-MHz crystal to the 8284A. The PCLK output pin contains a signal that is TTL compatible and at one half the CLK frequency.
7. Whenever the 8086/8088 is reset, it begins executing instructions at memory location FFFF0H and operating with the interrupts disabled.
8. Because the 8086/8088 buses are multiplexed and most memory and I/O devices aren't, the system must be demultiplexed before interfacing with a memory or I/O. Demultiplexing is accomplished by an 8-bit latch whose clock pulse is obtained from the ALE signal.
9. In a large system, the buses must be buffered because the 8086/8088 is capable of driving only up to 10 unit loads and large systems often have many more.
10. Bus timing is very important to the remaining chapters in this text. A bus cycle that consists of four clocking periods acts as the basic system timing. Each bus cycle is able to write or read one number between the microprocessor and the memory or I/O.
11. A bus cycle is broken into four states or T periods. T_1 is used by the microprocessor to send the address to the memory or I/O and the ALE signal to the demultiplexers; T_2 is used to send data to memory for a write and to test the READY pin and activate the control signals $\overline{\text{RD}}$ or $\overline{\text{WR}}$; T_3 allows the memory time to access data and allows

data to be transferred between the microprocessor and the memory or I/O; T_4 is where data are written.

12. The 8086/8088 allows the memory and I/O 460 ns to access data when they are operated with a 5-MHz clock.

13. Wait states (T_W) stretch the bus cycle by one or more clocking periods to allow the memory and I/O more access time. Wait states are inserted by controlling the READY input to the 8086/8088. READY is sampled at the end of T_2 and during T_W.

14. Minimum mode operation is similar to that of the Intel 8085A microprocessor, while maximum mode operation is new and specifically designed for the operation of the 8087 arithmetic coprocessor.

15. The 8288 bus controller must be used in the maximum mode to provide the control bus signals to the memory and I/O. This is because the maximum mode operation of the 8086/8088 removes some of the system's control signal lines in favor of control signals for the coprocessors. The 8288 reconstructs these removed control signals.

6-8   QUESTIONS AND PROBLEMS

1. List the differences between the 8086 and the 8088 microprocessors.
2. Is the 8086/8088 TTL compatible? Explain your answer.
3. What is the fanout from the 8086/8088 to the following devices?
   a. 74XXX TTL
   b. 74ALSXXX TTL
   c. 74HCXXX CMOS
   d. NMOS
4. What information appears on the address/data bus of the 8088 while ALE is active?
5. What is the purpose of status bits S_3 and S_4?
6. What condition does a logic 0 on the 8086/8088 $\overline{RD}$ pin indicate?
7. Explain the operation of the $\overline{TEST}$ pin and the WAIT instruction.
8. Describe the signal that is applied to the CLK input pin of the 8086/8088 microprocessor.
9. What mode of operation is selected when $MN/\overline{MX}$ is grounded?
10. What does the $\overline{WR}$ strobe signal from the 8086/8088 indicate about the operation of the 8086/8088?
11. When does ALE float to its high-impedance state?
12. When $DT/\overline{R}$ is a logic 1, what condition does it indicate about the operation of the 8086/8088?
13. What happens when the HOLD input to the 8086/8088 is placed at its logic 1 level?
14. What three minimum mode 8086/8088 pins are decoded to discover if the processor is halted?
15. Explain the operation of the $\overline{LOCK}$ pin.
16. What conditions do the QS_1 and QS_0 pins indicate about the 8086/8088?
17. What three housekeeping chores are provided by the 8284A clock generator?
18. By what factor does the 8284A clock generator divide the crystal oscillator's output frequency?

19. If the F/$\overline{C}$ pin is placed at a logic 1 level, the crystal oscillator is disabled. Where is the timing signal attached to the 8284A under this condition?

20. The PCLK output of the 8284A is _____ MHz if the crystal oscillator is operating at 14 MHz.

21. The $\overline{RES}$ input to the 8284A is placed at a logic _____ level in order to reset the 8086/8088.

22. What bus connections on the 8086 microprocessor are typically demultiplexed?

23. What bus connections on the 8088 microprocessor are typically demultiplexed?

24. What TTL integrated circuit is often used to demultiplex the buses on the 8086/8088?

25. What is the purpose of the demultiplexed $\overline{BHE}$ signal on the 8086 microprocessor?

26. Why are buffers often required in an 8086/8088-based system?

27. What 8086/8088 signal is used to select the direction of the data flows through the 74LS245 bidirectional bus buffer?

28. A bus cycle is equal to _____ clocking periods.

29. If the CLK input to the 8086/8088 is 4 MHz, how long is a bus cycle?

30. What two 8086/8088 operations occur during a bus cycle?

31. How many MIPS is the 8086/8088 capable of obtaining when operated with a 10-MHz clock?

32. Briefly describe the purpose of each T state listed:
    a. T_1
    b. T_2
    c. T_3
    d. T_4

33. How much time is allowed for memory access when the 8086/8088 is operated with a 5-MHz clock?

34. How wide is $\overline{DEN}$ if the 8088 is operated with a 5-MHz clock?

35. If the READY pin is grounded, it will introduce _____ states into the bus cycle of the 8086/8088.

36. What does the $\overline{ASYNC}$ input to the 8284A accomplish?

37. What logic levels must be applied to $\overline{AEN}_1$ and RDY_1 to obtain a logic 1 at the READY pin? (Assume that $\overline{AEN}_2$ is at a logic 1 level.)

38. Contrast minimum and maximum mode 8086/8088 operation.

39. What main function is provided by the 8288 bus controller when used with 8086/8088 maximum mode operation?

CHAPTER 7

Memory Interface

INTRODUCTION

Whether simple or complex, every microprocessor-based system has memory. The 8086/8088 is no different from any other microprocessor in this respect.

Almost all systems contain two main types of memory, read-only memory (ROM) and random access memory (RAM) or read/write memory. This chapter explains how to interface both types of memory to the 8086 and 8088.

OBJECTIVES

Upon completion of this chapter, you will be able to:

1. Decode the memory address and use the outputs of the decoder to select various memory components.
2. Explain how to interface both RAM and ROM to a microprocessor.
3. Explain how parity can detect memory errors.
4. Interface memory to the 8088 microprocessor.
5. Interface memory to the 8086 microprocessor.
6. Explain the operation of a dynamic RAM controller.
7. Interface dynamic RAM to the 8086 and 8088.

7-1   MEMORY DEVICES

It is essential to have a complete understanding of the operation of the memory components before attempting to interface memory to a microprocessor. In this section, we
explain the function of three common types of memory: read-only memory (ROM), static
random access memory (SRAM), and dynamic random access memory (DRAM).

Memory Connections

The connections that all memory devices have in common are address inputs, data outputs
and/or inputs, some type of selection input, and at least one control input used to read or
write data. See Figure 7–1 for ROM and RAM pseudo-memory devices.

Address Connections.   All memory devices have a set of address inputs used to select a
memory location within the memory device. The number of address pins found on a
memory device is determined by the number of memory locations found within it.

   Today, the more common memory devices have between 1K (1,024) and 1M memory locations, with 4M memory location devices on the horizon. A 1K memory device has
10 address pins; therefore, 10 address inputs are required to single out any one of its 1,024
memory locations. It takes a 10-bit binary number (1,024 different combinations) to select
any single location on a 1,024-location device. If a memory device has 11 address
connections, it has 2,048 (2K) internal memory locations. The number of memory locations can thus be extrapolated from the number of address pins. For example, a 4K
memory device has 12 address connections, an 8K device has 13, and so forth.

Data Connections.   All memory devices have a set of data outputs or inputs and outputs.
The device illustrated in Figure 7–1 has a common set of input/output (I/O) connections.

   The data connections are the points at which data are entered for storage or extracted
for reading. In this sample memory device, there are eight I/O connections, which means

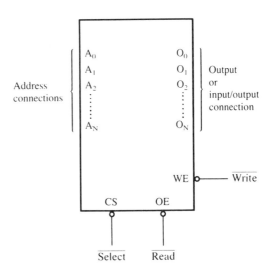

FIGURE 7–1 A pseudo-
memory component illustrating the address, data, and
control connections.

that the memory device can store 8 bits of data in each of its memory locations. An 8-bit-wide memory device is often called a *byte-wide memory*. Not all memory devices are 8 bits wide, however; some are 4 bits or even 1 bit wide.

Catalog listings of memory devices often refer to memory locations *times* bits per location. For example, a memory device with 1K memory locations and 8 bits in each location is listed as a 1K × 8 by the manufacturer. A 16K × 1 is a memory device with 16K 1-bit memory locations. Devices are also often classified according to total bit capacity. For example, a 1K × 8-bit memory device is sometimes listed as an 8K memory device, or a 64K × 4 memory device is listed as a 256K device.

Selection Connections.   Each memory device has an input—sometimes more than one— that selects or enables the memory device. This kind of input is most often called a *chip select* ($\overline{CS}$) or *chip enable* ($\overline{CE}$) input. RAM memory generally has at least one $\overline{CS}$ input, and ROM at least one $\overline{CE}$. If the $\overline{CE}$ or $\overline{CS}$ input is active (a logic 0 in this case), the memory device can do a read or a write; if it is inactive (a logic 1 in this case), the memory device cannot do a read or a write because it is turned off or disabled. If more than one $\overline{CS}$ connection is present, all must be activated to read or write data.

Control Connections.   All memory devices have some form of control or control input. A ROM usually has only one control input, while a RAM often has one or two control inputs.

The control input most often found on a ROM is the *output enable* ($\overline{OE}$) connection, which allows data to flow out of the output data pins of the ROM. If $\overline{OE}$ and the selection input are both active, then the output is enabled; if $\overline{OE}$ is inactive, the output is disabled at its high-impedance state. The $\overline{OE}$ input actually enables and disables a set of three-state buffers located within the memory device.

RAM memory devices can have either one or two control inputs. If there is one control input, it is often called R/$\overline{W}$. This pin selects a *read operation* or a *write operation* only if the device is selected by the selection input ($\overline{CS}$). If the RAM has two control inputs, they are usually labeled $\overline{WE}$ and $\overline{OE}$. Here $\overline{WE}$ must be active to perform a memory write, and $\overline{OE}$ must be active to perform a memory read operation. When these two controls ($\overline{WE}$ and $\overline{OE}$) are present, they must never both be active at the same time. If both control inputs are inactive (logic 1s), then data are neither written nor read and the data connections are at their high-impedance state.

ROM Memory

The read-only memory (ROM) permanently stores programs and data that are resident to the system and must not change when power is disconnected.

The ROM is available in many forms today. It is purchased in mass quantities from a manufacturer and programmed during its fabrication at the factory. The EPROM (erasable programmable read-only memory) is more commonly used when software must be changed often or when too limited a number are in demand to make the ROM economical.

EPROMs are programmed in the field on a device called an EPROM programmer. They are erasable if exposed to high-intensity ultraviolet light for about 30 minutes or less, depending on the type of EPROM. PROM memory devices are also available, but they are not as common today. The PROM (programmable read-only memory) can also be programmed in the field by burning open tiny Nichrome or silicon oxide fuses, but once programmed it cannot be erased.

Figure 7-2 illustrates the 2716 EPROM. This device contains 11 address inputs and 8 data outputs. The 2716 is a 2K × 8 memory device. The 27XXX series of the EPROM contains the following part numbers: 2704 (512 × 8), 2708 (1K × 8), 2716 (2K × 8), 2732 (4K × 8), 2764 (8K × 8), 27128 (16K × 8), 27256 (32K × 8), and 27512 (64K × 8). Each of these parts contains address pins, 8 data connections, one chip selection input ($\overline{CE}$), and an output enable pin ($\overline{OE}$).

Figure 7-3 illustrates the timing diagram for the 2716 EPROM. Data only appear on the output connections after a logic 0 is placed on both the $\overline{CE}$ and $\overline{OE}$ pin connections. If $\overline{CE}$ and $\overline{OE}$ are not both logic 0s, the data output connections remain at their high-impedance or off states.

One important piece of information provided by the timing diagram and data sheet is the *memory access time*—the time that it takes the memory to read information. As Figure 7-3 illustrates, memory access time (T_{acc}) is measured from the appearance of the address at the address inputs until the appearance of the data at the output connections. This is based on the assumption that the $\overline{CE}$ input goes low at the same time that the address inputs become stable. Also, $\overline{OE}$ must be a logic 0 for the output connections to become active. The basic speed of this EPROM is 450 ns. (Recall that the 8086/8088 operated with a 5-MHz clock allowed memory 460 ns to access data.) This type of memory component requires wait states to operate properly with the 8086/8088 microprocessor because of its rather long access time. If wait states are not desired, higher speed versions are available at an additional cost.

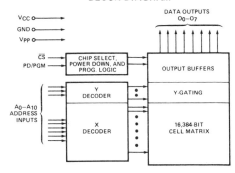

MODE SELECTION

PINS / MODE	PD/PGM (18)	$\overline{CS}$ (20)	V_{PP} (21)	V_{CC} (24)	OUTPUTS (9-11, 13-17)
Read	V_{IL}	V_{IL}	+5	+5	D_{OUT}
Deselect	Don't Care	V_{IH}	+5	+5	High Z
Power Down	V_{IH}	Don't Care	+5	+5	High Z
Program	Pulsed V_{IL} to V_{IH}	V_{IH}	+25	+5	D_{IN}
Program Verify	V_{IL}	V_{IL}	+25	+5	D_{OUT}
Program Inhibit	V_{IL}	V_{IH}	+25	+5	High Z

PIN CONFIGURATION

```
A7  [ 1      24 ] VCC
A6  [ 2      23 ] A8
A5  [ 3      22 ] A9
A4  [ 4      21 ] VPP
A3  [ 5      20 ] CS
A2  [ 6      19 ] A10
A1  [ 7      18 ] PD/PGM
A0  [ 8      17 ] O7
O0  [ 9      16 ] O6
O1  [ 10     15 ] O5
O2  [ 11     14 ] O4
GND [ 12     13 ] O3
```

BLOCK DIAGRAM

PIN NAMES

A0-A10	ADDRESSES
PD/PGM	POWER DOWN/PROGRAM
$\overline{CS}$	CHIP SELECT
O0-O7	OUTPUTS

FIGURE 7-2 The pinout of the 2716, 2K × 8 EPROM. (Courtesy of Intel Corporation)

A.C. Characteristics

$T_A = 0°C$ to $70°C$, $V_{CC}[1] = +5V \pm 5\%$, $V_{PP}[2] = V_{CC} \pm 0.6V$ [3]

Symbol	Parameter	Limits			Unit	Test Conditions
		Min.	Typ.[4]	Max.		
t_{ACC1}	Address to Output Delay		250	450	ns	PD/PGM = $\overline{CS}$ = V_{IL}
t_{ACC2}	PD/PGM to Output Delay		280	450	ns	$\overline{CS}$ = V_{IL}
t_{CO}	Chip Select to Output Delay			120	ns	PD/PGM = V_{IL}
t_{PF}	PD/PGM to Output Float	0		100	ns	$\overline{CS}$ = V_{IL}
t_{DF}	Chip Deselect to Output Float	0		100	ns	PD/PGM = V_{IL}
t_{OH}	Address to Output Hold	0			ns	PD/PGM = $\overline{CS}$ = V_{IL}

Capacitance[5] $T_A = 25°C$, $f = 1$ MHz

Symbol	Parameter	Typ.	Max.	Unit	Conditions
C_{IN}	Input Capacitance	4	6	pF	V_{IN} = 0V
C_{OUT}	Output Capacitance	8	12	pF	V_{OUT} = 0V

NOTE: Please refer to page 2 for notes.

A.C. Test Conditions:

Output Load: 1 TTL gate and C_L = 100 pF
Input Rise and Fall Times: ≤20 ns
Input Pulse Levels: 0.8V to 2.2V
Timing Measurement Reference Level:
Inputs   1V and 2V
Outputs   0.8V and 2V

WAVEFORMS

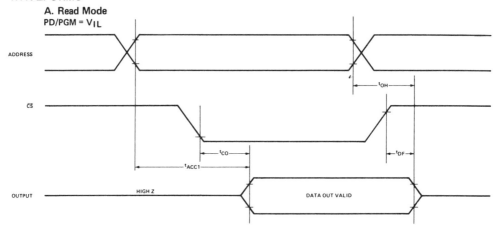

FIGURE 7–3 The timing diagram and AC characteristics of the 2716 EPROM. (Courtesy of Intel Corporation)

Static RAM (SRAM) Memory

Static RAM memory devices retain data as long as DC power is applied. Because no special action is required to retain the stored data, this device is called *static memory*. The main difference between a ROM and a RAM is that a RAM is written into under normal operation and a ROM is programmed outside the computer. The SRAM stores temporary data and is used when the size of the read/write memory is relatively small. Today, a small memory is under 256K bytes.

Figure 7–4 illustrates the 4016 SRAM, which is a 2K × 8 read/write memory. This device has 11 address inputs and 8 data input/output pins. The pinout of the 4016 is the same as that of the 2716 except for the program pin, which is changed to a write pin on

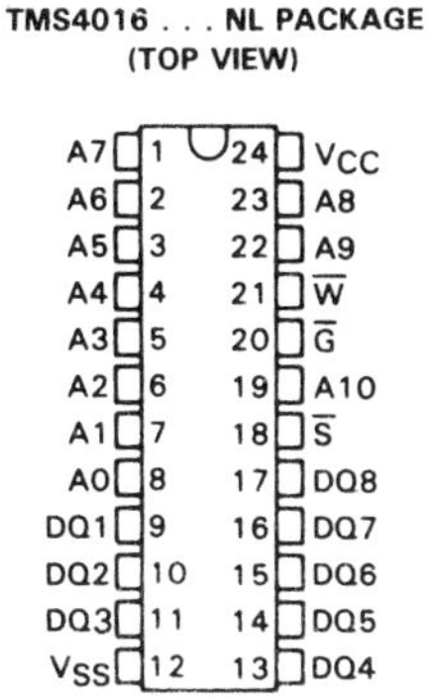

FIGURE 7-4 The pinout of the TMS4016, 2K × 8 static RAM (SRAM). (Courtesy of Texas Instruments Incorporated)

TMS4016 . . . NL PACKAGE
(TOP VIEW)

```
A7   1    24  VCC
A6   2    23  A8
A5   3    22  A9
A4   4    21  W̄
A3   5    20  Ḡ
A2   6    19  A10
A1   7    18  S̄
A0   8    17  DQ8
DQ1  9    16  DQ7
DQ2  10   15  DQ6
DQ3  11   14  DQ5
VSS  12   13  DQ4
```

PIN NOMENCLATURE	
A0 – A10	Addresses
DQ1 – DQ8	Data In/Data Out
Ḡ	Output Enable
S̄	Chip Select
VCC	+5-V Supply
VSS	Ground
W̄	Write Enable

the 4016. This interchangeability of an EPROM and a RAM is useful for system development and debugging. The software can initially be loaded into a 4016 RAM for debugging and modification, and, once the system is functioning properly, the program can be stored on the EPROM and plugged into the system.

The control inputs of this RAM are slightly different from those presented earlier. The $\overline{OE}$ pin is labeled $\overline{G}$, the $\overline{CS}$ pin $\overline{S}$, and the $\overline{WE}$ pin $\overline{W}$. Despite the altered designations, however, these control pins function exactly the same as those outlined previously. Other manufacturers make this popular SRAM under the part numbers 2016 and 6116.

Figure 7-5 depicts the timing diagram for the 4016 SRAM. As the read cycle timing reveals, access time is $t_a(A)$. On the slowest version of the 4016, this time is 250 ns, which is fast enough to connect to an 8088 or an 8086 operated at 5 MHz without wait states. Again, it is important to remember that the access time must be checked to determine the compatibility of memory components with the microprocessor.

Figure 7-6 (page 180) illustrates the pinout of the 62256, 32K × 8 static RAM. This device is packaged in a 28-pin integrated circuit, and is available with access times of 120 ns or 150 ns.

Dynamic RAM (DRAM) Memory

About the largest static RAM available today is a 32K × 8. Dynamic RAMs, on the other hand, are available in much larger sizes: up to 4M × 1. In all other respects, DRAM is essentially the same as SRAM except that it retains data for only about 2–4 ms on an integrated capacitor. After 2–4 ms, the contents of the DRAM must be completely rewritten or refreshed because the capacitors lose their charges.

electrical characteristics over recommended operating free-air temperature range (unless otherwise noted)

PARAMETER		TEST CONDITIONS		MIN	TYP[†]	MAX	UNIT
V_{OH}	High level voltage	$I_{OH} = -1$ mA,	$V_{CC} = 4.5$ V	2.4			V
V_{OL}	Low level voltage	$I_{OL} = 2.1$ mA,	$V_{CC} = 4.5$ V			0.4	V
I_I	Input current	$V_I = 0$ V to 5.5 V				10	µA
I_{OZ}	Off-state output current	$\overline{S}$ or $\overline{G}$ at 2 V or $\overline{W}$ at 0.8 V, $V_O = 0$ V to 5.5 V				10	µA
I_{CC}	Supply current from V_{CC}	$I_O = 0$ mA, $T_A = 0$°C (worst case)	$V_{CC} = 5.5$ V,		40	70	mA
C_i	Input capacitance	$V_I = 0$ V,	$f = 1$ MHz			8	pF
C_o	Output capacitance	$V_O = 0$ V,	$f = 1$ MHz			12	pF

[†]All typical values are at $V_{CC} = 5$ V, $T_A = 25$°C.

timing requirements over recommended supply voltage range and operating free-air temperature range

PARAMETER		TMS4016-12		TMS4016-15		TMS4016-20		TMS4016-25		UNIT
		MIN	MAX	MIN	MAX	MIN	MAX	MIN	MAX	
$t_{c(rd)}$	Read cycle time	120		150		200		250		ns
$t_{c(wr)}$	Write cycle time	120		150		200		250		ns
$t_{w(W)}$	Write pulse width	60		80		100		120		ns
$t_{su(A)}$	Address setup time	20		20		20		20		ns
$t_{su(S)}$	Chip select setup time	60		80		100		120		ns
$t_{su(D)}$	Data setup time	50		60		80		100		ns
$t_{h(A)}$	Address hold time	0		0		0		0		ns
$t_{h(D)}$	Data hold time	5		10		10		10		ns

switching characteristics over recommended voltage range, $T_A = 0$°C to 70°C with output loading of Figure 1 (see notes 3 and 4)

PARAMETER		TMS4016-12		TMS4016-15		TMS4016-20		TMS4016-25		UNIT
		MIN	MAX	MIN	MAX	MIN	MAX	MIN	MAX	
$t_{a(A)}$	Access time from address		120		150		200		250	ns
$t_{a(S)}$	Access time from chip select low		60		75		100		120	ns
$t_{a(G)}$	Access time from output enable low		50		60		80		100	ns
$t_{v(A)}$	Output data valid after address change	10		15		15		15		ns
$t_{dis(S)}$	Output disable time after chip select high		40		50		60		80	ns
$t_{dis(G)}$	Output disable time after output enable high		40		50		60		80	ns
$t_{dis(W)}$	Output disable time after write enable low		50		60		60		80	ns
$t_{en(S)}$	Output enable time after chip select low	5		5		10		10		ns
$t_{en(G)}$	Output enable time after output enable low	5		5		10		10		ns
$t_{en(W)}$	Output enable time after write enable high	5		5		10		10		ns

NOTES: 3. $C_L = 100$ pF for all measurements except $t_{dis(W)}$ and $t_{en(W)}$.
$C_L = 5$ pF for $t_{dis(W)}$ and $t_{en(W)}$.
4. t_{dis} and t_{en} parameters are sampled and not 100% tested.

(a)

FIGURE 7-5   (a) The AC characteristics of the TMS4016 SRAM. (b) The timing diagrams of the TMS4016 SRAM. (Courtesy of Texas Instruments Incorporated)

timing waveform of read cycle (see note 5)

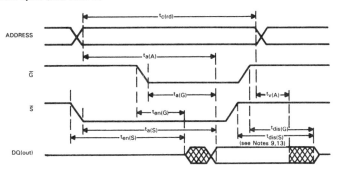

timing waveform of write cycle no. 1 (see note 6)

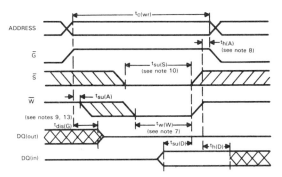

timing waveform of write cycle no. 2 (see notes 6 and 11)

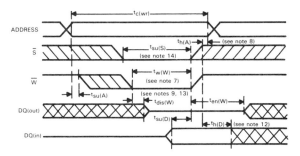

NOTES: 5. $\overline{W}$ is high for Read Cycle.

6. $\overline{W}$ must be high during all address transitions.

7. A write occurs during the overlap of a low $\overline{S}$ and a low $\overline{W}$.

8. $t_{h(A)}$ is measured from the earlier of $\overline{S}$ or $\overline{W}$ going high to the end of the write cycle.

9. During this period, I/O pins are in the output state so that the input signals of opposite phase to the outputs must not be applied.

10. If the $\overline{S}$ low transition occurs simultaneously with the $\overline{W}$ low transitions or after the $\overline{W}$ transition, output remains in a high impedance state.

11. $\overline{G}$ is continuously low ($\overline{G} = V_{IL}$).

12. If $\overline{S}$ is low during this period, I/O pins are in the output state. Data input signals of opposite phase to the outputs must not be applied.

13. Transition is measured ± 200 mV from steady-state voltage.

14. If the $\overline{S}$ low transition occurs before the $\overline{W}$ low transition, then the data input signals of opposite phase to the outputs must not be applied for the duration of $t_{dis(W)}$ after the $\overline{W}$ low transition.

(b)

FIGURE 7-5   *continued*

FIGURE 7–6 Pin diagram of the 62256, 32K $\times$ 8 static RAM.

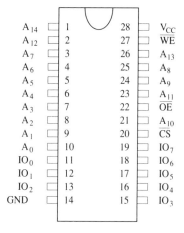

PIN FUNCTION

A_0 - A_{14}	Addresses
IO_0 - IO_7	Data connections
$\overline{CS}$	Chip select
$\overline{OE}$	Output enable
$\overline{WE}$	Write enable
V_{CC}	+5V Supply
GND	Ground

Rather than requiring the almost impossible task of reading the contents of each memory location with a program and then rewriting them, the manufacturer has internally constructed the DRAM so that, in the 64K $\times$ 1 version, the entire contents of the memory can be refreshed with 256 reads in a 4-ms interval. Refreshing will also occur during a write or during a special refresh cycle. Much more information on refreshing DRAMs is provided in Section 7–5.

Another disadvantage of DRAM memory is that it requires so many address pins that the manufacturers have multiplexed the address inputs. Figure 7–7 illustrates a 64K $\times$ 4 DRAM, the TMS4464. Notice that it contains only 8 address inputs where it should contain 16 — the number required to address 64K memory locations. The only way that 16 address bits can be crammed into 8 address pins is in 8-bit increments. This operation requires two special pins called *column address strobe* ($\overline{CAS}$) and *row address strobe* ($\overline{RAS}$). First, A_0–A_7 are placed on the address pins and strobed into an internal row latch by $\overline{RAS}$ as the row address. Next, the address bits A_8–A_{15} are placed on these eight address inputs and strobed into an internal column latch by $\overline{CAS}$ as the column address (see Figure 7–8 for this timing). The 16-bit address held in these internal latches addresses the contents of one of the 4-bit memory locations.

Figure 7–9 illustrates a set of multiplexers used to strobe the column and row addresses into the eight address inputs of a pair of TMS4464 DRAMs. Here the $\overline{RAS}$ not only strobes the row address into the DRAMs, but it also changes the address applied to

FIGURE 7-7 The pinout of the TMS4464, 64K × 4 dynamic RAM (DRAM). (Courtesy of Texas Instruments Incorporated)

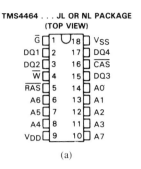

TMS4464 . . . JL OR NL PACKAGE
(TOP VIEW)

Ḡ	1	18	Vss
DQ1	2	17	DQ4
DQ2	3	16	CAS
W	4	15	DQ3
RAS	5	14	A0
A6	6	13	A1
A5	7	12	A2
A4	8	11	A3
VDD	9	10	A7

(a)

PIN NOMENCLATURE	
A0-A7	Address Inputs
CAS	Column Address Strobe
DQ1-DQ4	Data-In/Data-Out
Ḡ	Output Enable
RAS	Row Address Strobe
VDD	+5-V Supply
Vss	Ground
W	Write Enable

(b)

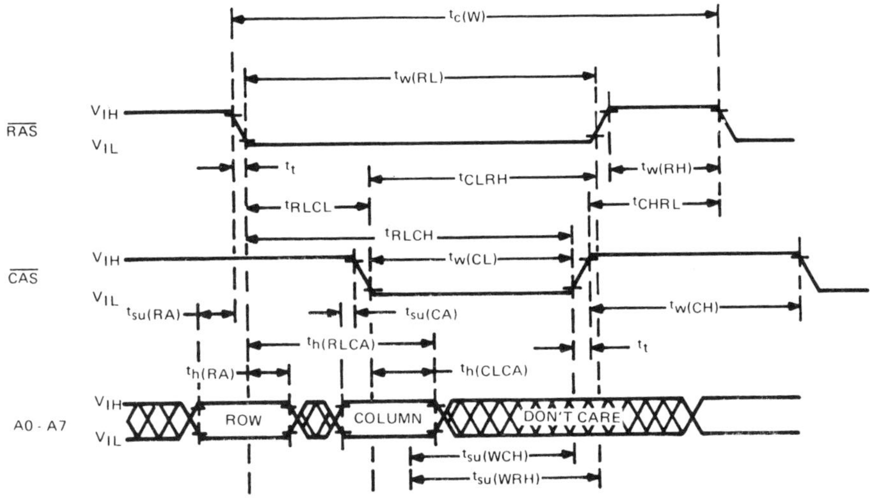

FIGURE 7-8 RAS, CAS, and address input timing for the TMS4464 DRAM. (Courtesy of Texas Instruments Incorporated)

the address inputs. This is possible due to the long propagation delay time of the multiplexers. When RAS is a logic 1, the B inputs are connected to the Y outputs of the multiplexers, and when the RAS input goes to a logic 0, the A inputs connect to the Y outputs. Because the internal row address latch is edge-triggered, it captures the row address before the address at the inputs changes to the column address. More detail on DRAM and DRAM interfacing is provided in Section 7-5.

FIGURE 7–9 Address multiplexer for the TMS4464 DRAM.

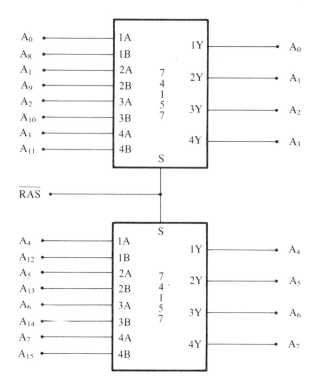

Here, as with the SRAM, the $\overline{W}$ pin writes data to the DRAM and the $\overline{G}$ pin enables the output connections for a read operation. ($\overline{W}$ replaces $\overline{WE}$, and $\overline{G}$ replaces $\overline{OE}$.) Figure 7–10 illustrates the pinout of 41256 dynamic RAM. This device is organized as a 256K × 1 memory requiring as little as 70 ns to access data.

More recently, a larger DRAM has become available that is organized as a 1M × 1 memory. On the horizon is the 4M × 1 memory currently produced by the IBM Corporation. Figure 7–11 illustrates the pinout of the TMX4C1024 by Texas Instruments. This device is also often numbered the 511000P.

7–2   ADDRESS DECODING

In order to attach a memory device to the microprocessor, it is necessary to decode the address from the microprocessor to make the memory function at a unique section or partition of the memory map. Without address decoders, only one memory device can be connected to a microprocessor, which would make it virtually useless. In this section, we describe a few of the more common address-decoding techniques as well as the decoders that are found in many systems.

Why Decode Memory?

As a comparison of the 8088 microprocessor and 2716 EPROM will reveal, the EPROM has 11 address connections and the microprocessor has 20. This means that the micro-

FIGURE 7-10 The 41256 dynamic RAM organized as a 256K × 1 memory device.

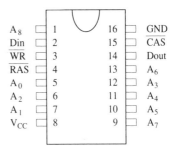

PIN FUNCTIONS

A_0 - A_8	Addresses
Din	Data in
Dout	Data out
$\overline{CAS}$	Column Address Strobe
$\overline{RAS}$	Row Address Strobe
$\overline{WR}$	Write enable
V_{CC}	+5V Supply
GND	Ground

FIGURE 7-11 The 1M × 1 DRAM.

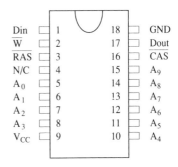

PIN FUNCTIONS

A_0 - A_9	Addresses
Din	Data in
Dout	Data out
$\overline{CAS}$	Column Address Strobe
$\overline{RAS}$	Row Address Strobe
$\overline{W}$	Write enable
V_{CC}	+5V Supply
GND	Ground

processor sends out a 20-bit memory address whenever it reads or writes data. Since the EPROM has only 11 address inputs, there is a mismatch that must somehow be corrected. If only 11 of the 8088's address pins are connected to the memory, then the 8088 will see only 2K bytes of memory instead of the 1M bytes that it "expects" the memory to contain. The decoder is used to match up the microprocessor with the memory component.

Simple NAND Gate Decoder

Address connections A_{10}–A_0 of the 8088 are connected to address inputs A_{10}–A_0 of the EPROM, and the remaining nine address pins (A_{19}–A_{11}) are connected to the inputs of a decoder (see Figure 7–12), which selects the EPROM for one of the many 2K-byte sections of the entire 1M-byte address range of the 8088.

In this circuit, a NAND gate decodes the memory address. The output of the NAND gate becomes a logic 0 whenever the nine leftmost 8088 address pins (A_{19}–A_{11}) are all logic 1s. The logic 0 output of the decoder is connected to the $\overline{CE}$ input, which selects (enables) the EPROM. Recall that if $\overline{CE}$ is a logic 0, data will be read from the EPROM only if $\overline{OE}$ is also a logic 0. $\overline{OE}$ is activated by the 8088 $\overline{RD}$ signal.

If the 20-bit binary address decoded by the NAND gate is written so that the leftmost 9 bits are 1s and the rightmost 11 bits are *don't cares* (X), the actual address range of the EPROM can be determined. (A *don't care* is a logic 1 or a logic 0, whichever is appropriate.)

Example 7–1 illustrates how the address range for this EPROM is determined by writing down the externally decoded address bits (A_{19}–A_{11}) and the address bits decoded by the EPROM (A_{10}–A_0) as *don't cares*. As the example illustrates, the *don't cares* are first written as 0s to locate the bottom address and then as 1s to find the top address.

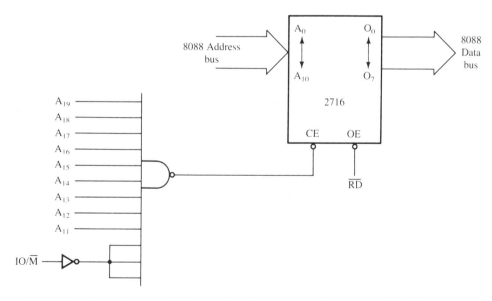

FIGURE 7–12   A simple NAND gate decoder used to select a 2716 EPROM memory component for memory locations FF800H–FFFFFH.

Example 7–1 also converts these top and bottom binary boundaries into hexadecimal. Here the 2K EPROM is decoded at memory address locations FF800H–FFFFFH. Notice that this is a 2K-byte section of the memory and is also located at the reset location for the 8088, a most likely place for an EPROM.

Although this example serves to make a point, NAND gates are rarely used to decode memory because each memory device requires its own NAND gate decoder. The excessive cost of this option requires that an alternate be found.

EXAMPLE 7–1

```
1111 1111 1XXX XXXX XXXX
          or
1111 1111 1000 0000 0000 = FF800H
          to
1111 1111 1111 1111 1111 =FFFFFH
```

The 3-to-8 Line Decoder (74LS138)

One of the more common integrated circuit decoders found in many microprocessor-based systems is the 74LS138 3-to-8 line decoder. Figure 7–13 illustrates this decoder and its truth table.

The truth table shows that only one of the eight outputs ever goes low at any time. For any of the decoder's outputs to go low, the three enable inputs—$\overline{E_1}$, $\overline{E_2}$, and E_3—must all be active. To be active, the $\overline{E_1}$ and $\overline{E_2}$ inputs must both be low (logic 0), and E_3 must be high (logic 1).

Once the 74LS138 is enabled, the address inputs (C, B, and A) select which output pin goes low. Imagine eight EPROM $\overline{CE}$ inputs connected to the eight outputs of the decoder! This is a very powerful device because it can decode eight different memory devices at the same time.

Sample Decoder Circuit. Notice that the outputs of the decoder illustrated in Figure 7–14 are connected to eight different 2764 EPROM memory devices. Here the decoder selects eight 8K-byte blocks of memory for a total of 64K bytes of memory. This figure also illustrates the address range of each of the memory devices and the common connections to the memory devices. Notice that all the address connections from the 8088 are connected to this circuit. Also notice that the decoder's outputs are connected to the $\overline{CE}$ inputs of the EPROMs, and the $\overline{RD}$ signal from the 8088 is connected to the $\overline{OE}$ inputs of the EPROMs. This allows only the selected EPROM to be enabled and to send its data to the microprocessor through the data bus whenever $\overline{RD}$ becomes a logic 0.

In this circuit, a 3-input NAND gate is connected to address bits A_{19}–A_{17}. When all four address inputs are high, the output of this NAND gate goes low and enables input $\overline{E_2}$. Input E_3 is connected directly to A_{16}. In other words, in order to enable this decoder, the first four address connections (A_{19}–A_{16}) must all be high.

The address inputs C, B, and A are connected to address pins A_{15}–A_{13}. These three address inputs determine which output pin goes low and which EPROM is selected whenever the 8088 outputs a memory address within this range to the memory system.

FIGURE 7–13 The
74LS138, 3-to-8-line decoder
and function table.

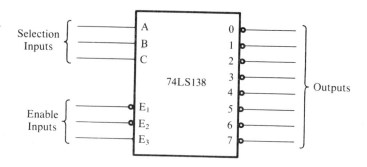

Inputs						Outputs							
Enable			Select										
$\overline{E_1}$	$\overline{E_2}$	E_3	C	B	A	$\overline{0}$	$\overline{1}$	$\overline{2}$	$\overline{3}$	$\overline{4}$	$\overline{5}$	$\overline{6}$	$\overline{7}$
1	X	X	X	X	X	1	1	1	1	1	1	1	1
X	1	X	X	X	X	1	1	1	1	1	1	1	1
X	X	0	X	X	X	1	1	1	1	1	1	1	1
0	0	1	0	0	0	0	1	1	1	1	1	1	1
0	0	1	0	0	1	1	0	1	1	1	1	1	1
0	0	1	0	1	0	1	1	0	1	1	1	1	1
0	0	1	0	1	1	1	1	1	0	1	1	1	1
0	0	1	1	0	0	1	1	1	1	0	1	1	1
0	0	1	1	0	1	1	1	1	1	1	0	1	1
0	0	1	1	1	0	1	1	1	1	1	1	0	1
0	0	1	1	1	1	1	1	1	1	1	1	1	0

Example 7–2 shows how the address range of the entire decoder is determined. Notice that the range is location F0000H–FFFFFH. This is a 64K-byte span of the memory.

How is it possible to determine the address range of each memory device attached to the decoder's outputs? Again, the binary bit pattern is written down, and this time the A, B, and C address inputs are *not don't cares*. Example 7–3 shows how output 0 of the decoder is made to go low to select the EPROM attached to that pin. Here C, B, and A are shown as logic 0s.

EXAMPLE 7–2

```
1111 XXXX XXXX XXXX XXXX
          or
1111 0000 0000 0000 0000 = F0000H
          to
1111 1111 1111 1111 1111 = FFFFFH
```

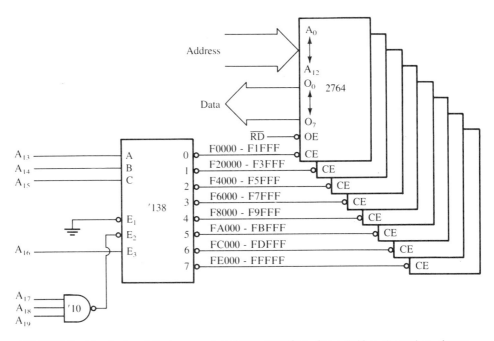

FIGURE 7–14 A circuit that uses eight 2764 EPROMs for a 64K × 8 section of memory in an 8088 microprocessor-based system. The addresses selected in this circuit are F0000H–FFFFFH.

EXAMPLE 7–3

```
      CBA
1111 000X XXXX XXXX XXXX
          or
1111 0000 0000 0000 0000 =F0000H
          to
1111 0001 1111 1111 1111 = F1FFFH
```

If the address range of the EPROM connected to output 1 of the decoder is required, it is determined in exactly the same way as that of output 0. The only difference is that now the C, B, and A inputs contain a 001 instead of a 000 (see Example 7–4). The remaining output address ranges are determined in the same manner by substituting the binary address of the output pin into C, B, and A.

EXAMPLE 7–4

```
      CBA
1111 001X XXXX XXXX XXXX
          or
```

```
1111 0010 0000 0000 0000 = F2000H
              to
1111 0011 1111 1111 1111 = F3FFFH
```

The Dual 2-to-4 Line Decoder (74LS139)

Another decoder that finds some application is the 74LS139 dual 2-to-4 line decoder. Figure 7–15 illustrates both the pinout and the truth table for this decoder. The 74LS139 contains two separate 2-to-4 line decoders—each with its own address, enable, and output connections.

PROM Address Decoder

The last of the common address decoders is the bipolar PROM, used because of its larger number of input connections, which reduces the number of other circuits required in a system memory address decoder. The 74LS138 decoder has six inputs used for address connections. Other types of the PROMs may have many more.

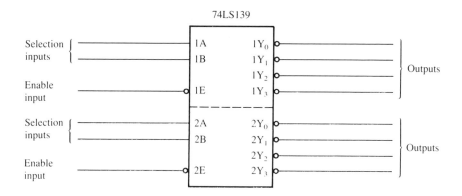

FIGURE 7–15 The pinout and truth table of the 74LS139, dual 2-to-4 line decoder.

$\overline{E}$	A	B	$\overline{Y_0}$	$\overline{Y_1}$	$\overline{Y_2}$	$\overline{Y_3}$
0	0	0	0	1	1	1
0	0	1	1	0	1	1
0	1	0	1	1	0	1
0	1	1	1	1	1	0
1	X	X	1	1	1	1

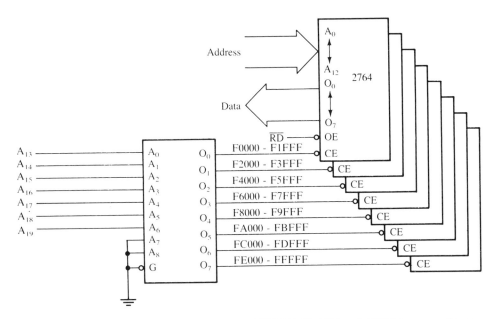

FIGURE 7-16 A memory system using the TPB28L42, 512 × 8 PROM as an address decoder.

For example, a TPB28L42 (512 × 8) PROM used as an address decoder has 10 input connections and 8 output connections. It can replace the circuit illustrated in Figure 7-14 without the extra 3-input NAND gate. This saves space on the printed circuit board and also reduces the cost of a system in volume production.

Figure 7-16 illustrates this address decoder with the PROM in place. The PROM is a memory device that must be programmed with the correct binary bit pattern to select the eight EPROM memory devices. The PROM itself has 9 address inputs that select one of the 512 internal 8-bit memory locations. The remaining input ($\overline{G}$) must be grounded because if this PROM's outputs float to their high-impedance state, then one or more of the EPROMs might be selected by noise impulses in the system.

Table 7-1 illustrates the binary bit pattern programmed into each PROM location in order to select the eight different EPROMs. The main advantage to using a PROM is that the address map is easily changed in the field. Because the PROM comes with all the locations programmed as logic 1s, only 8 of the 512 locations need to be programmed. This saves valuable time for the manufacturer.

PLA or PAL Programmable Decoders

The programmable logic array (PLA) or programmable array logic (PAL) is also a candidate for memory address decoding. This device is available in two types: one contains some internal flip-flop storage, and the other is merely a programmable combinational logic circuit. Only the second type is applicable to address decoding. The main problem with the PLA or PAL is that it doesn't offer as many output and input connections as the

TABLE 7–1   PROM programming bit pattern for Figure 7–16

$\overline{G}$	A_8	A_7	A_6	A_5	A_4	A_3	A_2	A_1	A_0	O_0	O_1	O_2	O_3	O_4	O_5	O_6	O_7
				Inputs									Outputs				
0	0	0	1	1	1	1	0	0	0	0	1	1	1	1	1	1	1
0	0	0	1	1	1	1	0	0	1	1	0	1	1	1	1	1	1
0	0	0	1	1	1	1	0	1	0	1	1	0	1	1	1	1	1
0	0	0	1	1	1	1	0	1	1	1	1	1	0	1	1	1	1
0	0	0	1	1	1	1	1	0	0	1	1	1	1	0	1	1	1
0	0	0	1	1	1	1	1	0	1	1	1	1	1	1	0	1	1
0	0	0	1	1	1	1	1	1	0	1	1	1	1	1	1	0	1
0	0	0	1	1	1	1	1	1	1	1	1	1	1	1	1	1	0
0			all other addresses							1	1	1	1	1	1	1	1

typical PROM. Today, the PAL or PLA is also more expensive. Therefore, in most cases, the PROM is the best choice for a programmed memory address decoder.

7–3   8088 MEMORY INTERFACE

This text contains separate sections on memory interfacing for the 8088 and the 8086 because the methods used to address the memory are slightly different in the two microprocessors. Hardware engineers or technicians who wish to broaden their expertise in interfacing 16-bit microprocessors should cover both sections. This section is much more complete than the section on the 8086 memory interface, which covers only material not covered in the 8088 section.

In this section, we examine the memory interface to both RAM and ROM and explain parity checking, which is becoming commonplace in many microprocessor-based computer systems. We also briefly mention error correction schemes currently available for memory systems.

Basic 8088 Memory Interface

The 8088 microprocessor has an 8-bit data bus, which makes it ideal to connect to the common 8-bit memory devices available today. For the 8088 to function correctly with the memory, however, the memory system must decode the address to select a memory component, and it must use the $\overline{RD}$, $\overline{WR}$, and IO/$\overline{M}$ control signals provided by the 8088 to control the memory.

The minimum mode configuration for the 8088 is used in this section and is essentially the same as the maximum mode system for memory interface. The main difference is that, in maximum mode IO/$\overline{M}$ is combined with $\overline{RD}$ to generate an $\overline{MRDC}$ signal, and IO/$\overline{M}$ is combined with $\overline{WR}$ to generate an $\overline{MWTC}$ signal. These maximum mode control signals are developed inside the 8288 bus controller. In the minimum mode, the memory sees the 8088 as a device with 20 address connections (A_{19}–A_0), 8 data bus connections (AD_7–AD_0), and the control signals IO/$\overline{M}$, $\overline{RD}$, and $\overline{WR}$.

Interfacing EPROM to the 8088.   You will find this section very similar to Section 7–2 on decoders. The only difference is that, in this section, we discuss wait states and the use of the IO/$\overline{M}$ signal to enable the decoder.

Figure 7–17 illustrates an 8088 microprocessor connected to eight 2732 EPROMs, 4K × 8 memory devices that are in very common use today. The 2732 has one more address input (A_{11}) than the 2716 and twice as much memory. The device in this illustration decodes eight 4K × 8 blocks of memory, or a total of 32K × 8 bits of the physical address space for the 8088.

The decoder is connected a little differently than might be expected because this type of EPROM has a memory access time of 450 ns. Recall from Chapter 6 that when the 8088 is operated with a 5-MHz clock, it allows 460 ns for memory access. Because of the decoder's added time delay, it is impossible for this memory to function within 460 ns. In order to correct this problem, the engineer must add a NAND gate to generate a signal to enable the decoder and a signal for the wait state generator, covered in Chapter 6. With a wait state inserted every time this section of the memory is accessed, the 8088 will allow 660 ns for the EPROM to access data. This is ample time for a 450-ns memory component to access data, even with the delays introduced by the decoder.

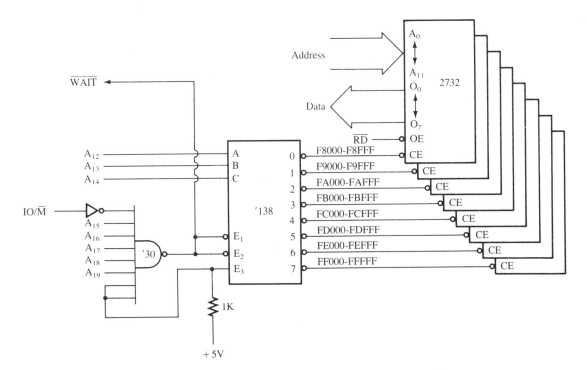

FIGURE 7–17 Eight 2732 EPROMs interfaced to the 8088 microprocessor. Note that the output of the NAND gate is used to cause a wait state whenever this section of the memory is selected.

Notice that the decoder is selected for a memory address range that begins at location F8000H and continues through location FFFFFH — the top 32K bytes of memory. This section of memory is an EPROM because FFFF0H is where the 8088 will start executing instructions after a hardware reset. The software stored in this section of memory contains a long JMP at location FFFF0H that jumps to location F8000H so that the remainder of the program can be executed.

Interfacing RAM to the 8088.   RAM is a little easier to interface than EPROM because most RAM memory components do not require wait states. An ideal section of the memory for the RAM is the very bottom, which contains vectors for interrupts. Interrupt vectors (discussed in more detail in Chapter 9) are often changed with different software packages, so it is rather important to encode this section of the memory with RAM.

In Figure 7–18 twenty-four 4016 2K × 8 static RAMS are interfaced to the 8088, beginning at memory location 00000H. This circuit board uses three decoders to select the twenty-four different RAM memory components and a fourth to select the other decoders for the appropriate memory sections. Twenty-four 2K RAMs fill memory from location 00000H through location 0BFFFH, for 48K bytes of memory.

The first decoder (A) in this circuit selects the other three decoders. An address beginning with 0000 00 selects decoder B, 0000 01 selects decoder C, and 0000 10 selects decoder D. Notice that five extra pins remain at the output of decoder A. These enable five more 16K × 8 blocks of RAM, for a total of 128K × 8, simply by adding the RAM and the extra secondary decoders.

Also notice from the circuit in Figure 7–18 that all the address inputs to this section of memory are buffered, as are the data bus connections and control signals $\overline{RD}$ and $\overline{WR}$. Buffering is important when many devices appear on a single board or in a single system. Suppose that three other boards like this are plugged into a system. Without the buffers on each board, the load on the system address, data, and control buses would be enough to prevent proper operation. (Excessive loading causes the logic 0 output to rise above the 0.8 V maximum allowed in a system.) Buffers are normally used if the memory will contain additions at some future date. If the memory will never grow, then buffers may not be needed.

Parity for Memory Error Detection

Because such large memories are available in today's systems, and because circuit costs are minimal, many memory board manufacturers have added parity checking to their RAM memory boards. Parity checking counts the number of 1s in data and indicates whether there is an even or odd number. If all data are stored as an even parity number (with an even number of 1s), a 1-bit error can be detected.

Figure 7–19 illustrates the 74AS280 parity generator/detector integrated circuit. This circuit has nine inputs and generates even or odd parity for the 9-bit number placed on its inputs. It also checks the parity of a 9-bit number connected to its inputs.

Figure 7–20 illustrates a 16K × 8 static RAM board that has parity generation and detection. Notice that a 74AS280 (A) generates a parity bit stored in one of four different TMS4044 4K × 1 RAM memories. Here the eight data bus connections are attached to the parity generator's inputs A–H. Input I is grounded so that if an even number of 1s appear on the data bus, a 1 (at the even output) is stored in the parity RAM. If an odd number of 1s appears, a 0 is stored in the parity RAM. Here odd parity is stored for each byte of data, including the parity bit written to the memory.

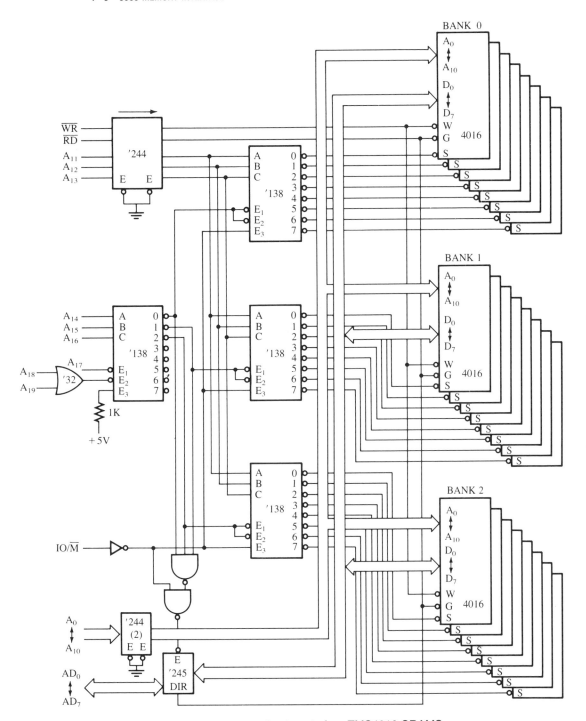

FIGURE 7–18 A 48K × 8 memory system using twenty-four TMS4016 SRAMS.

FIGURE 7–19 The pinout and function table of the 74AS280 9-bit parity generator/detector. (Courtesy of Texas Instruments Incorporated)

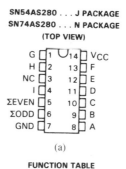

SN54AS280 . . . J PACKAGE
SN74AS280 . . . N PACKAGE
(TOP VIEW)

(a)

FUNCTION TABLE

NUMBER OF INPUTS A THRU I THAT ARE HIGH	OUTPUTS	
	Σ EVEN	Σ ODD
0,2,4,6,8	H	L
1,3,5,7,9	L	H

(b)

When data are read from the memory, each datum is connected to another 74AS280 (B) to check its parity. In this case, all the inputs to the checker are connected. Inputs A–H are connected to the data RAM's outputs, and input I is connected to the parity RAM. If parity is odd, as it is if everything is correct, the even parity output of the 74AS280 is a logic 0. If a bit of the information read from the memory changes for any reason, then the even output pin of the 74AS280 will become a logic 1.

This pin is connected to a special input of the 8088 called the nonmaskable interrupt (NMI) input. An NMI can never be turned off. If it is placed at its logic 1 level, the program being executed is interrupted, and a special subroutine indicates that a parity error has been detected by the memory system. (More detail on interrupts is provided in Chapter 9.)

The application of the parity error is timed so that the data read from the memory are settled to their final state before a NMI input occurs. The operation is timed by a D-type flip-flop that latches the output of the parity checker at the end of an $\overline{\text{RD}}$ cycle from this section of the memory. In this way, the memory has enough time to read the information and pass it through the generator before the output of the generator is sampled by the NMI input.

Error Correction

Error correction schemes have been around for a long time, but integrated circuit manufacturers have only recently started to produce error correcting circuits. One such circuit is the 74LS636, an 8-bit error correction and detection circuit that will automatically correct any single-bit memory read error and flag any 2-bit error.

This device corrects errors by storing 5 parity bits with each byte of memory data. This does increase the amount of memory required, but it also provides automatic correction of single-bit errors. If more than two bits are in error, this circuit may not detect it. Fortunately, this is rare, and the extra effort required to correct more than a single-bit error is very expensive and not worth the effort at this time. Whenever a memory component fails completely, its bits are all high or all low. In this case, the circuit flags the processor with a multiple-bit error indication.

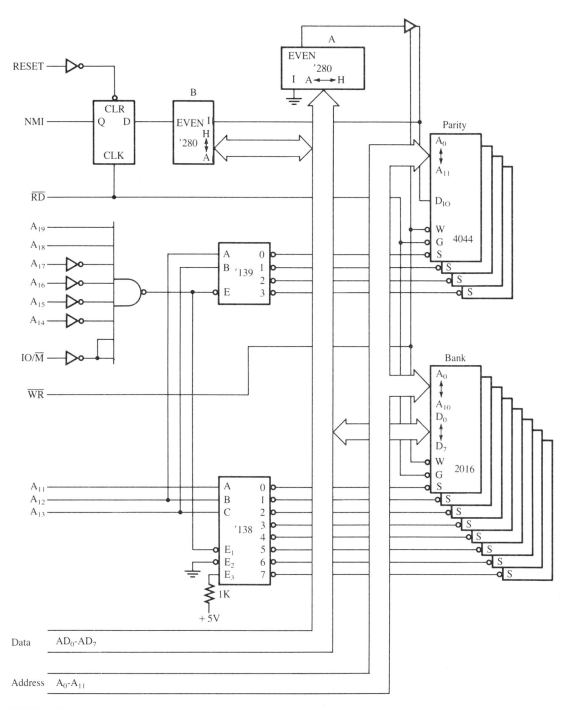

FIGURE 7–20   A 16K × 8 memory system that contains a parity error detection circuit.

Figure 7–21 depicts the pinout of the 74LS636. Notice that it has eight data I/O pins, five check bit I/O pins, two control inputs (S_0 and S_1), and two error outputs: single error flag (SEF) and double error flag (DEF). The control inputs select the type of operation to be performed and are listed in the truth table of Table 7–2.

When a single error is detected, the 74LS636 goes through an error correction cycle: it places a 01 on S_0 and S_1 by causing a wait and then a read following error correction.

Figure 7–22 illustrates a circuit used to correct single-bit errors with the 74LS636 and to interrupt the processor through the NMI pin for double-bit errors. To simplify the

pin assignments

J, N PACKAGES			
1	DEF	11	CB4
2	DB0	12	nc
3	DB1	13	CB3
4	DB2	14	CB2
5	DB3	15	CB1
6	DB4	16	CB0
7	DB5	17	SO
8	DB6	18	S1
9	DB7	19	SEF
10	GND	20	V_{CC}

(a)

functional block diagram

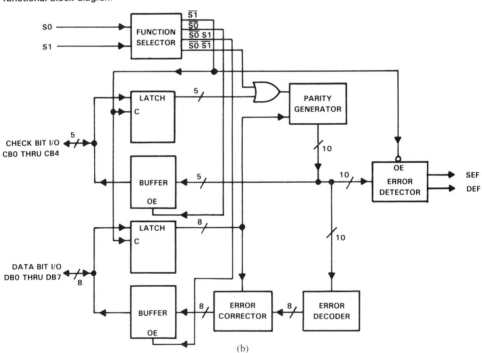

(b)

FIGURE 7–21 (a) The pin connections of the 74LS636. (b) The block diagram of the 74LS636. (Courtesy of Texas Instruments Incorporated)

TABLE 7–2 74LS636 control bits S_0 and S_1

			Error Flags	
S_0	S_1	Function	SEF	DEF
0	0	Write check word	0	0
0	1	Correct data word	*	*
1	0	Read data	0	0
1	1	Latch data	*	*

*These levels are determined by the type of error.

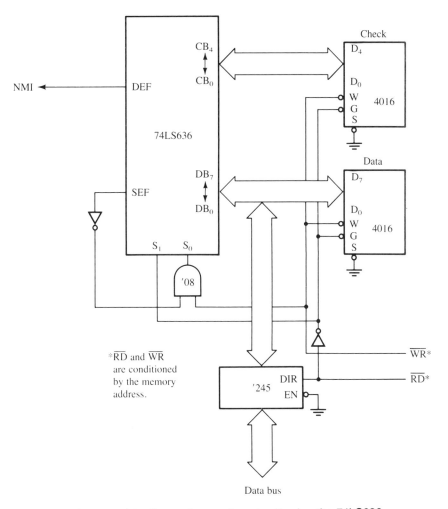

FIGURE 7–22 An error detection and correction circuit using the 74LS636.

illustration, we depict only one 2K × 8 RAM and a second 2K × 8 RAM to store the 5-bit check code.

The connection of this memory component is different from that of the previous example. Notice that the $\overline{S}$ or $\overline{CS}$ pin is grounded, and data bus buffers control the flow to the system bus. This is necessary if the data are to be accessed from the memory before the $\overline{RD}$ strobe goes low.

On the next negative edge of the clock after an $\overline{RD}$, the 74LS636 checks the single-error flag (SEF) to determine whether an error has occurred. If so, then a correction cycle causes the single-error defect to be corrected. If a double error occurs, then an interrupt request is generated by the double-error flag (DEF) output, which is connected to the NMI pin of the microprocessor.

7-4   8086 MEMORY INTERFACE

The 8086 microprocessor differs from the 8088 in three ways: (1) the data bus of the 8086 is 16 bits wide rather than 8 bits wide as on the 8088, (2) the IO/$\overline{M}$ bar pin of the 8088 is an M/$\overline{IO}$ pin on the 8086, and (3) there is a new control signal called *bus high enable* ($\overline{BHE}$). The address bit A_0 is also used differently. Because this section is based on information provided in Section 7-3, it is extremely important that you read the previous section first.

16-Bit Bus Control

The data bus of the 8086 is twice as wide as the bus for the 8088, and it has a unique set of problems that have not been encountered before. The 8086 must be able to write data to any 16-bit location or any 8-bit location. This means that the 16-bit data bus must be divided into two separate sections (banks) that are 8 bits in width so that the 8086 can write to either half or both halves. Figure 7-23 illustrates the two banks of the memory.

FIGURE 7-23 The high (odd) and low (even) 8-bit memory banks of the 8086 microprocessor.

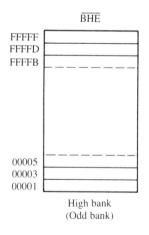

$\overline{BHE}$

FFFFF	
FFFFD	
FFFFB	
00005	
00003	
00001	

High bank
(Odd bank)

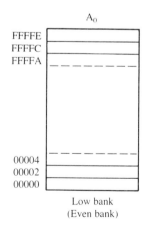

A_0

FFFFE	
FFFFC	
FFFFA	
00004	
00002	
00000	

Low bank
(Even bank)

One bank (low bank) holds all the even-numbered memory locations, and the other bank (high bank) holds all the odd-numbered memory locations.

The 8086 uses the $\overline{BHE}$ signal (high bank) and the A_0 address bit (low bank) to indicate whether one or both banks of memory are to be used in the data transfer. Table 7–3 depicts the logic levels on these two pins and the bank or banks selected.

Bank selection can be accomplished in two ways: (1) a separate $\overline{WR}$ signal can be developed for each bank of the memory, or (2) separate decoders can be used for each bank. As a careful comparison will reveal, the first technique is by far the least costly approach to memory interface for the 8086 microprocessor.

Separate Bank Decoders. The use of separate bank decoders is certainly the least effective way to handle memory address decoding for the 8086. This is sometimes done, but it is difficult to understand why.

Figure 7–24 illustrates two 74LS138 decoders used to select 64K RAM memory components. Here decoder A has the A_0 pin attached to $\overline{E}_1$, and decoder B has the $\overline{BHE}$ signal attached to its $\overline{E}_1$ input. Because the decoder will not activate until all its enable inputs are active, decoder A will only activate for a 16-bit operation or an 8-bit operation from the low bank, and decoder B will only activate for a 16-bit operation or an 8-bit operation to the high bank. These two decoders and the sixteen 64K-byte RAMs they control represent the entire 1M range of the memory. Yes, two decoders are used for the entire memory.

Notice from this figure that the A_0 address pin does not connect to the memory; instead it connects to the decoder. Also notice that address bus bit position A_1 is connected to memory address input A_0, A_2 is connected to A_1, and so forth. The reason is that A_0 from the 8086 is already connected to decoder A and does not need to be connected again to the memory. If A_0 is attached to the A_0 address pin of memory, every other memory location in each bank of memory would be used. This means that half of the memory is wasted if A_0 is connected to A_0.

Separate Bank $\overline{WR}$ Strobes. The most effective way to handle bank selection is to develop a separate write strobe for each memory bank. This technique requires only one decoder to select a 16-bit wide memory. This saves money in many systems and also reduces the number of components.

Why not separate $\overline{RD}$ strobes for each memory bank? This is an unnecessary expense, because the 8086 will read only the byte of data that it needs at any given time from the data bus. If 16-bit sections of data are always presented to the data bus during a read, the 8086 ignores the 8-bit sections it doesn't need without any conflicts.

TABLE 7–3 Truth table of $\overline{BHE}$ and A_0

$\overline{BHE}$	A_0	Function
0	0	Both banks active
0	1	High bank active
1	0	Low bank active
1	1	No banks active

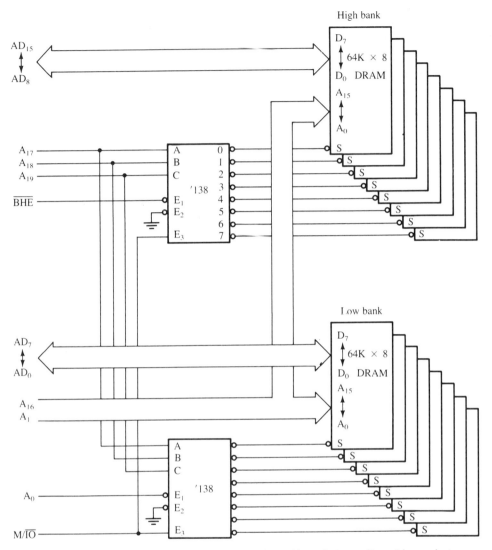

FIGURE 7–24   An 8086 1M byte memory interface. Note that no attempt is made to illustrate $\overline{RD}$, $\overline{WR}$, and the DRAM selection inputs $\overline{CAS}$ and $\overline{RAS}$.

Figure 7–25 depicts the generation of separate $\overline{WR}$ strobes for the memory. Here a 74LS32 OR gate combines A_0 with $\overline{WR}$ for the low bank selection signal ($\overline{LWR}$) and $\overline{BHE}$ with $\overline{WR}$ for the high bank selection signal ($\overline{HWR}$).

Figure 7–26 depicts a small memory system for the 8086 microprocessor that contains an EPROM section and a RAM section. Here there are eight 2764 EPROMs (8K × 8) that compose a 32K × 16-bit memory at location F0000H–FFFFFH and eight 4016 (2K × 8) RAMs that compose an 8K × 16-bit memory at location 00000H–03FFFH. (Remember that even though the memory is 16 bits wide, it is still numbered in bytes.)

FIGURE 7-25 The memory bank write selection inputs signals: $\overline{\text{HWR}}$ (high bank write) and $\overline{\text{LWR}}$ (low bank write).

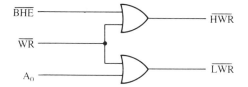

This circuit uses a 74LS139 dual 2-to-4 line decoder that selects EPROM with one half and RAM with the other half. It decodes memory that is 16 bits wide and not 8 bits as before. Notice that the $\overline{\text{RD}}$ strobe is connected to all the EPROM $\overline{\text{OE}}$ inputs and all the RAM $\overline{\text{G}}$ input pins. This is done because even if the 8086 is only reading 8 bits of data, the application of the remaining 8 bits to the data bus has no effect on the operation of the 8086.

The $\overline{\text{LWR}}$ and $\overline{\text{HWR}}$ strobes are connected to different banks of the RAM memory. Here it does matter if the microprocessor is doing a 16-bit or an 8-bit write. If the 8086 writes a 16-bit number to memory, both $\overline{\text{LWR}}$ and $\overline{\text{HWR}}$ go low and enable the $\overline{\text{W}}$ pins on both memory banks. But, if the 8086 does an 8-bit write, then only one of the write strobes goes low, writing to only one memory bank. Again, the only time that the banks make a difference is for a memory write operation.

Notice that an EPROM decoder signal is sent to the 8086 wait state generator because EPROM memory usually requires a wait state. The signal comes from the NAND gate used to select the EPROM decoder section so that if EPROM is selected, a wait state is requested.

7-5 DYNAMIC RAM CONTROLLERS

Because RAM memory in the 8086/8088 microprocessor is often very large, it requires many SRAM devices at a great cost or just a few DRAMs (dynamic RAMs) at a much reduced cost. DRAM memory, as briefly discussed in Section 7-1, is fairly complex because it requires address multiplexing and refreshing. Luckily, the integrated circuit manufacturers have provided a dynamic RAM controller that includes the address multiplexers and all the timing circuitry necessary for refreshing.

This section of the text covers the DRAM memory device in much more detail than Section 7-1 and provides information on the use of a dynamic RAM controller in a memory system.

DRAM Revisited

As mentioned in Section 7-1, a DRAM retains data for only 2-4 ms and requires the multiplexing of address inputs. We have already covered address multiplexers in Section 7-1, but we will examine the operation of the DRAM during refresh in detail here.

As we mentioned previously, a DRAM must be refreshed periodically because it stores data internally on capacitors that lose their charge in a short period of time. In order to refresh a DRAM, the contents of a section of the memory must periodically be read or

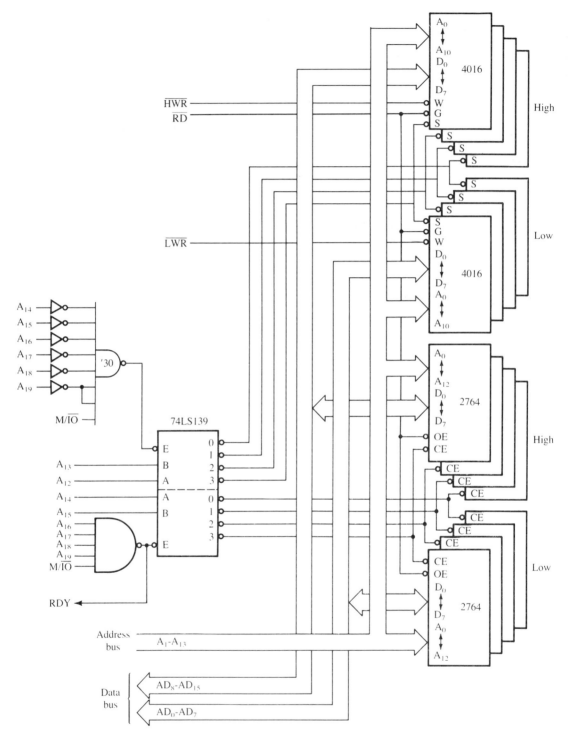

FIGURE 7–26 The 8086 interfaced to a 32K × 16 EPROM (F0000H–FFFFFH) and an 8K × 16 SRAM (00000H–03FFFH).

written. Any read or write will automatically refresh an entire section of bits inside the DRAM. The number of bits refreshed depends on the size of the memory component and its internal organization.

Refresh cycles can therefore be accomplished by doing a read, a write, or a special refresh cycle that doesn't read or write data. The refresh cycle is totally internal to the DRAM and can be accomplished while other memory components in the system operate. This type of refresh is called either *hidden refresh, transparent refresh,* or sometimes *cycle stealing.*

In order to accomplish a hidden refresh while other memory components are functioning, an $\overline{RAS}$-only cycle strobes a row address into the DRAM to select the row of bits to be refreshed. $\overline{RAS}$ also causes the selected row to be read out internally and rewritten into the selected bits. This recharges the internal capacitors that store the data. This type of refresh is hidden from the system because it occurs while the microprocessor is reading or writing to other sections of the memory.

The DRAM's internal organization contains a series of rows and columns. A 64K × A DRAM has 256 columns, each containing 256 bits, or rows. Whenever a memory location is addressed, the column address selects a column (or internal memory word) of 256 bits.

Figure 7–27 illustrates the timing for an $\overline{RAS}$-only refresh cycle. The main difference between the $\overline{RAS}$ and a read or write is that it applies *only* a refresh address, which is usually obtained from a 7- or 8-bit binary counter. The size of the counter is determined by the type of DRAM being refreshed. The refresh counter is incremented at the end of each refresh cycle so that all the rows will be refreshed in 2 or 4 ms, depending on the type of DRAM.

If there are 256 rows to be refreshed within 4 ms, as in a 64K × 4 DRAM, then the refresh cycle must be activated at least once every 15.6 μs in order to meet the refresh specification. For example, it takes the 8086/8088, running at a 5-MHz clock rate, 800 ns to do a read or a write. Because the DRAM must have a refresh cycle every 15.6 μs, this means that for every 19 memory reads or writes, the memory system must run a refresh cycle or memory data will be lost. This represents loss of 5 percent of the computer's time, a small price to pay for the savings represented by using the dynamic RAM.

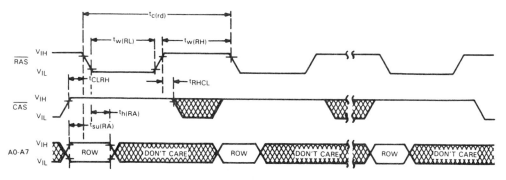

FIGURE 7–27 The timing diagram of the $\overline{RAS}$ refresh cycle for the TMS4464 DRAM. (Courtesy of Texas Instruments Corporation)

DRAM Controllers

Of the many DRAM controllers available, this text focuses on the TMS4500A (see Figure 7-28 for a block diagram). Like all dram controllers, the TMS4500A contains address multiplexers and some mechanisms for requesting a refresh, but, unlike the others, it does not need a special high-frequency clock signal for proper operation during a refresh. Notice that the TMS4500A has the internal multiplexer, the refresh counter, and all the timing necessary to accomplish a refresh.

Pin Description.   A complete understanding of the operation of the TMS4500A depends upon familiarity with the function of the pins described here:

1. RA_7–RA_0—Row Address Inputs: the pins connected to the microprocessor's address bus. They are often connected to address bus bits A_7–A_0.
2. CA_7–CA_0—Column Address Inputs: pins that are also connected to the address bus. If the row address inputs are connected to A_7–A_0, then these inputs are connected to A_{15}–A_8. The order of these connections doesn't really matter.
3. MA_7–MA_0—Memory Address Outputs: the pins connected directly to DRAM address pins A_7–A_0.
4. ALE—Address Latch Enable Input: a pin used to latch the 16 address inputs applied to RA_7–RA_0 and CA_7–CA_0, $\overline{CS}$, and REN_1. Notice how these latches

FIGURE 7-28   The block diagram of the TMS4500A dynamic RAM controller. (Courtesy of Texas Instruments Corporation)

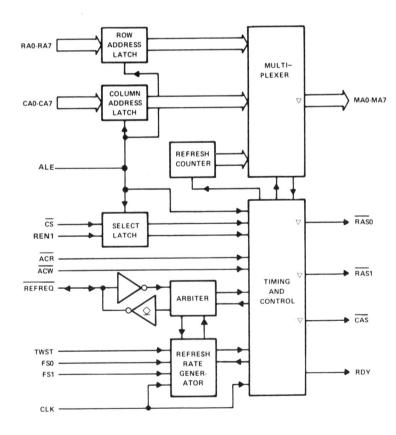

replace the address latches discussed in Chapter 6 if DRAM is the only memory in a system. Because this input must be active to cause a cycle, it must be connected to ALE.

5. $\overline{CS}$—Chip Select Input: the pin that starts a memory read or write from the DRAMs connected to the DRAM controller whenever it is a logic 0 at ALE's 1–0 transition.

6. REN_1—$\overline{RAS}$ Enable Input: the pin that selects one of two banks of DRAMs connected to the DRAM controller. (Notice that there are two $\overline{RAS}$ outputs.) When REN_1 is high, $\overline{RAS}_1$ is selected, and when it is low, $\overline{RAS}_2$ is selected.

7. $\overline{ACR}$—Access Control Read Input: the pin used to end a memory read cycle on the 0–1 transition. This pin is connected to the 8086/8088 minimum mode $\overline{RD}$ control signal or the $\overline{MRDC}$ signal for maximum mode operation.

8. $\overline{ACW}$—Access Control Write Input: the pin used to end a memory write cycle on the 0–1 transition. It is connected to $\overline{WR}$ or $\overline{MWTC}$.

9. CLK—Clock Input: the pin connected to the system clock of the 8086/8088 microprocessor.

10. REFREQ—Refresh Request: the pin used as an input to start a refresh cycle or as an output to indicate that an internal refresh cycle is in progress.

11. $\overline{RAS}_1$, $\overline{RAS}_0$—Row Address Strobes: the pins connected to the DRAM $\overline{RAS}$ inputs. Both go low for a refresh operation, but only one goes low during a read or a write. REN_1 selects which goes low during a memory operation.

12. $\overline{CAS}$—Column Address Strobe: the pin connected to the $\overline{CAS}$ inputs to all of the DRAM memories in both memory banks.

13. RDY—Ready Output: the pin connected to the RDY input of the 8284A clock generator. RDY becomes active when the DRAM controller does an internal refresh cycle.

14. TWST—Timing/Wait Strap Input: the pin used to select waits and/or certain timing constraints when used with the FS_1 and FS_0 inputs. A logic 1 on this pin will insert one wait state for every memory access.

15. FS_0, FS_1—Frequency Select Inputs: the pins used to select various mode and frequency options (refer to Table 7–4).

TABLE 7-4 Mode selection for the DRAM controller

TWST	FS_1	FS_0	Wait States	Refresh Rate	Minimum Clock (MHz)	Refresh Freq. (kHz)	Clocks per Refresh
0	0	0	0	External	—	REFREQ	4
0	0	1	0	CLK ÷ 31	1.984	64–95	3
0	1	0	0	CLK ÷ 46	2.944	64–85	3
0	1	1	0	CLK ÷ 61	3.904	64–82	4
1	0	0	1	CLK ÷ 46	2.944	64–85	3
1	0	1	1	CLK ÷ 61	3.904	64–80	4
1	1	0	1	CLK ÷ 76	4.864	64–77	4
1	1	1	1	CLK ÷ 91	5.824	64–88	4

TMS4500A Operation

Figure 7–29 illustrates the basic connection of the DRAM controller to the buses of the 8088 microprocessor in the minimum mode configuration. Here the $\overline{RD}$ and $\overline{WR}$ pins arc connected to the $\overline{ACR}$ and $\overline{ACW}$ pins, respectively. The $\overline{CS}$ input is connected to a 4-input NAND gate used to decode the three most significant address bits. REN_1 is connected to address bus connection A_{16} so that it selects one bank of memory or the other. If A_{16} is high, then the bank attached to $\overline{RAS}_1$ is selected, and if it is low, the bank that connects to $\overline{RAS}_0$ is selected. In this example, two banks of 64K × 8 DRAMs are selected for a total of 128K × 8 of memory. The address range begins at location 00000H and extends through location 1FFFFH.

The programming pins TWST, FS_1, and FS_0 are selected (0, 1, and 1) so that there are no waits, the refresh occurs every 61 clocks, and there are 4 clocks for every refresh. This will ensure that a refresh occurs once every 12.2 ms, which is well within the tolerance of the 15.6 ms calculated earlier.

When an internal clocking signal is generated every 61 clock periods, an internal refresh request occurs. The request is delayed until current bus cycle is completed, which

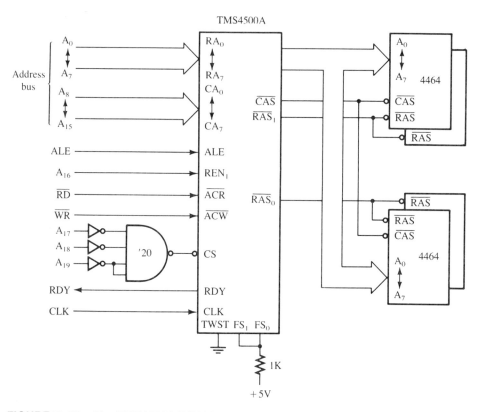

FIGURE 7–29   The TMS4500A DRAM controller used to interface to 128K bytes of DRAM. Here four TMS4464 DRAMs provide the memory located at locations 00000H–1FFFFH.

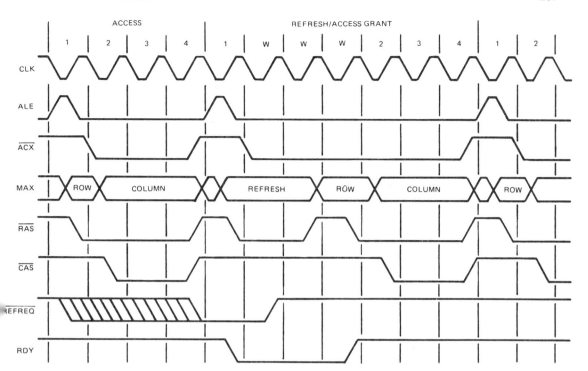

FIGURE 7–30 The timing for the TMS4500A dynamic RAM controller. (Courtesy of Texas Instruments Corporation)

can add another four clocks to the time. When the request is finally honored, the RDY pin goes to a logic 0. This causes wait states to be inserted while the DRAM controller refreshes the memory. After the refresh is completed, the bus is free to do a read or a write until the next refresh request.

Figure 7–30 shows the timing diagram for the TMS4500A during the request for and completion of a refresh. Notice that the RDY line goes low to request wait states during the refresh operation.

7–6 SUMMARY

1. All memory devices have address inputs; data inputs and outputs, or just outputs; a pin for selection; and one or more pins that control the operation of the memory.
2. Address connections on a memory component are used to select one of the memory locations within the device. Ten address pins have 1,024 combinations and therefore are able to address 1,024 different memory locations.
3. Data connections on a memory are used to enter information to be stored in a memory location and also to retrieve information read from a memory location. Manufacturers

list their memory as, for example, 4K × 4, which means that the device has 4K memory locations (4,096) and 4 bits are stored in each location.

4. Memory selection is accomplished via a chip selection pin ($\overline{CS}$) on many RAMs or a chip enable pin ($\overline{CE}$) on many EPROM or ROM memories.

5. Memory function is selected by an output enable pin (OE) for reading data and a write enable pin ($\overline{WE}$) for writing data.

6. EPROM memory is programmed by an EPROM programmer and can be erased if exposed to ultraviolet light. Today EPROMs are available in sizes from 1K × 8 all the way up to 64K × 8 and larger.

7. Static RAM (SRAM) retains data for as long as the system power supply is attached. These memory types are available in sizes up to 2K × 8.

8. Dynamic RAM (DRAM) retains data for only a short period, usually 2–4 ms. This creates problems for the memory system designer because the DRAM must be refreshed periodically. DRAMs also have multiplexed address inputs that require an external multiplexer to provide each half of the address at the appropriate time.

9. Memory address decoders select an EPROM or RAM at a particular area of the memory. Commonly found address decoders include the 74LS138 3-to-8 line decoder, the 74LS139 2-to-4 line decoder, and programmed selection logic in the form of a PROM.

10. PROM address decoders for microprocessors like the 8088 or the 8086 tend in many cases to reduce the number of integrated circuits required to complete a functioning memory system.

11. The 8088 minimum mode memory interface contains 20 address lines, 8 data lines, and 3 control lines: $\overline{RD}$, $\overline{WR}$, and IO/$\overline{M}$. The 8088 memory will function correctly only when all these lines are used.

12. The access speed of the EPROM must be compatible with the microprocessor to which it is interfaced. Many EPROMs available today have an access time of 450 ns, which is too slow for the 5-MHz 8088. In order to circumvent this problem, a wait state must be inserted to increase memory access time to 660 ns.

13. Parity checkers are becoming commonplace today in many 8086/8088-based microcomputer systems. An extra bit is stored with each byte of memory, making the memory 9 bits wide instead of 8.

14. Error correction features are also available for memory systems, but these require the storage of many more bits. If an 8-bit number is stored with an error correction circuit, it actually takes 13 bits of memory: 5 for an error checking code and 8 for the data. Most error correction integrated circuits are able to correct only a single-bit error.

15. The 8086 memory interface has a 16-bit data bus and contains an M/$\overline{IO}$ control pin, whereas the 8088 has an 8-bit data bus and contains an IO/$\overline{M}$ pin. In addition to these changes, there is an extra control signal, bus high enable ($\overline{BHE}$).

16. The 8086 memory is organized in two 8-bit banks: high bank and low bank. The high bank of memory is enabled by the $\overline{BHE}$ control signal and the low bank by the A_0 address signal.

17. Two common schemes for selecting the banks in an 8086-based system include (1) a separate decoder for each bank and (2) separate $\overline{WR}$ control signals for each bank with a common decoder.

18. Dynamic RAM controllers are designed to control DRAM memory components. Many DRAM controllers today contain address multiplexers, refresh counters, and the circuitry required to do a periodic DRAM memory refresh.

7–7 QUESTIONS AND PROBLEMS

1. What types of connections are common to all memory devices?
2. List the number of words found in each memory device for the following numbers of address connections:
   a. 8
   b. 11
   c. 12
   d. 13
3. List the number of data items stored in each of the following memory devices and the number of bits in each datum:
   a. 2K × 4
   b. 1K × 1
   c. 4K × 8
   d. 16K × 1
   e. 64K × 4
4. What is the purpose of the $\overline{CS}$ or $\overline{CE}$ pin on a memory component?
5. What is the purpose of the $\overline{OE}$ pin on a memory device?
6. What is the purpose of the $\overline{WE}$ or R/$\overline{W}$ pin on a RAM?
7. How many words of storage do the following EPROM memory devices contain?
   a. 2708
   b. 2716
   c. 2732
   d. 2764
   e. 27128
8. Why won't a 450-ns EPROM work directly with a 5-MHz 8088?
9. SRAM is an acronym for what type of device?
10. The 4016 memory has a $\overline{G}$ pin, an $\overline{S}$ pin, and a $\overline{W}$ pin. What are these pins used for in this RAM?
11. How much memory access time is required by the slowest 4016 RAM?
12. DRAM is an acronym for what type of device?
13. The TMS4464 has eight address inputs, yet it is a 64K DRAM. Explain how a 16-bit memory address is forced into eight address inputs.
14. What are the purposes of the $\overline{CAS}$ and $\overline{RAS}$ inputs of a DRAM?
15. How much time is required to refresh the typical DRAM?
16. Why are memory address decoders important?
17. Modify the NAND gate decoder of Figure 7–12 so that it selects the memory for address range DF800H–DFFFFH.
18. Modify the NAND gate decoder in Figure 7–12 so that it selects the memory for address range 40000H–407FFH.

19. When the $\overline{E}_1$ input is high and $\overline{E}_2$ and E_3 are both low, what happens to the outputs of the 74LS138 3-to-8 line decoder?

20. Modify the circuit of Figure 7–14 so that it addresses memory range 70000H–7FFFFH.

21. Modify the circuit of Figure 7–14 so that it addresses memory range 40000H–4FFFFH.

22. Describe the 74LS139 decoder.

23. Why is a PROM address decoder often found in a memory system?

24. Reprogram the PROM in Table 7–1 so that it decodes memory address range 80000H–8FFFFH.

25. Reprogram the PROM in Table 7–1 so that it decodes memory address range 30000H–3FFFFH.

26. The $\overline{RD}$ and $\overline{WR}$ minimum mode control signals are replaced by what two control signals in the maximum mode?

27. Modify the circuit of Figure 7–17 so that it selects memory at location 68000H–6BFFFH.

28. Modify the circuit of Figure 7–17 so that it selects eight 2764 8K × 8 EPROMs at memory location 10000H–1FFFFH.

29. Add another decoder to the circuit of Figure 7–18 so that an additional eight 4016 2K × 8 SRAMs are added at location 10000H–13FFFFH.

30. Redesign the main decoder in Figure 7–18 so that memory addressing begins at location 80000H.

31. Explain how odd parity is stored in a memory system and how it is checked.

32. The 74LS636 error correction and detection circuit stores a check code with each byte of data. How many bits are that check code?

33. What is the purpose of the SEF pin on the 74LS636?

34. The 74LS636 will correct _____ bits that are in error.

35. Outline the major difference between the buses of the 8086 and 8088 microprocessors.

36. What is the purpose of the $\overline{BHE}$ and A_0 pins on the 8086 microprocessor?

37. What two methods are used to select the memory in the 8086 microprocessor?

38. If $\overline{BHE}$ is a logic 0, then the _____ memory bank is selected.

39. If A_0 is a logic 0, then the _____ memory bank is selected.

40. Why don't separate bank read ($\overline{RD}$) strobes need to be developed when interfacing memory to the 8086?

41. Modify the circuit of Figure 7–27 so that the EPROM is located at memory range C0000H–CFFFFH and the RAM is located at memory range 30000H–33FFFH.

42. What is an $\overline{RAS}$-only cycle?

43. When DRAM is refreshed, can it be done while other sections of the memory operate?

44. If a 16K × 1 DRAM requires 2 ms for a refresh and has 128 rows to be refreshed, no more than _____ time must pass before another row is refreshed.

45. Where is the memory address applied to the TMS4500A DRAM controller?

46. What is the purpose of the REN_1 pin on the TMS4500A?

47. What is normally connected to the $\overline{ACW}$ pin of the TMS4500A?

48. What operating condition on the TMS4500A is TWST used to select?

49. Modify the circuit of Figure 7–29 so that it selects memory address range 40000H–5FFFFH.

CHAPTER 8

Basic I/O Interface

INTRODUCTION

A microprocessor is great at solving problems, but if it can't communicate with the outside world, it is of little worth. This chapter outlines some of the basic methods of communication, both serial and parallel, between human and microprocessor.

In this chapter, we will first introduce the basic I/O interface and discuss decoding. Then we will provide detail on parallel and serial interfacing, both of which have a wide variety of applications in the field.

OBJECTIVES

Upon completion of this chapter, you will be able to:

1. Explain the operation of the basic input/output device.
2. Decode an 8- or 16-bit I/O device so that it can be used at any I/O port address.
3. Define handshaking and explain how to use it with many I/O devices.
4. Interface and program the 8255 programmable parallel interface component.
5. Interface and program the 8279 programmable keyboard/display interface component.
6. Interface and program the 8254 programmable interval timer.
7. Interface and program the 8251A communications interface adapter.

8–1   ## BASIC I/O INTERFACE

In this section of the text, we explain the operation of the I/O instructions (IN and OUT), the concept of isolated I/O (sometimes called direct I/O) and memory-mapped I/O, the basic input and output interfaces, and handshaking. A working knowledge of these topics will make it easier to understand the connection and operation of the programmable interface components and I/O techniques presented in the remainder of this chapter and text.

I/O Instructions

The 8086/8088 instruction set contains one instruction to transfer information to an I/O device (OUT) and another to read information from an I/O device (IN). Four different versions of each of these instructions are available: two versions transfer 8- or 16-bit data using an 8-bit I/O address, and two versions transfer 8- or 16-bit data via a 16-bit I/O address. All eight instructions are listed in Table 8–1.

Both the IN and OUT instructions transfer data between an I/O device and the microprocessor. The I/O address is stored in register DX as a 16-bit I/O address or in the byte (d8) immediately following the opcode as an 8-bit I/O address. Intel calls the 8-bit address *fixed* because it is stored with the instruction, usually in a ROM. The 16-bit address is called *variable* because it is stored in a register, which can be varied.

Whenever data are transferred by IN or OUT instructions, the I/O address, often called a *port number,* appears on the address bus. The external I/O interface then decodes it in much the same manner as a memory address is decoded. If the port number is 8 bits, then it appears on A_7–A_0, and if it is 16 bits, it appears on A_{15}–A_0. In many systems, both types of I/O instructions can use an 8-bit port number because A_{15}–A_8 is decoded only if there are more than 256 I/O devices, which is rare in most systems except for computer systems like a PC that uses a 16-bit I/O address.

TABLE 8–1   Input/output instructions

Instruction	Data Width	Comment
IN AL,d8	8	Reads a byte from I/O address d8
IN AL,DX	8	Reads a byte from the I/O address indexed by register DX
IN AX,d8	16	Reads a word from I/O address d8
IN AX,DX	16	Reads a word from the I/O address indexed by register DX
OUT d8,AL	8	Writes a byte to I/O address d8
OUT DX,AL	8	Writes a byte to the I/O address indexed by register DX
OUT d8,AX	16	Writes a word to I/O address d8
OUT DX,AX	16	Writes a word to the I/O address indexed by register DX

Note: d8 is an 8-bit I/O address, and DX contains a 16-bit I/O address.

Isolated and Memory-Mapped I/O

There are two completely different methods of interfacing I/O to the 8086/8088 micro-processor: *isolated I/O* and *memory-mapped I/O*. In isolated I/O (or direct I/O, as it is sometimes called), IN and OUT transfer data between the microprocessor and an I/O device. In memory-mapped I/O, any instruction that references the memory can accomplish the transfer. Both methods are used in the field, so both will be discussed in this text.

Isolated I/O. The most common I/O transfer technique is isolated I/O, in which the I/O devices in a system are isolated from the memory. (Figure 8–1 provides an illustration of the memory and isolated I/O maps.) The addresses of isolated I/O devices, called I/O ports, are separate from the memory. As a result, the user can expand the memory to a full 1M bytes without using any of the memory space for I/O devices. A disadvantage of isolated I/O is that the data transferred between the I/O device and the microprocessor

FIGURE 8–1 The memory and I/O maps for the 8086/8088 microprocessor. (a) Isolated I/O. (b) Memory-mapped I/O.

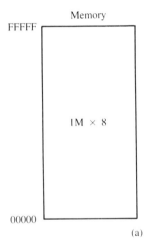

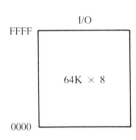

(a)

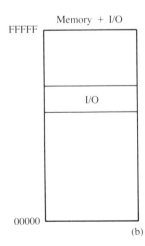

(b)

must be in either AL or AX. The IO/$\overline{\text{M}}$ signal (8088) or the M/$\overline{\text{IO}}$ signal (8086) indicates whether the address bus contains a memory address or an I/O port number.

Memory-Mapped I/O.   Unlike isolated I/O, memory-mapped I/O does not use the IN and OUT instructions to transfer data. Rather, it uses any instruction that transfers data between the microprocessor and memory. A memory-mapped I/O device is treated as a memory location in the memory map. The main disadvantage of this I/O technique is that it uses up part of the memory space. Therefore, no system that uses memory-mapped I/O can contain 1M bytes of memory. An advantage is that the IO/$\overline{\text{M}}$ (8088) or M/$\overline{\text{IO}}$ (8086) need not be used for decoding, because I/O instructions have no meaning in this system and are therefore never used.

Basic Input/Output Interface

The basic input device is a set of eight or sixteen three state buffers, and the basic output device is an 8- or 16-bit latch.

Basic Input Interface.   Eight three-state buffers are used to construct the 8-bit input port depicted in Figure 8–2. Notice that the external TTL data (simple toggle switches in this example) are connected to the inputs of the buffers, and the outputs of the buffers are attached to the 8086/8088 address/data bus. This connection allows the microprocessor to read the data from the address/data bus during an IN instruction into the AL or AX register, if a 16-bit buffer and sixteen switches are used with Figure 8–2.

When the 8086/8088 executes an IN, the I/O port address is decoded and generates a logic 0 on the control input to the buffers. A 0 on the control inputs causes the buffers

FIGURE 8–2   The basic input port using switches as input devices. Note the 72LS244 is a set of eight 3-state buffers that control the application of the switch data to the system data bus.

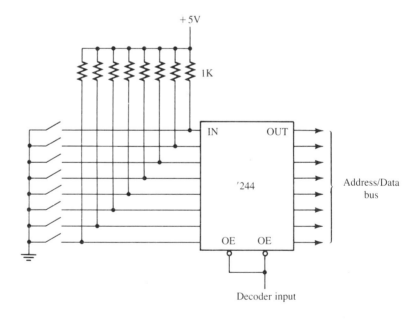

to pass the data from the switches through to the address/data bus where they are read into the AL or AX register.

This basic input circuit is not optional. It is always included inside an input device, or, if none exists, then it must be present as illustrated. Only simple switch-type inputs use the buffers as illustrated in the figure.

Basic Output Interface.   The basic output interface receives data from the microprocessor and must usually hold the data for some external device. Its latches, like those of the input interface, are also often built into the I/O device.

Figure 8–3 illustrates some simple light-emitting diodes (LEDs) connected to the microprocessor. Notice here that a latch is used to store the number that is output to the LEDs with the OUT instruction. Latches are needed to hold the data because the microprocessor takes only slightly longer than a microsecond to send data to an output device. Without a latch, the viewer would never see the LEDs illuminate.

When the OUT instruction is executed, the data from AL or AX are transferred to the latch via the address/data bus connections. Here the address/data bus is connected to the D inputs of the 74LS374 octal latch, and the outputs (Q) are connected to the eight LEDs. In this circuit, if a logic 0 is output to Q, the LED will light. Each time an OUT is executed, the decoder (not pictured) develops a clock pulse for the octal latch capturing the output from the address/data bus.

Handshaking

Many I/O devices accept or release information at a much slower rate than the microprocessor. Another method of I/O control, called *handshaking* or *polling,* synchronizes the I/O device with the microprocessor.

For example, if a printer is able to print only 100 characters per second (CPS), then the program to print information must slow down the microprocessor to match speeds with

FIGURE 8–3   The basic output port using LEDs as output devices. Note that the 74LS374 is an octal latch used to hold the data output from the microprocessor for the LEDs.

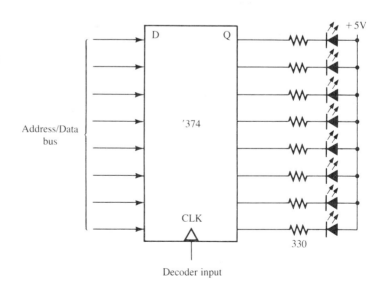

Address/Data bus

D   Q

'374

CLK

330

+5V

Decoder input

FIGURE 8-4   An interface between a printer and a computer system.

the printer. Figure 8-4 illustrates the typical input and output connections to a printer: data (D_7-D_0), BUSY, and $\overline{STB}$. The data inputs and $\overline{STB}$ are connected to an output port, and the BUSY line is connected to an input port.

The data (ASCII) to be printed are placed on D_7-D_0, and a pulse is sent to the $\overline{STB}$ input. The strobe input signals the printer that data are available. The printer responds by beginning to print the data and also by placing its BUSY pin at a logic 1 level. The BUSY pin tells the microprocessor not to send any more data. For the microprocessor to determine whether or not the printer is able to accept another character for printing, it must input the BUSY signal and check to see if it is a logic 0—not busy. This interrogation process is called a *handshake* or a *poll*.

Example 8-1 illustrates the software used to handshake with or poll the printer. Notice how the BUSY flag is tested to see if the printer is busy. When the printer is busy, the subroutine continues jumping to PRINT. If the printer is not busy, the subroutine outputs the data in the BL register to the printer. In this example, it is assumed that sending the data out to the printer also causes the $\overline{STB}$ signal to be activated.

EXAMPLE 8-1

```
                    ;procedure to print tne contents of the BL register
                    ;on the printer.
                    ;
0000                PRINT    PROC     NEAR

0000  E4 4B                  IN       AL,BUSY       ;input busy flag
0002  A8 04                  TEST     AL,BUSY_BIT   ;test it
0004  74 FA                  JE       PRINT         ;if busy
0006  8A C3                  MOV      AL,BL         ;print character
0008  E6 4A                  OUT      PRINTER,AL
000A  C3                     RET

000B                PRINT    ENDP
```

8–2 I/O PORT ADDRESS DECODING

I/O port address decoding is very similar to memory address decoding, especially with memory-mapped I/O devices. In fact, we do not discuss memory-mapped I/O decoding here because it is treated exactly the same as memory, except that the IO/$\overline{\text{M}}$ (8088) or M/$\overline{\text{IO}}$ (8086) signal is not used, since there is no IN or OUT instruction. The decision to use memory-mapped I/O is often determined by the types of I/O devices in a system.

The main difference between memory decoding and isolated I/O decoding is the number of address pins that must be decoded: A_{19}–A_0 for memory and A_{15}–A_0 or A_7–A_0 for isolated I/O. Another difference is the activity level of the IO/$\overline{\text{M}}$ (8088) or M/$\overline{\text{IO}}$ (8086) signal. In an isolated I/O system IO/$\overline{\text{M}}$ or M/$\overline{\text{IO}}$ must be used to decide the I/O address.

8-Bit and 16-Bit I/O Decoders (8088)

Eight-bit and 16-bit I/O devices are decoded differently in the 8086 microprocessor, but not in the 8088. This is because the data bus in the 8088 is 8 bits wide, so that a 16-bit IN or OUT simply transfers two consecutive bytes to two consecutive I/O port numbers. Figure 8–5 illustrates a decoder that generates the enable signals for eight different I/O devices in a system that uses only an 8-bit port number. Because most systems do not contain more than 256 different I/O devices, it is rather unusual to have to decode a 16-bit port number. All the examples in this text therefore assume an 8-bit port number even if register DX is used in the IN or OUT instruction.

Notice that the 8088 IO/$\overline{\text{M}}$ signal is used in this circuit along with address bits A_7–A_0 as inputs to the decoder. The outputs of this decoder will become active only when an I/O operation is performed (IO/$\overline{\text{M}}$) at isolated I/O port addresses 00H–07H. The outputs are used as clock pulses for latches when combined with the $\overline{\text{WR}}$ signal or as enable signals for three-state buffers when combined with the $\overline{\text{RD}}$ signal. Figure 8–6 illustrates how the $\overline{\text{RD}}$ and $\overline{\text{WR}}$ signals are combined with the $\overline{00\text{H}}$ output of this decoder to generate an $\overline{\text{RD } 00\text{H}}$ and a $\overline{\text{WR } 00\text{H}}$ strobe.

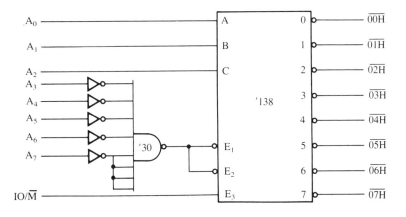

FIGURE 8–5 An I/O port decoder for the 8088 microprocessor that develops I/O enable signals for I/O ports 00H–07H.

FIGURE 8–6 A circuit that develops the $\overline{RD}$ and $\overline{WR}$ strobe signals for I/O port 00H.

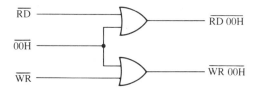

It is normally necessary to generate $\overline{RD}$ and $\overline{WR}$ strobes only when the I/O device is a buffer or a latch. The programmable I/O devices that are generally interfaced to microprocessors today generate the strobes internally via a connection to $\overline{RD}$, $\overline{WR}$, and IO/$\overline{M}$ (8088) or M/$\overline{IO}$ (8086). The most common I/O port decoder is the type found in Figure 8–6.

Systems that require latches and buffers are more likely to use a circuit such as that depicted in Figure 8–7. Here the $\overline{RD}$ and $\overline{WR}$ signals, as well as IO/$\overline{M}$, are connected to the decoder. This connection develops four $\overline{RD}$ strobes and four $\overline{WR}$ strobes for an 8088-based system. Notice that the port addresses are the same for pairs of I/O $\overline{RD}$ and $\overline{WR}$ strobes.

8-Bit I/O Decoders (8086)

Because the address and memory structure of the 8086 differs from that of the 8088, its 8-bit data transfers to I/O differ as well. The fact that the memory and I/O of the 8086 are organized into banks presents a problem for 8-bit I/O. Which bank is used? Are both banks used? The easiest and best approach in an 8086 system is to locate all the 8-bit I/O in one of the memory banks. If the I/O is located in the high bank, then $\overline{BHE}$ decodes the I/O address; if the I/O is located in the low bank, A_0 decodes the address. In both cases, the M/$\overline{IO}$ signal distinguishes the I/O port address from a memory address.

Figure 8–8 illustrates two decoders: one decodes the high bank and the other the low bank. Notice that the address is decoded in the same way as it was by the memory decoders discussed in Chapter 7. A_0 is not treated as an address pin, but as a signal used to select the low memory bank—in this case, the low I/O bank.

In this example, the low bank decoder develops the even I/O enable signals for ports F0H, F2H, F4H, F6H, F8H, FAH, FCH, and FEH. The high bank decoder develops the odd I/O enable signals for ports F1H, F3H, F5H, F7H, F9H, FBH, FDH, and FFH. The total of sixteen 8-bit I/O port numbers decoded here is often more than required even in medium-sized systems.

16-Bit I/O Decoders (8086)

Whenever 16-bit I/O devices are connected to the 8086, the $\overline{BHE}$ and A_0 pins are both ignored because they have significance only for 8-bit banks. The only commonly available 16-bit I/O devices are the analog-to-digital converter (ADC) and the digital-to-analog converter (DAC). These devices are usually 10 or 12 bits wide. They do not directly fit an 8-bit data bus but do fit a 16-bit data bus. Most microprocessor-compatible DAC and ADC circuits are designed to work with an 8-bit data bus even if the ADC or DAC is more than 8 bits wide.

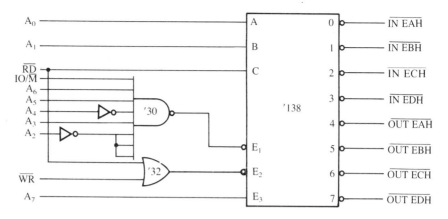

FIGURE 8–7 A 74LS138 decoder that develops four IN strobes and four OUT strobes for the 8088 microprocessor.

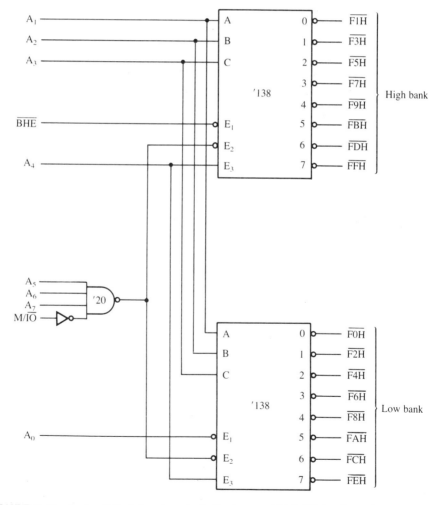

FIGURE 8–8 A circuit that develops both the low and high I/O bank strobes for the 8086 microprocessor.

FIGURE 8–9 A circuit that uses the 74LS138 to generate 16-bit I/O port strobes for the 8086 microprocessor.

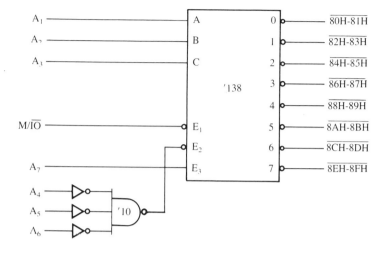

Figure 8–9 depicts a 16-bit decoder. Here 16-bit ports 80H–8FH are decoded. Only address bits A_7–A_1 and control line M/$\overline{\text{IO}}$ are connected to the decoder because, as in most cases, there are not enough I/O devices in the system to justify the use of a 16-bit port address decoder. Whenever memory is addressed as a 16-bit number, two 8-bit memory locations are accessed. Here the first 16-bit port is located at 80H and 81H. 80H represents the least significant 8 bits and 81H the most significant 8 bits of the 16 bits of I/O data.

8–3   THE 8255A PROGRAMMABLE PERIPHERAL INTERFACE

The 8255A programmable peripheral interface (PPI) is a very popular low-cost interfacing component found in many applications today. It has 24 pins for I/O, programmable in groups of 12, that are used in three separate modes of operation. The 8255A can interface any TTL-compatible I/O device to either the 8086 or 8088 microprocessor.

Basic Description of the 8255A

Figure 8–10 illustrates the pinout and block diagram of the 8255A. Its three 8-bit I/O ports (labeled A, B, and C) are programmed in groups of 12 pins. Programming group A consists of port A (PA_7–PA_0) and the upper half of port C (PC_7–PC_4), and programming group B consists of port B (PB_7–PB_0) and the lower half of port C (PC_3–PC_0). The 8255A is selected by a $\overline{\text{CS}}$ pin. Address bits A_1 and A_0 internally choose one of the ports or the command register for programing. Table 8–2 illustrates the I/O port numbers for programming.

This is a fairly simple device to connect to the 8086/8088 microprocessor. For the 8255A to do a read or a write, the $\overline{\text{CS}}$ pin must be low, and the correct internal I/O device location must be applied to the A_1 and A_0 inputs. The remaining port address pins are

PIN CONFIGURATION

PA3	1		40	PA4
PA2	2		39	PA5
PA1	3		38	PA6
PA0	4		37	PA7
RD	5		36	WR
CS	6		35	RESET
GND	7		34	D0
A1	8		33	D1
A0	9		32	D2
PC7	10	8255A	31	D3
PC6	11		30	D4
PC5	12		29	D5
PC4	13		28	D6
PC0	14		27	D7
PC1	15		26	VCC
PC2	16		25	PB7
PC3	17		24	PB6
PB0	18		23	PB5
PB1	19		22	PB4
PB2	20		21	PB3

PIN NAMES

D_7-D_0	DATA BUS (BI DIRECTIONAL)
RESET	RESET INPUT
CS	CHIP SELECT
RD	READ INPUT
WR	WRITE INPUT
A0, A1	PORT ADDRESS
PA7-PA0	PORT A (BIT)
PB7-PB0	PORT B (BIT)
PC7-PC0	PORT C (BIT)
V_{CC}	+5 VOLTS
GND	0 VOLTS

8255A BLOCK DIAGRAM

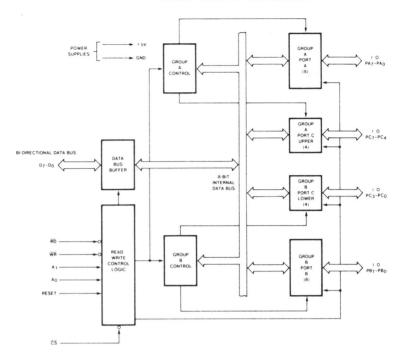

FIGURE 8–10   The pinout and block diagram of the 8255A programmable peripheral interface. (Courtesy of Intel Corporation)

TABLE 8–2   I/O port selection for the 8255A

A_7	A_6	A_5	A_4	A_3	A_2	A_1	A_0	Function
X	X	X	X	X	X	0	0	Port A
X	X	X	X	X	X	0	1	Port B
X	X	X	X	X	X	1	0	Port C
X	X	X	X	X	X	1	1	Command

Note: X = *don't cares* selected by external coding logic.

don't cares connected to an external decoder. In Figure 8–11, the 8255A is connected to the 8088 so that it functions at I/O ports C0H (port A), C1H (port B), C2H (port C), and C3H (command). Notice that the only pin connected to the 8088 besides $\overline{WR}$, $\overline{RD}$, A_1, A_0, and the data bus connections is RESET. The RESET input is used to set up ports A, B, and C as input ports when power is first applied to the system. This prevents any damage to the devices that are connected to the 8255A. After the RESET, no other commands are required to program all 8255A ports as input devices.

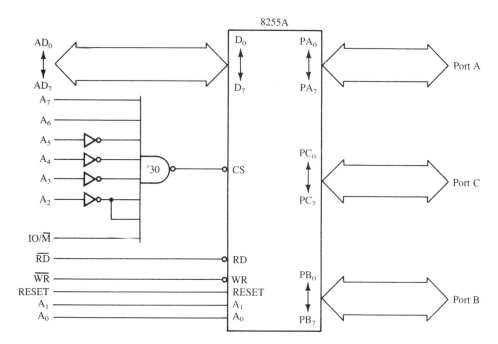

FIGURE 8-11   The 8255A programmable peripheral interface connected to the 8088 microprocessor.

Programming the 8255A

The 8255A is a rather simple device to program because it has only two internal command registers, as depicted in Figure 8-12. Figure 8-12(a) shows the main command word, which allows the user to program groups A and B separately. This word is selected when a 1 is output in the leftmost bit position of the command.

The group B pins (port B and lower port C) can be programmed as either inputs or outputs. Group B also allows the selection of either the mode 0 or mode 1 operation. Mode 0 is basic input/output, which means that the I/O pins are programmed as straight input or output port pins. Mode 1 is strobed input or output, which means that for group B, port B is either an input or an output, with the handshaking (polling) for port B supplied by port C.

Group A programs port A and the upper half of port C as input or output ports in modes 0 and 1 and as bidirectional pins in mode 2. Mode 0 is basic I/O for ports A and C; mode 1 is strobed I/O for port A, with port C acting as handshaking signals; and mode 2 sets up port A as a bidirectional bus with handshaking on port C.

If a 0 is placed in the leftmost bit of the command register (see Figure 8-12(b)), then the bits of port C can be set or reset if operated in mode 1 or 2. (*Note:* This command word will not function if port C is programmed in mode 0.) Each bit of port C is addressable by this command word, so any bit can be set or reset. This command and the

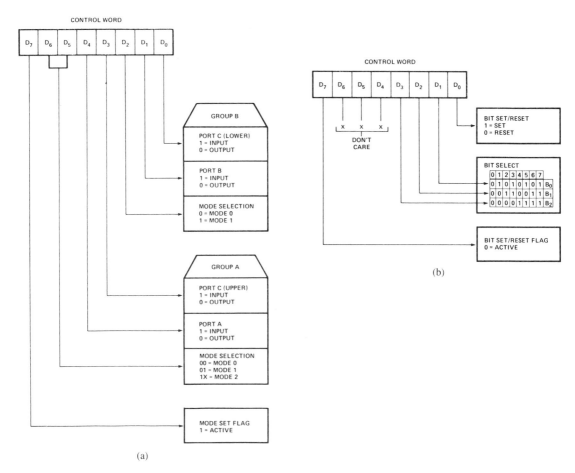

FIGURE 8-12   8255A command words. (a) Programs ports A, B, and C. (b) Sets or resets any bit of port C as long as port C is programmed in modes 1 or 2. Note that the leftmost bit selects the type of control word. (Courtesy of Intel Corporation)

pins of port C are useful for generating control strobe signals, as a mode 1 example later in this section will demonstrate.

Mode 0 Example

Figure 8-13 illustrates an 8255A connected to an eight-digit multiplexed LED display. In this example, both ports A and B are programmed as simple output ports. Port A provides the segment inputs of the displays with the seven-segment coded data, and port B selects a display position. Example 8-2 shows the software required to program the 8255A for this application. Notice that the leftmost bit of the command word is a 1. This selects the command that programs the ports. In this case, both group A and group B are programmed for mode 0 outputs (see Figure 8-12(a) for the command word).

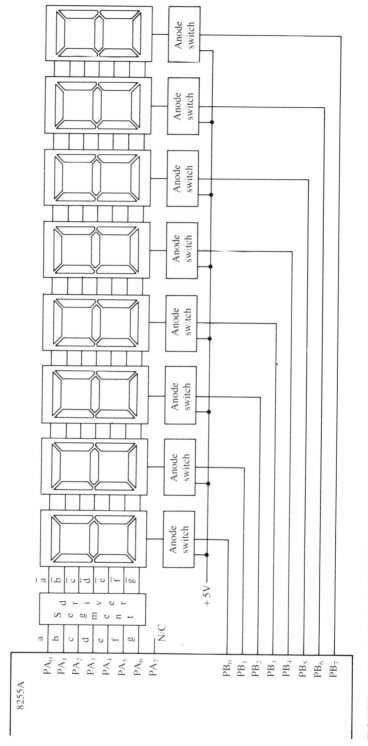

FIGURE 8–13 An 8-digit LED display using the 8255A in mode 0 operation.

224

EXAMPLE 8-2

```
                        ;Software to initialize the 8255A
                        ;
0000  B0 80             MOV        AL,10000000B  ;set up command
0002  E6 F0             OUT        COMMAND,AL    ;program 8255A
```

The procedure to display data on these LEDs appears in the listing of Example 8–3. This procedure saves all the registers that it uses first and then loads BX with a count of 8, AH with a pattern that selects the display digits, and SI with the address of the display RAM minus 1. This display RAM contains the eight seven-segment codes to be displayed on each digit. Next, a digit is selected, and data from the display RAM are sent to port A, which connects to the segments of the displays. After the information is displayed, a 1-ms delay procedure is called (not shown) to slow the rate of display scanning. The manufacturers of most LED displays state that the scan rate—the number of times a display flashes—should be about 100 times a second. To complete the procedure, the contents of AH are rotated to select the next digit, and the count is decremented to determine whether all the digits have had data displayed on them.

For the information to remain visible, this procedure must be frequently called from another program, most commonly by an interrupt that ensures continual display regardless of the activity of the program. Chapter 9 deals with interrupts in more detail.

EXAMPLE 8-3

```
                        ;Procedure to scan the eight digits of the
                        ;multiplexed LED display.  This procedure must
                        ;be called continuously from a program to
                        ;display information.
                        ;

0000              DISPLAY   PROC     NEAR

0000  9C                    PUSHF                   ;save registers
0001  50                    PUSH     AX
0002  53                    PUSH     BX
0003  56                    PUSH     SI

              ;Setup registers

0004  BB 0008             MOV        BX,8
0007  B4 7F               MOV        AH,7FH
0009  BE FFFF R           MOV        SI,OFFSET DISPLAY_RAM-1

              ;Display eight digits

000C                      DISPLAY1:

000C  8A C4               MOV        AL,AH         ;select digit
000E  E6 02               OUT        PORTB,AL
0010  8A 00               MOV        AL,[BX+SI]    ;get display data
0012  E6 01               OUT        PORTA,AL
```

```
0014   E8 0110 R              CALL      DELAY        ;wait 1 ms
0017   D0 CC                  ROR       AH,1         ;adjust select code
0019   4B                     DEC       BX
001A   75 F0                  JNZ       DISPLAY1     ;repeat 8 times

001C   5E                     POP       SI           ;restore registers
001D   5B                     POP       BX
001E   58                     POP       AX
001F   9D                     POPF
0020   C3                     RET

0021                          DISPLAY   ENDP
```

Mode 1 Strobed Input

Mode 1 operation selects handshaking for port A or port B through the port C pins. Figure 8–14 illustrates the internal configuration of the 8255A for strobed input operation under mode 1 and also the mode 1 strobed input timing diagrams.

Signal Definitions for Mode 1 Strobed Input.

1. $\overline{STB}$—Strobe: an input used to load data into the port latch, which holds the information until it is input to the microprocessor via an IN instruction.
2. IBF—Input Buffer Full: an output that indicates the input latch contains information. The $\overline{STB}$ signal causes IBF to become a logic 1, and the IN instruction clears it to a 0.
3. INTR—Interrupt Request: an output used to request an interrupt. INTR becomes a logic 1 when the $\overline{STB}$ signal becomes a logic 1 and is cleared when the IN instruction is executed.
4. INTE—Interrupt Enable: neither an input nor an output, but an internal bit programmed via the bit set and reset command word. INTE A is programmed as bit position PC_4 and INTE B as bit position PC_2.
5. PC_7, PC_6—Port Pins 6 and 7: general-purpose I/O pins in mode 1 strobed input operation. The bit set and reset command word controls them.

Strobed Input Example.
An excellent example of a strobed input device is a keyboard. The keyboard encoder debounces the keyswitch and provides a strobe whenever a key is depressed; the data outputs contain the ASCII character typed on the keyboard. Figure 8–15 illustrates the keyboard connected to strobed input port A. Here the $\overline{DAV}$ signal from the keyboard becomes active for 1 μs when a key is pressed. The $\overline{DAV}$ pulse is applied to the $\overline{STB}$ input of port A, causing IBF (PC_5) to become a logic 1 and the ASCII data from the keyboard to be held or strobed into an internal port A latch.

Port C control signal information is read whenever port C is read; there is no special I/O port for this. So, if an IN AL, PORTC instruction is executed, bit position 5 of the AL register will contain PC_5 or IBF from port A.

A procedure that reads this keyboard and returns with the character from the keyboard in the AL register appears in Example 8–4.

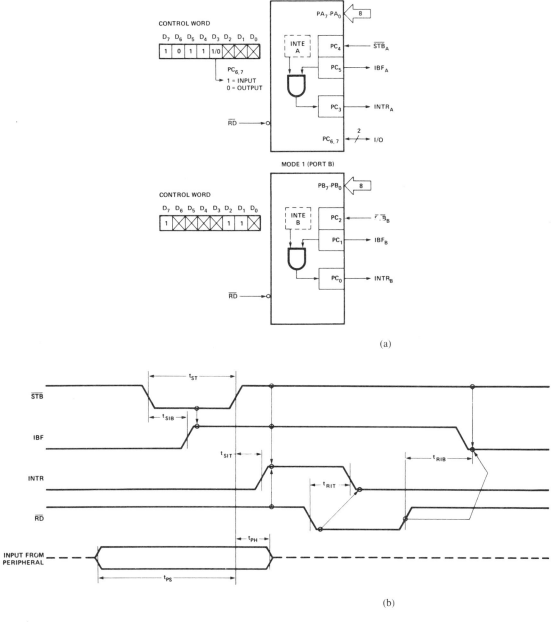

FIGURE 8–14 Strobed input operation of the 8255A. (a) Internal structure. (b) Timing diagrams. (Courtesy of Intel Corporation)

FIGURE 8–15 Using the
8255A for strobed input operation of a keyboard.

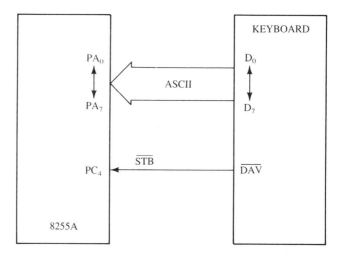

EXAMPLE 8–4

```
                ;Procedure that reads an ASCII character from the
                ;keyboard via Port A.
                ;
                ;ASCII data found in AL after a return.
                ;
= 0020              BIT5      EQU       20H        ;mask for PC5
                ;
0000                READ_KEY  PROC      NEAR

0000  E4 03                   IN        AL,PORTC   ;input IBF
0002  A8 20                   TEST      AL,BIT5    ;check IBF
0004  74 FA                   JZ        READ_KEY   ;if IBF = 0
0006  E4 01                   IN        AL,PORTA   ;read data
0008  C3                      RET


0009                READ_KEY  ENDP
```

Mode 1 Strobed Output

Figure 8–16 illustrates the internal configuration and the timing diagram of the 8255A
when it is operated as a strobed output under mode 1.

Signal Definitions for Mode 1 Strobed Output.

1. $\overline{OBF}$—Output Buffer Full: an output that goes low whenever data are output (OUT) to
   the port A or port B latch. This signal is set to a logic 1 whenever the $\overline{ACK}$ pulse
   returns from the external device, indicating it has received the data, and is cleared
   when data are written to the port.
2. $\overline{ACK}$—Acknowledge Input: a signal that causes the $\overline{OBF}$ pin to return to a logic 1
   level. $\overline{ACK}$ is a response from the external device that indicates it has received the data
   from the 8255A.

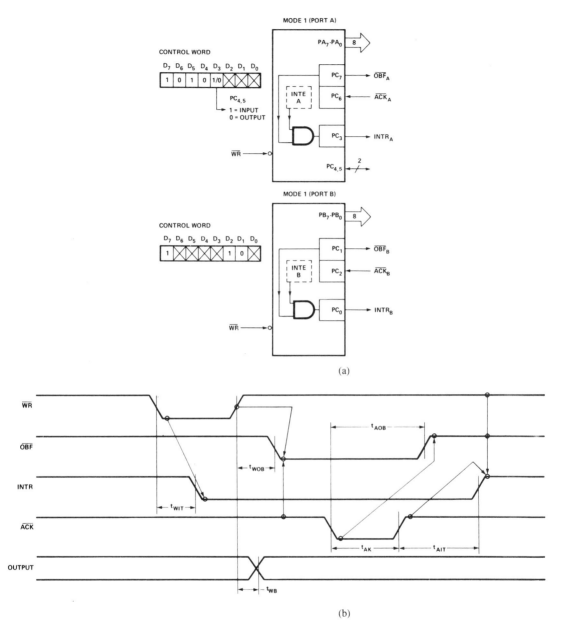

FIGURE 8-16 Strobed output operation of the 8255A. (a) Internal structure. (b) Timing diagrams. (Courtesy of Intel Corporation)

3. INTR—Interrupt Request: a signal that interrupts the processor when the external device sends the $\overline{ACK}$ signal back to the 8255A.
4. INTE—Interrupt Enable: neither an input nor an output, but an internal bit programmed via the bit set and reset command word. INTE A is programmed as bit position PC_6, and INTE B as bit position PC_2.
5. PC_5, PC_4—Port Pins 5 and 4: general-purpose I/O pins in strobed output operation of mode 1. The bit set and reset command word controls these pins.

Strobed Output Example.   The printer interface discussed in Section 8–1 is used here to demonstrate how to achieve strobed output operation. Figure 8–17 illustrates port B connected to a parallel printer with eight data inputs for receiving ASCII-coded data, a $\overline{DS}$ input to strobe the data into the printer, and an $\overline{ACK}$ output to acknowledge the receipt of the ASCII character.

In this circuit, there is no signal to generate the $\overline{DS}$ input to the printer, so PC_4 is used along with software that generates the $\overline{DS}$ signal. The $\overline{ACK}$ signal that is returned from the printer acknowledges receipt of data. The software for this interface is illustrated in Example 8–5. Here the procedure first tests $\overline{OBF}$ to find out whether the printer is available. If the output buffer is full, the procedure waits until it is empty before printing the character in AH. If it is empty, the character is sent to the printer, and the software generates the $\overline{DS}$ signal.

EXAMPLE 8–5

```
                    ;Procedure that transfers the contents of the
                    ;AH register to the printer.
                    ;
  = 0002            BIT1      EQU       2H
                    ;
  0000              PRINT     PROC      NEAR

                    ;check printer ready

  0000   E4 03                IN        AL,PORTC  ;get OBF
  0002   A8 02                TEST      AL,BIT1   ;test OBF
  0004   74 FA                JZ        PRINT     ;if OBF = 0

                    ;send character

  0006   8A C4                MOV       AL,AH
  0008   E6 02                OUT       PORTB,AL

                    ;send DS

  000A   B0 08                MOV       AL,8        ;clear DS
  000C   E6 00                OUT       COMMAND,AL
  000E   B0 09                MOV       AL,9        ;set DS
  0010   E6 00                OUT       COMMAND,AL
  0012   C3                   RET

  0013              PRINT     ENDP
```

FIGURE 8-17 The 8255A
connected to a parallel
printer interface that illustrates the strobed output
mode of operation for the
8255A.

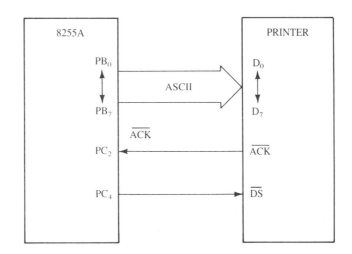

Mode 2 Bidirectional Operation

In mode 2 operation, which is allowed only for group A, port A becomes bidirectional, allowing data to be transmitted or received over the same eight wires. Bidirectional bused data are useful when interfacing two computers. Figure 8-18 illustrates the internal configuration band timing diagram for mode 2 bidirectional operation.

Signal Definitions for Bidirectional Mode 2 Operation.

1. INTR—Interrupt Request: an output used to interrupt the processor for both input and output conditions.
2. $\overline{OBF}$—Output Buffer Full: an output that indicates that the output buffer contains data for the bidirectional bus.
3. $\overline{ACK}$—Acknowledge: an input that enables the three-state output connections of the bidirectional bus to send data. If $\overline{ACK}$ is a logic 1, the bidirectional bus is in its high-impedance state.
4. $\overline{STB}$—Strobe: an input used to load the input latch from the bidirectional bus.
5. IBF—Input Buffer Full: an output that indicates that the input buffer is loaded with data.
6. INTE—Interrupt Enable: an internal bit that allows the INTR pin to function. The state of INTE is controlled with the bit set and reset command word. INTE 1 is controlled by bit PC_6, and INTE 2 by PC_4.
7. PC_2–PC_0—general-purpose I/O pins in mode 2 controlled by the bit set and reset command word.

The Bidirectional Bus. The bidirectional bus can be used only if all input (IN) and output (OUT) instructions reference port A. To transmit data through the bidirectional bus, the program checks the $\overline{OBF}$ signal to determine whether the output buffer is empty. If it is, then the data are sent to the buffer with an OUT instruction. The external circuit also monitors $\overline{OBF}$ and extracts data from the buffer by activating the $\overline{ACK}$ input. $\overline{ACK}$ turns on the three-state output buffers so the external device can retrieve the data and also places $\overline{OBF}$ back at its logic 1 level. Example 8-6 shows the software procedure required to transmit the data in register AH through the bidirectional bus.

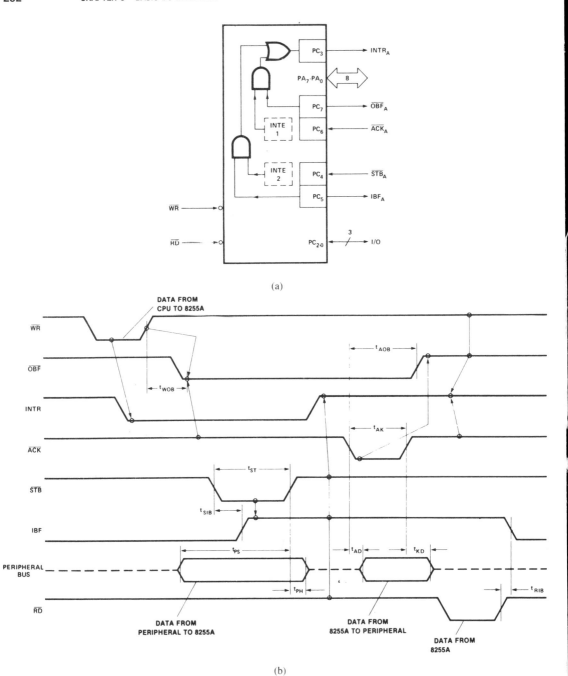

(a)

(b)

FIGURE 8–18   Mode 2 operation of the 8255A. (a) Internal structure. (b) Timing diagram. (Courtesy of Intel Corporation)

EXAMPLE 8-6

```
                ;Procedure that transfers AH through the bidirectiona
                ;bus of Port A
                ;
= 0080          BIT7        EQU       80H        ;OBF test bit
0000            TRANSMIT    PROC      NEAR

                ;test OBF

0000 E4 03                  IN        AL,PORTC   ;get status
0002 A8 80                  TEST      AL,BIT7    ;check OBF
0004 74 FA                  JZ        TRANSMIT   ;if full

                ;SEND DATA

0006 8A C4                  MOV       AL,AH      ;get data
0008 E6 01                  OUT       PORTA,AL   ;send data
000A C3                     RET

000B            TRANSMIT    ENDP
```

To receive data through the bidirectional bus of port A, the IBF bit is tested with software to determine whether data are available at port A. These data are then input with an IN instruction. The external interface sends data into the bus by activating the $\overline{STB}$ signal, which latches the data into port A and causes IBF to go high. When IBF is a logic 1, it indicates that the port contains data for the microprocessor. Example 8-7 lists a procedure that will check IBF and input data to the AL register before returning.

EXAMPLE 8-7

```
                ;Procedure that inputs data from the bidirectional
                ;bus and saves it in AL.
                ;
= 0200 BIT5 EQU 20H                        ;IBF test bit

0000            RECEIVE     PROC      NEAR

        ;check IBF

0000 E4 03                  IN        AL,PORTC   ;get status
0002 A8 20                  TEST      AL,BIT5    ;check IBF
0004 74 FA                  JZ        RECEIVE    ;if no data

        ;read data

0006 E4 01                  IN        AL,POTA    ;get data
0008 C3                     RET

0009            RECEIVE     ENDP
```

	MODE 0		MODE 1		MODE 2
	IN	OUT	IN	OUT	GROUP A ONLY
PA_0	IN	OUT	IN	OUT	◄────►
PA_1	IN	OUT	IN	OUT	◄────►
PA_2	IN	OUT	IN	OUT	◄────►
PA_3	IN	OUT	IN	OUT	◄────►
PA_4	IN	OUT	IN	OUT	◄────►
PA_5	IN	OUT	IN	OUT	◄────►
PA_6	IN	OUT	IN	OUT	◄────►
PA_7	IN	OUT	IN	OUT	◄────►
PB_0	IN	OUT	IN	OUT	───
PB_1	IN	OUT	IN	OUT	───
PB_2	IN	OUT	IN	OUT	───
PB_3	IN	OUT	IN	OUT	───
PB_4	IN	OUT	IN	OUT	───
PB_5	IN	OUT	IN	OUT	───
PB_6	IN	OUT	IN	OUT	───
PB_7	IN	OUT	IN	OUT	───
PC_0	IN	OUT	$INTR_B$	$INTR_B$	I/O
PC_1	IN	OUT	IBF_B	$\overline{OBF}_B$	I/O
PC_2	IN	OUT	$\overline{STB}_B$	$\overline{ACK}_B$	I/O
PC_3	IN	OUT	$INTR_A$	$INTR_A$	$INTR_A$
PC_4	IN	OUT	$\overline{STB}_A$	I/O	$\overline{STB}_A$
PC_5	IN	OUT	IBF_A	I/O	IBF_A
PC_6	IN	OUT	I/O	$\overline{ACK}_A$	$\overline{ACK}_A$
PC_7	IN	OUT	I/O	$\overline{OBF}_A$	$\overline{OBF}_A$

MODE 0
OR MODE 1
ONLY

FIGURE 8–19 The mode definition summary of the 8255A programmable peripheral interface. (Courtesy of Intel Corporation)

Mode Summary

As the preceding section indicates, the 8255A is a very flexible peripheral interface component. It can be used in applications that range from simple I/O to complex I/O requiring handshaking and bidirectional buses. Figure 8–19 provides a summary of the three operating modes for the 8255A.

8–4   THE 8279 PROGRAMMABLE KEYBOARD/DISPLAY INTERFACE

The 8279 is a programmable keyboard and display interfacing component that can scan and encode up to a 64-key keyboard and up to a 16-digit numerical display. The keyboard section of this integrated circuit has a built-in first-in, first-out (FIFO) buffer that allows it to store up to eight keyboard characters before the microprocessor must retrieve a character. The display section can scan up to 16 numeric displays from an internal 16×8 RAM memory that stores the coded display patterns.

Basic Description of the 8279

As we shall see, the 8279 is designed for easy interfacing with the 8086 or 8088 microprocessor. Figure 8–20 illustrates the pinout, pin names, and logic symbol for the 8279.

Pin Definitions for the 8279.

1. DB_7–DB_0—Data Bus: bidirectional pins that connect to the address/data bus of the 8086/8088 microprocessor.
2. CLK—Clock: an input used to generate internal timing for the 8279. It is normally connected to the PCLK pin of the 8284A clock generator in an 8086/8088-based system.
3. RESET—Reset: an input that connects to the RESET pin of the 8086/8088 microprocessor.
4. $\overline{CS}$—Chip Select: an input used to enable the 8279 for programming, reading keyboard and status information, and writing control and display data.
5. A_0—Address Input A_0: a pin used to select data or control for reads and writes between the microprocessor and the 8279. A logic 0 on the pin selects data, and a logic 1 selects control.
6. $\overline{RD}$—Read: an input directly connected to the 8086/8088 $\overline{RD}$ pin in minimum mode or the $\overline{IORDC}$ pin in maximum mode.
7. $\overline{WR}$—Write: an input directly connected to the 8086/8088 $\overline{WR}$ pin in minimum mode or the $\overline{IOWTC}$ pin in maximum mode.
8. IRQ—Interrupt Request: an output that becomes a logic 1 whenever keyboard data are available for the microprocessor.

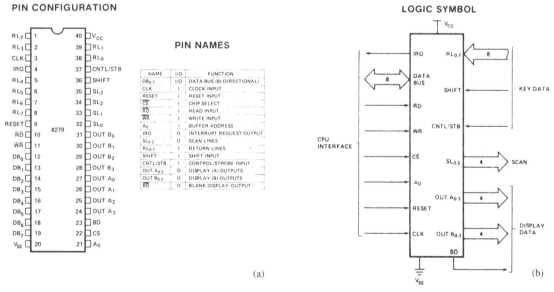

FIGURE 8–20 The pinout and logic symbol of the 8279 programmable keyboard/display interface. (Courtesy of Intel Corporation)

9. V_{ss}—Ground: a pin connected to a system ground.
10. V_{cc}—Supply: a pin connected to the +5V of the system.
11. SL_3–SL_0—Scan Lines: outputs used to scan both the keyboard and displays.
12. RL_7–RL_0—Return Lines: inputs used to sense any key depression in the keyboard matrix.
13. SHIFT—Shift: an input normally connected to the shift key on a keyboard.
14. CNT/STB—Control/Strobe: an input normally connected to the control key (CTRL) on a keyboard.
15. OUT A_3–OUT A_0—Outputs: pins used to send data to the displays (most significant).
16. OUT B_3–OUT B_0—Outputs: pins used to send data to the displays (least significant).
17. $\overline{BD}$—Blank: an output used to blank the displays.

Interfacing the 8279 to the 8086/8088.   In Figure 8–21, the 8279 is connected to the 8088 microprocessor. There are two versions of the 8279. The 8279-5, used here, is compatible with the 5-MHz version of the 8086/8088, and the 8279 is not. A higher speed version of the 8086/8088 would require a wait state for compatibility. Notice that the PCLK signal is applied to the CLK input, which means that the CLK input to the 8279-5 is 2.5 MHz for the 5-MHz version of the 8086/8088 microprocessor. The 8279 is able to have only a 2-MHz clock input, whereas the 8279-5 version may have a maximum clock input frequency of 3.125 MHz.

In this figure, the 8279-5 is decoded at I/O byte port address FEH for data and address FFH for control. A_0 is connected to address connection A_0 in the 8088-based system. If this interface is connected to the 8086, then A_1 is connected to the A_0 pin and removed from the decoder. With this connection, I/O ports for the 8086 are FCH or FDH for data and FEH or FFH for control.

The only signal not connected to the 8086/8088 microprocessor is the IRQ output. This is an interrupt request pin and is beyond the scope of this section of the text. The next chapter covers interrupts, and at that point, the IRQ input will be explained.

FIGURE 8–21   The 8279-5 interfaced to a minimum mode 8088 microprocessor.

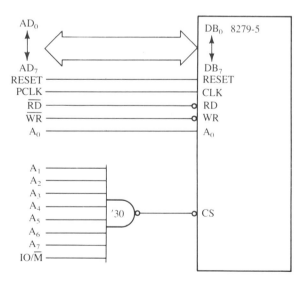

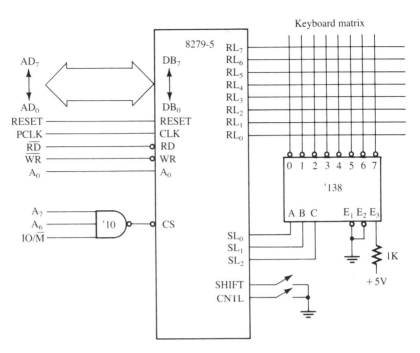

FIGURE 8-22 A 64-key keyboard connected to the 8279-5 and the 8088 microprocessor.

Keyboard Interface

Suppose that a 64-key keyboard (with no numeric displays) is connected through the 8279-5 to the 8086/8088 microprocessor. Figure 8-22 shows the interface of the 8279-5 to an 8088 microprocessor as well as the connections for the keyboard. With the 8279-5, the keyboard matrix is an 8 × 8 or anything smaller. (Note that each cross point in the matrix contains a normally open pushbutton keyswitch that connects one vertical and one horizontal line when pressed.)

The I/O port number decoded for this example is not complete. Not all of the address bits are used for decoding, so there are many possible choices for the address. If the missing bits are made 0, then I/O port FEH is data and FFH is control.

The 74LS138 decoder generates eight active-low strobes for the keyboard. The selection output pins SL_2–SL_0 sequentially scan each column of the keyboard, and the internal circuitry of the 8279-5 scans the RL inputs to test each row for a closure. Pullup resistors are not needed because the RL inputs have internal pullups.

Programming the Keyboard Interface. Before any keystroke can be detected, the 8279-5 must be programmed, a more involved procedure than the programming of the 8255A in the last section of the text. The 8279-5 has eight different command words to consider before it is programmed. The first 3 bits of the number output to the control port contain the number of the command word. Table 8-3 lists the eight different command words and briefly describes them.

TABLE 8–3   The 8279-5 command word summary

D_7	D_6	D_5	Function	Purpose
0	0	0	Mode set	Selects the number of display position, left or right entry, and type of keyboard scan
0	0	1	Clock	Programs the internal clock
0	1	0	Read FIFO	Selects the type of FIFO read and the address
0	1	1	Read display	Selects the type of display read and the address
1	0	0	Write display	Selects the type of display write and the address
1	0	1	Display write inhibit	Allows half bytes to be blanked or inhibited
1	1	0	Clear	Allows the display or FIFO to be cleared
1	1	1	End interrupt	Clears the IRQ pin

Command Descriptions.

1. 000DDKKK—Mode Set: a command with an opcode of 000 and two fields programmed to select the mode of operation for the 8279: DD (display mode) and KKK (keyboard mode). Table 8–4 lists the bit assignments for DD, and Table 8–5 lists the bit assignments for KKK.

    DD selects an 8- or 16-digit display and determines whether new data are entered to the rightmost or leftmost display position. KKK is quite a bit more complex. It provides encoded, decoded, or strobed keyboard operation.

    In encoded mode, the SL outputs are active-high and follow the binary bit pattern 0–7 or 0–15 depending on whether 8- or 16-digit displays are selected. In decoded mode, the SL outputs are active-low, and only one of the four outputs is low at any time. The outputs repeat the following pattern: 1110, 1101, 1011, and 0111. In strobed mode, an active-high pulse on the CNTR/STB input pin strobes the data on the RL pins into the internal FIFO.

    It is also possible to select either two-key lockout or N-key rollover. Two-key lockout prevents two keys from being recognized if pressed simultaneously. N-key rollover will accept all keys pressed simultaneously, from first to last.

2. 001PPPPP—Clock: a command word that programs the clock divider. PPPPP is a prescaler that divides the CLK input pin to achieve the desired operating frequency of approximately 100 KHz. An input clock of 1 MHz thus requires a prescaler of 10.

3. 010I0AAA—Read FIFO: a command that reads a keystroke from the internal FIFO buffer. Bit positions AAA select the desired FIFO location from 000 to 111, and I selects auto-increment for this address. Under normal operation, this command word is used only with the sensor matrix operation.

4. 011IAAAA—Read Display: a command that reads a position in the display RAM. AAAA is the address of the position to be read, and I selects auto-increment mode. This command is used if the information stored in the display RAM must be read.

5. 100IAAAA—Write Display: a command that displays new data at a particular position. AAAA is the address of the display to be written, and I selects auto-increment so that a subsequent write will be automatically sent to the next display location.

TABLE 8-4 Binary bit assignments for DD of mode set

D	D	Function
0	0	8-character display with left entry
0	1	16-character display with left entry
1	0	8-character display with right entry
1	1	16-character display with right entry

TABLE 8-5 Binary bit assignment for KKK of mode set

K	K	K	Function
0	0	0	Encoded keyboard with 2-key lockout
0	0	1	Decoded keyboard with 2-key lockout
0	1	0	Encoded keyboard with N-key rollover
0	1	1	Decoded keyboard with N-key rollover
1	0	0	Encoded sensor matrix
1	0	1	Decoded sensor matrix
1	1	0	Strobed input, encoded display scan
1	1	1	Strobed input, decoded display scan

6. 1010WWBB—Display Write Inhibit: a command that inhibits writing to either half of each display RAM location. The leftmost W inhibits writing to the leftmost 4 bits of a display RAM location, and the rightmost W inhibits writing to the rightmost 4 bits. The BB bits work the same way, except that they blank either output.
7. 1100CCFA— Clear: a command that clears the display, the FIFO, or both display and FIFO. F clears the FIFO, the display RAM status, and sets the pointer to 0. CC clears the display RAM to all 0s, all 1s, or all 20H. 00 and 01 will clear to 0, 10 will clear to 20H, and 11 will clear to all 1s.
8. 111E0000 —End Interrupt: a command that clears the IRQ in sensor matrix mode.

The large number of commands make programming the keyboard interface appear very complex, so let's go through the process step by step. The input clock to the 8279-5 is 2.5 MHz. To program the clock prescaler for 100 KHz, this must be divided by a factor of 25. The next step is keyboard programming. In this example, the keyboard is an encoded type. Notice from the logic diagram that an external decoder is used to convert the encoded data from the 8279-5 into column selection signals. We are free to choose either two-key or N-key rollover, but two-key rollover is preferable for most applications. Next, the 8279-5 must be programmed to read the FIFO. Once this is done, there is no need to reprogram as long as we intend only to read the FIFO, because each byte read will contain the next character from the keyboard. Example 8-8 provides the initialization dialogue for programming the 8279-5 for this keyboard interface.

EXAMPLE 8-8

```
                 ;Initialization dialog for the keyboard

= 00 FF          COMMAND    EQU      OFFH


                 ;program clock

0000 B0 39                  MOV      AL,00111001B
0002 E6 FF                  OUT      COMMAND,AL

                 ;program mode

0004 B0 00                  MOV      AL,0
0006 E6 FF                  OUT      COMMAND,AL

                 ;program to read FIFO and keyboard

0008 B0 A0                  MOV      AL,010100000B
000A E6 FF                  OUT      COMMAND,AL
```

Our next step is to write a procedure that will read data from the keyboard, but first we must find a way to determine if there are data to be read. This we can accomplish by looking at the FIFO status word, illustrated in Table 8-6 along with the function of each bit. FIFO status is obtained by reading the control port of the 8279-5. In most cases, the read program is interested in whether or not there are data in the FIFO to be read. The procedure listed in Example 8-9 reads the keyboard. Here the status word is first checked to see if data are present in the FIFO from the keyboard; these data are read from the FIFO, and a return occurs with the character in the AL register.

Upon returning, the AL register contains the data from the keyboard FIFO. Figure 8-23(a) depicts the format of the keyboard data from the FIFO for scanned keyboard mode. In most cases, this code is translated into ASCII code with a lookup table and the XLAT instruction. Figure 8-23(b) shows the pattern received when the keyboard is operated in strobed mode.

TABLE 8-6   FIFO status word

D	S/E	O	U	F	N_2	N_1	N_0

D—Display Unavailable: a bit that indicates a clear command currently clearing the displays.

S/E—Sensor Closure/Error Flag: a bit that indicates multiple key closures.

O—Overrun Error: a bit that indicates the FIFO has filled up and been overrun with data.

U—Underrun Error: a bit that indicates the FIFO has been read while it is empty.

F—Full: a bit that indicates the FIFO is full.

N_2, N_1, N_0—bits that indicate the number of characters in the FIFO.

(a)   (b)

FIGURE 8–23 8279-5 FIFO data patterns for (a) scanned keyboard data, and (b) strobed keyboard data. (Courtesy of Intel Corporation)

EXAMPLE 8–9

```
              ;Procedure to read keyboard and leave the
              ;character in AL.

= 0007        MASKS       EQU    7
= 00FF        STATUS      EQU    0FFH
= 00FE        DATA        EQU    0FFEH

0000          READ_KEY    PROC   NEAR

              ;check status

0000 E4 FF                IN     AL,STATUS    ;get status
0002 A8 07                TEST   AL,MASKS     ;check N bits
0004 74 FA                JZ  '  READ_KEY     ;if empty

              ;read FIFO

0006 E4 FE                IN     AL,DATA      ;get data
0008 C3                   RET

0009          READ_KEY    ENDP
```

Six-Digit Display Interface

Figure 8–24 depicts the 8279-5 interfaced to the 8088 microprocessor and a six-digit numeric display. The port numbers decoded for this interface must begin with a 100; the remaining bits are *don't cares* except for A_0. The software for this example uses port 80H for the data and 81H for control. In this circuit, the segment data are supplied by the output A and B pins. B_0 is the rightmost bit of the data output to the displays, and A_3 is the leftmost bit. These outputs are sent through a segment driver (ULN2003A) to the segments of the displays.

A 74LS138 3-to-8-line decoder enables the anode switches of each display position. $SL_3–SL_0$ supplies the encoded display position to the 74LS138 from the 8279-5. Notice that the left-hand display is number 0 (0000) and the right-hand display is number 5 (0101). These are the addresses of each display as indicated in the command words.

It is necessary to choose resistor values that will cause 100 mA of current to flow through each segment. (The voltage across the resistor is approximately 3.3 V due to the

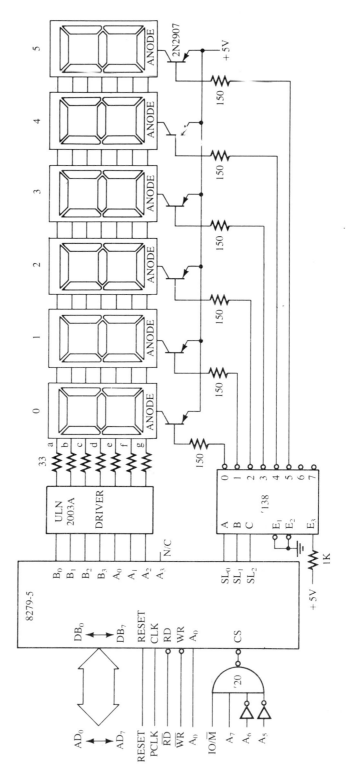

FIGURE 8–24 A 6-digit numeric display interfaced to the 8279-5 programmable keyboard/display interface.

drop across the LED and the anode switch.) Because each segment is turned on for only one sixth of the time, the average current per segment is 16.7 mA, which causes it to light with normal intensity. Connected to each anode switch are resistors chosen to accommodate 700 mA of peak segment current supplied by the anode switch. If the current gain of each anode switch is a minimum of 40, current supplied to the anode is 920 mA. This allows for any variation in the base resistor, the drop across the emitter–base junction, and the logic 0 output voltage of the 74LS138 decoder.

Example 8–10 lists the initialization dialogue for programming the 8279-5 to function properly for this display. This software programs the display and clears the display RAM.

EXAMPLE 8-10

```
                          ;Initialization dialog for the display.

   = 0081                           COMMAND    EQU   81H

                          ;program clock

0000  B0 39                         MOV        AL,00111001B
0002  E6 81                         OUT        COMMAND,AL

                          ;program mode

0004  B0 00                         MOV        AL,0
0006  E6 81                         OUT        COMMAND,AL

                          ;clear display

0008  B0 C1                         MOV        AL,11000001B
000A  E6 81                         OUT        COMMAND,AL
```

Example 8–11 illustrates a procedure for displaying information on the display RAM. Data are transferred to the procedure through the AX register. AH contains the seven-segment coded information to be displayed, and AL contains the address of the display.

EXAMPLE 8-11

```
                          ;Procedure to display AH on the display addressed
                          ;by register AL

 = 0080                   MASKS     EQU   80H
 = 0081                   COMMAND   EQU   81H
 = 0080                   DATA      EQU   80H

0000                      DISPLAY   PROC  NEAR

0000  0C 80                         OR    AL,MASKS
0002  E6 81                         OUT   COMMAND,AL
```

;display data

```
0004   8A C4               MOV     AL,AH
0006   E6 80               OUT     DATA,AL
0008   C3                  RET

0009                       DISPLAY ENDP
```

8-5 8254 PROGRAMMABLE INTERVAL TIMER

The 8254 programmable interval timer consists of three independent 16-bit programmable counters. Each counter is capable of counting in binary or binary-coded decimal (BCD). The allowable input frequency to any counter is DC to 10 MHz. This device is useful wherever the microprocessor must control real-time events. Some examples of usage for the 8254 include: real-time clock, events counter, and motor speed and direction controller.

8254 Functional Description

Figure 8–25 illustrates the block diagram and pinout of the 8254 programmable timer. Notice that the three internal timers in Figure 8–25(a) each have a clock input, and output, and a gate input, which is at times used to enable or disable the counter.

The signals that connect to the microprocessor are the data bus pins (D_7–D_0), $\overline{RD}$, $\overline{WR}$, $\overline{CS}$, and address bits A_1 and A_0. The two address inputs are present so that any of four internal registers may be chosen for programming, reading, or writing.

Pin Definitions.
1. V_{cc}—Power: the pin connected to the +5-V power supply.
2. $\overline{WR}$—Write: the pin connected to the 8086/8088 $\overline{WR}$ pin.
3. $\overline{RD}$—Read: the pin connected to the 8086/8088 $\overline{RD}$ pin.
4. $\overline{CS}$— Chip Select: the pin that selects the 8254 and is usually connected to an I/O port decoder.
5. A_1–A_0—Address Inputs: pins that are connected to A_1 and A_0 in the 8088 or A_2 and A_1 in the 8086. These inputs are used to select the counters or control word. Table 8–7 illustrates internal functions selected by A_1 and A_0.
6. CLK_0, CLK_1, and CLK_2— Clock Inputs: the timing inputs to the counter. They may be clocked from any TTL-compatible source with a frequency of DC–10 MHz.
7. OUT_0, OUT_1, and OUT_2—Outputs: the outputs of the counters. They can be programmed to generate square waves or pulses.
8. $GATE_0$, $GATE_1$, and $GATE_2$—Gate Inputs: pins used to enable (1) the counter or disable (0) the counter.
9. GND—Ground: a pin connected to the system ground connection.

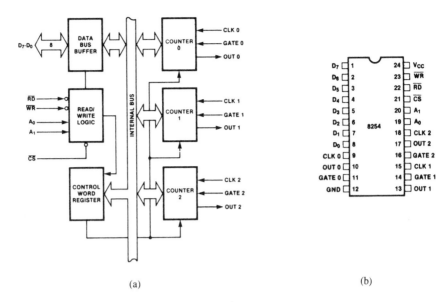

FIGURE 8–25   The 8254 programmable interval timer. (a) Internal structure. (b) Pinout. (Courtesy of Intel Corporation.)

TABLE 8–7 Address selection for the 8254

A_1	A_0	Function
0	0	Counter 0
0	1	Counter 1
1	0	Counter 2
1	1	Control word

Programming the 8254. Each counter can be individually programmed by writing a control word followed by the initial count. Figure 8–26 lists the program control word and the function of each bit. The control word allows the programmer to select the counter, the mode of operation, and the type of operation (read/write). The programmer can also determine whether the counter is to be BCD or binary. Each 16-bit counter may be programmed with a count of 1–FFFFH–0. A count of 0 is equal to FFFFF + 1 (64K in binary) or 9,999 + 1 (10,000 in BCD). The minimum count of 1 applies to all modes of operation except modes 2 and 3, which have a minimum count of 2.

RW_1 and RW_0 determine how the data are read or written to the counter. The program is able to select a write to either the most significant or least significant halves of the counter or both halves with the least significant byte followed by the most significant.

Each counter has a program control word used to select the way the channel is programmed. If 2 bytes are programmed into a channel, then the first byte (LSB) will stop the count, and the second byte (MSB) will start the counter with the new count. The order

D₇	D₆	D₅	D₄	D₃	D₂	D₁	D₀
SC1	SC0	RW1	RW0	M2	M1	M0	BCD

SC — Select Counter:

SC1	SC0	
0	0	Select Counter 0
0	1	Select Counter 1
1	0	Select Counter 2
1	1	Read-Back Command (See Read Operations)

M — MODE:

M2	M1	M0	
0	0	0	Mode 0
0	0	1	Mode 1
X	1	0	Mode 2
X	1	1	Mode 3
1	0	0	Mode 4
1	0	1	Mode 5

RW — Read/Write:

RW1	RW0	
0	0	Counter Latch Command (see Read Operations)
0	1	Read/Write least significant byte only.
1	0	Read/Write most significant byte only.
1	1	Read/Write least significant byte first, then most significant byte.

BCD:

0	Binary Counter 16-bits
1	Binary Coded Decimal (BCD) Counter (4 Decades)

NOTE: DON'T CARE BITS (X) SHOULD BE 0 TO INSURE
COMPATIBILITY WITH FUTURE INTEL PRODUCTS.

FIGURE 8–26   The control word and bit definitions of the 8254. (Courtesy of Intel Corporation)

of programming is important for each counter, but the programming of different counters may be interleaved for better control. For example, the control word may be sent to each counter for individual programming. The order of control words does not matter. Example 8–12 illustrates a few ways to program counters.

EXAMPLE 8–12

```
OUTPUT    CONTROL CNT0
OUTPUT    CONTROL CNT1
PROGRAM LSB         CNTI
PROGRAM LSB         CNT0
PROGRAM MSB         CNT0
PROGRAM MSB         CNT1
```

or

```
OUTPUT    CONTROL CNT0
OUTPUT    CONTROL CNT1
PROGRAM LSB         CNT0
PROGRAM MSB         CNT0
OUTPUT    CONTROL CNT2
PROGRAM LSB         CNT1
PROGRAM LSB         CNT2
PROGRAM MSB         CNT1
PROGRAM MSB         CNT2
```

Six modes of operation are available for each of the 8254's counters (mode 0–mode 5). Figure 8–27 illustrates the timing of each mode. A description of each follows:

1. *Mode 0* allows the 8254 counter to be used as an events counter. In this mode, the output becomes a logic 0 when the control word is written to the counter and remains there until $N + 1$ input clock pulses have occurred. (N = programmed count.) Suppose that the counter is to count 100 pulses at its clock input. In order to do this, the counter is programmed for a count of 99. After 100 input pulses, the output pin returns to a logic 1 level. Note that the gate input must be a logic 1 for the counter to count.

2. *Mode 1* allows the counter to function as a retriggerable monostable multivibrator (one-shot). Here the gate input is used as a trigger input to fire the one-shot. For example, if the counter is loaded with a 10 and a trigger (a logic 1) occurs on the gate input, the out connection will go low for 10 input clocks. If a second trigger occurs before 10 clocks, then the output time will be extended for 10 additional clocks.

3. *Mode 2* allows the counter to generate a series of continuous pulses that are one clock pulse in width. The separation between pulses is determined by the count. For example, if the count is a 10, the output will be a logic 1 for nine clock pulses and low for one. This cycle is repeated until the counter is reprogrammed with a new count. The gate input is used to start (a logic 1) and stop (a logic 0) the count.

4. *Mode 3* allows the counter to generate a continuous square-wave output. If the count is even, then the high and low times of the output are each equal to one half the count. If the count is odd, the low time is one count less than the high time. For example, if the counter is programmed with a 10, the output will be low for five clocks and high for five clocks. If the count is 11, the output will be low for five clocks and high for six clocks. As with other modes, the gate input is used to stop (a logic 0) or start (a logic 1) the count.

5. *Mode 4* allows the counter to produce one pulse. This mode is like mode 0 except that instead of producing a continuous stream of pulses, it produces only one pulse. For example, if the count is a 10, the output will be high for 10 clock pulses after the count is programmed and then low for one. After the pulse, the output returns to a logic 1 until the counter is reprogrammed (software-controlled one-shot). The gate input is used to inhibit the count if required.

6. *Mode 5* allows the counter to generate a single pulse after it is triggered with the gate input. It is similar to mode 4 except that the trigger is hardware instead of software. For example, if a count of 5 is programmed, the output will remain high until five clocks after the gate trigger pulse (a logic 1) and then go low for an additional clock. Like mode 1, this mode is retriggerable.

Reading a Counter.   Each counter has an internal latch that is read with the read counter port operation. These latches will normally follow the count. If the contents of the counter are needed at a particular time, then the latch can remember a count by programming the counter latch control word (see Figure 8–28), which causes the contents of the counter to be held in the latch until it is read. Whenever the count is read from the latch or the counter is reprogrammed, the latch returns to following the count.

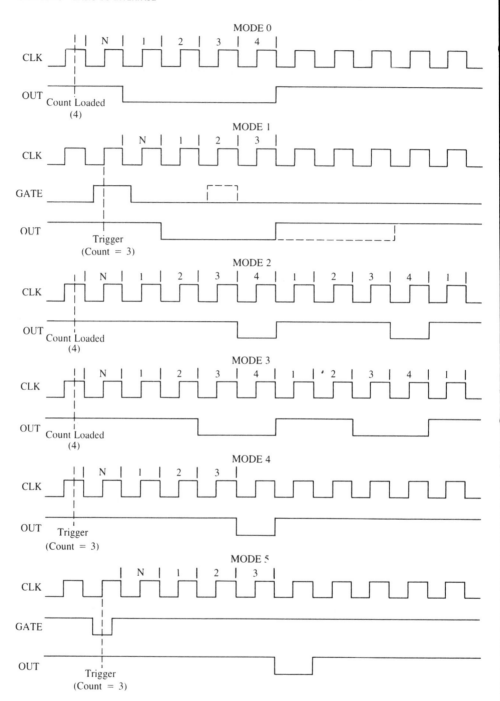

FIGURE 8–27   The six modes of operation for the 8254 programmable interval timer.

FIGURE 8–28 The 8254 counter latch control word. (Courtesy of Intel Corporation)

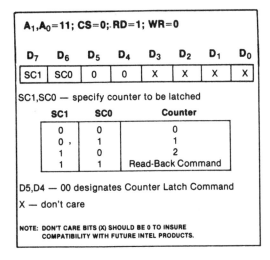

FIGURE 8–29 The 8254 read-back control word. (Courtesy of Intel Corporation)

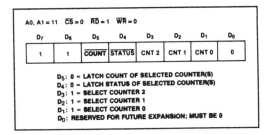

FIGURE 8–30 The 8254 status word. (Courtesy of Intel Corporation)

When it is necessary for the contents of more than one counter to be read at the same time, it is desirable to latch more than one counter. This is accomplished with the read-back control word illustrated in Figure 8–29. Here the $\overline{\text{COUNT}}$ bit is a 0 if the contents of counters CNT_2, CNT_1, and CNT_0 are to be latched. If the status of the counter is latched, then the $\overline{\text{STATUS}}$ bit is a 0. Figure 8–30 illustrates the status word, which allows the programmer to determine what state the output pin is in, whether the counter is at 0 (null count), and how the counter is programmed (RW_1, RW_0, M_2, M_1, M_0, and BCD).

DC Motor Speed and Direction Control

One application for the 8254 is the speed and direction control of a DC motor. Figure 8–31 illustrates the schematic diagram of the motor and its associated driver circuitry.

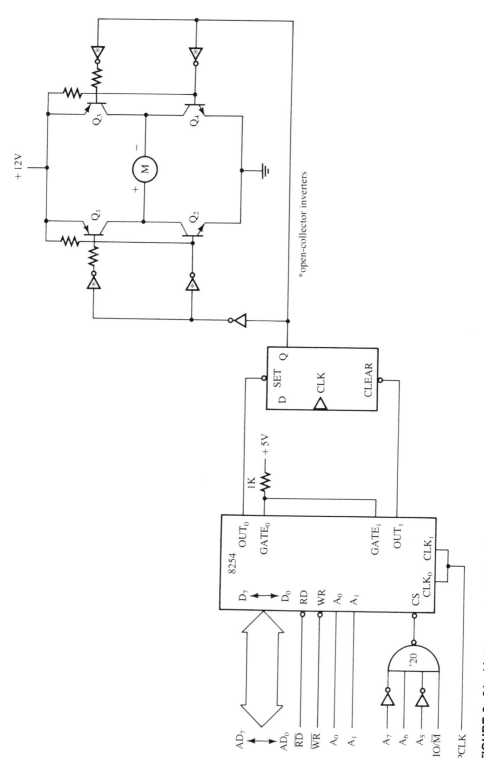

FIGURE 8–31 Motor speed and direction control using the 8254 programmable interval timer.

The operation of the driver circuitry is fairly straightforward. If the Q output of the flip-flop is a logic 1, the bases of Q_1 and Q_2 are both pulled up to $+$ 12 V through the base pullup resistors. This means that Q_1 is off and Q_2 is on, with ground applied to the positive lead of the motor. Transistors Q_3 and Q_4 both have ground attached to their bases. Q_3 is on, and Q_4 is off. This applies $+$ 12V to the negative lead of the motor and makes it run backward. If the Q output of the flip-flop becomes a logic 0, these conditions are reversed so that Q_4 and Q_1 are on and Q_2 and Q_3 are off. This applies $+$12V to the positive terminal of the motor and ground to the negative lead, causing the motor to spin forward.

If the output of the flip-flop is alternated between a logic 1 and 0, the motor spins in either direction and at various speeds. If the duty cycle of the Q output is 50 percent, then the motor will not spin at all. Figure 8–32 shows some timing diagrams and their

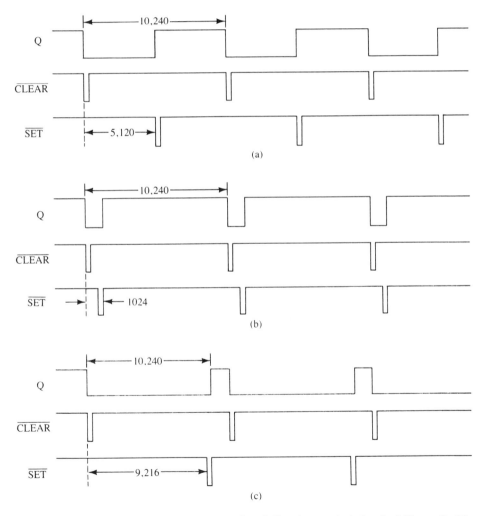

FIGURE 8–32   Timing for the motor speed and direction control circuit of Figure 8–31.
(a) Causes no rotation. (b) Causes a fairly high-speed rotation in the reverse direction.
(c) Causes a fairly high-speed rotation in the forward direction.

effects on the speed and direction of the motor. Notice how each counter is generating pulses at different positions to vary the duty cycle at the output of the flip-flop.

To generate these waveforms, counters 0 and 1 are both programmed to divide the input clock by 10,240. The point at which counter 0 is started in relation to counter 1 is varied to change the duty cycle and hence the speed and direction of the motor. But why divide the 2.5-MHz PCLK by 10,240? 10,240 is divisible by 256. In fact, it is divisible by a factor of 40. This allows the software to watch the most significant part of counter 1 to determine where to start counter 0 to develop different duty cycles. The most significant part will be checked for numbers 1–39. A 1 causes the motor to spin in the reverse direction at full speed, a 20 causes it to sit still, and a 39 causes it to spin in the forward direction at full speed.

EXAMPLE 8–13

```
                         ;Procedure to program the duty cycle of Q
                         ;
                         ;AH contains a number between 1 and 39 to
                         ;select both the speed and direction.

= 0043                        CONTROL  EQU    43H              ;control port
= 0040                        CNT0     EQU    40H              ;counter 0
= 0041                        CNT1     EQU    41H              ;counter 1
= 0028                        FORTY    EQU    40               ;MSB of 10,240

0000                          COUNTER PROC   NEAR

                         ;stop both counters and program LSB

0000  B0 34                            MOV    AL,00110100B ;control CNT0
0002  E6 43                            OUT    CONTROL,AL
0004  B0 74                            MOV    AL,01110100B ;control CNT1
0006  E6 43                            OUT    CONTROL,AL
0008  32 C0                            XOR    AL,AL        ;program LSB
000A  E6 40                            OUT    CNT0,AL      ;stop CNT0
000C  E6 41                            OUT    CNT1,AL      ;stop CNT1

                         ;start CNT1 (clear signal)

000E  B0 28                            MOV    AL,FORTY     ;program MSB
0010  E6 41                            OUT    CNT1,AL      ;start CNT1

                         ;wait for CNT1 to reach AH - 1 before starting CNT0

0012  FE CC                            DEC    AH           ;adjust AH
0014  B0 64                            MOV    AL,01100100B ;control CNT1
0016  E6 43                            OUT    CONTROL,AL   ;setup to read MSB

0018                          LOOPS:

0018  E4 41                            IN     AL,CNT1      ;read MSB
001A  3A C4                            CMP    AL,AH        ;test count
001C  75 FA                            JNE    LOOPS        ;wait till equal
```

```
                         ;start CNT0

001E  B0 28                         MOV      AL,FORTY
0020  E6 40                         OUT      CNT0,AL
0022  C3                            RET


0023                      COUNTER            ENDP
```

Example 8–13 illustrates a procedure that is called whenever power is first applied. It sets the duty cycle to 50 percent either to stop the motor or to change the speed or direction of the motor, depending on the number in register AH. If AH = 20, the duty cycle is 50 percent, and the motor is stopped. Speed will increase in either direction as the number is either increased or decreased from 20 to a maximum of 39 or a minimum of 1.

To perform this procedure, it is first necessary to stop both counters by programming the LSB of their counts. When counter 1 is started, it begins generating the clear signal for the flip-flop. Next, the MSB of the first counter is checked to see if it has counted down to the contents of AH − 1. Why AH − 1? Because this is a down counter, it begins counting at 40 MSB, 00 LSB, or 2800H toward 0. In order to sense an MBS of 20 or 14H (half the count for a duty cycle of 50 percent), for example, the program must go through a count of 14FFH before reaching 1400H. To make this procedure sense 1400H as closely as possible, it is necessary to find a count of 13FFH by looking for 14H − 1 in the most significant byte of the count register. Once this is found (for a duty cycle of 50 percent in this case), counter 0 can begin to generate the set pulse for the flip-flop. Notice that mode 2 is selected so that each counter generates a continuous stream of pulses.

8–6   8251A PROGRAMMABLE COMMUNICATIONS INTERFACE

The 8251A is a programmable communications interface designed to connect to virtually any type of serial interface. The 8251A is a universal synchronous/asynchronous receiver/transmitter (USART) that is fully compatible with the Intel 8086/8088 microprocessor. The 8251A is capable of operating at DC–64K baud (bits per second) in the synchronous mode and DC–19.2K baud in the asynchronous mode. *Baud rate* is the number of bits transmitted per second, including start, stop, data, and parity. The programmer of the 8251A can select the number of data bits, number of stop bits, type of parity (even or odd), and the clock rate in the asynchronous mode and the number of data bits, parity, and number of sync characters (one or two) in the synchronous mode.

Asynchronous Data

Asynchronous data are information that is transmitted and received without a clock or timing signals. Figure 8–33 illustrates two frames of asynchronous data. Each of these frames contains a start bit, seven data bits, parity, and one stop bit. In this figure, a frame,

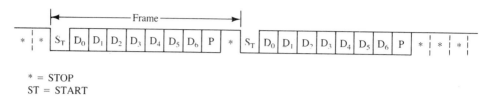

* = STOP
ST = START

FIGURE 8–33   Asynchronous serial data.

which contains one character (ASCII), has 10 bits: 1 start bit, 7 data bits, 1 parity bit, and 1 stop bit. Most asynchronous data communications function with 10 bits per frame.

Synchronous Data

Figure 8–34 illustrates synchronous data. Notice that this information contains no start bit and no stop bits, only data bits. Also notice that the data are referenced or synchronized to a clock signal. The start of a frame of data is indicated by the use of sync characters. The use of two sync characters, often referred to as *bysync,* is the most common technique.

8251A Functional Description

Figure 8–35 illustrates the block diagram and pinout of the 8251A. Two completely separate sections within the 8251A are responsible for data communications: the receiver and the transmitter. Because the sections are independent of each other, the 8251A is able to function in the *simplex, half-duplex,* or *full-duplex* modes. In simplex operation, either the transmitter or the receiver is used by itself. An example of simplex communications is an FM broadcasting station, because it only transmits and never receives. In a half-duplex operation, data are transmitted and received, but only in one direction at a time. An example of a half-duplex operation is a CB radio, which receives and transmits, but not in both directions at the same time. A full-duplex operation allows data to be transmitted and received simultaneously. The telephone is a full-duplex system because you can talk and hear on it simultaneously.

The 8251A is also capable of controlling a *modem* (modulator/demodulator), which is a device that converts TTL serial data to or from audio tones that can be passed by the telephone system. Four lines that control the modem are provided or accepted by the 8251A— $\overline{\text{DSR}}$, $\overline{\text{DTS}}$, $\overline{\text{CTS}}$, and $\overline{\text{RTS}}$. A modem is often referred to as a *data set,* and the 8251A and its microprocessor-based system are often referred to as the *data terminal.*

Pin Functions.

1. RESET—Reset Input: a pin that clears the internal circuitry of the 8251A. This input is connected to the 8086/8088 RESET pin to reset the 8251A with the 8086/8088.
2. CLK—Clock Input: a pin that is connected to the PCLK output of the 8251A clock generator. Note that the frequency of this input does not determine the receive or transmit baud rate of the 8251A.
3. $\overline{\text{WR}}$—Write Input: a pin used to strobe data into the transmitter or the internal command register.
4. $\overline{\text{RD}}$—Read Input: a pin used to strobe data out of the receiver or the status register.

FIGURE 8–34
Synchronous serial data.

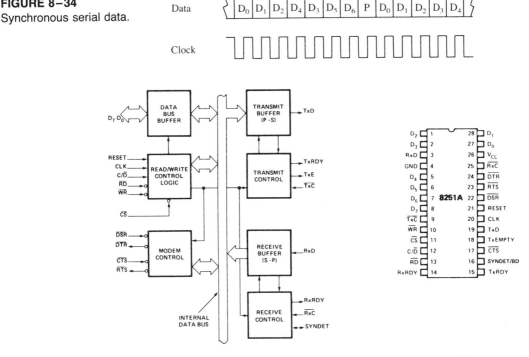

FIGURE 8–35 The pinout and block diagram of the 8251A programmable communications interface. (Courtesy of Intel Corporation)

5. C/$\overline{D}$— Command/Data Input: a pin that selects either data or command. If this input is high, data are written to the command register or read from the status register. If it is low, data are transmitted or received by the USART.

6. $\overline{CS}$— Chip Select Input: a pin that, when low, enables the 8251A so that data or commands may be read from or written to the USART.

7. $\overline{DSR}$— Data Set Ready: an inverting input bit often used to test the $\overline{DSR}$ signal from the modem (data set). $\overline{DSR}$ indicates that the modem or data set is operational.

8. $\overline{DTR}$— Data Terminal Ready: an inverting output bit often used to signal the modem that the data terminal (USART) is operational.

9. $\overline{RTS}$— Request to Send: an inverting output bit often used to ask the modem to turn the line around in a half-duplex system, so that the data may be transmitted.

10. $\overline{CTS}$— Clear to Send: an inverting input bit often used to test the modem to see if it has turned the line around for transmission in a half-duplex system. Note that this input must be grounded for the transmitter to function.

11. D_7–D_0—Data Bus: pins connected to the 8086/8088 address/data bus.

12. TxD—Transmit Data: the serial output data pin.

13. TxRDY—Transmitter Ready: a pin used to indicate that the transmitter is able to receive another character from the microprocessor for transmission.

14. TxEMPTY—Transmitter Empty: a pin that indicates that the transmitter section has completely sent all of the data.

15. $\overline{\text{TxC}}$—Transmitter Clock: an input that supplies the transmitter with a timing signal. The baud rate of the transmitter is programmable, and a divider of 1, 16, or 64 used with this input generates the baud rate of the transmitted data. Note that the baud rate divider for synchronous data is only 1.

16. RxD—Receiver Data: the serial input to the receiver.

17. RxRDY—Receiver Ready: a pin that indicates that the receiver section of the USART has received a character and is being held for the microprocessor.

18. $\overline{\text{RxC}}$—Receiver Clock: a pin that provides a baud clock to the receiver. (See $\overline{\text{TxC}}$ for details about the internal programmable divider.)

19. SYNDET/BD—Sync Detect/Break Detect: an output that indicates that the sync or sync characters are detected in synchronous operation or that a break character is detected in asynchronous operation. A break character is two complete frames of start pulses.

Programming the 8251A. Programming the 8251A is a rather simple task when compared to some of the other programmable interfaces discussed in this chapter. It is a two-part process including initialization dialogue and operational programming.

Initialization programming, which occurs after a reset, consists of two parts: reset and mode. Because of an apparent design flaw, the 8251A does not reset properly from the reset input pin. Instead it must be reset by a command word preceded by three 0s.

Once the 8251A is reset, it may then be programmed with the mode word, which directs the 8251A to function in either the synchronous or asynchronous mode. Figure 8–36 shows both the synchronous and asynchronous mode command words. Both words specify the number of data bits and the parity, but this is where the similarity ends. In

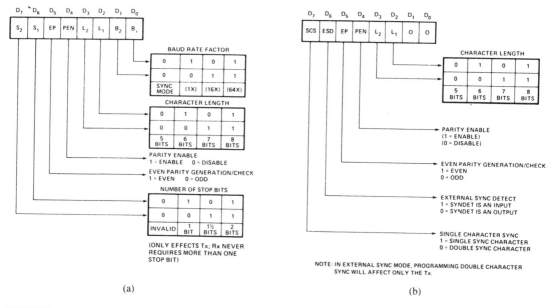

FIGURE 8–36 8251A mode instruction words. (a) Asynchronous. (b) Synchronous. (Courtesy of Intel Corporation)

asynchronous operation, the number of stop bits and the clock divider are programmed. In synchronous operation, the number of sync characters and the function of the SYNDET pin are programmed. SYNDET is programmed as either an input or an output. As an input, it indicates that sync characters are received; as an output, it indicates that sync characters are transmitted.

In the asynchronous mode, once the mode instruction is sent to the 8251A, the initialization programming is complete. In the synchronous mode, the one or two sync characters are sent to the 8251A before the initialization programming is complete.

Suppose that an asynchronous operation requires seven data bits, odd parity, a clock divider of 64, and one stop bit. Example 8–14 illustrates the software required to initialize the 8251A so that it functions in this manner. Figure 8–37 shows the 8251A interfaced to the 8088 so that it operates at I/O ports FEH and FFH, here the control port and the data port, respectively.

EXAMPLE 8–14

```
                    ;Initialization dialog for the 8251A used in
                    ;synchronous operation.


   = 00FF           CONTROL    EQU      0FFH
   = 0040           RESET      EQU      40H

   0000             INITA      PROC     NEAR

                    ;reset 8251A

   0000   32 C0                XOR      AL,AL
   0002   E6 FF                OUT      CONTROL,AL
   0004   E6 FF                OUT      CONTROL,AL
   0006   E6 FF                OUT      CONTROL,AL
   0008   B0 40                MOV      AL,RESET
   000A   E6 FF                OUT      CONTROL,AL

                    ;program mode

   000C   B0 5B                MOV      AL,01011011B
   000E   E6 FF                OUT      CONTROL,AL

                    ;enable receiver and transmitter

   0010   B0 15                MOV      AL,00010101B
   0012   E6 FF                OUT      CONTROL,AL
   0014   C3                   RET
   0015                INITA   ENDP
```

If the 8251A is operated with synchronous data, the programming sequence is very similar except that after initialization, the one or two sync characters are also sent to the 8251A. Example 8–15 illustrates how the 8251A is programmed for synchronous operation with seven data bits, even parity, SYNDET programmed as an output, and two sync characters.

FIGURE 8–37 The 8251A connected to the 8088 so that it functions at I/O ports FEH and FFH.

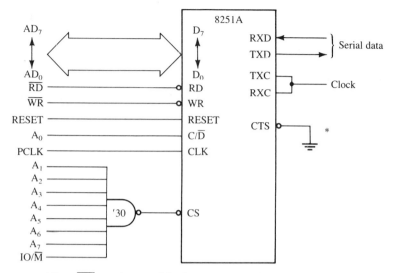

Note: $\overline{CTS}$ *must be ground for the transmitter to function.*

EXAMPLE 8–15

```
                           ;Initialization dialog for the 8251A used for
                           ;synchronous operation.

= 00FF                     CONTROL EQU   0FFH
= 0040                     RESET         EQU   40H
= 007F                     SYNC1         EQU   7FH
= 007E                     SYNC2         EQU   7EH

0000                       INITS         PROC  NEAR

                 ;reset 8251A

0000   32 C0                     XOR     AL,AL
0002   E6 FF                     OUT     CONTROL,AL
0004   E6 FF                     OUT     CONTROL,AL
0006   E6 FF                     OUT     CONTROL,AL
0008   B0 40                     MOV     AL,RESET
000A   E6 FF                     OUT     CONTROL,AL

             ;program mode

000C   B0 B8                     MOV     AL,10111000B
000E   E6 FF                     OUT     CONTROL,AL

         ;send sync characters

0010   B0 7F                     MOV     AL,SYNC1
0012   E6 FF                     OUT     CONTROL,AL
0014   B0 7E                     MOV     AL,SYNC2
0016   E6 FF                     OUT     CONTROL,AL
```

```
                        ;enable receiver and transmitter

0018   B0 15                        MOV     AL,00010101B
001A   E6 FF                        OUT     CONTROL,AL
001C   C3                           RET


001D                       INITS    ENDP
```

Even when the 8251A mode instruction is programmed, the 8251A is still not ready to function. The next step is operational programming, where the command word is sent to the 8251A to tell it how to function. Figure 8–38 illustrates the command word, used in both synchronous and asynchronous operation, that enables the receiver and the transmitter, controls DTR and RTS, sends a break in asynchronous mode, resets errors, resets the 8251A, and enters into the hunt mode for synchronous operation. Refer to Examples 8–14 and 8–15 in which both the transmitter and receiver are enabled.

Before it is possible to write software for the 8251A to send or receive data, it is necessary to know the status word (illustrated in Figure 8–39). The status word indicates error conditions about the received data, the state of DSR, SYNDET/BD, TxEMPTY, RxRDY, and Tx/RDY.

FIGURE 8–38 The 8251A command word. (Courtesy of Intel Corporation)

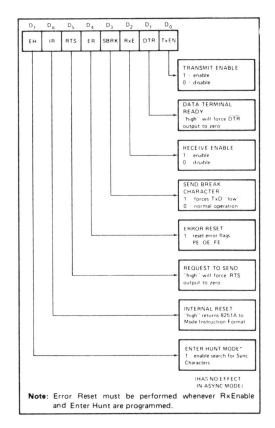

FIGURE 8–39 The 8251A status word. (Courtesy of Intel Corporation)

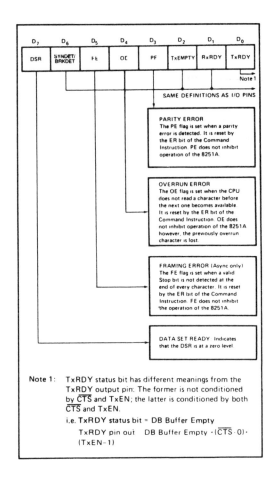

Note 1: TxRDY status bit has different meanings from the TxRDY output pin. The former is not conditioned by $\overline{CTS}$ and TxEN; the latter is conditioned by both $\overline{CTS}$ and TxEN.

i.e. TxRDY status bit = DB Buffer Empty

TxRDY pin out   DB Buffer Empty $\cdot (\overline{CTS}\cdot 0)\cdot$ (TxEN-1)

Suppose that a procedure (see Example 8–16) is written to transmit the ASCII data in the AH register to the 8251A. If the TxRDY bit of the status word indicates that the transmitter is ready to receive data, then the data are sent to it for transmission. Again, this sample procedure uses the circuit of Figure 8–37.

EXAMPLE 8–16

```
                    ;Procedure to transmit the contents of AH
                    ;to the 8251A

    = 00FF          CONTROL EQU    0FFH
    = 00FE          DATA    EQU    0FEH

    0000            TRANS   PROC   NEAR

                    ;test txRDY
```

```
0000   E4 FF                       IN    AL,CONTROL    ;get status
0002   D0 C8                       ROR   AL,1          ;move txRDY to C
0004   73 FA                       JNC   TRANS         ;wait till ready

               ;transmit data

0006   8A C4                       MOV   AL,AH
0008   E6 FE                       OUT   DATA,AL
000A   C3                          ·RET

000B                 TRANS    ENDP
```

To read information from the 8251A receiver, the RxRDY bit of the status word must be tested. Example 8–17 illustrates a procedure that waits until the receiver contains data for the microprocessor. Upon reception of valid data, it is returned in the AL register. Next, the error bits are tested to determine whether the received data contain any errors. If an error is detected, a return is made with a question mark in AL.

EXAMPLE 8–17

```
               ;Procedure to read data from the 8251A.
               ;Data is left in AL upon return.

= 00FF                 CONTROL    EQU   0FFH
= 00FE                 DATA       EQU   0FEH
= 0004                 MASKS      EQU   4
= 0038                 ERROR            EQU   38H
= 0015                 ERR_RESET  EQU   15H
= 003F                 QUESTION   EQU   '?'

0000                   READ       PROC NEAR

               ;check rxRDY

0000   E4 FF                       IN    AL,CONTROL    ;read status
0002   A8 04                       TEST  AL,MASKS      ;test rxRDY
0004   74 FA                       JZ    READ          ;if not ready

               ;test for errors

0006   A8 38                       TEST  AL,ERROR
0008   75 03                       JNZ   ERR

               ;read data

000A   E4 FE                       IN    AL,DATA
000C   C3                          .RET

               ;error
```

```
000D                              ERR:

000D   B0  15                     MOV    AL,ERR_RESET
000F   E6  FF                     OUT    CONTROL,AL
0011   B0  3F                     MOV    AL,QUESTION
0013   C3                         RET

0014                    READ      ENDP
```

The types of errors detected by the 8251A include parity, framing, and overrun errors. Parity errors occur if the received data have the wrong number of 1s expressed as even or odd. A framing error occurs if the start and stop bit or bits are not in their proper locations, generally as a result of data received at the incorrect baud rate. Finally, an overrun error occurs if the data are not removed from the receiver before the next character is received. Notice that the error flags must be reset by the error reset bit in the command word before the next error is detected.

8-7   SUMMARY

1. The 8086/8088 has two basic I/O instructions: IN and OUT. Both are available in four versions: two are fixed port, and two are variable port instructions. A fixed port instruction transfers 8 or 16 bits of data to an 8-bit I/O port where the port number is stored in the memory location following the opcode. The variable I/O instructions transfer 8 or 16 bits of data to a 16-bit I/O port where the I/O port number is stored in the DX register.

2. Isolated I/O, sometimes called direct I/O, uses a separate map for the I/O, freeing the entire memory for use by a program. Isolated I/O uses the IN and OUT instructions to transfer data between the I/O device and the 8086/8088. The control structure of the I/O map uses $\overline{RD}$, $\overline{WR}$, and I/O/$\overline{M}$ (8088) or M/$\overline{IO}$ (8086) to effect the transfer.

3. Memory-mapped I/O actually uses a portion of the memory space for I/O. This reduces the amount of memory available, but it negates the need to use the I/O/$\overline{M}$ (8088) or M/$\overline{IO}$ (8086) signal. In addition, any instruction that references the memory is used to transfer data between the microprocessor and I/O.

4. All input devices must use a three-state buffer to connect the I/O device to the address/data bus during an IN. The buffer is either built into a programmable peripheral device or located separately.

5. All output devices usually use a latch to capture the data when they are output from the microprocessor. This is necessary because the data appear on the address/data bus for only a brief period of time and will most likely be missed without the latch.

6. Handshaking or polling is the act of two independent devices synchronizing with a few control signals. For example, the computer asks a printer if it is busy by inputting the BUSY signal from the printer. If it isn't busy, the computer outputs the data and informs the printer with a data strobe ($\overline{STB}$) signal. This communication between the computer and the printer is a handshake or a poll.

7. The I/O port number appears on the address connections A_7–A_0 for a fixed port I/O instruction and on A_{15}–A_0 for a variable port I/O instruction. In many systems, even if the variable I/O instructions are used, only an 8-bit port number is decoded because it is fairly difficult to have more than 256 different I/O devices in a system.

8. The main differences between the I/Os of the 8086 and the 8088 microprocessors is their data bus widths (8 bits for the 8088 and 16 bits for the 8086) and their memory and I/O control signal ($IO/\overline{M}$ for the 8088 and $M/\overline{IO}$ for the 8086).

9. I/O port decoders are much like memory address decoders, except that the memory address decoder looks at all 20 bits of the address, while in many cases the I/O port decoder looks at only 8 bits of the address.

10. The 8255A is a programmable peripheral interface that has 24 I/O pins that are programmable in two groups of 12 pins (group A and group B). The 8255A operates in three modes: simple I/O, strobed I/O, and bidirectional I/O.

11. The 8279 is a programmable keyboard/display interface that can control a 64-key keyboard and a 16-digit numeric display.

12. The 8254 is a programmable interval timer that contains three 16-bit counters that count in binary or binary-coded decimal (BCD). Each counter is independent of the other, and each operates in six different modes. The six modes of operation are (1) events counter, (2) retriggerable monostable multivibrator, (3) pulse generator, (4) squarewave generator, (5) software-triggered pulse generator, and (6) hardware-triggered pulse generator.

13. The 8251A is a programmable communications interface capable of receiving and transmitting either asynchronous or synchronous data.

8-8   QUESTIONS AND PROBLEMS

1. Explain which way the data flow for an IN and an OUT instruction.
2. Where is the I/O port number stored for a fixed I/O instruction?
3. Where is the I/O port number stored for a variable I/O instruction?
4. To which register are data input by the 16-bit IN instruction?
5. Contrast memory-mapped I/O with isolated I/O.
6. What is the basic input interface?
7. What is the basic output interface?
8. Explain the term *handshaking* as it applies to computers.
9. List the differences between the 8086 and the 8088 with respect to I/O interface.
10. Modify the decoder of Figure 8–5 so that it generates eight enable signals at I/O ports 10H–17H.
11. Modify the decoder of Figure 8–5 so that it generates eight enable signals at I/O ports 28H–2FH.
12. How is an I/O read strobe generated?
13. Modify the circuit of Figure 8–7 so that it decodes eight $\overline{WR}$ strobes for ports E0H–E7H.

14. Modify the circuit of Figure 8–7 so that it decodes eight $\overline{RD}$ strobes for ports A8H–AFH.
15. Why is it wise to locate all the 8-bit I/O data for an 8086 in either the high or the low banks?
16. Modify the circuit of Figure 8–8 so that it decodes I/O ports 20H–2FH.
17. Why are both BHE and A_0 ignored in a 16-bit 8086 I/O port decoder?
18. Develop a decoder that will decode I/O ports C8H–CFH for the 8088 microprocessor.
19. Develop a decoder that will decode I/O ports D0H, D2H, D4H, D6H, D8H, DAH, DCH, and DEH for the 8086.
20. The 8255A has how many programmable I/O pins?
21. List the pins that belong to group A and group B of the 8255A.
22. Which two pins accomplish internal port selection on the 8255A?
23. Modify Figure 8–11 so that the 8255A functions at I/O ports 10H–13H.
24. When the 8255A is reset, its I/O ports are all initialized as _____.
25. What three modes of operation are available for the 8255A?
26. Explain what happens each time the procedure listed in Example 8–3 is called by a program.
27. In strobed input operation of the 8255A, what is the purpose of the $\overline{STB}$ pulse?
28. What sets IBF in strobed input operation of the 8255A, and what clears it?
29. Write the software required to place a logic 1 on bit PC_7 during strobed input operation.
30. What is the purpose of the $\overline{ACK}$ signal in strobed output operation of the 8255A?
31. In strobed output operation of the 8255A, what sets the $\overline{OBF}$ signal, and what clears it?
32. Write the software required to read PC_4 in the strobed output for the 8255A.
33. Which group is used for bidirectional I/O in the 8255A?
34. What pins are general-purpose I/O pins during mode 2 operation of the 8255A?
35. What is normally connected to the CLK pin of the 8279-5 in an 8088-based system?
36. Why is the 8279-5 used in place of the 8279 in an 8086/8088-based system?
37. If the 8279-5 CLK pin is connected to a 3-MHz clock, then program the internal clock.
38. In the 8279-5 what is an overrun error?
39. Develop a procedure using the XLAT instruction to reference a lookup table for the keyboard in Figure 8–22. (Provide the procedure—not the lookup table.)
40. What is the difference between *encoded* and *decoded?*
41. The counters inside the 8254 function from DC to _____.
42. Each timer in the 8254 functions in how many different modes?
43. Interface an 8254 so that it resides at I/O ports 80H–83H for an 8088. Write software to cause counter number 2 to generate a 1-kHz square wave if the clock input is 2.5 MHz.
44. For the 8254 operated in mode 0, what number is programmed to count 300 events?
45. If a 16-bit count is programmed into the 8254, which byte of the count must be programmed first?
46. Explain how the read-back control word functions in the 8254.
47. What 8254 mode of operation is used for the circuit of Figure 8–31?
48. Why does a 50 percent duty cycle in Figure 8–31 cause the motor to stand still?

49. If Q in Figure 8–31 is a logic 1, then the motor will rotate in which direction? Which transistors are turned on?
50. A 1 placed in AH when the procedure of Example 8–13 is called will cause the motor to spin at full speed in which direction?
51. Program the 8251A for asynchronous operation using six data bits, even parity, one stop bit, and a baud rate divider of 1. (Assume that the I/O ports are numbered 20H and 21H.)
52. What is a frame of asynchronous data?
53. What is baud rate?
54. Describe the following terms: simplex, half-duplex, and full-duplex.
55. How must the 8251A be reset with the software?

CHAPTER 9

Interrupts

INTRODUCTION

In this chapter, we expand our coverage of basic I/O and programmable peripheral interfaces by examining a technique called interrupt-processed I/O. An interrupt is a hardware- or software-initiated subroutine call that interrupts whatever a program is being executed by the microprocessor.

This chapter provides examples and detailed explanation of the interrupt structure of the 8086/8088 microprocessor.

OBJECTIVES

Upon completion of this chapter, you will be able to:

1. Explain the interrupt structure of the 8086/8088.
2. Explain the operation of software interrupt instructions INT, INTO, and INT 3.
3. Explain how the interrupt enable (I) flag bit applies to interrupts.
4. Describe the function of the trap (T) flag bit and the operation of trap-generated single-stepping or tracing.
5. Develop interrupt service subroutines that control lower speed external peripheral devices.
6. Expand the interrupt structure of the 8086/8088 so that additional interrupt inputs can be added.
7. Use the 8259A to expand and enhance the interrupt structure of the 8086/8088.

9-1   **BASIC INTERRUPT PROCESSING**

In this section, we discuss the function of an interrupt in a microprocessor-based system and the structure and features of interrupts available in the 8086/8088 microprocessor.

The Purpose of Interrupts

Interrupts are particularly useful when interfacing I/O devices that provide or require data at relatively low rates. In Chapter 8, for instance, we saw a keyboard example of strobed input operation in the 8255A, in which the software polled the 8255A and its IBF bit to find out when data were available from the keyboard. If the person using the keyboard typed one character a second, then the software would ask the 8255A through the IBF bit if keyboard data were available for a second. This process is such a tremendous waste of time that designers have come up with an alternative technique called *interrupt processing* to handle this common situation.

Unlike the polling technique, interrupt processing allows the microprocessor to execute any type of program while the keyboard operator is thinking about what to type next. As soon as a key is pressed, the keyboard encoder debounces the switch and puts out a pulse that interrupts the microprocessor. In this way, the microprocessor reads data from the keyboard only when a key has actually been pressed. As a result, it can print a report or complete any other software task while the operator is typing a document and thinking about which key to type next.

8086/8088 Interrupts

The interrupts of the 8086 and 8088 are identical. Both microprocessors have two hardware interrupt inputs (INTR and NMI) and one interrupt output ($\overline{\text{INTA}}$), two interrupt-related flags (I and T) in the flag register, and four types of software interrupt instructions: INT, INTO, INT 3, and IRET.

Interrupt Vectors. The interrupt vector table is crucial to an understanding of hardware and software interrupts. It is located in the first 1,024 bytes of memory at locations 00000H–003FFH. It contains 256 different 4-byte *interrupt vectors*, which are the addresses of the interrupt service subroutine or procedure.

Figure 9–1 illustrates the interrupt vector table for the 8086/8088 microprocessor. Notice that the first 5 vectors or pointers are dedicated functions in the 8086/8088, 27 are reserved for future use by Intel in newer products, and 224 are available to the user. Each vector is 4 bytes long and contains the starting address of the interrupt service procedure—the first 2 bytes of the vector contain the IP offset address, and the next 2 bytes contain the CS segment address.

In the following list, we describe the functions of all the dedicated interrupt vectors.

1. Type 0—Divide Error: an interrupt that occurs whenever the result of a division overflows. This occurs when an attempt is made to divide by 0 or when the quotient is too large to be held in the quotient register (AX for 16-bit division and AL for 8-bit division).

FIGURE 9–1 The interrupt vector table for the 8086/8088 microprocessor. (Courtesy of Intel Corporation)

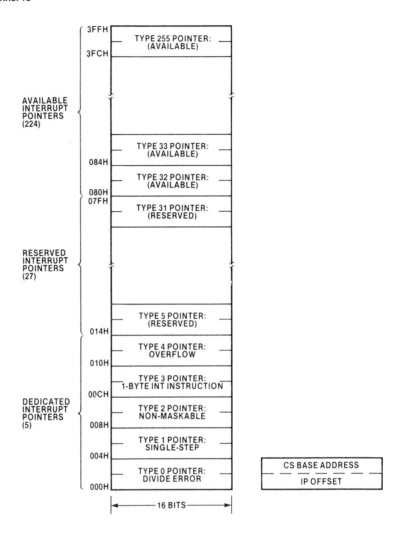

2. Type 1 — Single-Step or Trace: an interrupt that occurs after each instruction when the trap (T) flag is set. This allows the writing of software that will trace or single-step, provided the correct address for the interrupt service procedure is located at this vector. More detail about this procedure follows later in this section.

3. Type 2 — Nonmaskable Hardware Interrupt: a function that occurs when a logic 1 is applied to the NMI pin on the 8086/8088. *Nonmaskable* means that it cannot be turned off.

4. Type 3 — 1-Byte Interrupt Instruction: a special instruction discussed later in this section.

5. Type 4 — Overflow: an interrupt that occurs if the INTO instruction is used in a program and the overflow (O) flag is set. The INTO instruction is a conditional interrupt instruction covered later in this section.

Interrupt Instructions: INTO, INT, INT 3, and IRET. Of the four software interrupt instructions available in the 8086/8088, INT and INT 3 are very similar, while INTO, a conditional interrupt, and IRET, a special return instruction, are quite distinct.

INTO checks the overflow flag. If it is set, INTO calls the interrupt procedure that begins at the location addressed by interrupt vector type 4 (00010H–00013H). If the overflow flag is cleared, INTO is a NOP, and execution continues with the next sequential instruction in the program.

INT *n* calls the interrupt service procedure that begins at vector type *n*. For example, an INT 80H or INT 128 calls the interrupt service procedure located at the address pointed to by interrupt vector type 80H (00200H-00203H). To determine the vector address, just multiply the vector number (*n*) by 4. This gives the beginning location of the 4-byte interrupt vector. For example, INT 4 = 4 × 4 or 16 (10H). The vector of INT 4 begins at address 10H and continues to location 13H. Each INT is 2 bytes long, except for the INT 3 instruction, which is 1 byte long. INT 3 is often used as a breakpoint interrupt because it is easy to insert 1 byte in a program. Breakpoints are often used when debugging software.

IRET is a special return instruction that terminates execution of an interrupt service procedure. It is much like a normal RET except that, in addition to retrieving the return address from the stack, it also retrieves a copy of the flag register. IRET is thus a combination RET and POPF instruction. (Interrupt service procedures can end with a POPF followed by a RET, but IRET is much more efficient.)

The Operation of an Interrupt. When the 8086/8088 completes executing the current instruction, it determines whether an interrupt is active by checking (1) trap and divide error (highest priority), (2) the software interrupts, and (3) the hardware interrupt inputs (INTR and NMI) (lowest priority). If any interrupt is present, the following sequence of events occurs:

1. The contents of the flag register are pushed onto the stack.
2. Both the interrupt (I) and trap (T) flags are cleared. This disables future INTR hardware interrupts and also a trap or single-step interrupt.
3. The contents of the code segment (CS) register are pushed onto the stack.
4. The contents of the instruction pointer (IP) are pushed onto the stack.
5. The interrupt vector contents are fetched and placed into both IP and CS so that the next instruction executes at the interrupt service procedure addressed by the vector.

Whenever an interrupt is accepted, therefore, the microprocessor stacks the contents of the flags, CS, and IP; clears both the I and T flags; and jumps to the procedure addressed by the vector. Please note that two of the flags are also affected by the acceptance of an interrupt. When the IRET instruction is encountered, the flags are retrieved from the stack, which restores the prior state of both T and I. Therefore, if interrupts were enabled prior to the interrupt, they are automatically reenabled by the IRET instruction upon return.

Interrupt Flag Bits. Let us look more closely at the operation of the I and T flags, which are cleared when an interrupt is accepted by the 8086/8088. (Refer to Figure 9–2 for the flag register.) When the I bit is set, it allows the INTR pin to cause an interrupt; when

FIGURE 9–2 The
8086/8088 flag register.
(Courtesy of Intel Corporation)

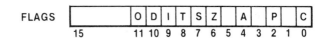

cleared, it prevents the INTR input from causing an interrupt. When the T bit is set, it
causes a trap interrupt to occur after the execution of each instruction. When T is cleared,
normal program execution continues.

I is set and cleared by the STI and CLI instructions, respectively. There are no
special instructions to clear and set the T flag. It is set to begin a trace or single-step and
cleared to turn trace or single-step off. Example 9–1 shows an interrupt service procedure
for turning trace on, and Example 9–2 shows an interrupt service procedure for turning
it off.

EXAMPLE 9–1

```
                        ;Procedure to turn trace on.
                        ;

0000                    TRACE_ON        PROC FAR

0000   50                              PUSH AX          ;save registers
0001   55                              PUSH BP
0002   8B EC                           MOV  BP,SP        ;get SP
0004   8B 46 08                        MOV  AX,[BP+8]    ;get flags
0007   80 CC 01                        OR   AH,1         ;set T flag
000A   89 46 08                        MOV  [BP+8],AX    ;save flags
000D   5D                              POP  BP           ;restore registers
000E   58                              POP  AX
000F   CF                              IRET

0010                    TRACE_ON        ENDP
```

EXAMPLE 9–2

```
                        ;Procedure to turn trace off.
                        ;

0000                    TRACE_OFF       PROC FAR

0000   50                              PUSH AX          ;save registers
0001   55                              PUSH BP
0002   8B EC                           MOV  BP,SP        ;get SP
0004   8B 46 08                        MOV  AX,[BP+8]    ;get flags
0007   80 E4 FE                        AND  AH,0FEH      ;clear T flag
000A   89 46 08                        MOV  [BP+8],AX    ;save flags
000D   5D                              POP  BP           ;restore registers
000E   58                              POP  AX
000F   CF                              IRET

0010                    TRACE_OFF ENDP
```

In both these examples, the flag register is retrieved from the stack via the BP register, which normally addresses data within the stack segment. After the flags are retrieved, the T bit is either set (TRACE _ ON) or cleared (TRACE _ OFF) before a return from interrupt occurs.

Trace Procedure

When the software illustrated in Example 9-3 is used to perform a trace, INT 40 is inserted in a program and the T flag is turned on to allow the instruction following INT 40 to execute. Then the type 1 trace interrupt is called. The procedure listed in Example 9-3 will display all the registers on the CRT screen between the INT 40 (TRACE _ ON) and INT 41 (TRACE _ OFF) instructions. The example shows everything in this procedure except the display subroutine that accesses the register names from the code segment with a segment override prefix. Each register is displayed in the following form: AX = 0000, BX = 1011, and so forth. DISPLAY is used to actually display the contents of registers in hexadecimal form.

EXAMPLE 9-3

```
                         ;Procedure to display all the registers on the CRT
                         ;screen in response to a TRACE interrupt.
                         ;

0000                     TRACE     PROC  FAR

0000  50                           PUSH  AX                ;save registers
0001  55                           PUSH  BP
0002  53                           PUSH  BX

0003  BB 0059 R                    MOV   BX,OFFSET NAMES ;address names

                         ;display registers

0006  E8 0075 R                    CALL  CRLF              ;display CR and LF
0009  E8 0084 R                    CALL  DISPLAY           ;display AX
000C  58                           POP   AX
000D  50                           PUSH  AX
000E  E8 0084 R                    CALL  DISPLAY           ;display BX
0011  8B C1                        MOV   AX,CX
0013  E8 0084 R                    CALL  DISPLAY           ;display CX
0016  8B C2                        MOV   AX,DX
0018  E8 0084 R                    CALL  DISPLAY           ;display DX
001B  8B C4                        MOV   AX,SP
001D  05 000C                      ADD   AX,12
0020  E8 0084 R                    CALL  DISPLAY           ;display SP
0023  8B C5                        MOV   AX,BP
0025  E8 0084 R                    CALL  DISPLAY           ;display BP
0028  8B C6                        MOV   AX,SI
002A  E8 0084 R                    CALL  DISPLAY           ;display SI
002D  8B C7                        MOV   AX,DI
002F  E8 0084 R                    CALL  DISPLAY           ;display DI
0032  8B EC                        MOV   BP,SP
```

```
0034   8B 46 06              MOV     AX,[BP+6]
0037   E8 0084 R             CALL    DISPLAY          ;display IP
003A   8B 46 0A              MOV     AX,[BP+10]
003D   E8 0084 R             CALL    DISPLAY          ;display Flags
0040   8B 46 08              MOV     AX,[BP+8]
0043   E8 0084 R             CALL    DISPLAY          ;display CS
0046   8C D8                 MOV     AX,DS
0048   E8 0084 R             CALL    DISPLAY          ;display DS
004B   8C D0                 MOV     AX,SS
004D   E8 0084 R             CALL    DISPLAY          ;display SS
0050   8C C0                 MOV     AX,ES
0052   E8 0084 R             CALL    DISPLAY          ;display ES
0055   5B                    POP     BX               ;restore registers
0056   5D                    POP     BP
0057   58                    POP     AX
0058   CF                    IRET

0059                  TRACE  ENDP

0059   41 58         NAMES:  DB      'AX'
005B   42 58                 DB      'BX'
005D   43 58                 DB      'CX'
005F   44 58                 DB      'DX'
0061   53 50                 DB      'SP'
0063   42 50                 DB      'BP'
0065   53 49                 DB      'SI'
0067   44 49                 DB      'DI'
0069   49 50                 DB      'IP'
006B   46 4C                 DB      'FL'
006D   43 53                 DB      'CS'
006F   44 53                 DB      'DS'
0071   53 53                 DB      'SS'
0073   45 53                 DB      'ES'


0075                  CRLF   PROC    NEAR

0075   50                    PUSH    AX               ;save registers
0076   52                    PUSH    DX
0077   B4 06                 MOV     AH,6
0079   B2 0D                 MOV     DL,0DH
007B   CD 21                 INT     21H              ;display CR
007D   B2 0A                 MOV     DL,0AH
007F   CD 21                 INT     21H              ;display LF
0081   5A                    POP     DX               ;restore registers
0082   58                    POP     AX
0083   C3                    RET

0084                  CRLF   ENDP

0084                  DISPLAY PROC   NEAR

0084   52                    PUSH    DX               ;save registers
0085   57                    PUSH    DI
0086   51                    PUSH    CX
0087   50                    PUSH    AX
```

```
0088   B4 06                        MOV    AH,6
008A   2E: 8A 17                    MOV    DL,CS:[BX]
008D   CD 21                        INT    21H              ;display name
008F   43                           INC    BX
0090   2E: 8A 17                    MOV    DL,CS:[BX]
0093   CD 21                        INT    21H
0095   43                           INC    BX
0096   B2 3D                        MOV    DL,'='
0098   5F                           POP    DI               ;get value
0099   57                           PUSH   DI
009A   B6 04                        MOV    DH,4

009C                        DISPLAY1:

009C   B9 0004                      MOV    CX,4             ;load count
009F   D3 C7                        ROL    DI,CL
00A1   8B C7                        MOV    AX,DI
00A3   B4 06                        MOV    AH,6
00A5   8A D0                        MOV    DL,AL
00A7   80 E2 0F                     AND    DL,15
00AA   80 C2 30                     ADD    DL,30H           ;convert to ASCII
00AD   CD 21                        INT    21H
00AF   FE CE                        DEC    DH
00B1   75 E9                        JNZ    DISPLAY1

00B3   B0 20                        MOV    AL,' '
00B5   CD 21                        INT    21H
00B7   58                           POP    AX               ;restore registers
00B8   59                           POP    CX
00B9   5F                           POP    DI
00BA   5A                           POP    DX
00BB   C3                           RET

00BC                        DISPLAY   ENDP
```

Storing the Interrupt Vector in the Vector Table. In order to install an interrupt vector, the assembler must address absolute memory. Example 9–4 illustrates how a new vector is added to the memory by means of the assembler. The address of the interrupt service subroutine is initialized by using a DOS function. Refer to Appendix A for more detail.

EXAMPLE 9–4

```
                       ;Using the DOS BIOS function 21H for installing interrupt
                       ;vector 40H.  This assumes that you have stored the correct
                       ;interrupt service procedure address at NEW_OFFSET and
                       ;NEW_SEG.

0000                        SETUP_40   PROC   FAR

0000   1E                           PUSH   DS
0001   B4 35                        MOV    AH,35H           ;get current vector
0003   B0 40                        MOV    AL,40H           ;vector number
```

```
0005   CD 21                    INT     21H
0007   8B 1E 0008 R             MOV     BX,OLD_OFFSET      ;save old vector
000B   8E 06 000A R             MOV     ES,OLD_SEG
000F   8E 1E 000E R             MOV     DS,NEW_SEG         ;get new vector
0013   8B 16 000C R             MOV     DX,NEW_OFFSET
0017   B4 25                    MOV     AH,25H             ;set new vector
0019   B0 40                    MOV     AL,40H
001B   CD 21                    INT     21H
001D   1F                       POP     DS
001E   CB                       RET

001F              SETUP_40      ENDP
```

9-2   HARDWARE INTERRUPTS

The 8086/8088 has two hardware interrupt inputs: nonmaskable interrupt (NMI) and interrupt request (INTR). Because the NMI is internally decoded, a type-2 interrupt is executed whenever this pin is activated. The INTR input must be externally decoded to select a vector. Any vector is allowed for INTR, but in most cases it is chosen above the reserved interrupt vectors. The $\overline{\text{INTA}}$ output provides a vector number in response to an INTR. (Refer to Figure 9-3 for the interrupt pins on the 8086/8088 microprocessor.)

NMI

The nonmaskable interrupt (NMI) is an edge-triggered input that requests an interrupt on the positive edge (0-1) transition. This input must go low for at least two clocking periods before the positive edge is recognized by the 8086/8088.

NMI is often used for parity error or other major system interrupt requirements like power failures. Power failures are detected by monitoring the AC power line and causing an NMI interrupt whenever AC power drops out. In response to this type of interrupt, the processor will store the contents of the internal registers in a battery-backed-up memory.

FIGURE 9-3 The 8086/8088 interrupt pins.

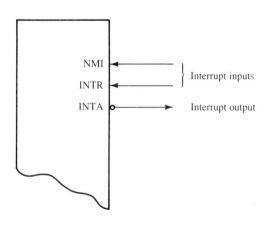

Figure 9–4 depicts a powerful-failure detection circuit that provides a logic 1 to the NMI input whenever power is interrupted.

In this circuit, an optical coupler provides isolation from the AC power line. The output of the coupler is shaped by a Schmitt trigger circuit so that it provides a 60-Hz square wave to the 74LS122 retriggerable single-shot. R and C are chosen so that the single shot can be fired for a period of time equal to two periods of the 60-Hz signal or 33.3 ms. As long as AC power is applied, the 74LS122 will be triggered and provide a logic 0 to the NMI pin. Three cycles after the AC power fails, the NMI pin of the 8086/8088 will become a logic 1, which requests an NMI interrupt. The interrupt service procedure (not shown here) stores all the registers in a battery-backed-up memory. In order for this to function properly, the filter capacitor in the microprocessor's power supply must provide enough power, for long enough, for the microprocessor to store all the data.

Figure 9–5 illustrates a circuit that supplies power to the memory when DC power fails. Here diodes switch the supply voltage between the + 5-V DC input and the battery. Because the diodes are germanium, the amount of voltage drop is minimal. The type of battery is either an NiCAD or a gel cell. Notice also that there is a pullup register for the

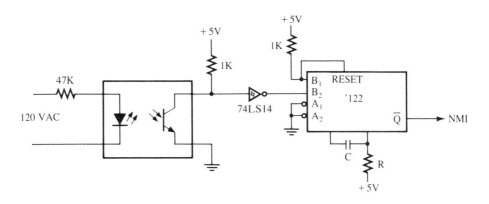

FIGURE 9–4 A power-failure detection circuit.

FIGURE 9–5 Battery backup for the memory. Note that the $\overline{WR}$ signal is provided with a pullup so that when DC power fails, the $\overline{WR}$ pin remains at a logic 1 level.

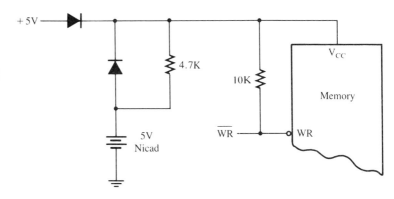

$\overline{\text{WR}}$ pin of the memory from the battery supply so that when power to the rest of the system decays to 0, the $\overline{\text{WR}}$ pin is pulled high to prevent an erroneous memory write.

INTR and $\overline{\text{INTA}}$

The interrupt request (INTR) input is level-sensitive. It must be held at a logic 1 level until it is recognized and must be returned to a logic 0 level before the end of the interrupt service procedure. This input is automatically disabled at its acceptance by the micro-processor and automatically reenabled at the end of the interrupt service procedure by the IRET instruction.

$\overline{\text{INTA}}$ (interrupt acknowledge) forces an interrupt type number onto the data bus in response to the INTR input (see Figure 9–6). Figure 9–7 shows how a simple circuit

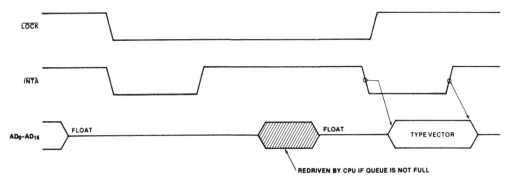

FIGURE 9–6 Timing for an interrupt acknowledge ($\overline{\text{INTA}}$). (Courtesy of Intel Corporation)

FIGURE 9–7 A simple method for causing a type-255 Interrupt in response to an INTR input. Note the re-sistors ensure that the data bus is at an FFH (255) when-ever an $\overline{\text{INTA}}$ occurs.

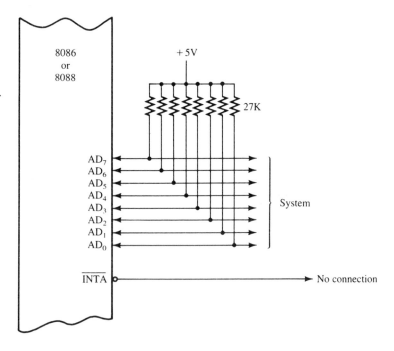

(only resistors) can cause a type-255 interrupt in response to INTR. Notice that the $\overline{\text{INTA}}$ pin is not connected. The microprocessor fetches the vector number from the data bus during the $\overline{\text{INTA}}$ pulse, but here an FFH (255) is fetched because the resistors have ensured that the data bus will be pulled up to FFH during the $\overline{\text{INTA}}$ cycle. If only one external interrupt is added, then this is the best method for handling a single interrupt.

Using a Three-State Buffer for $\overline{\text{INTA}}$. Figure 9–8 shows how a type 128 interrupt is caused in response to an INTR input. An $\overline{\text{INTA}}$ on 8086/8088 enables the 74LS244, which causes the 80H (128) to be applied to the data bus, where it is fetched as the interrupt type number.

This circuit works only in the minimum mode. In the maximum mode, the $\overline{\text{LOCK}}$ signal is logically combined with $\overline{\text{INTA}}$ to generate the enable signal to the 74LS244 three-state buffer. Figure 9–9 shows the NAND gate used to generate the enable signal in the maximum mode.

The 8255A Keyboard Interrupt

The keyboard example presented in the last chapter provides a simple example of the operation of the INTR input and an interrupt.

Figure 9–10 illustrates the interconnection of the 8255A with the 8088 microprocessor operated in the minimum mode and the keyboard. It also shows how the 74LS244 three-state buffer is connected to provide the 8088 with vector number 40H (INT 40H) during an $\overline{\text{INTA}}$.

The 8255A is operated in mode 1, the strobed input mode, so that whenever a key is pressed, the INTR output (PC_3) goes high, requesting an INTR interrupt. It remains high until the data are input from port A. In other words, every time a key is pressed, the

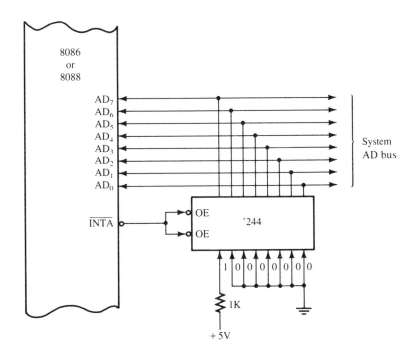

FIGURE 9–8 A type-80H response to an $\overline{\text{INTA}}$ (minimum mode operation).

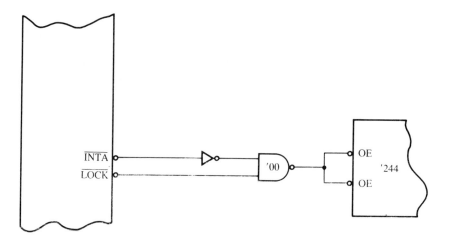

FIGURE 9-9   Generating an $\overline{\text{INTA}}$ enable signal in the maximum mode.

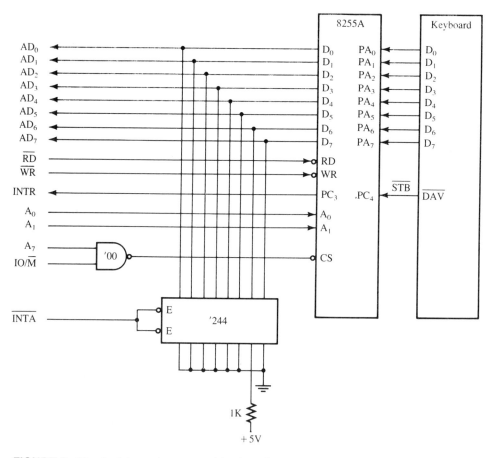

FIGURE 9-10   An interrupt processed keyboard.

8255A calls a type-40H interrupt. The $\overline{DAV}$ signal from the keyboard causes data to be strobed into port A from the keyboard whenever it is active. This action also causes INTR to be placed at the logic 1 level through the 8255A.

Example 9–5 illustrates the interrupt service procedure for the keyboard. It is very important for all registers affected by an interrupt service procedure to be saved before they are used. In the software required to initialize the 8255A (not shown here), the FIFO is initialized with both pointers equal, and the 8255A is programmed. The 8255A is decoded in this example as I/O port number 80H–83H.

EXAMPLE 9–5

```
                          ;Interrupt service procedure for a keyboard.

= 0080                    PORTA     EQU   80H
= 0083                    CONTROL   EQU   83H

0000                      KEYBOARD  PROC  FAR

0000   50                           PUSH  AX                    ;save registers
0001   53                           PUSH  BX
0002   57                           PUSH  DI

0003   8B 1E 0010 R                 MOV   BX,IN_POINT           ;address FIFO
0007   8B 3E 0012 R                 MOV   DI,OUT_POINT
000B   FE C3                        INC   BL                    ;test for full
000D   3B DF                        CMP   BX,DI
000F   74 0D                        JE    FULL                  ;if full

0011   FE CB                        DEC   BL
0013   E4 80                        IN    AL,PORTA              ;read data
0015   88 07                        MOV   [BX],AL               ;save data
0017   FE 06 0010 R                 INC   BYTE PTR IN_POINT
001B   EB 05 90                     JMP   DONE

001E                      FULL:

001E   B0 08                        MOV   AL,00001000B          ;disable interrupts
0020   E6 83                        OUT   CONTROL,AL

0022                      DONE:

0022   5F                           POP   DI                    ;restore registers
0023   5B                           POP   BX
0024   58                           POP   AX
0025   CF                           IRET

0026                      KEYBOARD  ENDP
```

This procedure is fairly short because the 8086/8088 already knows that keyboard data are available when the procedure is called. Data are input from the keyboard and then stored in a FIFO (first-in, first-out) buffer, a very common software feature in the I/O-microprocessor interface. The FIFO in this example is 256 bytes, which is more than adequate for any keyboard interface. Many computers use a 16-byte FIFO.

This procedure first checks to see if the FIFO is full. This status is indicated when the input pointer (IN _ POINT) is one less than the output pointer (OUT _ POINT). If the FIFO is full, the interrupt is turned off with the bit set/reset command for the 8255A, and a return is made. If it is not full, then the data are input from the 8255A, which turns off the INTR signal. The data are then stored in the FIFO, and a return occurs.

Example 9–6 illustrates the procedure used to read the FIFO. This procedure first determines whether the FIFO is empty by comparing the pointers. If they are equal, then the FIFO is empty and the software waits. The EMPTY loop is interrupted by the interrupt service procedure when another byte of keyboard data is placed in the FIFO. If the FIFO is not empty, the data are moved from the FIFO to AH, the interrupt output of the 8255A is turned on, and the output pointer is incremented before the return is made with the character in AH.

EXAMPLE 9–6

```
                       ;Procedure to read keyboard data from the FIFO
                       ;
                       ;keyboard character is returned in AH
                       ;

 = 0083                CONTROL   EQU   83H

0000                   READ_KEY  PROC  NEAR

0000   53                        PUSH  BX              ;save registers
0001   57                        PUSH  DI

0002                   EMPTY:

0002   8B 1E 0010·R             MOV   BX,IN_POINT     ;test for empty
0006   8B 3E 0012 R             MOV   DI,OUT_POINT
000A   3B FB                    CMP   DI,BX
000C   74 F4                    JE    EMPTY           ;if empty

000E   8A 25                    MOV   AH,[DI]         ;read character

0010   B0 09                    MOV   AL,9            ;enable 8255A interrupt
0012   E6 83                    OUT   CONTROL,AL
0014   FE 06 0012 R             INC   BYTE PTR OUT_POINT

0018   5F                       POP   DI              ;restore registers
0019   5B                       POP   BX
001A   C3                       RET

001B                   READ_KEY  ENDP
```

9–3   EXPANDING THE INTERRUPT STRUCTURE

This text covers three of the more common methods of expanding the interrupt structure of the 8086/8088 microprocessor. In this section, we explain how, with software and some modification of the circuit of Figure 9–8, it is possible to add six interrupt pins to the

INTR input. We also explain how to "daisy chain" interrupts by software polling. In the next section, we describe a third technique in which up to 63 interrupt inputs can be added by means of the 8259 programmable interrupt controller.

Using the 74LS244 to Expand Interrupts

The modification shown in Figure 9–11 allows the circuit of Figure 9–8 to accommodate up to seven additional interrupt inputs. The only hardware change is the addition of an eight-input NAND gate, which provides the INTR input with a signal if any of the interrupt request lines ($\overline{IR}$) is active. This makes the interrupt request inputs active-low instead of active-high, which means that the outputs of most peripheral components with interrupt request outputs must be inverted.

Operation. If any of the $\overline{IR}$ inputs become a logic 0, then the output of the NAND gate goes to a logic 1 level and requests an interrupt. Which interrupt vector is fetched depends on which interrupt request input becomes active. Table 9–1 illustrates the interrupt vectors used by a single interrupt request input.

If two or more interrupt request inputs are simultaneously active, a new interrupt vector is called. For example, if $\overline{IR}_1$ and $\overline{IR}_0$ are both active, then the vector fetched is an

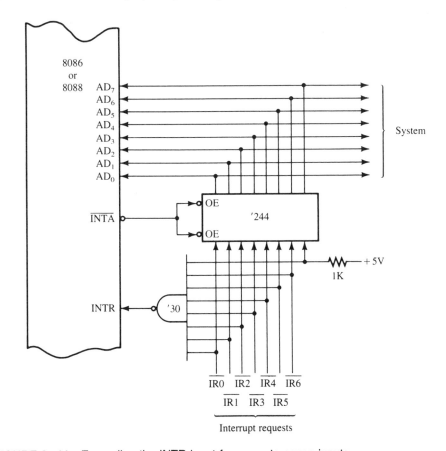

FIGURE 9–11 Expanding the INTR input from one to seven inputs.

TABLE 9–1   Single interrupt requests

AD_7	IR_6	R_5	IR_4	IR_3	IR_2	IR_1	IR_0	Vector
1	1	1	1	1	1	1	0	FEH (254)
1	1	1	1	1	1	0	1	FDH (253)
1	1	1	1	1	0	1	1	FBH (251)
1	1	1	1	0	1	1	1	F7H (247)
1	1	1	0	1	1	1	1	EFH (239)
1	1	0	1	1	1	1	1	DFH (223)
1	0	1	1	1	1	1	1	BFH (191)

FCH (252). Priority is resolved at this vector location. If the $\overline{IR}_0$ input is to have the higher priority, then the vector address for $\overline{IR}_0$ is stored at vector location FCH. If the $\overline{IR}_1$ input is to have the higher priority, then the address of the $\overline{IR}_1$ interrupt service procedure is stored at FCH. The entire top half of the interrupt vector table and its 128 vectors must be used to accommodate all the possible combinations of these seven interrupt request inputs. This seems wasteful, but in many dedicated applications it is a cost effective approach.

Daisy-Chained Interrupts

Expansion by means of the daisy-chained interrupt is in many ways better than 74LS244 interrupt expansion because it requires only one interrupt vector location. The task of determining priority is left to the interrupt service procedure. Setting the priority for these inputs does require some additional software and time, but in general this is a much better approach to expanding the interrupt structure of the 8086/8088.

Figure 9–12 illustrates a set of two 8255A peripheral interfaces with their four INTR outputs daisy chained and connected to the single INTR input pin of the 8086/8088. If any interrupt output goes high, so does the INTR input to the 8086/8088.

It is possible to reduce the amount of hardware required for this technique by using resistors to pull up the data bus so that interrupt vector FFH (255) is assigned for this circuit. Any interrupt output will cause INTR to go high, requesting an interrupt at vector FFH. Vector FFH is fetched because the 8086/8088 sees an FFH when it looks to the data bus during the $\overline{INTA}$ pulse.

When INTR does go high, there is no direct way to cause an interrupt to different vectors with this technique. Instead, the interrupt service procedure located at vector address FFH polls each 8255A to determine which INTR pin is active and then calls the appropriate procedure.

The command ports assigned to the 8255As of Figure 9–12 are 03H and 07H, with the decoder connected as shown. Example 9–7 illustrates the interrupt service procedure that is called from vector FFH in this example. Notice that the procedure polls the 8255A at I/O address 03H first, so this has the highest priority of the two 8255As. It also checks the INTR B output first, so that the INTR B output of the 8255A located at I/O port 03H

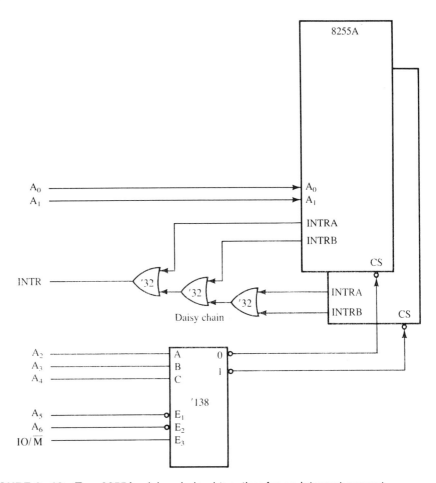

FIGURE 9-12 Two 8255As daisy chained together for an interrupt request.

has the highest priority and the INTR A output of the 8255A located at I/O port 07H has the lowest priority.

EXAMPLE 9-7

```
                        ;Interrupt service procedure that resolves priority
                        ;in a daisy-chained interrupt scheme.


 = 0003                 CONTROL_1 EQU    03H                ;first 8255A
 = 0007                 CONTROL_2 EQU    07H                ;second 8255A
 = 0001                 MASK_1    EQU    1                  ;INTRB
 = 0008                 MASK_2    EQU    8                  ;INTRA


0000                    INTERRUPT PROC   FAR
```

```
0000  50                          PUSH  AX              ;save registers

0001  E4 03                       IN    AL,CONTROL_1
0003  A8 01                       TEST  AL,MASK_1
0005  75 0D                       JNZ   LEVEL_0         ;if INTRB of first
                                                        ;8255A

0007  A8 08                       TEST  AL,MASK_2
0009  75 29                       JNZ   LEVEL_1         ;if INTRA of first
8255A

000B  E4 07                       IN    AL,CONTROL_2
000D  A8 01                       TEST  AL,MASK_1
000F  75 37                       JNE   LEVEL_2         ;if INTRB of 2nd.
8255A
0011  EB 73 90                    JMP   LEVEL_3         ;if INTRA of 2nd.
8255A


0014                              INTERRUPT  ENDP
```

9–4   8259A PROGRAMMABLE INTERRUPT CONTROLLER

The 8259A interrupt controller adds eight vectored priority interrupts to either the 8086 or 8088 microprocessor. This controller can be expanded without additional hardware to accept up to 64 interrupt request inputs. This expansion requires a master 8259A and eight slave 8259As.

General Description of the 8259A

Figure 9–13 illustrates the pinout and block diagram of the 8259A programmable interrupt controller. As the internal component parts of the 8259A indicate, the interface to the microprocessor contains the following pins: D_7-D_0, $\overline{WR}$, $\overline{RD}$, and A_0, and a $\overline{CS}$ that is used for selection. A cascade section is provided when the 8 interrupt inputs must be expanded to 64. The remainder of the block diagram is devoted to interrupt processing or 8259A control.

Pin Definitions.

1. D_7-D_0 — Bidirectional Data Bus: pins normally connected to the 8086/8088 address/data bus pins AD_7-AD_0.
2. IR_7-IR_0 — Interrupt Request: inputs used to request an interrupt and to connect to a slave if this is a master.
3. $\overline{WR}$ — Write: an input that connects to the system $\overline{WR}$ signal.

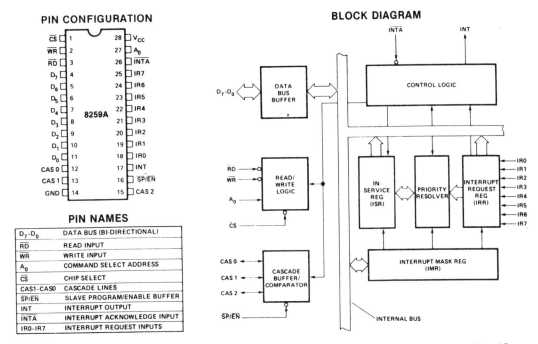

FIGURE 9-13 The pinout and block diagram of the 8259A programmable interrupt controller. (Courtesy of Intel Corporation)

4. $\overline{RD}$—Read: an input that connects to the system $\overline{RD}$ signal.

5. INT—Interrupt: an output connected to the INTR pin on the 8086/8088 or, if a slave, to one of the IR inputs of the master.

6. $\overline{INTA}$—Interrupt Acknowledge: an input connected to the 8086/8088 $\overline{INTA}$ pin. Only the master has its $\overline{INTA}$ pin connected to the 8086/8088 $\overline{INTA}$ pin.

7. A_0—Address: an input used to select different command words for the 8259A.

8. $\overline{CS}$—Chip Select: an input used to enable the 8259A.

9. $\overline{SP}/\overline{EN}$—Slave Program/Enable Buffer: A dual-function fin. When the 8259A is in buffered mode, this is an output that controls the data bus transceivers. When the 8259A is not in buffered mode, this is an input pin used to designate master (1) or slave (0).

10. CAS_2–CAS_0—Cascade Lines: outputs from the master to the slave used for cascading 8259As.

Connecting a Single 8259A

Figure 9-14 illustrates a single 8259A connected to an 8088 microprocessor operated in the minimum mode. (The same basic connection is followed when attaching the 8259A to an 8086 microprocessor operated in the minimum mode. Make sure that AD_7–AD_0 are connected to D_7–D_0 and A_0 is connected to A_1.) Here $\overline{SP}/\overline{EN}$ is pulled high so that the 8259A is programmed as a master. Also notice that this interface is decoded at I/O addresses 40H and 41H.

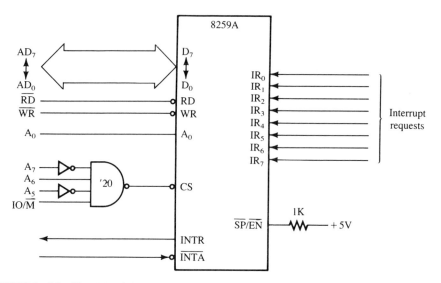

FIGURE 9–14   The 8259A interfaced to a minimum mode, unbuffered 8088 microprocessor.

Maximum mode connections differ slightly, as illustrated in the circuit of Figure 9–15, which shows an 8086 operated in the maximum mode. Here, too, the 8086 and the 8088 are connected in the same fashion. The main difference between this circuit and the one pictured in Figure 9–14 is that it contains buffers. This is because a maximum mode system is normally large enough to require buffers on both the address and data buses. In this circuit, the I/O address is decoded on the buffered side of the system, and the data I/O pins of the 8259A are connected on the microprocessor side of the data bus buffers.

Connecting Multiple 8259s to a Large Maximum Mode System

Figure 9–16 illustrates three 8259As connected to the 8088/8086 operated in maximum mode. Here all the 8259As are buffered to allow them to drive the 8286 (7LS245) bidirectional bus buffers connected to the system data bus. This occurs in very large 8088- or 8086-based systems. In this circuit, there are 22 interrupt inputs to work with. Two are to be used on the master for interconnecting with the slaves.

Programming the 8259A

The 8259A is programmed by initialization and operation command words. Initialization command words are programmed before the 8259A is able to function and dictate the basic mode of operation for the 8259A. Operation command words are used during the normal course of operation to make the 8259A function properly.

Initialization Command Words.   There are four initialization command words (ICWs) for the 8259A that are selected when $A_0 = 1$. When the 8259A is first powered up, it must be sent ICW_1 and ICW_2. ICW_3 is needed only if ICW_1 is programmed for cascade operation (SNGL = 0). ICW_4 must be programmed for 8086/8088 operation because, if

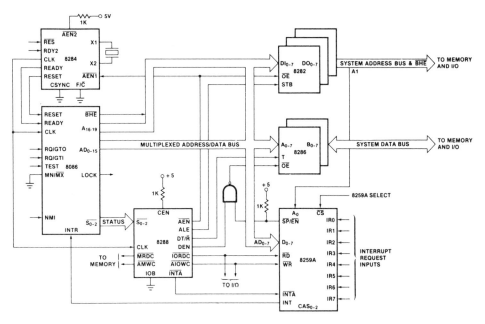

FIGURE 9-15   The 8086 connected to an 8259A. Here the 8086 is operated in the maximum mode. (Courtesy of Intel Corporation)

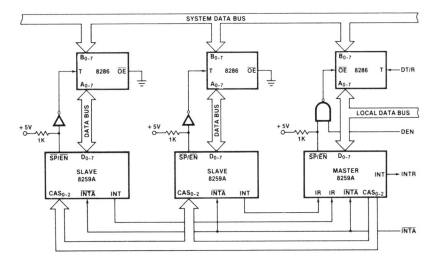

FIGURE 9-16   Cascaded 8259As connected to the 8086/8088 bus. (Courtesy of Intel Corporation)

IC_4 of ICW_1 is a logic 0, then all the bits of ICW_4 are cleared to 0, which sets up the 8259A in the MCS-80/85 mode. So single-mode operation requires ICW_1, ICW_2, and ICW_4 to be programmed, and cascaded operation requires all four ICWs to be programmed. Refer to Figure 9-17 for the formats of all ICWs. The following sections contain descriptions of each.

FIGURE 9–17 The 8259A
initialization command words
(ICWs). (Courtesy of Intel
Corporation)

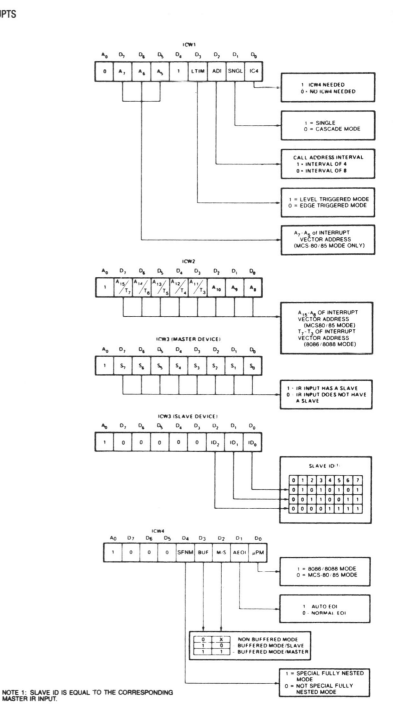

NOTE 1: SLAVE ID IS EQUAL TO THE CORRESPONDING
MASTER IR INPUT.

ICW$_1$. For 8086/8088 operation. IC$_4$ is high, and ADI, A$_7$, A$_6$, and A$_5$ are *don't cares.* Only two of these 8 bits are programmed for 8086/8088 operation. As mentioned, SNGL is programmed for single (0) or cascade (1) operation. LTIM selects the type of triggering on all eight interrupt request input pins. If LTIM is a logic 1, positive-level triggering is selected, and, if it is a logic 0, positive-edge triggering is selected.

ICW$_2$. This ICW selects the interrupt vector number T$_7$-T$_3$ for the 8086/8088 micropro- cessor. T$_2$-T$_0$ (A$_{10}$-A$_8$) are selected by the interrupt request input whenever it is accepted. For example, if this command word is programmed with a 40H, then the interrupt vectors generated by the 8259A will be 40H-47H (40H for IR$_0$, 41H for IR$_1$, etc.).

ICW$_3$. A master is programmed differently than a slave, and that is why two ICW$_3$ words are illustrated in Figure 9-17. The master ICW$_3$ is programmed to indicate which slaves are connected in the system. A logic 1 in an S bit indicates that a slave is present; a logic 0 indicates that no slave is present. The slave INT pins must be connected to an IR pin on the master. The S bit that corresponds to the IR pin is activated in the ICW.
   The slave ICW$_3$ is used to identify the slave, so it must correspond to the IR pin connected to INT on the master. Only the master $\overline{\text{INTA}}$ pin is connected to the 8086/8088, never the slave $\overline{\text{INTA}}$ pins.

ICW$_4$. The rightmost bit of the ICW$_4$ must be programmed as a logic 1 to select 8086/8088 operation. The remaining bits are programmed to select the functions indi- cated.
   The SFNM bit selects special fully nested mode (1). This mode allows the highest interrupt from a slave to be recognized by the master in cascaded mode even while an interrupt is being processed from the slave. Normally, only one interrupt request at a time is recognized from a slave by the master.
   This special mode also requires a nonspecific EOI command to be sent to the master at the end of the interrupt service subroutine if no more interrupts are pending in the slave. (The EOI command is described in the section on operation command words.)
   The BUF bit selects buffered operation as illustrated in Figure 9-16. Buffered operation is used in large systems, and nonbuffered operation is used in smaller systems like those illustrated in Figure 9-14 and Figure 9-15. M/S is used with BUF to select buffered master or slave.
   AEOI selects auto or normal end of interrupt (EOI) (discussed more fully in the OCW$_2$ section). The EOI command words are used only if the AEOI mode is not selected. If AEOI is selected, the interrupt automatically resets the interrupt request bit and does not modify priority. This is the preferred mode of operation wherever possible because it reduces the length of the interrupt service procedure.

Operation Command Words. The operation command words (OCWs) are used to direct the operation of the 8259A once it is programmed with the ICWs. OCWs are selected when A$_0$ = 0, except for OCW$_1$, which is selected when A$_0$ = 1. Figure 9-18 lists the three operation command words for the 8259A.

OCW$_1$. OCW$_1$ is used to set and read the interrupt mask register. When a mask bit is set, it will turn off (mask) the corresponding interrupt input. OCS$_1$ may also be read to determine which interrupt inputs are masked. Because the state of the internal masks is

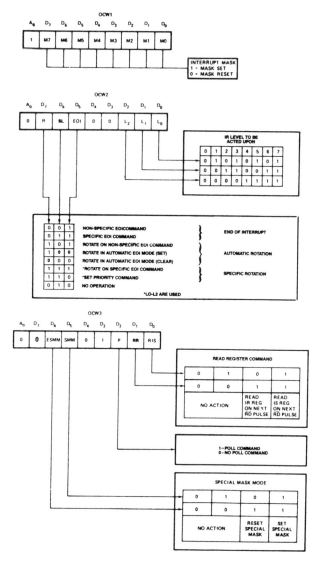

FIGURE 9–18 The 8259A operational command words (OCWs). (Courtesy of Intel Corporation)

unknown when the system is first powered up, it is important to set or reset these mask bits to configure the system. This is normally done after the ICWs are sent to the 8259A. This word *must* be sent to the 8259A to guarantee proper operation.

OCW$_2$. Bits R, L, and EOI select various command modes of operation for the interrupt level selected with bits L_2–L_0. These modes are described in the following list:

1. Nonspecific End-of-Interrupt: a command sent by the interrupt service procedure to the 8259A to signal an end of the procedure. The 8259A automatically determines which interrupt level was active and resets the correct bit of the interrupt status register. Resetting the status bit allows the interrupt to take action again or a lower priority interrupt to take effect.

2. Specific End-of-Interrupt: a command that allows a specific interrupt request to be reset. The exact position of the bit is specified with bits L_2–L_0 of OCW_2.
3. Rotate-on-Nonspecific EOI: A command that functions exactly like the nonspecific EOI command except that it rotates interrupt priorities after resetting the interrupt bit. The level reset by this command now becomes the lowest interrupt level. For example, if IR_4 was just serviced, then it would have the lowest priority after this command and IR_5 the highest. See Figure 9–19 for an illustration of this priority rotation.
4. Rotate-on-Automatic EOI: a command that causes an automatic rotate priority mode to be entered when sent to the 8259A one time. From that point forward, priorities will automatically rotate after each interrupt. To select this mode of operation, use the rotate-on-automatic EOI set command. To turn it off, use the rotate-on-automatic EOI clear command.
5. Rotate-on-Specific EOI: a command that allows the user to reset a mask bit like the rotate-on-nonspecific EOI command and also to select which interrupt input receives the lowest priority. Selection is accomplished with bits L_2–L_0 of OCW_2.
6. Set Priority: a command that allows the programmer to select the lowest priority for the interrupts with bits L_2–L_0 of OCW_2.

OCW$_3$. This command word selects the register to be read, the operation of the special mask register, and the poll command.

If polling is selected, the P bit must be set and then output to the 8259A. The next read operation will read the poll word. The rightmost 3 bits of the poll word indicate, in binary code, the active interrupt input with the highest priority. The leftmost bit indicates whether there is an interrupt, and must be checked to determine whether the rightmost 3 bits contain valid information.

Status Register. Three status registers are readable in the 8259A: interrupt request register (IRR), in-service register (ISR), and interrupt mask register (IMR). (Refer to Figure 9–20 for all three status registers.) IRR is an 8-bit register that indicates which interrupt request inputs are active. ISR is an 8-bit register that contains the levels of the interrupts being serviced. IMR is an 8-bit register that holds the interrupt mask bits and indicates which interrupts are masked off.

The IRR and ISR are read by programming through OCW_3, and IMR is read through OCW_1. A read with $A_0 = 1$ will always read the IMR; a read with $A_0 = 0$ will read IRR or ISR. IRR can be read by placing a 10 in bits D_1 and D_0 of OCW_3. After this is written to the 8259A, every read with $A_0 = 0$ will read IRR. IRR is also selected when the 8259A is initialized.

FIGURE 9–19 The 8259A in-service register (ISR). (a) Before IR4 is accepted, and (b) after IR4 is accepted. (Courtesy of Intel Corporation)

FIGURE 9–20   The 8259A status registers. (a) Interrupt request register (IRR), (b) Inservice register (ISR), and (c) Interrupt mask register (IMR).

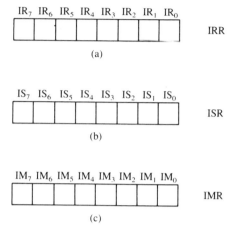

8259A Programming Example

Figure 9–21 illustrates the 8259A programmable interrupt controller (PIC) connected to an 8251A programmable communications controller. In this circuit, three interrupt output pins (TxRDY, RxRDY, and BD) are connected to the PIC's IR_0, IR_1, and IR_2 pins. An IR_0 occurs whenever the transmitter is ready to send another character. When the receiver has a character for the 8088, IR_1 is active. IR_2 is used for a break character detection. Notice that the 8251A is decoded at I/O ports 40H and 41H, and that the 8259A is decoded at I/O ports 42H and 43H.

Initialization Software.   The first portion of the software for this system must program both the 8251A and the 8259A and then enable the INTR pin of the 8088 so that interrupts can take effect. Example 9–8 illustrates the software that initializes this system.

     The first portion of this procedure resets the 8251A; programs it for seven data, even parity, one stop, and a clock divider of 64; and then enables both the transmitter and the receiver.

     The second portion of the procedure programs the 8259A with three ICWs and one OCW. An examination of the ICWs shows that ICW_1 programs the 8259A with interrupt vector numbers, which, in this example, are 80H–87H. ICW_4 selects the 8086/8088 and turns on automatic EOI so that no software is required to acknowledge interrupt requests in the 8259A.

     After the ICWs are sent to the 8259A,.the only OCW is transmitted. Here the IR pins are enabled for the receiver and break detection interrupts, but not for the transmitter interrupt. (The transmitter interrupt is only enabled when data are available for transmission.) The last step of this procedure is to enable the 8086/8088 INTR pin so that any interrupts from the receiver or the break detection pin of the 8251A can take effect immediately.

     The only other time OCW is ever sent to the 8259A in this example is when the transmitter or receiver needs to be enabled or disabled. In these situations, OCW_1 is read, modified, and again sent to mask or unmask the IR_0 or IR_1 pin, which is connected to TxRDY and RxRDY of the 8251A.

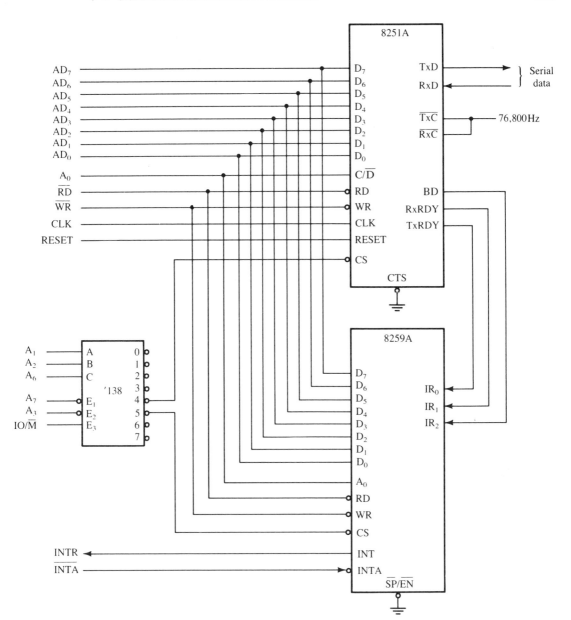

FIGURE 9–21   An example communications circuit using the 8251A and the 8259A.

EXAMPLE 9–8

```
                ;Initialization dialog for the 8251A and the 8259A
                ;
= 0041          PCIA_C EQU      41H         ;8251A control
= 0042          PIC_C1    EQU    42H         ;8259A control A0 = 0
= 0043          PIC_C2    EQU    43H         ;8259A control A0 = 1
```

```
= 0028                    FORTY    EQU   40        ;reset command
= 007B                    INST_1   EQU   7BH       ;8251A mode word
= 0015                    INST_2   EQU   15H       ;8251A command word
= 001B                    ICW1     EQU   1BH       ;8259A ICW1
= 0080                    ICW2     EQU   80H       ;8259A ICW2
= 0003                    ICW4     EQU   03H       ;8259A ICW4
= 00F9                    OCW1     EQU   0F9H      ;8259A OCW1

0000                      START_UP  PROC  FAR

                          ;Setup the 8251A for 7 data bits, even parity, one stop
                          ;bit, and a clock divide by factor of 64.

                          ;program the 8251A

0000   32 C0                        XOR   AL,AL        ;reset 8251A
0002   E6 41                        OUT   PCIA_C,AL
0004   E6 41                        OUT   PCIA_C,AL
0006   E6 41                        OUT   PCIA_C,AL
0008   B0 28                        MOV   AL,FORTY
000A   E6 41                        OUT   PCIA_C,AL

000C   B0 7B                        MOV   AL,INST_1    ;program 8251A mode
000E   E6 41                        OUT   PCIA_C,AL

0010   B0 15                        MOV   AL,INST_2    ;program 8251A command
0012   E6 41                        OUT   PCIA_C,AL

                          ;program 8259A

0014   B0 1B                        MOV   AL,ICW1      ;program ICW1
0016   E6 42                        OUT   PIC_C1,AL

0018   B0 80                        MOV   AL,ICW2      ;program ICW2
001A   E6 43                        OUT   PIC_C2,AL
001C   B0 03                        MOV   AL,ICW4      ;program ICW4
001E   E6 43                        OUT   PIC_C2,AL

0020   B0 F9                        MOV   AL,OCW1      ;program OCW1
0022   E6 43                        OUT   PIC_C2,AL

0024   FB                           STI                ;enable INTR
0025   CB                           RET

0026                      START_UP  ENDP
```

Receiving Data from the 8251A.   The data received from the 8251A are stored in an FIFO memory until the software in the main program can use them. Here the FIFO memories for both receiving and transmitting data are 16K bytes long, so that many characters of data are easily received or transmitted before any intervention from the 8086/8088 main program. Both FIFOs are stored in the extra segments, so the string operations and DI, which is in the extra segment, are used for any reference to the FIFO data.

Receiving data from the 8251A requires two procedures: one reads data from the FIFO and is used in the main program, and the other—the interrupt service procedure—writes data to the FIFO whenever RxRDY indicates that data are available to the 8251A.

EXAMPLE 9-9

```
                        ;Main read procedure for the 8251A.
                        ;AL = Character or 0FEH if empty.

   = 0043               OCW1      EQU     43H
   = 00FD               MASK1     EQU     0FDH
   = 1FFF               TOP_FIFO  EQU     1FFFH
   = 1000               BOT_FIFO  EQU     1000H

0000                    READ      PROC    FAR

0000  53                          PUSH    BX              ;save registers
0001  57                          PUSH    DI

                        ;test for empty FIFO

0002  8B 3E 0012 R              MOV     DI,OUT_POINT
0006  8B 1E 0010 R              MOV     BX,IN_POINT
000A  3B DF                     CMP     BX,DI
000C  B0 FE                     MOV     AL,0FEH           ;indicate FIFO empty
000E  74 11                     JE      DONE

                        ;get character from ES

0010  AC                          LODSB

                        ;modify and save pointer

0011  89 3E 0012 R              MOV     OUT_POINT,DI
0015  81 FF 1FFF               CMP     DI,TOP_FIFO       ;test boundary
0019  76 06                    JBE     DONE
001B  C7 06 0012 R 1000        MOV     OUT_POINT,BOT_FIFO

                        ;enable RxRDY interrupt

0021                            DONE:

0021  50                          PUSH    AX
0022  E4 43                       IN      AL,OCW1
0024  24 FD                       AND     AL,MASK1
0026  E6 43                       OUT     OCW1,AL
0028  58                          POP     AX
0029  5F                          POP     DI
002A  5B                          POP     BX
002B  CB                          RET

002C                    READ      ENDP
```

Example 9–9 illustrates the procedure used to read data from the FIFO. This procedure assumes that the pointers (IN _ PNTR and OUT _ PNTR) are initialized in the initialization dialogue for the system (not shown). It also assumes that both the top (TOP _ FIFO) and bottom (BOT _ FIFO) locations of the FIFO are defined elsewhere. The data are found in AL after a return. Any character is valid, and FEH is used to indicate no data—the FIFO-empty condition. Also notice that before the return is made, the interrupt mask register of the 8259A is modified so that the interrupt for IR_1 is enabled when the FIFO is full.

EXAMPLE 9–10

```
                        ;Interrupt service procedure for RxRDY

= 0040              DATA       EQU    40H        ;8251A data port
= 0043              OCW1       EQU    43H        ;8259A command port
= 0002              MASK2      EQU    02H        ;turn IR1 off
= 1FFF              TOP_FIFO   EQU    1FFFH
= 1000              BOT_FIFO   EQU    1000H

0000                RXRDY      PROC   FAR

0000  50                       PUSH   AX
0001  53                       PUSH   BX
0002  57                       PUSH   DI
0003  56                       PUSH   SI
0004  8B 1E 0012 R             MOV    BX,OUT_POINT
0008  8B 36 0010 R             MOV    SI,IN_POINT

                    ;Is FIFO full?

000C  8B FE                    MOV    DI,SI
000E  46                       INC    SI
000F  81 FE 1FFF               CMP    SI,TOP_FIFO
0013  76 03                    JBE    NEXT
0015  BE 1000                  MOV    SI,BOT_FIFO

0018                    NEXT:

                    ;read character and ignore error

0018  E4 40                    IN     AL,DATA
001A  AA                       STOSB
001B  89 36 0010 R             MOV    IN_POINT,SI
001F  EB 07 90                 JMP    DONE

0022                    FULL:

0022  E4 43                    IN     AL,OCW1
0024  0C 02                    OR     AL,MASK2
0026  E6 43                    OUT    OCW1,AL

0028                    DONE:
```

```
0028    5E                              POP     SI
0029    5F                              POP     DI
002A    5B                              POP     BX
002B    58                              POP     AX
002C    CF                              IRET

002D                                    RXRDY       ENDP
```

Example 9–10 illustrates the RxRDY interrupt service procedure that is called whenever the 8251A has a character for the microprocessor. In this example, this interrupt uses vector type number 81H, which contains the address of the RxRDY interrupt service procedure. RxRDY retrieves data from the 8251A and stores them in the FIFO. This is very nearly identical to the procedure in Example 9–9, except that the data are stored in the FIFO. If the FIFO is full, then the IR_1 interrupt input is disabled. This may result in lost data, but at least it will not cause a continuous IR_1 interrupt that will disrupt system operation.

Transmitting Data to the 8251A.   Data are transmitted to the 8251A in much the same manner as they are received, except that the interrupt service procedure removes them from a second FIFO.

Example 9–11 illustrates the procedure used to fill the output FIFO. It is similar to the procedure illustrated in Example 9–9, except that it determines whether the FIFO is full instead of empty.

Example 9–12 illustrates the interrupt service procedure for the 8251A transmitter TxRDY, using vector number 80H. This procedure is similar to the interrupt service procedure for RxRDY in Example 9–10, except that it determines whether the FIFO is empty rather than full.

EXAMPLE 9–11

```
                        ;Main transmit procedure for the 8251A.
                        ;AL = the character transmitted.

= 0043                  OCW1       EQU     43H            ;8259A command port
= 00FE                  MASK3      EQU     0FEH           ;turn IR0 on
= 1FFF                  TOP_FIFO   EQU     1FFFH
= 1000                  BOT_FIFO   EQU     1000H

0000                    TRANS      PROC    FAR

0000    53                         PUSH    BX
0001    57                         PUSH    DI
0002    56                         PUSH    SI

                        ;Check if FIFO full

0003    8B 36 0010 R               MOV     SI,IN_POINT
0007    8B 1E 0012 R               MOV     BX,OUT_POINT
000B    8B FE                      MOV     DI,SI
000D    46                         INC     SI
```

```
000E  81 FE 1FFF              CMP    SI,TOP_FIFO
0012  76 03                   JBE    NEXT
0014  BE 1000                 MOV    SI,BOT_FIFO

0017                   NEXT:

0017  3B DE                   CMP    BX,SI
0019  74 05                   JE     DONE          ;if full
001B  AA                      STOSB
001C  89 36 0010 R            MOV    IN_POINT,SI

0020                   DONE:

0020  E4 43                   IN     AL,OCW1
0022  24 FE                   AND    AL,MASK3
0024  E6 43                   OUT    OCW1,AL
0026  5E                      POP    SI
0027  5F                      POP    DI
0028  5B                      POP    BX
0029  CB                      RET

002A                   TRANS  ENDP
```

EXAMPLE 9-12

```
                   ;Interrupt service procedure for TxRDY
                   ;

= 0040             DATA      EQU   40H         ;8251A data port
= 0043             OCW1      EQU   43H         ;8259A command port
= 0001             MASK4     EQU   01H         ;turn IR0 off
= 1FFF             TOP_FIFO  EQU   1FFFH
= 1000             BOT_FIFO  EQU   1000H

0000               TXRDY     PROC  FAR

0000  50                     PUSH  AX
0001  53                     PUSH  BX
0002  57                     PUSH  DI
0003  8B 1E 0010 R           MOV   BX,IN_POINT
0007  8B 3E 0012 R           MOV   DI,OUT_POINT

                   ;FIFO empty?

000B  3B DF                  CMP   BX,DI
000D  74 13                  JE    EMPTY

                   ;write character

000F  AC                     LODSB
0010  E6 40                  OUT   DATA,AL
0012  81 FF 1FFF             CMP   DI,TOP_FIFO
0016  76 03                  JBE   NEXT
0018  BF 1000                MOV   DI,BOT_FIFO
```

```
001B                            NEXT:

001B   89 3E 0012 R               MOV    OUT_POINT,DI
001F   EB 07 90                   JMP    DONE

0022                            EMPTY:

0022   E4 43                      IN     AL,OCW1
0024   0C 01                      OR     AL,MASK4
0026   E6 43                      OUT    OCW1,AL

0028                            DONE:

0028   5F                         POP    DI
0029   5B                         POP    BX
002A   58                         POP    AX
002B   CF                         IRET

002C               TXRDY          ENDP
```

9–5   SUMMARY

1. An interrupt is a hardware- or software-initiated call that interrupts the currently executing program at any point and calls a procedure. The procedure called by the interrupt is an interrupt service procedure or subroutine.
2. Interrupts are useful when an I/O device needs to be serviced only occasionally at low data transfer rates.
3. The 8086/8088 has four instructions that apply to interrupts: INT, INTO, INT 3, and IRET, INT and INT 3 call procedures with addresses stored in an interrupt vector, the type number of which is stored with the instruction. INTO is a conditional interrupt that interrupts on an overflow. Finally, IRET is a special return instruction that pops the flags off the stack and then returns to the program at the point of interruption.
4. The 8086/8088 has three pins that apply to interrupts: INTR, NMI, and $\overline{\text{INTA}}$. INTR and NMI are inputs used to request interrupts. $\overline{\text{INTA}}$ is an output used to acknowledge an INTR input.
5. Interrupts are referenced through a vector table that occupies memory locations 00000H–003FFH. Each vector is 4 bytes in length and contains the IP and CS register for the interrupt service procedures.
6. Two flag bits are used with the interrupt structure of the 8086/8088: trap (T) and interrupt enable (I). The I flag enables or disables INTR, and the T flag causes interrupts after the execution of each instruction when T is active.
7. Five predefined interrupt vectors exist in the 8086/8088: divide error, single-step, NMI, 1-byte interrupt (INT 3), and interrupt on an overflow.
8. Whenever an interrupt is accepted, the following events occur: (1) the flags are pushed onto the stack, (2) the I and T flags are cleared, (3) the IP and CS registers are pushed onto the stack, and (4) the interrupt vector is fetched from the vector table, and the interrupt service procedure is called.

9. Tracing or single-stepping is accomplished by setting the T flag. This causes an interrupt to occur after the execution of each instruction.
10. The nonmaskable interrupt (NMI) inputs calls the procedure whose address is stored at vector number 2. This input is positive edge-sensitive.
11. The INTR pin is not internally decoded like the NMI input. Instead, the $\overline{\text{INTA}}$ (interrupt acknowledge) must be used to fetch the correct vector from the data bus.
12. Methods of applying the interrupt vector type to the data bus via $\overline{\text{INTA}}$ vary widely. Two methods use resistors to apply an FFH and a three-state buffer to apply any interrupt vector-type number.
13. The 8259A is a programmable interrupt controller (PIC) that adds at least eight interrupt inputs to the 8086/8088 microprocessor. If more interrupts are required, the 8259A can be expanded to 64 inputs.
14. Programming the 8259A is a two-step process. First a series of initialization command words (ICWs) are issued to the 8259A, and then operational command words (OCWs) are programmed as needed.
15. The 8259A contains three status registers: IMR (interrupt mask register), ISR (in-service register), and IRR (interrupt request register).

9-6   QUESTIONS AND PROBLEMS

1. What does an interrupt interrupt?
2. Define the term *interrupt*.
3. What is called by an interrupt?
4. Why do interrupts save microprocessor execution time?
5. List the interrupt pins.
6. List the four interrupt instructions.
7. What is an interrupt vector?
8. Where are the interrupt vectors located in the 8086/8088 memory?
9. How many different interrupt vectors are located in the interrupt vector table?
10. List the predefined interrupts.
11. Explain how a type-0 interrupt occurs.
12. Describe the operation of the INTO instruction.
13. What memory locations contain the vector for an INT 44H instruction?
14. Explain the operation of the IRET instruction.
15. List the events that occur for any interrupt input or instruction.
16. Explain the purpose of the interrupt (I) flag.
17. How is the I flag set and cleared?
18. Explain the purpose of the trap (T) flag.
19. Explain how the T flag bit is set.
20. The NMI interrupt will automatically vector through which interrupt vector type number? ____
21. Does the $\overline{\text{INTA}}$ signal activate for an NMI interrupt?
22. The INTR input is _____ -sensitive.

23. The NMI input is _____ -sensitive.
24. When INTA becomes a logic 0, it indicates that the 8086/8088 is waiting for an interrupt _____ number to be placed on the data bus.
25. What is a FIFO?
26. Modify the circuit of Figure 9–6 so that interrupt type number 86H is applied to the data bus in response to an $\overline{\text{INTA}}$.
27. Explain why the addition of pullup resistors to the data bus will automatically cause an interrupt type number of FFH to be applied in response to an $\overline{\text{INTA}}$.
28. What is a daisy chain?
29. Why must the 8255A be polled in Example 9–7?
30. What is the 8259A?
31. How many 8259As are required in order to have 64 interrupt inputs?
32. What is the purpose of the $\text{IR}_7–\text{IR}_0$ pins on the 8259A?
33. When the 8259A is not in the buffered mode, what is the function of the $\overline{\text{SP}/\overline{\text{EN}}}$ pin?
34. When are the $\text{CAS}_2–\text{CAS}_0$ lines used on the 8259A?
35. Where is the slave 8259A INT pin connected on the master 8259A?
36. What is an ICW?
37. What is an OCW?
38. How many ICWs are normally required to program a single 8259A for use with the 8086/8088?
39. Where is the vector address programmed into the 8259A?
40. Where is the sensitivity of the IR pins programmed with the 8259A?
41. What is the purpose of OCW_1?
42. Which ICW is used to select the poll status word?
43. What is a nonspecific end-of-interrupt command?
44. How is the automatic priority rotation selected for the 8259A?
45. What is the purpose of the IRR?

CHAPTER 10

Direct Memory Access

INTRODUCTION

In previous chapters, we discussed basic and interrupt-processed I/Os. Now it is time to turn to the final form of I/O—**direct memory access** (DMA). DMA provides direct access to the memory while the microprocessor is turned off. This allows data to be transferred between the memory and the I/O device at a rate of speed that is limited only by the speed of the memory components in a system. DMA speeds can often approach 8–10M-byte transfer rates with today's high-speed RAM memory components.

DMA transfers are used for many purposes, but the more common are CRT screen refreshing and disk memory system reads and writes. DMA is also sometimes used to do high-speed memory-to-memory data transfers.

OBJECTIVES

Upon completion of this chapter, you will be able to:

1. Describe a DMA transfer.
2. Explain the function of the 8086/8088 minimum mode control signals HOLD and HLDA.
3. Explain the function of the 8086/8088 maximum mode control signal $\overline{RQ}/\overline{GT}$.
4. Use the 8237-2 for minimum mode DMA transfers.
5. Explain the operation and function of the 8289 bus arbiter.
6. Describe how multiple processors can function in a common system.

10-1   MINIMUM MODE DMA

The two control signals used to request and acknowledge a DMA when the 8086/8088 is operating in the minimum mode are, respectively, the HOLD input pin and the HLDA (hold acknowledge) output pin. Figure 10–1 illustrates the HOLD and HLDA timing diagrams.

DMA Control Pins

Whenever the HOLD input pin is placed at its logic 1 level, a HOLD is requested. The 8086/8088 responds to the request by placing its address, data, and control buses at their high-impedance state. This procedure allows an external DMA I/O device to control the memory through the buses. (The only control bus signal that does not go to its high-impedance state is the ALE signal, which is a logic 0 during a HOLD.)

As the timing diagram indicates, HOLD is sampled prior to T_1 or T_4 only. Thus it can take effect in any bus cycle. It can occur in the middle of any instruction because many instructions require more than one bus cycle to execute. The HOLD input has a higher priority than any interrupt. The only input in the 8086/8088 with a higher priority than a HOLD is RESET.

The HLDA output signal becomes active to indicate that the 8086/8088 has indeed placed its buses at their high-impedance states. After the buses are floated, HLDA signals a HOLD by becoming a logic 1. HLDA again goes to its logic 0 level before the buses return to normal, but not until the HOLD input goes to a logic 0.

To operate properly, the HOLD input to the 8086/8088 microprocessor must be synchronized with the system clock through the connection of a D-type flip-flop to the HOLD pin of the 8086/8088 (see Figure 10–2). Notice that RESET is connected to the reset (CLR) input of the flip-flop. RESET initially clears the flip-flop so that no HOLD will be requested when the 8086/8088 is powered up.

Basic DMA Definitions

DMAs normally occur between an I/O device and the memory. A *DMA read* transfers data from the memory (memory read) to an I/O device. A *DMA write* transfers data from the I/O to the memory. In both cases, the memory and I/O must be controlled simultaneously.

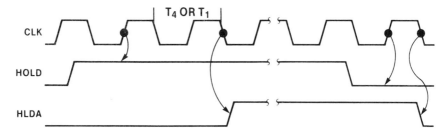

FIGURE 10–1   HOLD and HLDA timing for the 8086/8088 microprocessor.

FIGURE 10–2 HOLD syn-
chronization.

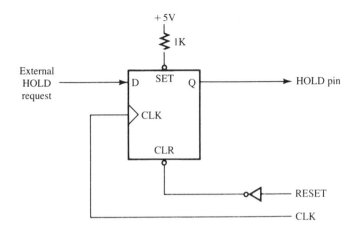

A *verify cycle* sends the DMA addresses to the memory, but does not do a read or a write to either the memory or the I/O.

New Control Bus. In order to control both the memory and I/O devices in a system, a new system control structure must be developed in the minimum mode. $\overline{RD}$, $\overline{WR}$, and IO/$\overline{M}$ are designed to control either the memory or I/O; they will not allow both to be accessed simultaneously.

DMA requires four new signals to control memory and I/O. Two signals—$\overline{MEMR}$ (memory read) and $\overline{MEMW}$ (memory write)—control the memory, and two signals—$\overline{IOR}$ (I/O read) and $\overline{IOW}$ (I/O write)—control the I/O. During a DMA read, the $\overline{MEMR}$ and $\overline{IOW}$ signals are active, and during a DMA write, the $\overline{MEMW}$ and $\overline{IOR}$ signals are active. These signals must be connected to all memory and I/O devices in the system.

Figure 10–3 illustrates a circuit that generates the new control signals for use with a DMA. The circuit illustrated here is for use in the 8088 microprocessor. It uses the B input to the 74LS257B Quad Multiplexer to select the B inputs for I/O and the A inputs for memory. $\overline{RD}$ is steered through the 74LS257B to the $\overline{IOR}$ pin when B is high and to the $\overline{MEMR}$ pin when B is low. The same applies to $\overline{WR}$, except that it is steered through to $\overline{IOW}$ (B pin high) or $\overline{MEMW}$ (B pin low). The HLDA signal disables the output pins of the 74LS257B during a DMA.

When this circuit is used in the 8086, the outputs are relabeled from top to bottom—$\overline{MEMR}$, $\overline{MEMW}$, $\overline{IOR}$, and $\overline{IOW}$—because B is connected to the M/$\overline{IO}$ signal instead of the IO/$\overline{M}$ signal as in the 8088.

8237A-5 DMA Controller

The 8237A-5 DMA controller supplies the memory and I/O with control signals and memory address information during a DMA transfer. It is actually a special-purpose microprocessor whose only job is high-speed data transfer between the memory and the I/O. Figure 10–4 illustrates the pinout and block diagram of the 8237A-5 programmable DMA controller.

The 8237A-5 is a four-channel 8086/8088-compatible DMA controller with internal DMA channel priority selected through programming. It can be expanded to any number of DMA channel inputs, although four DMA channels seem to be adequate for many

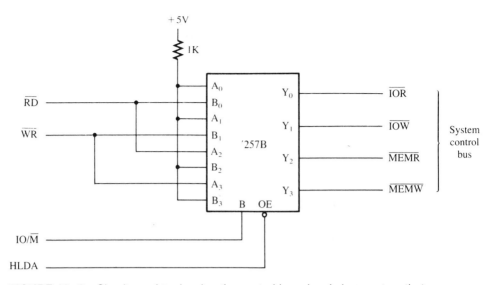

FIGURE 10-3 Circuit used to develop the control bus signals in a system that uses minimum mode DMA for the 8088 microprocessor.

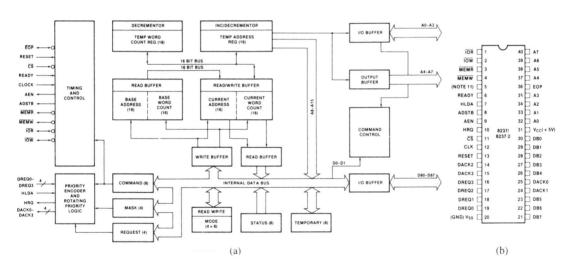

FIGURE 10-4 The 8237A-5 programmable DMA controller. (a) Block diagram, and (b) pinout. (Courtesy of Intel Corporation)

systems. The 8237A-5 is capable of DMA transfers at rates of up to 1.6M bytes per second. Each channel of the controller is capable of addressing a full 64K-byte section of memory and can transfer 64K bytes with a single programming.

Pin Definitions.

1. CLK (clock) is connected to the 5-MHz system CLK signal. (It must be inverted for proper operation with the 8086/8088 microprocessor, and its maximum is 5 MHz.)

2. $\overline{CS}$ (chip select) is used to select the 8237A-5 during programming. It is normally connected to the output of a decoder. The decoder does not use IO/$\overline{M}$ or M/$\overline{IO}$ because the controller already has the new control signal inputs.

3. RESET (reset) is used to clear the command, status, request, and temporary registers. It also clears the first/last flip-flop and sets the mask register. This primes the 8237A-5 so that it is disabled until programmed otherwise.

4. READY (ready) is an input used in the 8086/8088-based system to cause wait states for slower memory and/or I/O.

5. HLDA (hold acknowledge) is an input to the 8237A-5 that indicates that the 8086/8088 has floated its buses.

6. DREQ$_3$–DREQ$_0$ (DMA request) are the DMA request inputs for each of the four DMA channels. Because the polarity of these inputs is programmable, they are either active-high or active-low. The RESET input initializes these pins as active-high inputs.

7. DB$_7$–DB$_0$ (data bus) are pins connected to the 8086/8088 address/data bus and used during programming and DMA operations. During a DMA, these pins contain the most significant 8 bits of the DMA-transfer 16-bit memory address (A$_{15}$–A$_8$). They contain data only during a transfer for the special block move mode of operation.

8. $\overline{IOR}$ (I/O read) is a bidirectional pin used during programming and during a DMA write cycle.

9. $\overline{IOW}$ (I/O write) is a bidirectional pin used during programming and during a DMA read cycle.

10. $\overline{EOP}$ (end-of-process) is a bidirectional signal used as an input to terminate a DMA or as an output to indicate the end of a DMA transfer. This pin is often used to interrupt the processor at the end of a DMA cycle.

11. A$_3$–A$_0$ (address) are pins used during programming to select the internal register to be programmed or read and during a DMA transfer cycle to indicate the least significant 4 bits of the DMA transfer address.

12. A$_7$–A$_4$ (address) are outputs used to provide the address bits A$_7$–A$_4$ of the DMA transfer address.

13. HRQ (hold request) is an output connected to the HOLD synchronization flip-flop of Figure 10–2.

14. DACK$_3$–DACK$_0$ (DMA channel acknowledge) are outputs used to acknowledge a channel DMA request. These outputs, like the request inputs, are programmable for active-high or active-low levels. The RESET input defines these outputs as active-low outputs until programmed differently.

15. AEN (address enable) is an output used to enable the DMA address latch connected to DB$_7$–DB$_0$. It also disables the normal 8086/8088 address and data bus buffers and the control signal multiplexer.

16. ADSTB (address strobe) is a pin that functions like the ALE signal, except that it is used by the 8237A-5 to strobe the upper address (A$_{15}$–A$_8$) into an external address latch.

17. $\overline{MEMR}$ (memory read) is an output used during a DMA read to read data from the system memory.

18. $\overline{MEMW}$ (memory write) is an output used during a DMA write to write data into the system memory.

Internal Registers.

1. *Current address register* is used to hold the 16-bit memory address used for the DMA transfer. Each channel has its own current address register for this purpose. When a byte of data is transferred during a DMA, this register is either incremented or decremented, depending on how it is programmed.

2. *Current word count register* is used to program a channel for the number of bytes (up to 64K) transferred during a DMA. The number loaded into this register is one less than the number of bytes transferred. For example, if a 10 is loaded onto this register, then 11 bytes are transferred during the DMA.

3. *Base address and base word count registers* are used when autoinitialization is selected for a channel. In this mode, these registers are used to reload automatically both the count and the address into the current address and current count registers of the channel after the DMA transfer is completed. When the current address and count registers are programmed, these two registers are also programmed even if autoinitialization mode is not used.

4. *Command register* is used to program the 8237A-5. It is cleared by a RESET or a master clear instruction. Figure 10–5 illustrates the binary bit pattern of the command register.

   The command register selects the memory-to-memory DMA transfer mode. Memory-to-memory transfers use DMA channel 0 to hold the source address of the transfer and DMA channel 1 to hold the destination address. (This is similar to the MOVSB or MOBSW command in the 8086/8088, except that transfers occur at a much higher rate of speed.) A byte is read from the addfess pointed to by channel 0 and saved in an internal temporary register. Next, the contents of the temporary registers are stored in the memory address pointed to by the channel 1 register. The number of bytes transferred in this manner is determined by the channel 1 count register.

FIGURE 10–5 8237A-5 command register. (Courtesy of Intel Corporation)

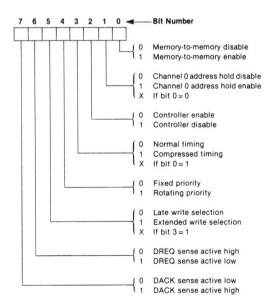

The channel 0 address-hold enable bit programs channel 0 for memory-to-memory transfers. For example, if you wish to fill an area of memory with data, channel 0 can be held at the same address while channel 1 changes for memory-to-memory transfers.

The controller enable bit turns the entire controller on and off in single or cascade mode. The normal and compressed timing bits determine whether a byte is transferred in four clocks or two. If normal timing is selected, the extended write bit extends write time to one clocking period earlier.

The fixed-priority bit gives channel 0 the highest priority and channel 3 the lowest. The rotating-priority bit causes the most recently serviced DMA request channel to assume the lowest priority level after being honored. This procedure closely approximates equal priority.

The two remaining bits program all the DACK outputs and DREQ inputs.

5. *Mode register* is used to program the mode of operation for a channel. Each DMA channel has its own internal mode register (see Figure 10–6). Its rightmost 2 bits select the channel to be programmed, and the remaining bits select the operation, autoinitialization, increment/decrement, and mode. Verification operations generate the DMA addresses without generating the DMA memory and I/O control signals.

The modes of operation include demand mode, single mode, block mode, and cascade mode. Demand mode transfers data until an external $\overline{EOP}$ is input or until the DREQ input becomes inactive. Single mode releases the HOLD after each byte of data is transferred. If the DREQ pin is held high, the 8237A-5 will again request a DMA through the HRQ output pin. Block mode automatically transfers the number of bytes indicated by the count register for the channel. DREQ need not be held high throughout the transfer. Cascade mode is used when more than one 8237A-5 is connected in a system.

6. *Request register* is used to request a DMA via software (see Figure 10–7). This is very useful in memory-to-memory DMA transfers. The channel must be programmed for block mode for a software DMA.

FIGURE 10–6   8237A-5 mode register. (Courtesy of Intel Corporation)

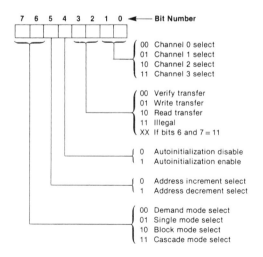

00	Channel 0 select
01	Channel 1 select
10	Channel 2 select
11	Channel 3 select
00	Verify transfer
01	Write transfer
10	Read transfer
11	Illegal
XX	If bits 6 and 7 = 11
0	Autoinitialization disable
1	Autoinitialization enable
0	Address increment select
1	Address decrement select
00	Demand mode select
01	Single mode select
10	Block mode select
11	Cascade mode select

7. *Mask register set/reset* is used to turn a DMA channel off or on (see Figure 10–8). If the mask is set, the channel is disabled. (Recall that the masks are set by a reset.)

8. *Mask register* is used to set or clear all the masks at the same time (see Figure 10–9).

9. *Status register* is used to determine the status of the channels and to identify a terminal count in any channel (see Figure 10–10). The TC bits indicate when a channel has transferred all its data. The TC automatically disables the channel. The request bits indicate which channel is currently requesting a DMA action.

Software Commands.   Three software commands are used to control the operation of the 8237A-5. These commands do not have a particular binary bit pattern for operation. A simple output to the correct port will enable a command. Figure 10–11 illustrates the I/O

FIGURE 10–7   8237A-5 request register. (Courtesy of Intel Corporation)

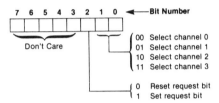

FIGURE 10–8   8237A-5 mask register set/reset mode. (Courtesy of Intel Corporation)

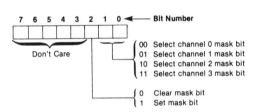

FIGURE 10–9   8237A-5 mask register. (Courtesy of Intel Corporation)

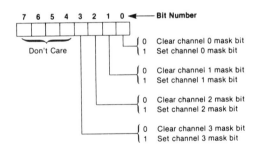

FIGURE 10–10   8237A-5 status register. (Courtesy of Intel Corporation)

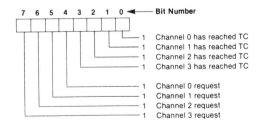

FIGURE 10–11 8237A-5 command and control port assignments. (Courtesy of Intel Corporation)

Signals						
A3	A2	A1	A0	IOR	IOW	Operation
1	0	0	0	0	1	Read Status Register
1	0	0	0	1	0	Write Command Register
1	0	0	1	0	1	Illegal
1	0	0	1	1	0	Write Request Register
1	0	1	0	0	1	Illegal
1	0	1	0	1	0	Write Single Mask Register Bit
1	0	1	1	0	1	Illegal
1	0	1	1	1	0	Write Mode Register
1	1	0	0	0	1	Illegal
1	1	0	0	1	0	Clear Byte Pointer Flip/Flop
1	1	0	1	0	1	Read Temporary Register
1	1	0	1	1	0	Master Clear
1	1	1	0	0	1	Illegal
1	1	1	0	1	0	Clear Mask Register
1	1	1	1	0	1	Illegal
1	1	1	1	1	0	Write All Mask Register Bits

ports required to access the software commands and also the internal status and control registers.

The functions of these commands are explained in the following list:

1. *Clear first/last flip-flop* is used to clear the first/last (F/L) flip-flop (byte pointer flip-flop), which selects the least significant byte and current address of the base and the current count when F/L = 0. The MSB is selected when F/L = 1. Any write to the address or count registers of the 8237A-5 will automatically toggle the F/L flip-flop.
2. *Master clear* acts exactly the same as a hardware RESET. It clears all the internal registers and sets the mask register, which disables all the DMA request inputs.
3. *Clear mask register* enables all four DMA channels.

Programming the Address and Count Registers.   Figure 10–12 illustrates the I/O port locations for programming and count and address registers for each channel. Notice that the state of the first/last flip-flop determines whether the MSB or LSB is programmed. If this state is not known before programming, the count and address will be incorrect. It is also important for a DMA channel to be disabled while it is being programmed.

There are four steps to programming an address and count: (1) the first/last flip-flop is cleared, (2) the channel is disabled, (3) first the LSB and then the MSB of the address are programmed, and (4) first the LSB and then the MSB of the count are programmed. When a channel is programmed, the data are written into both the current and base registers simultaneously. When a count or address is read, the data are read only from the current register.

Connection of the 8088 to the 8237A-5

Figure 10–13 illustrates a system in which the 8088 microprocessor is connected to the 8237A-5 DMA controller.

The address enable (AEN) output of the 8237A-5 controls the output pins of the latches and the outputs of the 74LS257 (E). During normal 8088 operation (AEN = 0), latches A and C and the multiplexer (E) provide address bus bits A_{19}–A_{16} and A_7–A_0. The multiplexer provides the system control bus signals at this time. During a DMA action

Channel	Register	Operation	Signals							Internal Flip-Flop	Data Bus DB0–DB7
			$\overline{CS}$	$\overline{IOR}$	$\overline{IOW}$	A3	A2	A1	A0		
0	Base and Current Address	Write	0	1	0	0	0	0	0	0	A0–A7
			0	1	0	0	0	0	0	1	A8–A15
	Current Address	Read	0	0	1	0	0	0	0	0	A0–A7
			0	0	1	0	0	0	0	1	A8–A15
	Base and Current Word Count	Write	0	1	0	0	0	0	1	0	W0–W7
			0	1	0	0	0	0	1	1	W8–W15
	Current Word Count	Read	0	0	1	0	0	0	1	0	W0–W7
			0	0	1	0	0	0	1	1	W8–W15
1	Base and Current Address	Write	0	1	0	0	0	1	0	0	A0–A7
			0	1	0	0	0	1	0	1	A8–A15
	Current Address	Read	0	0	1	0	0	1	0	0	A0–A7
			0	0	1	0	0	1	0	1	A8–A15
	Base and Current Word Count	Write	0	1	0	0	0	1	1	0	W0–W7
			0	1	0	0	0	1	1	1	W8–W15
	Current Word Count	Read	0	0	1	0	0	1	1	0	W0–W7
			0	0	1	0	0	1	1	1	W8–W15
2	Base and Current Address	Write	0	1	0	0	1	0	0	0	A0–A7
			0	1	0	0	1	0	0	1	A8–A15
	Current Address	Read	0	0	1	0	1	0	0	0	A0–A7
			0	0	1	0	1	0	0	1	A8–A15
	Base and Current Word Count	Write	0	1	0	0	1	0	1	0	W0–W7
			0	1	0	0	1	0	1	1	W8–W15
	Current Word Count	Read	0	0	1	0	1	0	1	0	W0–W7
			0	0	1	0	1	0	1	1	W8–W15
3	Base and Current Address	Write	0	1	0	0	1	1	0	0	A0–A7
			0	1	0	0	1	1	0	1	A8–A15
	Current Address	Read	0	0	1	0	1	1	0	0	A0–A7
			0	0	1	0	1	1	0	1	A8–A15
	Base and Current Word Count	Write	0	1	0	0	1	1	1	0	W0–W7
			0	1	0	0	1	1	1	1	W8–W15
	Current Word Count	Read	0	0	1	0	1	1	1	0	W0–W7
			0	0	1	0	1	1	1	1	W8–W15

FIGURE 10–12 8237A-5 DMA channel I/O port addresses. (Courtesy of Intel Corporation)

(AEN = 1), latches A and C are disabled along with the multiplexer. Latches D and B now provide address bits A_{19}–A_{16} and A_{15}–A_8. Address bus bits A_7–A_0 are provided directly by the 8237A-5 DMA controller as well as the control signals $\overline{MEMR}$, $\overline{MEMW}$, $\overline{IOR}$, and $\overline{IOW}$.

The address strobe output (ADSTB) of the 8237A-5 strobes the address (A_{15}–A_8) into latch D during the DMA so that the entire address becomes available on the address bus. Address bus bits A_{19}–A_{16} are provided by the I/O port latch (B), which must be programmed with these address bits before the controller is enabled. The DMA action of this circuit is limited to one 64K-byte block of memory beginning at any 64K-byte memory boundary.

The decoder (F) selects the 8237A-5 for programming and also the 4-bit latch (B) for the uppermost 4 bits of the DMA address. The decoder enables the 8237A-5 for I/O port addresses 70H–7FH and the latch for any I/O port number 10H–1FH. Notice that the output of the decoder is combined with $\overline{IOW}$ to generate an active-high gate pulse for latch B.

During normal 8088 operation, therefore, the DMA controller and integrated circuits B and D are disabled. During a DMA action, integrated circuits A, C, and E are

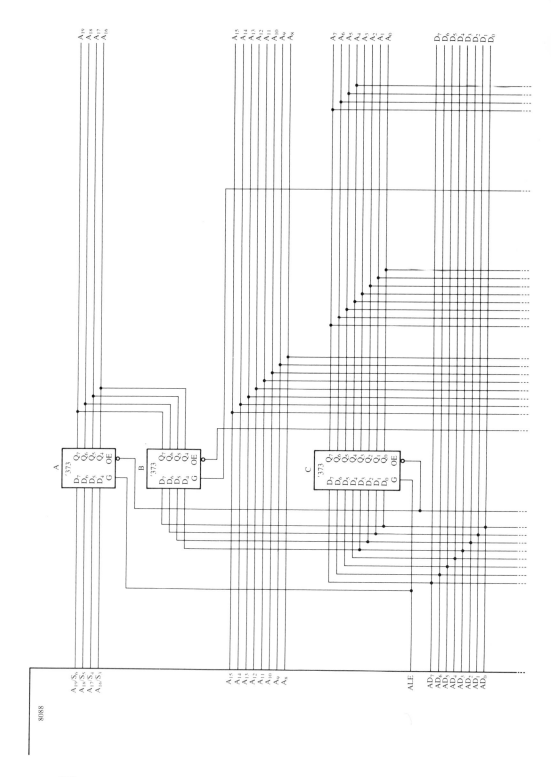

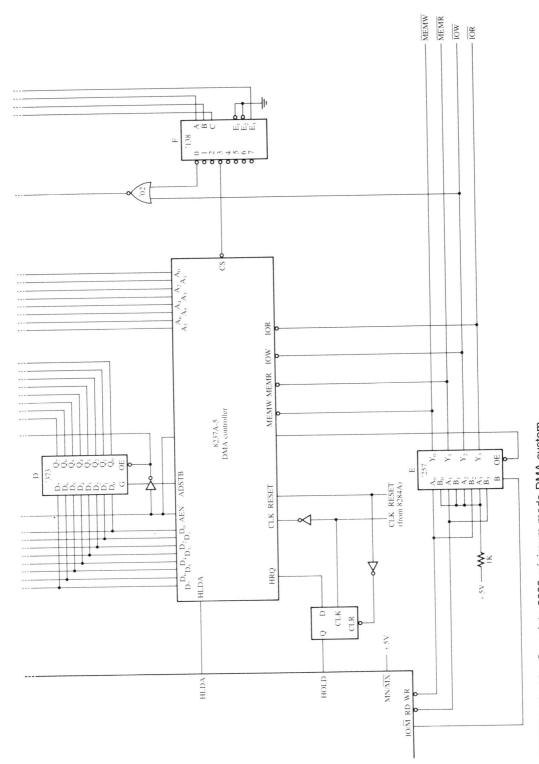

FIGURE 10–13 Complete 8088 minimum mode DMA system.

disabled so that the 8237A-5 can take over the buses and control the memory and DMA I/O device attached to the system.

Memory-to-Memory Data Transfer with the 8237A-5

The memory-to-memory DMA transfer is much more powerful than even the automatically repeated REP MOVSB instruction. While the REP MOVSB instruction takes the 8086/8088 4.2 μs per byte, it takes the 8237A-5 only 2.0 μs per byte. This is over twice as fast as a software data transfer.

EXAMPLE 10-1

```
                    ;Procedure that will transfer a block of data using the 8237A-5
                    ;DMA controller.  This transfer is a memory-memory transfer.
                    ;
                    ;Source address is assumed to be in SI
                    ;Destination address is assumed to be in DI
                    ;Count is assumed to be in CX
                    ;
                    ;All data are assumed to be in the ES which contains the location
                    ;of the 64K byte block.
                    ;
= 0010              LATCHB      EQU  10H              ;latch (B)
= 007C              CLEAR_FL    EQU  7CH              ;F/L flip-flop
= 0070              CH0_ADD     EQU  70H              ;CH0 address
= 0072              CH1_ADD     EQU  72H              ;CH1 address
= 0073              CH1_CNT     EQU  73H              ;CH1 count
= 007B              MODE        EQU  7BH              ;mode
= 0078              CMMD        EQU  78H              ;command
= 007F              MASKS       EQU  7FH              ;mask
= 0079              REQ         EQU  79H              ;request register
= 0078              STATUS      EQU  78H              ;status register

0000                TRANSFER    PROC FAR

0000   50                       PUSH AX

0001   8C C0                    MOV  AX,ES            ;program latch (B)
0003   8A C4                    MOV  AL,AH
0005   D0 E8                    SHR  AL,1
0007   D0 E8                    SHR  AL,1
0009   D0 E8                    SHR  AL,1
000B   D0 E8                    SHR  AL,1
000D   E6 10                    OUT  LATCHB,AL

000F   E6 7C                    OUT  CLEAR_FL,AL      ;clear F/L

0011   8B C6                    MOV  AX,SI            ;program source
0013   E6 70                    OUT  CH0_ADD,AL
0015   8A C4                    MOV  AL,AH
0017   E6 70                    OUT  CH0_ADD,AL

0019   8B C7                    MOV  AX,DI            ;program destination
001B   E6 72                    OUT  CH1_ADD,AL
001D   8A C4                    MOV  AL,AH
001F   E6 72                    OUT  CH1_ADD,AL

0021   8B C1                    MOV  AX,CX            ;program count
0023   48                       DEC  AX               ;adjust count
0024   E6 73                    OUT  CH1_CNT,AL
0026   8A C4                    MOV  AL,AH
0028   E6 73                    OUT  CH1_CNT,AL
```

```
002A   B0 88            MOV   AL,88H          ;program mode
002C   E6 7B            OUT   MODE,AL
002E   B0 85            MOV   AL,85H
0030   E6 7B            OUT   MODE,AL

0032   B0 01            MOV   AL,1            ;enable block move
0034   E6 78            OUT   CMMD,AL

0036   B0 0E            MOV   AL,0EH          ;unmask channel 0
0038   E6 7F            OUT   MASKS,AL

003A   B0 04            MOV   AL,4            ;request DMA
003C   E6 79            OUT   REQ,AL

003E            AGAIN:

003E   E4 78            IN    AL,STATUS       ;wait till DMA complete
0040   A8 01            TEST  AL,1
0042   74 FA            JZ    AGAIN

0044   58               POP   AX
0045   CB               RET

0046            TRANSFER   ENDP
```

Sample Memory-to-Memory DMA Transfer.   Suppose that the contents of memory locations 10000H–13FFFH are to be transferred into memory locations 14000H–17FFH. This is accomplished with the string move instruction or, at a much faster rate, with the DMA controller.

Example 10–1 illustrates the software required to initialize the 8237A-5 and program latch B in Figure 10–13 for this DMA transfer.

Programming the 8237A-5 is a rather simple task, as illustrated in the software listing. The leftmost digit of the 5-digit hexadecimal DMA address is sent to latch B. Next, the channels are programmed after the F/L flip-flop is cleared. The count is then decremented because one more byte than programmed will be transferred by a DMA. After this, the mode of each channel is programmed, the command register is programmed to select block move, channel 0 is enabled, and a software DMA is requested. Before a return is made, the status register is checked for a terminal count, which indicates that all the bytes have been transferred. TC also disables the channel until the next DMA action.

Sample Memory Fill with the 8237A-5.   In order to fill an area of memory with the same data, the channel 0 source register is programmed to point to the same address (channel 0 hold mode). The controller copies the contents of the location addressed by channel 0 into all the memory at the destination block that is addressed by channel 1. This is useful in many applications. For example, to clear the screen in a CRT terminal, an ASCII space (20H) must be stored in each location of the screen memory. If the display contains 80 columns and 24 lines, the count is 1,919, which is one less than the actual number of bytes (1,920).

EXAMPLE 10–2

```
                  ;Procedure that will clear the screen.
                  ;
  = 0002          ADDRESS   EQU   02H          ;screen address
  = 0010          LATCHB    EQU   10H          ;latch (B)
```

```
= 007C              CLEAR_FL  EQU   7CH                    ;F/L flip-flop
= 0070              CH0_ADD   EQU   70H                    ;CH0 address
= 0072              CH1_ADD   EQU   72H                    ;CH1 address
= 0073              CH1_CNT   EQU   73H                    ;CH1 count
= 007B              MODE      EQU         7BH              ;mode
= 0078              CMMD      EQU         78H              ;command
= 007F              MASKS     EQU   7FH                    ;mask
= 0079              REQ       EQU         79H              ;request register
= 0078              STATUS    EQU   78H                    ;status register
= 0020              SPACE     EQU   ' '                    ;ASCII space

0000                CLEAR_SCREEN  PROC   FAR

0000  50                        PUSH   AX
0001  06                        PUSH   ES
0002  53                        PUSH   BX

0003  B0 02                     MOV    AL,ADDRESS
0005  E6 10                     OUT    LATCHB,AL
0007  D0 E0                     SHL    AL,1
0009  D0 E0                     SHL    AL,1
000B  D0 E0                     SHL    AL,1
000D  D0 E0                     SHL    AL,1
000F  8A E0                     MOV    AH,AL
0011  32 C0                     XOR    AL,AL
0013  8E C0                     MOV    ES,AX        ;address segment

0015  E6 7C                     OUT    CLEAR_FL,AL     ;clear F/L

0017  B8 0014 R                 MOV    AX,OFFSET SCREEN
001A  8B D8                     MOV    BX,AX
001C  26: C6 07 20              MOV    BYTE PTR ES:[BX],SPACE

0020  E6 70                     OUT    CH0_ADD,AL
0022  8A C4                     MOV    AL,AH
0024  E6 70                     OUT    CH0_ADD,AL

0026  8B C3                     MOV    AX,BX
0028  40                        INC    AX
0029  E6 72                     OUT    CH1_ADD,AL
002B  8A C4                     MOV    AL,AH
002D  E6 72                     OUT    CH1_ADD,AL
002F  B8 077E                   MOV    AX,1918   ;program count
0032  E6 73                     OUT    CH1_CNT,AL
0034  8A C4                     MOV    AL,AH
0036  E6 73                     OUT    CH1_CNT,AL

0038  B0 88                     MOV    AL,88H     ;program mode CH0
003A  E6 7B                     OUT    MODE,AL

003C  B0 85                     MOV    AL,85H     ;program mode CH1
003E  E6 7B                     OUT    MODE,AL

0040  B0 03                     MOV    AL,3       ;program copy
0042  E6 78                     OUT    CMMD,AL

0044  B0 0E                     MOV    AL,0EH     ;unmask CH0
0046  E6 7F                     OUT    MASKS,AL

0048  B0 04                     MOV    AL,4       ;request DMA
004A  E6 79                     OUT    REQ,AL

004C                AGAIN:

004C  E4 78                     IN     AL,STATUS ;wait until complete
004E  A8 01                     TEST   AL,1
```

0050	74 FA		JZ	AGAIN
0052	5B		POP	BX
0053	07		POP	ES
0054	58		POP	AX
0055	CB		RET	
0056		CLEAR_SCREEN	ENDP	

Example 10–2 illustrates the screen-clearing procedure. Here the address of the screen is known, as is the number of bytes in the screen memory. To clear the screen, the user need only call this procedure. Notice that it is very nearly the same as the procedure listed in Example 10–1, except that the command register is programmed so that the channel 0 address is held.

DMA-Processed Printer Interface. Figure 10–14 illustrates the hardware added to Figure 10–13 for a DMA-controlled printer interface. Notice that little additional circuitry is

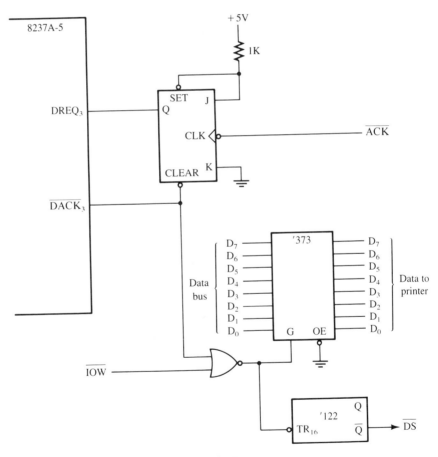

FIGURE 10–14 DMA processed printer interface.

required to provide the data to the printer. A latch is used to capture data during the DMA transfer and hold it for the printer. The write pulse passed to the latch during the DACK$_3$ is also used to fire a single shot that generates the $\overline{DS}$ pulse to strobe the data into the printer. The $\overline{ACK}$ pulse that returns from the printer after data are printed requests the next DMA transfer.

Notice that the I/O device is not selected by decoding the address on the address bus. During a DMA, the address bus contains the memory address of the DMA transfer and cannot contain the I/O device address. In place of an I/O address, the DACK$_3$ output is used as a kind of I/O port number to gate the $\overline{IOW}$ pulse through to the latch.

Software to control this interface is simple because only the address of the data and the number of characters to be printed are programmed. Once this has been accomplished, the channel is enabled, and DMA action transfers 1 byte at a time to the printer interface latch each time the previous character is acknowledged $\overline{ACK}$.

EXAMPLE 10–3

```
                    ;Procedure that prints data beginning at the location
                    ;addressed by DS:BX.  The number of characters printed is
                    ;in CX when this procedure is called.
                    ;
= 0010              LATCHB     EQU   10H              ;latch (B)
= 007C              CLEAR_FL   EQU   7CH              ;F/L flip-flop
= 0076              CH3_ADD    EQU   76H              ;CH3 address
= 0077              CH3_CNT    EQU   77H              ;CH3 count
= 007B              MODE       EQU   7BH              ;mode
= 0078              CMMD       EQU   78H              ;command
= 007F              MASKS      EQU   7FH              ;mask
= 0079              REQ        EQU   79H              ;request register

0000                PRINT      PROC  FAR

0000  50                       PUSH  AX
0001  51                       PUSH  CX
0002  53                       PUSH  BX

0003  8C D8                    MOV   AX,DS            ;program A19--A16
0005  B1 04                    MOV   CL,4
0007  D3 EB                    SHR   BX,CL
0009  03 C3                    ADD   AX,BX
000B  B1 0C                    MOV   CL,12
000D  50                       PUSH  AX
000E  D3 E8                    SHR   AX,CL
0010  E6 10                    OUT   LATCHB,AL
0012  58                       POP   AX
0013  5B                       POP   BX
0014  B1 04                    MOV   CL,4
0016  D3 E0                    SHL   AX,CL
0018  83 E3 0F                 AND   BX,15
001B  03 C3                    ADD   AX,BX

001D  E6 7C                    OUT   CLEAR_FL,AL      ;clear F/L

001F  E6 76                    OUT   CH3_ADD,AL       ;program
address
0021  8A C4                    MOV   AL,AH
0023  E6 76                    OUT   CH3_ADD,AL

0025  58                       POP   AX               ;program count
0026  50                       PUSH  AX
```

```
0027   53                              PUSH    BX
0028   48                              DEC     AX

0029   E6 77                           OUT     CH3_CNT,AL
002B   8A C4                           MOV     AL,AH
002D   E6 77                           OUT     CH3_CNT,AL
002F   B0 00                           MOV     AL,0      ;enable controller
0031   E6 78                           OUT     CMMD,AL

0033   B0 07                           MOV     AL,7      ;unmask CH3
0035   E6 7F                           OUT     MASKS,AL

0037   5B                              POP     BX
0038   59                              POP     CX
0039   58                              POP     AX
003A   CB                              RET

003B              PRINT     ENDP
```

The procedure that prints data from the current data segment is illustrated in Example 10-3. This procedure only programs the 8237A-5 and doesn't print anything. The printing is done by the DMA controller and the printer interface.

A secondary procedure is needed to test the printer to determine if the DMA action has been completed. Example 10-4 illustrates this secondary procedure. TEST_P is called before programming the DMA controller for printing. It could be included in the print procedure, but that would prevent the software from double buffering the data.

EXAMPLE 10-4

```
                   ;Procedure to test for a completed DMA action.
                   ;
= 0078             STATUS    EQU    78H              ;status

0000               TEST_P    PROC   NEAR

0000   E4 78                  IN     AL,STATUS        ;test CH3
0002   A8 08                  TEST   AL,8
0004   74 FA                  JZ     TEST_P
0006   C3                     RET

0007               TEST_P    ENDP
```

Data to be printed can be double-buffered by first loading a buffer (buffer 1) with data for the printer. Next, the PRINT procedure is called. Because it takes very little time to program the DMA controller, a second buffer is filled with the next block of data to be printed while the contents of buffer 1 are printed. Before printing the contents of the second buffer, the TEST procedure is called to ensure that the contents of buffer 1 have been completely printed. As soon as buffer 1 has been printed, buffer 2 is programmed and buffer 1 is again filled with data. Before the data in buffer 1 are printed, TEST is again called to ensure that those in buffer 2 have been printed. This process is repeated until all the data are printed.

10–2   MAXIMUM MODE DMA

The main difference between maximum mode and minimum mode DMA is that the former is designed to operate with a family of coprocessors and the latter to operate with standard DMA controllers. A coprocessor is microprocessor designed for a specific application. Chapter 11 presents a coprocessor produced by INTEL: the 8087 arithmetic coprocessor. This device accesses data via DMA in the maximum mode.

In this section, we define the DMA control pins for maximum mode operation and explain the timing involved.

$\overline{RQ}/\overline{GT}$ Pins

The 8086/8088 uses two pins for DMA called *request/grant pins:* $\overline{RQ}/\overline{GT}_0$ and $\overline{RQ}/\overline{GT}_1$. These are bidirectional pins that basically function like HOLD and HLDA. Each is a request input (HOLD) and grant output (HLDA) for two external DMA devices. Figure 10–15 illustrates the basic timing diagram for an $\overline{RQ}/\overline{GT}$ pin.

Each of these pins transfers three pieces of information: request, grant, and release. The first pulse, which requests a DMA action from the 8086/8088, comes from the external controller. Once the microprocessor recognizes the request, it sends a grant to the controller through the same line. The grant signals the controller that the 8086/8088 buses are three-state, just as the HLDA signal does in minimum mode operation.

The DMA controller now uses the buses to transfer data between memory and I/O. When the controller is finished with the buses, it sends the 8086/8088 a release pulse to signal that the controller has completed its operation. After this, the 8086/8088 resumes normal operation. You could think of the request signal as the 0–1 transition of the HOLD pin, the grant as HLDA, and the 1–0 transition of HOLD as the release.

The $\overline{RQ}/\overline{GT}_0$ input has the highest priority. If both $\overline{RQ}/\overline{GT}_0$ and $\overline{RQ}/\overline{GT}_1$ are activated simultaneously, then the 8086/8088 will accept the $\overline{RQ}/\overline{GT}_0$ input. If $\overline{RQ}/\overline{GT}_1$ has already received a grant from the 8086/8088, then the $\overline{RQ}/\overline{GT}_0$ input must wait for a release on the $\overline{RQ}/\overline{GT}_1$ line before it is accepted.

Maximum mode is used only when the 8087 coprocessor exists in a system. Refer to Chapter 11 for more information on maximum mode operations, the coprocessors, and the use of the $\overline{RQ}/\overline{GT}$ pins.

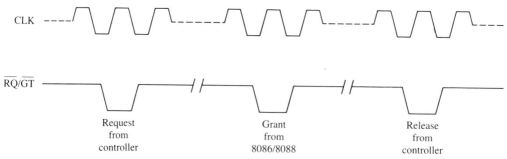

FIGURE 10–15 $\overline{RQ}/\overline{GT}$ timing.

Figure 10–16 shows the 8088 microprocessor connected to the 8087 coprocessor. Here the processors share the same clock generator and the same local bus—the bus before the system bus buffers. Only one of these processors is active at a given time in the system, and all share memory and I/O devices.

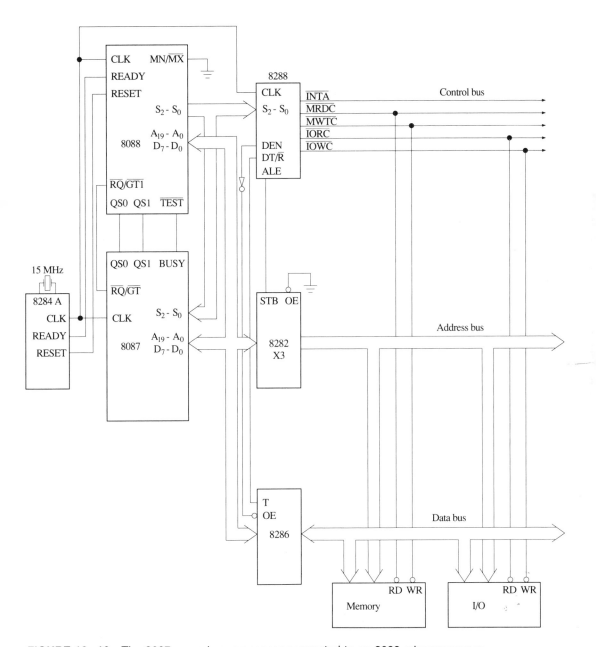

FIGURE 10–16 The 8087 numeric coprocessor connected to an 8088 microprocessor.

10-3   SHARED BUS OPERATION (MULTITASKING)

Complex present-day computer systems have so many tasks to perform that some systems are using more than one microprocessor to accomplish the work. In systems that contain more than one microprocessor, some method of control must be developed and employed. In the *multitasking* environment, there are two types of microprocessor configurations used in systems that contain more than one microprocessor: (1) the local bus and (2) the remote bus configurations. The local bus is a bus connected to memory and I/O that is accessed by a microprocessor without any special protocol. The remote bus is a bus that contains memory and I/O that is accessed or shared by more than one microprocessor.

Types of Buses Defined

The *local bus* is the bus that is resident to the microprocessor, and on this bus are memory and I/O that the microprocessor can access. All of the microprocessor systems studied so far are considered local bus systems. This local memory and local I/O are only accessed by the microprocessor that is directly connected to them. A microprocessor operating in the local bus mode contains its own data, address, and control bus connected to the local memory and I/O, as well as to a remote data bus, address, and control bus that are connected to the remote bus. The remote bus is a *shared bus* that is accessible by all microprocessors in a system. The remote bus may have its own memory and I/O as does the local bus. The difference is that remote bus memory and I/O are shared between all of the microprocessors on a system, while the local bus is resident to just one microprocessor.

Figure 10–17 illustrates an 8088 microprocessor connected as a remote bus master. The term *bus master* applies to any device (microprocessor or otherwise) that can control a bus containing memory and I/O. The DMA controller presented earlier in this chapter is an example of a bus master, as is a microprocessor. In order to control the access of the shared bus, the bus master must request access through a bus arbiter. The *bus arbiter* is a device that controls access to the shared or remote bus. It also resolves priority when more than one bus master requests access to the shared bus.

In Figure 10–17 notice that the 8088 microprocessor has its own local memory and I/O spaces and also an interface to the shared or remote bus. This configuration allows the 8088 to access local memory and I/O or, through the bus arbiter and buffers, the remote or shared bus. The task assigned to this microprocessor might be data communications and it may, after collecting data from a data communications interface, pass those data on to the shared bus and shared memory so that other microprocessors in the system may gain access to the data. This allows the data to be shared between more than one microprocessor. In this manner each microprocessor on the shared bus can be assigned tasks to perform that are independent of each other although performed at the same time.

The Bus Arbiter

Before Figure 10–17 can be fully understood, the operation of the bus arbiter must be grasped. The 8289 bus arbiter controls the interface of a bus master to a shared bus system. Each bus master or microprocessor requires an arbiter for the interface to the

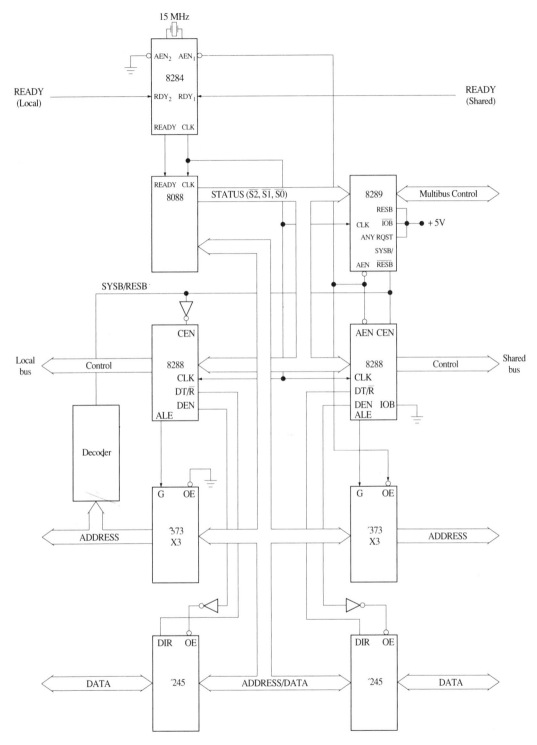

FIGURE 10–17 The 8088 operated in the remote mode illustrating the local and shared bus connections.

323

shared bus, which Intel calls the Multibus[*] and IBM calls the Micro Channel[†]. The shared bus is used to pass information from one bus master to another; otherwise, the bus masters function in their own local bus modes using their own local programs, memory, and I/O space. Microprocessors connected in a system such as this are often called *parallel processors* or *distributed processors* because they can execute software in parallel independently of each other.

8289 Architecture

Figure 10–18 illustrates the pinout and block diagram of the 8289 bus arbiter. The left side of the block diagram depicts the connections to a microprocessor (8086 or 8088). It is possible to attach more than one 8086 or 8088 to a system using this device and a set of buffers. The right side of the block diagram denotes the 8289 connection to the shared bus (remote bus) or the Multibus.

The 8289 controls the shared bus by causing the READY pin on the microprocessor to become a logic 0 (not ready) if access to the shared bus is blocked. *Blocking* occurs whenever another microprocessor is accessing the shared bus. As a result, the microprocessor requesting access never realizes that it doesn't have access to the shared bus, because access is blocked by a logic 0 applied to the READY pin. When the READY pin

FIGURE 10–18   The 8289 pinout and block diagram. (Courtesy of Intel Corporation)

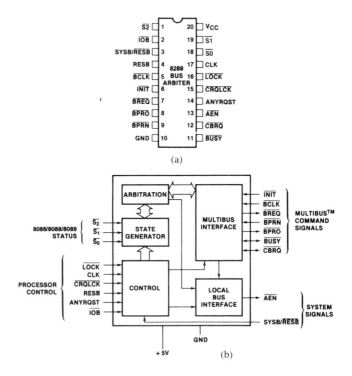

*Multibus is a trademark of Intel Corporation.

†Micro Channel is a trademark of International Business Machines.

is a logic 0, the microprocessor and its software wait until access to the shared bus is granted by the arbiter. In this manner, one microprocessor at a time gains access to the shared bus. No special instructions are required for bus arbitration with the 8289 bus arbiter since arbitration is accomplished strictly by hardware.

Pin Definitions.

1. $\overline{\text{AEN}}$ (address enable output) causes the bus drivers in a system to switch to their three-state, high-impedance outputs.
2. ANYRQST (any request input) is a strapping option that allows a lower priority microprocessor from gaining access to the shared system bus. If tied to a logic 0, normal operation occurs, but it allows a lower priority microprocessor to gain access to the shared bus if the $\overline{\text{CBRQ}}$ pin is also at a logic 0.
3. $\overline{\text{BCKL}}$ (bus clock input) is used to synchronize all shared-bus masters.
4. $\overline{\text{BPRN}}$ (bus priority input) is used to allow the 8289 to acquire the shared bus on the next falling edge of the $\overline{\text{BCKL}}$ signal.
5. $\overline{\text{BPRO}}$ (bus priority output) is a signal that is used to resolve priority.
6. $\overline{\text{BREQ}}$ (bus request output) is a signal used by a microprocessor to request access to the shared bus.
7. $\overline{\text{BUSY}}$ (busy input/output) indicates, as an output, that an 8289 has acquired the shared bus, and is also used as an input to detect that another 8289 has acquired the shared bus.
8. $\overline{\text{CBRQ}}$ (common bus request input/output) is used when a lower priority microprocessor is asking the use of the shared bus. As an output, $\overline{\text{CBRQ}}$ becomes a logic 0 whenever the 8289 requests the shared bus, and remains low until the 8289 obtains access of the shared bus.
9. CLK (clock input) is generated by the 8284A clock generator and provides the internal clock timing signal for the 8289 arbiter.
10. $\overline{\text{CRQLCK}}$ (common request lock input) prevents the 8289 from surrendering the shared bus to any other 8289 in the system. This signal functions in conjunction with the $\overline{\text{CBRQ}}$ input pin.
11. $\overline{\text{INIT}}$ (initialization input) is used to reset the 8289 arbiter.
12. $\overline{\text{IOB}}$ (I/O bus input) determines whether the 8289 will operate in a shared-bus system (if selected by RESB) with I/O ($\overline{\text{IOB}} = 0$) or with memory and I/O ($\overline{\text{IOB}} = 1$).
13. $\overline{\text{LOCK}}$ (lock input) is used to prevent the 8289 from allowing any other microprocessor to gain access to the shared bus. An 8086/8088 instruction with the lock prefix attached can retain access to the shared bus without intervention from any other microprocessor because of this feature.
14. RESB (resident-bus input) is a strapping connection that allows the 8289 to operate in systems that have either a shared-bus or a resident-bus system. If RESB is connected to a logic 1, the 8289 is configured as a shared-bus master, and if connected to a logic 0, it is configured as a local-bus master. When configured as a shared-bus master the bus is requested through the SYSB/$\overline{\text{RESB}}$ input connection.
15. $\overline{\text{S2}}$, $\overline{\text{S1}}$, and $\overline{\text{S0}}$ (status input pins) initiate shared-bus requests and surrenders. These pins are connected to the 8086 or 8088 status output pins.
16. SYSB/$\overline{\text{RESB}}$ (system-bus/resident-bus input) selects the shared-bus system when placed at a logic 1 or the unshared resident (local) bus when placed at a logic 0.

General 8289 Operation.   As the pin descriptions demonstrate, the 8289 can be operated in three basic modes: (1) I/O peripheral bus mode, (2) resident bus mode, and (3) single-bus mode. Refer to Table 10–1 for the connections required to operate the 8289 in these modes. In the *I/O peripheral bus mode,* all devices on the local bus are treated as I/O, including memory, and are accessed by I/O instructions. All memory references access the shared bus and all I/O instructions access the local bus in the I/O peripheral bus mode. The *resident-bus mode* allows memory and I/O access on both the local and the shared bus. Finally, the *single-bus mode* interfaces a microprocessor to a shared bus, but the microprocessor has no access to a local bus. In many systems one microprocessor is set up as the shared-bus master, which means that it is operated in the single-bus mode. The *shared-bus master* controls the entire system through the shared memory and I/O. Additional microprocessors are connected to the shared bus as resident or I/O peripheral bus masters. These additional bus masters usually perform independent tasks that are reported to the shared-bus master through the shared bus.

System Illustrating Single-Bus and Resident-Bus Connections.   Single-bus operation interfaces a microprocessor to a shared bus that contains both I/O and memory resources that are shared by other microprocessors. Figure 10–19 illustrates three 8088 microprocessors, each connected to operate in a shared-bus environment. Two of the three microprocessors are connected to operate in the resident-bus mode, while the third is operated in the single-bus mode. Microprocessor A in Figure 10–19 is operated in the single-bus mode and has no local or resident bus. This microprocessor can only access memory and I/O that are present on the shared bus. This microprocessor is often referred to as the *system master* because it is responsible for coordinating the main system memory and I/O tasks. The remaining two microprocessors (B and C) are connected in the resident (local) -bus mode, which allows them to access their own local memory and I/O and also the shared memory and I/O. These resident-bus microprocessors are used to perform tasks that are independent from the system master. In fact, the only time that the system master is interrupted from performing its task is when one of the two resident-bus microprocessors needs to transfer data between itself and the shared bus. This connection allows all three microprocessors to perform tasks simultaneously, yet data can be shared between the microprocessors if needed.

TABLE 10–1   8289 modes of operation

Mode	Pin Connections
Single bus	$\overline{IOB}$ = 1 RESB = 0
Resident bus	$\overline{IOB}$ = 1 RESB = 1
I/O bus	$\overline{IOB}$ = 0 RESB = 0
I/O bus and resident bus	$\overline{IOB}$ = 0 RESB = 1

In this example, the bus master (A) is used to allow the user to operate with a video terminal, to execute programs, and to generally control the computer system. Microprocessor B is used to handle all telephone communications. This means that it waits for each character to be transmitted or received and controls the protocol used for the transfers. For example, suppose that a 1K-byte block of data is to be transmitted across the telephone lines and this transfer occurs at the rate of 100 characters per second. This means that the transfer will take 10 seconds. Rather than tie up the bus master for 10 seconds, microprocessor B accesses the shared memory for a few hundred microseconds to transfer the entire 1K-byte block of data from the shared memory into its local memory. From that point forward, the communications is handled completely by microprocessor B. It accomplishes this by taking data from its own local memory and sending them out through the local communications channel. This frees the bus master for other tasks during the entire period of time required to send the data, except for the few hundred microseconds when the data are transferred between it and microprocessor B.

Microprocessor C, in this system, is used as a print spooler. Its task is to print data on a printer. Whenever the bus master requires printed output, it transfers the task to microprocessor C. Microprocessor C then accesses the shared memory and captures the data to be printed in its own local memory. Data are then printed from the local memory, freeing the bus master to perform other tasks in the system. It can be seen that this system could be executing a program, with the bus master, transferring data through the communications channel, via microprocessor B, and printing information on the printer via microprocessor C. These tasks are executed simultaneously. There is no limit to the number of microprocessors connected to a system or the number of tasks performed simultaneously using this technique. The only limit is that introduced by the system design and the designer's ingenuity.

Priority Logic for the 8289

In applications that use the 8289, there is always more than one microprocessor connected to a shared bus. Because each can access the shared bus at the same time, some method for resolving priority must be employed. Priority prevents two microprocessors from accessing the shared bus at exactly the same time. The two methods for resolving priority in the 8289 are the daisy-chain (serial) and the parallel-priority schemes.

Daisy-Chain Priority. The daisy-chain priority scheme connects the $\overline{\text{BPRO}}$ output to the $\overline{\text{BPRN}}$ input of the next-lower priority 8289 and is the least expensive to implement. Figure 10–20 illustrates the daisy-chain scheme for connecting several 8289s in a system. Because the $\overline{\text{BPRN}}$ input of the higher priority 8289 is grounded, it gets an immediate acknowledgment whenever its microprocessor requests access to the shared bus. The $\overline{\text{BPRO}}$ output is a logic 0 if the 8289 is inactive and a logic 1 if the 8289 is actively using the shared bus. If no requests are active, all $\overline{\text{BPRN}}$ inputs will see a logic 0. As soon as the highest priority 8289 receives a bus acknowledgment, its $\overline{\text{BPRO}}$ output goes high, disabling all lower priority 8289s. If more than one 8289 receives an acknowledgment at the same time, more than one 8289 *will* function at the same time. This scheme is seldom used because when two microprocessors access the shared bus simultaneously, serious bus conflicts occur. For this reason, Intel recommends that this scheme be used for up to three

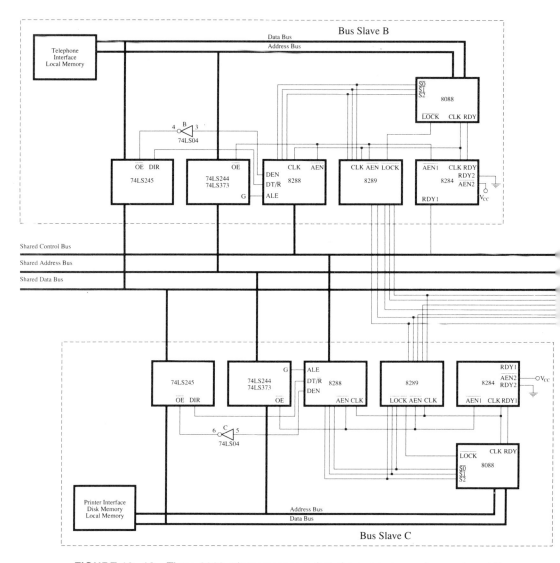

FIGURE 10–19   Three 8088 microprocessors that share a common bus system. Microprocessor A is the bus master in control of the shared memory and CRT terminal. Microprocessor B is a bus slave controlling its local telephone interface and memory. Microprocessor C is also a slave that controls a printer, disk memory system, and local memory.

8289s in a system that uses a bus clock of 10 MHz or less. With this frequency bus clock, no conflict can occur and only one microprocessor can gain access to the shared bus at a time. If more arbiters are connected, Intel suggests that the priority be resolved using the parallel scheme because a conflict can occur.

Parallel Priority.   Figure 10–21 illustrates a parallel-priority scheme in which four 8289 bus arbiters are connected by a parallel priority circuit. Here a 74LS148, eight-input

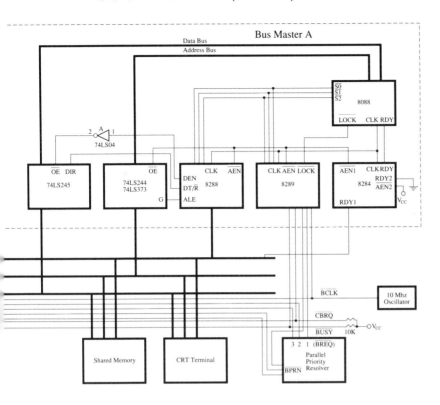

priority encoder is used to resolve priority conflicts in parallel. In this example, only four of the eight inputs are actually used to resolve priority of the four 8289s. The four unused priority encoder inputs are pulled to a logic 1 to disable these unneeded inputs to the encoder. These additional four inputs can be used to expand the circuit so that a system with eight 8289s can be constructed by merely connecting additional 8289s.

This circuit functions as follows. If all 8289 arbiters are idle (no requests for the shared bus through the SYSB/$\overline{\text{RESB}}$ input pin), all $\overline{\text{BREQ}}$ outputs are high and the outputs of the 74LS148 are logic 1s ($\overline{\text{A}}$ and $\overline{\text{B}}$ both are 1). This places a logic 0 on the $\overline{\text{BPRN}}$ input of the highest priority 8289 and logic 1s on the remaining three. This means that the highest priority 8289 will gain immediate access to the shared bus if a request is placed in its SYSB/$\overline{\text{RESB}}$ input connection. On the other hand, if a lower priority request is made, the $\overline{\text{BREQ}}$ output becomes a logic 0. This causes the priority encoder to place a logic 0 on the corresponding $\overline{\text{BPRN}}$ input pin of the 8289 allowing a bus request. For example, if the rightmost 8289 places a logic 0 on its $\overline{\text{BREQ}}$ output pin in response to a bus request, the priority encoder will have a zero on the input pin $\overline{3}$. This causes the 74LS148 to generate a 00 on its output pins. The 00 causes the 74LS138 to activate the $\overline{\text{BPRN}}$ input on the rightmost 8289, giving it access to the shared bus. This action also locks out any other request if it occurs during this access because the $\overline{\text{BUSY}}$ signal becomes a logic 0. If simultaneous requests occur, they are automatically prioritized by the 74LS148, preventing conflicts no matter how many 8289s are connected in the system. For this reason, this priority scheme is most often recommended.

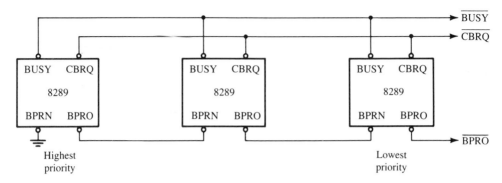

FIGURE 10–20   Daisy-chain 8289 priority resolver.

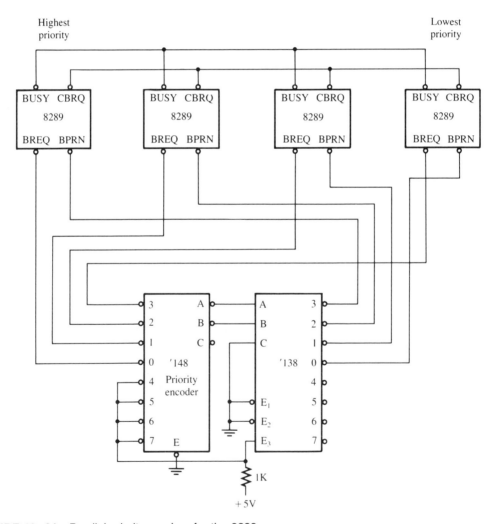

FIGURE 10–21   Parallel-priority resolver for the 8289.

Printer Spooler and Interface

Figure 10–22 illustrates the block diagram of a printer interface and spooler (printer queue) controlled by an 8088 microprocessor. Here two microprocessors are placed in a system with one, the system master (8088), operated in single mode, and a second 8088 operated in resident-bus mode. Because two microprocessors exist, one can print information while the other is used to process new information in the interim.

In this interface the slave microprocessor is used to transfer data to the printer from its local memory without intervention from the bus master. Data are transferred to the local memory of the slave by the slave microprocessor whenever it accesses the shared memory for additional data.

Single-Mode–Bus-Master Interface. Figure 10–23 illustrates the 8088 bus master interfaced to the shared bus operated in the single mode. This 8088 microprocessor has access to every memory location on the shared bus as well as every I/O device. The $\overline{BLCK}$ signal is generated by an 8284A used as an oscillator to generate the 10-MHz bus clock signal.

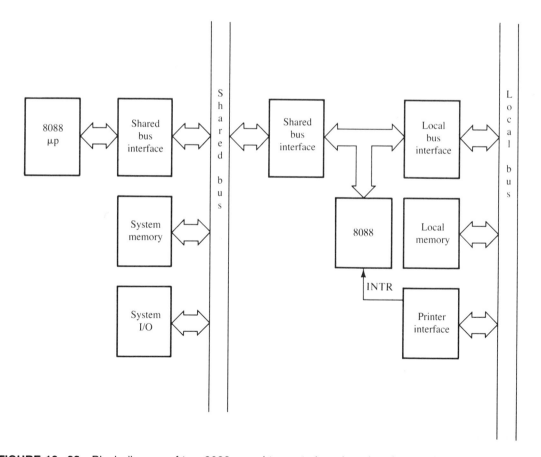

FIGURE 10–22 Block diagram of two 8088s used to control a printer interface and print spooler.

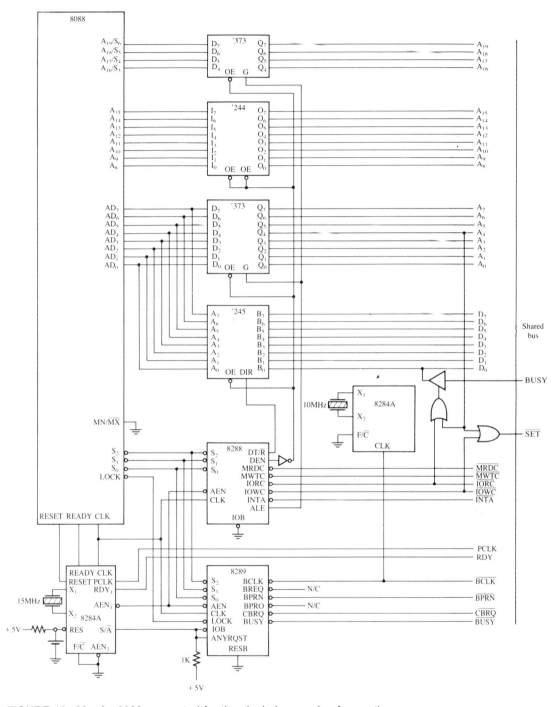

FIGURE 10–23   An 8088 connected for the single bus mode of operation.

The 8289 arbiter is operated with no I/O bus, no resident bus, and ANYRQST pulled high so that the shared bus can be accessed for all I/O or memory requests. This system uses the daisy-chain priority scheme, which means that the $\overline{\text{BREQ}}$ signal is not connected. The interface allows the slave 8088 microprocessor to access shared memory whenever necessary and thus prevents the slave 8088 from locking the bus for too long.

In addition to the normal bus signals, this circuit also provides the shared bus with a 2.5-MHz PCLK signal for any I/O devices and the $\overline{\text{BCLK}}$ signal. The RDY input is shown in case system memory and I/O components require wait states to stretch out access time. It is also tied to the RDY line of the 8088 slave portion of the system to allow the master to force the slave to wait for access to the shared bus.

Resident-Bus Operation of the Slave 8088. Figure 10–24 illustrates the slave 8088 print spooler controller connected as a resident-bus master. The resident–local bus interface is depicted as well as the shared-bus interface.

Whenever the 8088 slave microprocessor accesses memory that is above location 7FFFFH, it places a logic 1 on the SYSB/$\overline{\text{RESB}}$ pin of the 8289 and the CEN pin of the shared bus 8288. This procedure requests access to the shared bus through the 8289 bus arbiter. If the address is below 80000H, the SYSB/$\overline{\text{RESB}}$ pin on the 8289 is grounded and a logic 1 is placed on the CEN input of the local bus 8288. This requests access to the resident local bus for control of the printer and the resident memory. Notice that no attempt is made to access shared-bus I/O because the purpose of this slave 8088 is to access the printer interface on its local bus as local I/O.

Figure 10–25 illustrates the memory maps of both the slave 8088 local memory and the shared memory and also the memory of the bus-master 8088. The bus master has access to all of the shared memory, while the bus slave has access to only the top half of the shared memory. Transfers to the print spooler are made through the upper half of the shared memory.

The resident local bus in this system contains EPROM, DRAM, and a printer interface. The EPROM stores the task programs for the slave 8088, the DRAM stores the data for the queue of the spooler, and the printer interface controls the printer. Figure 10–26 illustrates these devices on the resident local bus of the slave 8088 microprocessor.

The decoder in this illustration selects the EPROM for locations 00000H–0FFFFH, the printer for locations 10000H–1FFFFH, and the DRAM for locations 20000H–7FFFFH. This allows the spooler to hold up to 384K bytes of data (see Figure 10–27). If the printer can produce 2,000 lines per minute (high-speed printer), then this represents about a minute and a half of printing and about an average of about 50–75 printed pages of data. If the system is expanded to spool the data onto a disk drive that is placed on the local bus, the capacity of this spooler can become almost boundless because of the huge memory capacity of modern disk memory. For simplicity's sake this is not done in this example.

The printer is interfaced to the slave 8088 microprocessor through a 74LS244 that is operated as a strobed output interrupting device. Whenever the printer has printed a character, as signaled by its BUSY interface connection, an interrupt is generated, causing the slave 8088 microprocessor to retrieve data from the queue for the printer. This process is continued until the queue is empty, at which time the slave 8088 disables interrupt requests until new information is placed in the queue for printing.

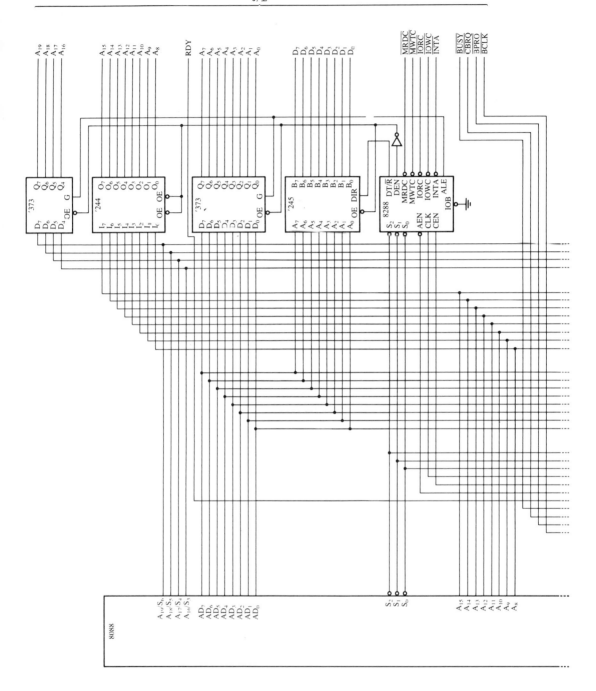

334

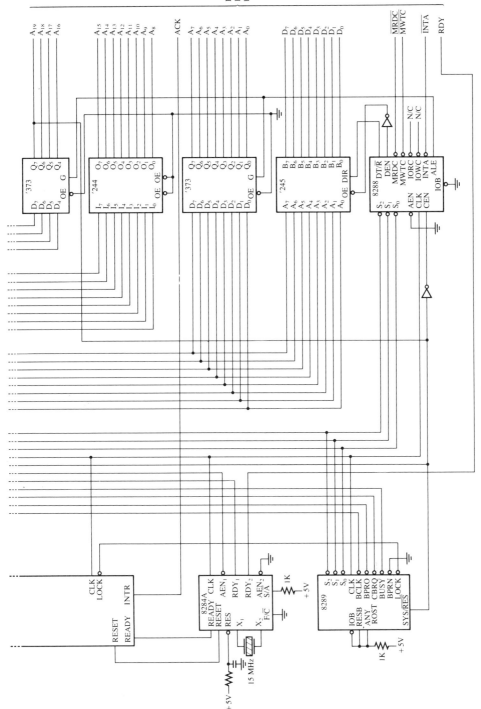

FIGURE 10–24 The 8088 shown with both a shared and a local bus.

FIGURE 10–25 Memory maps for the print spooler. (a) Shared-bus master. (b) Bus-slave memory map.

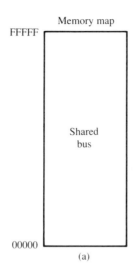

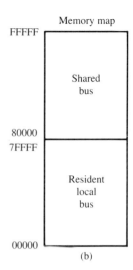

Print Spooler Software.   The software for the print spooler is fairly straightforward. The entire software listing is provided in sections, so that a study can be made of initialization, data transfer software, and interrupt-controlled printer service procedures. The only software not illustrated is that which is required to program and initialize the system. When the system is initialized, the input and output pointers of the queue are both set up with address 20000H. This condition (equal pointers) indicates that the queue is void of data. The segment portion of these pointers contains 2000H and the offset portion contains a 0000H.

Example 10–5 illustrates the software required to transfer data into the print spooler from the 8088 bus master. In this software interface, the 8088 bus master loads a block of shared memory, called a print buffer (BUFFER beginning at location 80002H), with printer data and then signals the slave 8088 that data are available through a flip-flop, which acts as an indicator to the slave. This flag flip-flop is set by the master whenever printer data are available and cleared by the slave whenever the slave has processed all of the data. One additional piece of information is also placed in shared memory for the slave. The length of the block of data (LENGTH at location 80000H) to be printed is stored in shared memory as a word count for the slave 8088.

EXAMPLE 10–5

```
;Procedure found in the master microprocessor that tests the
;FLAG to determine if the slave is busy.  If the slave is not busy
;data are transferred into the print buffer and the flag is set
;to indicate that data are available for the slave to print.
;
;The contents of CX = the number of characters to be loaded
```

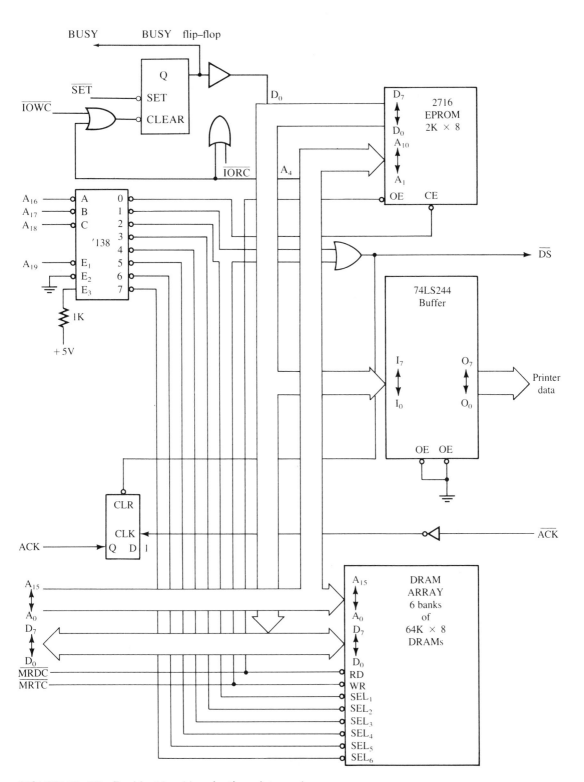

FIGURE 10–26 Resident local bus for the print spooler.

337

FIGURE 10–27 8088 resident local bus memory map.

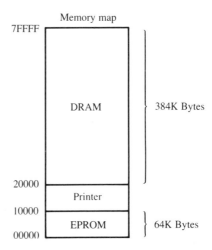

```
;The contents of DS:SI = the location of the data to be sent to
;the slave for printing
;
0000                           LOAD    PROC  FAR

0000  E4 00                            IN    AL,00H
0002  A8 01                            TEST  AL,1
0004  75 FA                            JNZ   LOAD    ;wait for slave to finish

0006  06                               PUSH  ES
0007  BF 0002 R                        MOV   DI,OFFSET BUFFER
000A  B8 8000                          MOV   AX,8000H
000D  8E C0                            MOV   ES,AX
000F  26: 89 0E 0000 R                 MOV   ES:LENGTH,CX

0014  F3/ A4                           REP   MOVSB

0016  07                               POP   ES
0017  B0 FF                            MOV   AL,0FFH
0019  E6 00                            OUT   00H,AL  ;set data available flag

001B  CB                               RET

001C                           LOAD    ENDP
```

The maximum size of the buffer is constrained to 64K bytes.

Once the data are stored in the print buffer located in the shared memory, the slave microprocessor begins to transfer it from the shared memory into its own local memory. The data are stored in the local memory organized as an FIFO or queue. In this example, the size of the queue is 384K bytes. Example 10–6 lists the software used by the slave microprocessor to load the queue from the shared-memory print buffer.

EXAMPLE 10-6

```
                  ;Procedure found in the slave microprocessor that tests the
                  ;FLAG to determine if data are available for printing.  If
                  ;data are available, this procedure transfers it into the
                  ;local memory of the slave processor for printing.
                  ;
0000                        TRANSFER   PROC  FAR

0000  E4 00                 IN    AL,00H
0002  A8 01                 TEST  AL,1
0004  74 FA                 JZ    TRANSFER          ;if no data

0006  B8 8000               MOV   AX,8000H          ;load segments
0009  8E D8                 MOV   DS,AX
000B  BE 0000               MOV   SI,0              ;load source
000E  8B 0C                 MOV   CX,[SI]           ;get count
0010  83 C6 02              ADD   SI,2              ;adjust pointer

0013  E8 0023 R             CALL  FILL_QUEUE        ;fill queue

0016  FB                    STI                     ;enable interrupt

0017  E6 00                 OUT   00H,AL            ;clear flip-flop
0019  EB E5                 JMP   TRANSFER

001B               TRANSFER   ENDP


001B  0000         IN_POINT_SEG    DW    ?          ;input pointer
001D  0000         IN_POINT_OFF    DW    ?
001F  0000         OUT_POINT_SEG   DW    ?          ;output pointer
0021  0000         OUT_POINT_OFF   DW    ?

                  ;Procedure that will transfer data from the master BUFFER to
                  ;the slave queue.  DS:SI address the source data in the
                  ;shared memory and CX contains the count.
                  ;
0023                        FILL_QUEUE PROC  NEAR

0023  FC                    CLD
0024  2E: A1 001B R         MOV   AX,CS:IN_POINT_SEG
0028  8E C0                 MOV   ES,AX
002A  2E: 8B 3E 001D R      MOV   DI,CS:IN_POINT_OFF

002F                        FULL:

002F  E8 0046 R             CALL  TEST_FULL         ;test for full
0032  74 FB                 JZ FULL                 ;if full

0034  A4                    MOVSB
0035  E8 005C R             CALL  INC_IN_POINT ;increment
                                               ;in_pointer
0038  8C C0                 MOV   AX,ES
```

```
003A   2E: A3 001B R              MOV      CS:IN_POINT_SEG,AX
003E   2E: 89 3E 001D R           MOV      CS:IN_POINT_OFF,DI
0043   E2 EA                      LOOP     FULL           ;repeat for all data
0045   C3                         RET

0046                       FILL_QUEUE     ENDP
```

;Procedure to test for a full queue
;
```
0046                       TEST_FULL   PROC   NEAR

0046   1E                         PUSH     DS
0047   57                         PUSH     DI
0048   E8 005C R                  CALL     INC_IN_POINT
004B   8C D8                      MOV      AX,DS
004D   2E: 3B 06 001F R           CMP      AX,CS:OUT_POINT_SEG
0052   75 05                      JNE      TEST_FULL_END
0054   2E: 3B 3E 0021 R           CMP      DI,OUT_POINT_OFF

0059                       TEST_FULL_END:

0059   5F                         POP      DI
005A   1F                         POP      DS
005B   C3                         RET

005C                       TEST_FULL      ENDP
```

;Procedure to increment the in_pointer.
;
```
005C              INC_IN_POINT PROC      NEAR

005C   47      ·                  INC      DI
005D   0B FF                      OR DI,DI
005F   75 0F                      JNE      INC_IN_POINT_END
0061   8C C0                      MOV      AX,ES
0063   05 1000                    ADD      AX,1000H
0066   3D 8000                    CMP      AX,8000H
0069   75 03                      JNE      INC_IN_POINT1
006B   B8 2000                    MOV      AX,2000H

006E                       INC_IN_POINT1:

006E   8E C0                      MOV      ES,AX

0070                       INC_IN_POINT_END:

0070   C3                         RET

0071              INC_IN_POINT      ENDP
```

In this software the slave tests the flag flip-flop to see whether the master microprocesso
has filled the print buffer. If the buffer is filled, the slave microprocessor transfers it
contents from the shared memory into its queue. Once the transfer is complete, the slav

microprocessor clears the flag flip-flop to indicate that the master may transfer additional data to the slave for printing.

Example 10–7 illustrates the software used to actually print data from the queue.

EXAMPLE 10–7

```
;Interrupt service procedure that prints data from the queue.
;If all data are printed, interrupts are disabled by this
;procedure.
;
0071                     PRINT   PROC    FAR

0071  50                         PUSH    AX              ;save registers
0072  55                         PUSH    BP
0073  1E                         PUSH    DS
0074  57                         PUSH    DI
0075  06                         PUSH    ES

0076  E8 009D R                  CALL    TEST_EMPTY
0079  75 0E                      JNE     PRINT1          ;if not empty

007B  8B EC                      MOV     BP,SP
007D  8B 46 0C                   MOV     AX,[BP+12]
0080  80 E4 FD                   AND     AH,0FDH         ;interrupt off
0083  89 46 0C                   MOV     [BP+12],AX
0086  EB 0F 90                   JMP     PRINT_END

0089               PRINT1:

0089  B8 1000                    MOV     AX,1000H
008C  8E C0                      MOV     ES,AX
008E  8A 05                      MOV     AL,[DI]
0090  26: A2 0000 R              MOV     ES:DATA,Al      ;print character

0094  E8 00B5 R                  CALL    INC_OUT

0097               PRINT_END:

0097  07                         POP     ES              ;restore registers
0098  5F                         POP     DI
0099  1F                         POP     DS
009A  5D                         POP     BP
009B  58                         POP     AX
009C  CF                         IRET

009D                     PRINT   ENDP

009D               TEST_EMPTY    PROC    NEAR

009D  2E: Al 001F R              MOV     AX,CS:OUT_POINT_SEG
00A1  8E D8                      MOV     DS,AX
00A3  2E: 8B 3E 0021 R           MOV     DI,CS:OUT_POINT_OFF
00A8  2E: 3B 06 001B R           CMP     AX,CS:IN_POINT_SEG
00AD  75 05                      JNE     TEST_EMPTY_END
```

```
00AF   2E: 3B 3E 001D R            CMP         DI,CS:IN_POINT_OFF
00B4                               TEST_EMPTY_END:

00B4   C3                          RET

00B5                     TEST_EMPTY          ENDP

00B5                     INC_OUT PROC        NEAR

00B5   47                          INC         DI
00B6   0B FF                       OR          DI,DI
00B8   75 0D                       JNE         INC_OUT_END
00BA   8C C0                       MOV         AX,DS
00BC   05 1000                     ADD         AX,1000H
00BF   3D 8000                     CMP         AX,8000H
00C2   75 03                       JNE         INC_OUT_END
00C4   B8 2000                     MOV         AX,2000H

00C7                               INC_OUT_END:

00C7   2E: A3 001F R               MOV         CS:OUT_POINT_SEG,AX
00CB   2E: 89 3E 0021 R            MOV         CS:OUT_POINT_OFF,DI
00D0   C3                          RET

00D1                     INC_OUT ENDP
```

This software is interrupt driven, and therefore runs as a background program virtually hidden from the software listed in Example 10–6 except for the interrupt enable instruction located there. Whenever the printer interface, through the 8255, indicates that it is ready to accept additional data, an interrupt occurs calling this interrupt service procedure. The procedure itself extracts data from the queue, if they are available, and sends them to the printer. If data are not found in the queue, the interrupts are disabled until more information is placed into the queue. In other words, every time that data are stored in the queue, interrupts are enabled, causing the interrupt service procedure to be called. The interrupt service procedure then transfers data from the queue to the printer until the queue is empty. When the queue is empty future interrupts are disabled until more information is loaded into the queue.

10–4   SUMMARY

1. Direct memory access (DMA) is an I/O technique that bypasses the microprocessor for data transfers. In fact, the microprocessor is shut off during a DMA data transfer.
2. DMA data transfers are used in applications that require very high-speed data transfer rates. With modern memory devices, DMA transfer rates approach 8–10M bytes per second.
3. A DMA read is a high-speed data transfer from the memory to the I/O device. A DMA write is a high-speed data transfer from an I/O device to the memory.

4. In the minimum mode, the 8086/8088 uses two pins for DMA: HOLD and HLDA. The HOLD pin requests a DMA action, and the HLDA pin acknowledges the DMA action.

5. Whenever HOLD is activated, the address, data, and control buses of the 8086/8088 become three-state, going to their high-impedance state. ALE becomes a logic 0 during a hold.

6. The HOLD input to the 8086/8088 requires external synchronization with the clock. To accomplish this, a D-type flip-flop is connected to the HOLD pin and the external hold request signal.

7. The 8086/8088 bus control signals $\overline{RD}$, $\overline{WR}$, and IO/$\overline{M}$ are not able to control DMA devices. To correct this situation, these three controls are converted into four control signals for DMA-based I/O: $\overline{MEMR}$, $\overline{MEMW}$, $\overline{IOR}$, and $\overline{IOW}$.

8. A DMA controller is a special-purpose microprocessor designed to transfer data through the data bus between I/O and memory. The basic DMA controller contains an address register and a counter to count the number of bytes transferred.

9. The 8237A-5 programmable DMA controller is a four-channel device capable of transferring up to 64K bytes of data using DMA techniques without the intervention of the 8086/8088. Transfer rates for this controller approach 1.6M bytes per second when operated with a 5-MHz clock.

10. The 8237A-5 DMA controller operates in four basic modes: demand, single, block, and cascade. Demand mode will transfer data as long as the request input for a channel is active. Single mode will transfer one byte each time the request is active. Block mode performs memory-to-memory transfer by means of software. Cascade mode expands the system beyond the original four channels.

11. The address and count registers of the 8237A-5 are 16 bits wide. This allows the controller to address the data at a 16-bit memory boundary and transfer up to 64K bytes of data with one programming.

12. In order to use the 8237A-5 with the 8086/8088, an external address latch must capture the address bits A_{15}–A_8, and an additional 4-bit latch must hold the upper 4 bits of the memory address (A_{19}–A_{16}).

13. Maximum mode 8086/8088 DMA is designed to function with the 8089 and 8087 coprocessors.

14. $\overline{RQ}/\overline{GT}$ pins of the 8086/8088 are bidirectional request/grant pins. Each available pin is able to handle one external DMA controller or coprocessor.

15. $\overline{RQ}/\overline{GT}$ is used to request a DMA, grant a DMA, and release the 8086/8088 from a DMA. The external DMA controller applies the first pulse to this pin to request a DMA. The 8086/8088 applies the second pulse to grant the DMA. The controller applies the third pulse to release the 8086/8088 from the DMA.

16. The 8289 bus arbiter connects microprocessors to shared-bus systems. It allows the master to operate in three different modes: single, I/O bus, and resident bus. Single-bus mode allows a microprocessor to access a shared bus. I/O bus mode allows a microprocessor to access a shared bus and a local I/O bus. Resident-bus mode allows the microprocessor to access a shared bus and a local I/O and memory bus.

17. Priority is resolved in the 8288 system via a daisy-chain priority circuit or a priority circuit.

10–5   QUESTIONS AND PROBLEMS

1. At what speed is DMA transfer mainly used to transfer data?
2. With what types of I/O devices is DMA particularly useful?
3. What limits the speed of a DMA transfer?
4. Explain what happens when a logic 1 is applied to the 8086/8088 HOLD input.
5. What 8086/8088 condition is HLDA used to indicate?
6. At what point in the bus timing is a HOLD accepted?
7. What is the purpose of the circuit of Figure 10–2?
8. A DMA write transfers data from ＿＿＿＿＿＿＿ to ＿＿＿＿＿＿ .
9. A DMA read transfers data from ＿＿＿＿＿＿＿ to ＿＿＿＿＿＿ .
10. What is a verify cycle?
11. Why is it impossible to use the $\overline{RD}$, $\overline{WR}$, and IO/$\overline{M}$ signals to accomplish a DMA?
12. What system control signals are used in place of $\overline{RD}$, $\overline{WR}$, and IO/$\overline{M}$ for DMA?
13. Explain how the circuit of Figure 10–3 functions.
14. At what rate is the 8237A-5 capable of making DMA transfers?
15. How many DMA channels are available in the 8237A-5?
16. The 8237A-5 is able to transfer up to ＿＿＿＿ bytes without being reprogrammed.
17. What is the purpose of the DREQ pins on the 8237A-5?
18. What is the ADSTB signal used for with the 8237A-5?
19. The current count register holds a count that is always ＿＿＿＿ less than the number of bytes transferred by the 8237A-5.
20. What are the purposes of the 8237A-5 base address and count registers?
21. Briefly define each bit of the 8237A-5 command register.
22. The mode register is used to program each channel for autoincrement/decrement operation. What is meant by this?
23. What is the request register normally used for in the 8237A-5?
24. What is a terminal count?
25. If a mask for channel 1 is set, then channel 1 is ＿＿＿＿＿＿＿ .
26. What is the F/L flip-flop of the 8237A-5?
27. Briefly describe how channel 1 is programmed for the count and address of the DMA transfer.
28. Assume that I/O ports A0H/AFH are decoded, and write the software required to program channel 3 for a DMA address of 1000H and a count to transfer 100H bytes of data.
29. Assuming that I/O ports 10H–1FH are decoded, program the 8237A-5 so that the channel 2 DMA address is 2345H and the count is 123H.
30. How long does it take the 8237A-5 to transfer one byte of data in memory-to-memory transfer mode?
31. In memory-to-memory transfers, channel 0 holds the ＿＿＿＿＿＿＿ address, and channel 1 holds the ＿＿＿＿＿＿＿ address.
32. Where is the count for a memory-to-memory transfer held?
33. Which channel is programmed with the software request to start a memory-to-memory DMA transfer?
34. Explain the effect of a channel 0 hold for memory-to-memory DMA transfers.

35. What signal from the 8237A-5 is used to enable the I/O device for a DMA transfer?
36. What is a double buffer?
37. What is the main purpose of maximum mode 8086/8088 operation?
38. Explain the operation of the $\overline{RQ}/\overline{GT}$ pins.
39. The main purpose of the bus arbiter is to control access to a _____ bus.
40. Is an 8289 required for all microprocessors and coprocessors that access the shared-system bus?
41. What is the purpose of the SYSB/$\overline{RESB}$ input to the 8289?
42. A device operated in the single-bus mode is connected to the _____ bus of the system.
43. Resident bus operation allows a device to address the _____ bus and also local _____ and _____ .
44. Which mode of operation is used to address a shared-system bus and a local I/O bus?
45. Define the term *parallel processing*.
46. The 8289 allows two priority schemes. List them.
47. Redraw the circuit of Figure 10–21 so that five 8289s are connected.
48. Is the 8289 $\overline{BCLK}$ signal used in a parallel-priority scheme?
49. In the circuit of Figure 10–24, how is the access of the shared bus and the resident bus selected by the 8088?
50. The resident local bus of Figure 10–26 addresses EPROM at which section of the 8088 local memory?
51. Briefly explain how the printer interface functions in Figure 10–26.

CHAPTER 11

The 8087 Family of Arithmetic Coprocessors

INTRODUCTION

The 8087 family of coprocessors performs arithmetic and comparisons on a wise variety of data types. It is also capable of performing transcendental functions such as tangent and log. This chapter provides the details required to interface the 8087 to either an 8086 or 8088 microprocessor and details the programming of the 8087 family.

The 8087 family is able to multiply, add, subtract, divide, and find the square root, partial tangent, partial arctangent, and log. Data types operated upon by the 8087 include 16-, 32-, and 64-bit integers; 10-digit BCD; and 32-, 64-, and 80-bit floating-point numbers. The operations performed by the 8087 generally execute about 100 times faster than equivalent operations written with the most efficient 8086/8088 software.

OBJECTIVES

Upon completion of this chapter, you will be able to:

1. Convert data to and from the data types used by the 8087 family of coprocessors.
2. Explain the operation of the 8087 when interfaced to an 8086/8088.
3. Interface the 8087 to the 8086/8088.
4. Explain the operation of each of the 8087 family instructions.
5. Develop software with the 8087 family instruction set.

11–1   DATA FORMATS FOR THE 8087 FAMILY

This section of the text presents the types of data used with the 8087 family of numeric processors. These include integer, BCD, and floating point. Each has a specific use in a system, and many systems may require all three types.

Integers

Integers are signed. There are word integers (16 bits), short integers (32 bits), and long integers (64 bits). Conversion to and from these integers is handled in exactly the same manner as it is for the 8-bit signed integers presented in the introductory chapters of this text. As you will recall, positive numbers are stored with the leftmost sign bit of a 0, and negative numbers are stored in the two's complement form with the leftmost sign bit of a 1.

   The word integers range in value from $-32,768$ to $+32,767$, the short integers from -2×10^9 to $+2 \times 10^9$, and the long integers from -9×10^{18} to $+9 \times 10^{18}$. Integer data types are used in many of the operations performed by the 8087 family. Figure 11–1 illustrates the three forms of integer data types for the 8087 family.

Binary Coded Decimal (BCD)

The binary coded decimal (BCD) form requires 80 bits to be stored in the memory. Each number is stored as 18 BCD digits that are packed in memory as two digits per byte. The leftmost byte contains only the sign of the BCD number. Each digit is valued between 0 and 9. It is always stored as a positive number, and never in ten's complement form. Figure 11–2 illustrates the form of the BCD number as used by the 8087 family.

Floating Point

Floating-point numbers are often called *real numbers* because they may hold integers, fractions, or mixed numbers. A floating-point number has two parts: a *biased exponent*

FIGURE 11–1 Integer forms of data for the 8087 family of numeric coprocessors. (a) Word, (b) short, and (c) long.

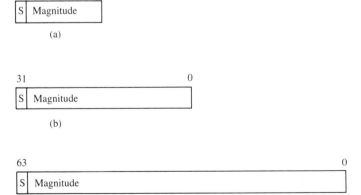

79		72	71																		0
S	X	D_{17}	D_{16}	D_{15}	D_{14}	D_{13}	D_{12}	D_{11}	D_{10}	D_9	D_8	D_7	D_6	D_5	D_4	D_3	D_2	D_1	D_0		

FIGURE 11–2   BCD data format for the 8087 family of numeric coprocessors.

and a *significand*. Floating-point numbers are written in *scientific binary notation*. The 8087 family supports three types of floating-point numbers: short (32 bits), long (64 bits), and temporary (80 bits). Refer to Figure 11–3 for these three types of floating-point numbers. Floating-point numbers used with the numeric coprocessor conform to the IEEE-754 standard that is adopted by major software producers.

Converting to Floating-Point Form.   Converting a decimal number to floating point is a simple task that is accomplished by following these steps:

1. Convert the decimal number into binary.
2. Normalize the binary number.
3. Calculate the biased exponent.
4. Store the number in floating-point form.

   These four steps are illustrated for the decimal number 100.25 in Example 11–1. Here the decimal number is converted to a short floating-point number.

EXAMPLE 11–1

Step	Result
1	100.25 = 1100100.01
2	1100100.01 = 1.10010001 × 2^6
3	110 = 110 + 01111111 = 10000101
4	01000010 11001000 10000000 00000000
	SEEEEEEE ESSSSSSS SSSSSSSS SSSSSSSS

   In step 4, the positions are identified as sign (S), exponent (E), and significand. The original number is positive, so S is a 0 and the biased exponent is a 110 plus a 01111111. The bias value for the short real number is + 127 or 01111111. Biases for other forms are listed in the caption of Figure 11–3. Notice that in step 4 the significand is stored without the first bit 1.XXXX. (As a result, it may have appeared that the significand was stored improperly.) Only the fractional portion is stored because all numbers contain this integer 1 (called an implied 1). The only exceptions to this rule are a 0 and an overflow. A 0 is stored as 0 in all bit positions of the floating-point number. An overflow condition is stored with a logic 1 in every bit of the exponent with a fraction of all zeros.

Converting from Floating-Point Form.   Conversion to a decimal number from the floating-point form is summarized in the following steps.

FIGURE 11–3

Floating-point (real) numbers. (a) Short with a bias of 127 (7FH) and an implicit 1, (b) long with a bias of 1023 (3FFH) and an implicit 1, and (c) temporary with a bias of 16,383 (3FFFH) and a non-implicit 1.

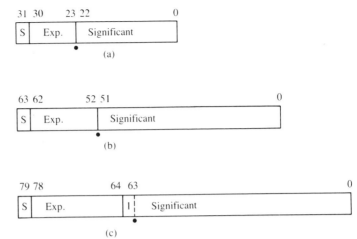

1. Separate the sign, biased exponent, and significand.
2. Convert the biased exponent into a true exponent by subtracting the bias.
3. Write the number as a normalized binary number.
4. Convert it to an unnormalized binary number.
5. Convert ,the unnormalized binary number into decimal.

These five steps are used to convert a short floating-point number to decimal in Example 11–2. Notice how the sign bit of 1 makes the decimal result negative. Also notice that the implied 1 is added back to the normalized binary result in step 3.

EXAMPLE 11–2

Step	Result
1	1 10000011 10010010000000000000000
2	10000011 = 10000011 − 01111111 = 100
3	1.1001001×2^4
4	11001.001
5	− 25.125

11–2   8087 ARCHITECTURE

The 8087 is a coprocessor designed to run in parallel with the 8086/8088. Its performance exceeds the speed of software written for the 8086/8088 100 times. The 8087 executes 68 numeric instructions with the 8086/8088 microprocessor. The 8086/8088 executes all the normal instructions, while the 8087 executes just its own. Figure 11–4 illustrates the

FIGURE 11–4 The pinout of the 8087 numeric data processor (NDP). (Courtesy of Intel Corporation)

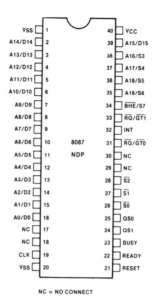

		8087		
VSS	1		40	VCC
A14/D14	2		39	A15/D15
A13/D13	3		38	A16/S3
A12/D12	4		37	A17/S4
A11/D11	5		36	A18/S5
A10/D10	6		35	A19/S6
A9/D9	7		34	BHE/S7
A8/D8	8		33	RQ/GT1
A7/D7	9		32	INT
A6/D6	10	8087	31	RQ/GT0
A5/D5	11	NDP	30	NC
A4/D4	12		29	NC
A3/D3	13		28	S2
A2/D2	14		27	S1
A1/D1	15		26	S0
A0/D0	16		25	QS0
NC	17		24	QS1
NC	18		23	BUSY
CLK	19		22	READY
VSS	20		21	RESET

NC = NO CONNECT

pinout of the 8087 arithmetic coprocessor. Other family members include the 80187, 80287, and 80387. The 80187 interfaces to the 80186/80188, the 80287 to the 80286, and the 80387 to the 80386. In addition to the 80387, a 16-bit version, the 80387SX, interfaces to the 80386SX. The 80486 includes an 80387 built into the same integrated circuit. Except for the microprocessor they are interfaced with, the architectures of these other family members are essentially the same as the 8087.

Pin Definition

The following list describes all the pins of the 8087:

1. AD_{15}–AD_0 (address data bus) are normally connected to AD_{15}–AD_0 of the 8086 or AD_7–AD_0 and A_{15}–A_8 of the 8088 microprocessor. When attached to the 8088, the function of AD_{15}–AD_8 is changed to A_{15}–A_8. These connections contain address and data.

2. A_{19}/S_6–A_{16}/S_3 (address/status bus) hold address bits A_{19}–A_{16}, but no status information. As output, S_6–S_5 are always a logic 1, and S_3 is always a logic 0. As inputs, the status bits are monitored by the 8087.

3. $\overline{BHE}/S_7$ (bus high enable/status) indicates that AD_{15}–AD_8 contains valid data. As an output, S_7 is always a logic 0. As an input, it is monitored by the 8087.

4. $\overline{S_2}$–$\overline{S_0}$ (status) are I/O pins that provide status during 8087 operation and are monitored by the 8087 during normal bus operation. Table 11–1 illustrates the function of the $\overline{S_2}$–$\overline{S_0}$ pins whenever the 8087 is using the bus.

5. $\overline{RQ/GT_0}$ (request/grant) is a bidirectional pin that requests a DMA and grants and releases a DMA. This pin must be connected to either the $\overline{RQ/GT_0}$ or $\overline{RQ/GT_1}$ pin on the 8086/8088.

6. $\overline{RQ/GT_1}$ (request/grant) is a bidirectional pin that forces the 8087 to request the bus. The 8087 is not in control of the bus, but the request is passed through the 8087 for

TABLE 11-1 Function of the 8087 status bits

$\overline{S}_2$	$\overline{S}_1$	$\overline{S}_0$	Function
0	X	X	Unused
1	0	0	Unused
1	0	1	Reads memory
1	1	0	Writes memory
1	1	1	Passive

this I/O pin. This input is often used to connect an 8089 to the 8086/8088 through the 8087.

7. QS_1 and QS_0 (queue status) are used by the 8087 to track the 8086/8088 queue.
8. INT (interrupt output) requests an interrupt for errors such as division overflow.
9. BUSY (busy output) indicates that the 8087 is currently executing an instruction. Output is normally connected to the $\overline{TEST}$ input of the 8086/8088 so that the 8086/8088 is able to wait for the numeric coprocessor to complete an operation.
10. READY (ready input) is normally tied to the 8086/8088 READY pin so that slow memory can be accessed.
11. RESET (reset input) causes the 8087 to be reset, which immediately terminates its current operation.
12. CLK (clock input) provides timing for the 8087 and is normally tied in parallel with the CLK pin of the 8086/8088.

Internal Structure of the 8087

Figure 11-5 depicts the internal structure of the 8087. Notice that this device is broken down into two major components: the *control unit* and the *numeric execution unit*.

The control unit is responsible for synchronizing the operation of the 8087 with that of the 8086/8088. Both the 8086/8088 and the 8087 fetch instructions in parallel. That is, each executes its own instructions. If an 8087 instruction is fetched, the 8086/8088 does an NOP, and if an 8086/8088 instruction is fetched, the 8087 does an NOP.

The numeric execution unit (NEU) is responsible for executing all 68 instructions that the 8087 will respond to in a system. The NEU has an eight-register stack that holds operands for arithmetic operations and the results from these operations. Instructions may address data in specific registers or use a PUSH or POP instruction to store or retrieve data. Other registers contained in the NEU are status word, control word, tag word, and exception pointers.

Status Word. The status word (see Figure 11-6) reflects the overall operation of the 8087. It can be accessed by executing the 8087 instruction that reads the status word and stores it in the system memory so that the 8086/8088 can interrogate it.

The B (busy) bit indicates whether the 8087 is currently executing a task. The 8087 is busy if it is a logic 1; otherwise, it is idle. After the operation, bits C_3–C_0 indicate the condition of some of the instructions, such as compare and test.

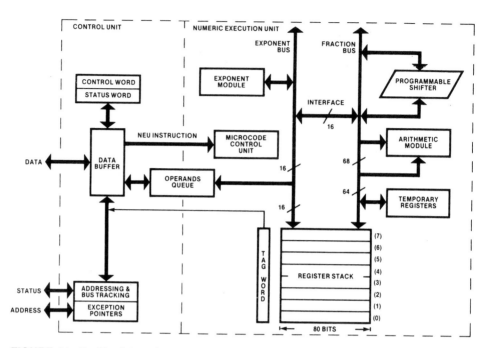

FIGURE 11–5   The internal structure of the 8087. (Courtesy of Intel Corporation)

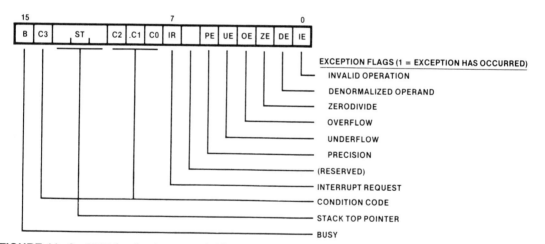

FIGURE 11–6   8087 family status word. (Courtesy of Intel Corporation)

The ST field indicates which register is currently at the top of the stack. This memory is cyclic—that is, one location higher than the top location of 111 is 000 and vice versa.

Bits 5–0 indicate specific conditions about exceptions that the 8087 has detected during an operation. An exception will cause an interrupt if the interrupts are enabled.

Control Word.   The control word is illustrated in Figure 11–7. The interrupt mask bits enable the corresponding exception if unmasked (mask = 0) and disable the exception if masked (mask = 1). The control word itself is sent to the 8087 with an 8087 instruction.

Tag Word.   The tag word is not used by the programmer. It is an internal word that optimizes the performance of the 8087.

Exception Pointers.   Exception pointers (see Figure 11–8) are provided for exception-handling programs. Whenever the 8087 executes an instruction, the 8087 holds the

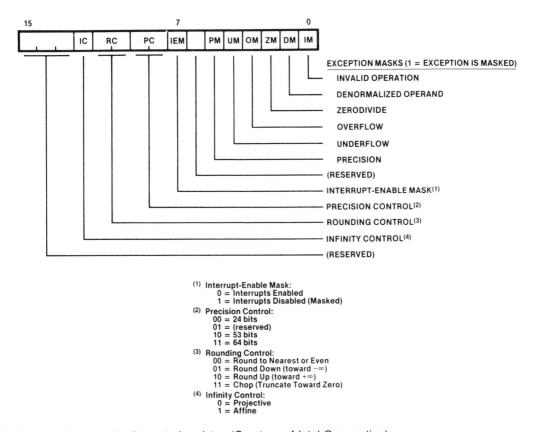

(1) Interrupt-Enable Mask:
   0 = Interrupts Enabled
   1 = Interrupts Disabled (Masked)
(2) Precision Control:
   00 = 24 bits
   01 = (reserved)
   10 = 53 bits
   11 = 64 bits
(3) Rounding Control:
   00 = Round to Nearest or Even
   01 = Round Down (toward −∞)
   10 = Round Up (toward +∞)
   11 = Chop (Truncate Toward Zero)
(4) Infinity Control:
   0 = Projective
   1 = Affine

FIGURE 11–7   8087 family control register. (Courtesy of Intel Corporation)

FIGURE 11–8   8087 Exception pointers.

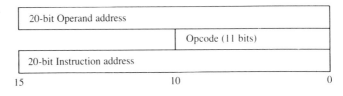

11 least significant bits of the Opcode are stored

instruction's address and opcode in the exception pointers. It is often possible for an exception handler (interrupt service procedure) to use this information to correct the exception error.

Reset

The 8087 is reset by the hardware and the RESET input or by a software reset (the FINIT and FSAVE instructions). After a reset, the 8087 initializes itself to put the conditions listed in Table 11–2 into effect.

Definitions

It is essential to understand some of the fields and their meaning in the control word before attempting to use the 8087. Terms that require explanation are *rounding control, precision control,* and *infinity control*. Each of these features is selected and controlled by the control word.

Rounding Control. The rounding control field in the control word selects one of four different rounding modes: round to nearest, round down, round up, and chop. The round-to-nearest mode is selected upon a reset and is the mode most often used in a program. This mode causes the 8087 to round the result from an operation to the nearest value (up or down). The chop mode truncates the result. This is most often used in integer arithmetic where a fractional portion must be chopped from the result. The round-up and round-down modes round a number up to the next higher value or down to the next lower value.

TABLE 11–2 State of the 8087 after reset

Field	Value	Condition
Infinity	0	Projective
Rounding control	00	Round-to-nearest
Precision control	11	64 bits
Interrupt mask	1	Disabled
Exception masks	11111	Exceptions masked
Busy	0	Not busy
Condition code	????	Unknown
Stack top	000	Register 000
Interrupt request	0	No request
Exception flags	00000	No exceptions
Tags	11	Registers empty
Registers	—	Not changed
Instruction code	—	Not changed
Instruction address	—	Not changed
Operand address	—	Not changed

Precision Control. This field of the control word selects the number of binary bits used in the calculation. Three widths are selected by the precision control field: 64, 53, or 24 bits. The default setting specified at a reset is 64 bits. The speed of the 8007 is affected by selecting the different sizes of precision, since the 53-bit precision operation takes less time than the 64- or 80-bit ones.

Infinity Control. The infinity control bit in the control word selects either projective or affine closures for infinity. The projective infinity mode selects an unsigned infinity value for both positive and negative infinity. The affine closure elects to keep the signs of positive and negative infinity.

Interrupts

The 8087 has one interrupt output pin, INT. The INT pin becomes a logic 1 whenever the interrupt pin is enabled (by a 0 in the interrupt-enable mask bit of the control word) and an unmasked exception is active. The exceptions detected by the 8087 include denormalization (if unmasked), invalid operation, division by 0, denormalization (if masked), over/underflow, and precision.

11–3   PROCESSOR INTERFACE

The interface of the 8087 and the 8086/8088 is much simpler than the interface of the 8237 and the 8086/8088. This is because the 8087 works only in the local mode. As a result, everything is connected in parallel except for the INT, $\overline{RQ}/\overline{GT}_0$, and $\overline{RQ}/\overline{GT}_1$ pins.

Figure 11–9 illustrates the connection of the 8088 microprocessor with the 8087 arithmetic coprocessor. Notice that this connection is very straightforward. It requires no decoder or additional hardware because the 8087 is never programmed with an IN or an OUT. Programming is handled by 8087 instructions stored in the memory of the 8086/8088 along with normal 8086/8088 instructions. The 8087 instructions are actually an extension of the 8086/8088 instruction set. Whenever an 8087 instruction is encountered in a program, the 8087 responds to it, and the 8086/8088 treats it as an NOP instruction and merely proceeds to the next instruction in the program.

The interface in Figure 11–9 uses the $\overline{RQ}/\overline{GT}_0$ pin of the 8087 to cause a DMA whenever the 8087 requires transfers between itself and the memory. The second request/grant pin ($\overline{RQ}/\overline{GT}_1$) is used if an additional coprocessor, such as the 8089, is connected in the local bus configuration. If the additional coprocessor is connected, its $\overline{RQ}/\overline{GT}$ pin is connected to the $\overline{RQ}/\overline{GT}_1$ input pin of the 8087. The coprocessor connected to $\overline{RQ}/\overline{GT}_1$ has a higher priority than the 8087.

The INT output pin is either connected to the NMI or INTR pin of the 8086/8088 or to an 8259A programmable interrupt controller, depending on the system's configuration. If no other interrupts are present in the system, then INT is connected directly to the 8086/8088's INTR pin. It is rare for this to be the only interrupt, so, in most cases, the INT output pin is connected to an input of the 8259A PIC.

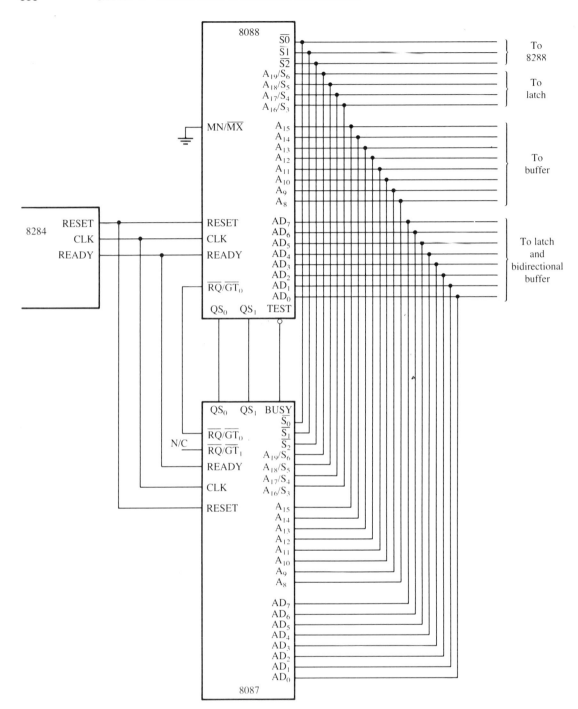

FIGURE 11–9 An 8088 interfaced with an 8087.

The BUSY output is connected to the $\overline{\text{TEST}}$ input pin of the 8088 so that the WAIT instruction can determine whether the 8087 is busy. Recall that the WAIT instruction will cause a delay until the $\overline{\text{TEST}}$ pin is a logic 0 before any instructions are executed. If $\overline{\text{TEST}}$ is a 1, then the 8086/8088 waits; if it is a 0, it continues with the next instruction in the program. BUSY is a logic 1 when the 8087 is executing an instruction.

11–4 INSTRUCTION SET

The 8087 arithmetic coprocessor is able to execute 68 different instructions. Whenever an instruction references the memory, the 8086/8088 automatically generates the memory address for the 8087. The 8087 sends or receives the data in memory reference operations, while the 8086/8088 receives the data in normal reference operations.

This section of the text describes the function of each instruction and lists its assembly language form. Because the 8087 uses the 8086/8088 addressing modes, not all of the possible assembly language instruction forms are included; the list would be far too extensive. All the 8087 opcodes are recognized by most 8086/8088 assemblers. The assembler generates an ESC instruction followed by an 11-bit code that represents the opcode of the 8087 instruction.

Data Transfer Instructions

There are three basic forms of data transfers: floating-point, integer, and BCD. Figure 11–10 illustrates the way that each type of data used by the 8087 is stored in the system memory.

Data types are defined with assembler directives, as indicated in Table 11–3. The assembler then automatically selects the type of memory transfer used with an instruction.

Floating-Point Data Transfers.   There are four floating-point data transfer instructions: FLD (load real), FST (store real), FSTP (store real and pop), and FXCH (exchange registers).

FLD loads (pushes) memory data to the top of the stack. This instruction decrements the stack pointer by one and then stores the data at this new location. Data loaded to the stack top are either from the memory or any other internal register. An FLD ST(2) instruction will copy the contents of register 2 to the stack top, which is usually, but not always, initially register 0. FLD DATA will copy the contents of memory location DATA to the stack top. FLD ARRAY[BX] will copy the contents of memory beginning at the location addressed by BX + ARRAY to the stack top. Again, any 8086/8088 memory-addressing mode may be used with an 8087 instruction.

FST stores the floating-point number from the top of the stack into a destination. The significand of the number stored is rounded to the width of the destination if the number is short or long. The data are rounded according to RC field of the control register. Data are stored in the memory or in the stack at any register location selected by the instruction.

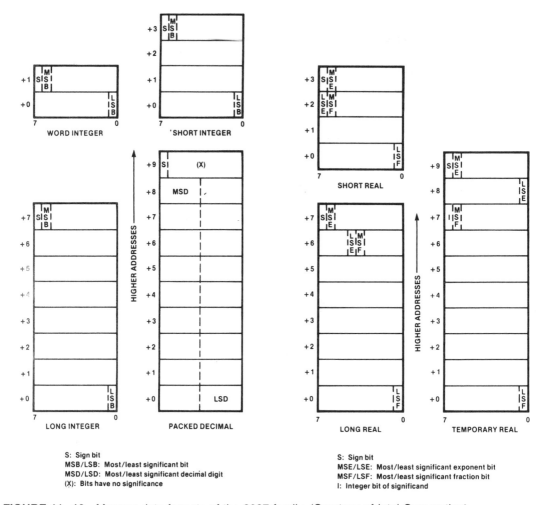

S: Sign bit
MSB/LSB: Most/least significant bit
MSD/LSD: Most/least significant decimal digit
(X): Bits have no significance

S: Sign bit
MSE/LSE: Most/least significant exponent bit
MSF/LSF: Most/least significant fraction bit
I: Integer bit of significand

FIGURE 11–10   Memory data formats of the 8087 family. (Courtesy of Intel Corporation)

TABLE 11–3   Assembler data storage directives

	Definition	Type	Example
DW	Define word	Word integer	DW 1234H
DD	Define doubleword	Short integer, short real	DD 12333333H
DQ	Define quadword	Long integer, long real	DQ 8888888888888888H
DT	Define tenbyte	Packed decimal, temporary real	DT 121212121212121212H

Note: Real numbers are floating-point numbers.

FSTP stores data and pops the stack. The only difference between FST and the FSTP instruction is that FSTP increments the stack pointer after data are stored, and FST does not change it. You might think of FSTP as *removing* the data from the stack and FST as *copying* them.

FXCH exchanges the register indicated by the instruction with the top of the stack. For example, an FXCH ST(2) instruction will exchange the contents of the top of the stack with register number 2.

Integer Data Transfers. The 8087 supports three integer data transfer instructions: FILD (integer load), FIST (integer store), and FISTP (integer store and pop).

FILD converts the integer from its binary form into a floating-point number and pushes it onto the stack. Data from memory may be loaded onto the stack with this instruction. Register data may not be loaded onto the stack with FILD.

FIST converts the contents of the stack top into an integer and rounds it as dictated by the RC bits of the control register. A register may not be used with this instruction.

FISTP functions like FIST, except that it also pops the stack by incrementing the stack pointer.

BCD Data Transfers. Two instructions are used with BCD data to push (FBLD) and pop (FBSTP) data between the stack and the memory. When data are moved from memory to the stack, they are converted to floating-point form from BCD. When data are removed (popped) from the stack, they are converted back into BCD numbers before being stored in the memory. Note that all stack data are in the floating-point form.

Arithmetic Instructions

Arithmetic instructions for the 8087 include addition, subtraction, multiplication, division, and finding square root. Arithmetic-related instructions include scaling, rounding to integer, finding absolute value, and changing sign.

Table 11-4 illustrates the basic addressing modes allowed for the arithmetic operations in the 8087 instruction set. Each addressing mode is illustrated with an example that uses the FADD instruction. All arithmetic operations are floating-point operations that use temporary 80-bit floating-point numbers. The only time the numbers are not in floating-point form is when they are transferred between the memory and the 8087.

TABLE 11-4 Arithmetic addressing modes

Form	Forms	Examples
Stack	ST(N),ST	FADD
Register	ST(n),ST or ST,ST(n)	FADD FADD ST,ST(2)
Register pop	ST(n),ST	FADDP ST(2).ST
Memory	ST,FPN ST,integer	FADD DATA[BX] FIADD NUMBER__ONE

Notes: n = any register number 0–7; N = the next stack data; and FPN = floating-point number.

The classic stack form pops the first operand datum from the top of the stack and then takes, without popping, the second operand datum from the next stack location. The operation is performed, and the result is then pushed back onto the stack. This causes the result from the operation to replace the first operand datum, but doesn't change the second. (Note that the first operand datum is the destination and the second is the source.)

The register-addressing form uses the ST (stack top) and one other register as operands. For example, the FADD ST,ST(2) instruction will add the contents of register 2 to the stack top.

The register-pop-addressing mode allows data at the stack to be used as a source operand. After the operation is performed, the source data are effectively erased by a pop. For example, FADDP ST(3),ST will add the data at the top of the stack to register 3 and then do a pop to erase the data at the stack top.

The memory-addressing mode allows floating-point or integer, but not BCD, data to be directly used as the source data that are added to the stack top. The result erases the old stack top data and replaces them.

The Arithmetic Operations.   The letter P in an opcode specifies the register pop mode (FADDP as opposed to FADD), or, in the case of subtraction and division, the letter R indicates the reverse mode. For example, FSUB ST.ST(2) will subtract the contents of register 2 (source) from the stack top and then replace the stack top with the difference. The FSUBR ST.ST(2) (R is for reverse mode) allows the data at the stack top to be subtracted from the data in register 2. The difference still replaces the data at the stack top, as in normal subtraction.

The letter I (second letter in all cases) indicates that the memory operation is integer as opposed to floating point. For example, the FADD DATA instruction adds the floating-point number at memory location DATA to the stack top, and the FIADD adds the integer at DATA to the stack top.

The same rules apply to all the main arithmetic instructions: FADD, FSUB, FMUL, and FDIV.

Arithmetic-Related Operations.   Other operations that are arithmetic in nature include FSQRT (find square root), FSCALE (scale a number), FPREM (find partial remainder), FRNDINT (round to integer), FXTRACT (extract exponent and significand), FABS (find absolute value), and FCHG (change sign).

FSQRT calculates the square root of the number located at the top of the stack. The resultant square root replaces the data at the stack top.

FSCALE uses the data stored in the next stack element and adds this value to the exponent of the data at stack top. It is important that the value located in the next stack element be an integer, or an error will result.

FPREM performs a modulo division to the stack top by the next stack element. The most common use of this instruction is to reduce the operands of a periodic transcendental function (tangent or arctangent) to a value of less than $\pi/4$.

FRNDINT rounds the data in the stack top to an integer. The RC field of the control register determines whether the number is rounded up or truncated (chopped).

FXTRACT decomposes the number at the stack top into two numbers that represent the value of the unbiased exponent and the significand, which includes the integer 1 bit.

The stack top contains the significand expressed as a floating-point number, and the next stack element contains the unbiased exponent also expressed as a floating-point number.

FABS returns the absolute (positive) value to the stack top and clears the sign bit of the floating-point number at the stack top.

FCHS complements the sign bit of the data at the stack top.

Comparison Instructions

The comparison instructions all examine the data at the stack top in relation to another element and return with the result of the comparison in the status word condition code bits. Comparisons allowed by the 8087 include FCOM (floating-point comparison), FCOMP (floating-point comparison and pop), FCOMPP (floating-point comparison and pop twice), FICOM (integer comparison), FICOMP (integer comparison and pop), FTST (test), and FXAM (examination).

FCOM compares the floating-point data at the stack top with an operand, which may be any register or any short or long floating-point memory operand. If the operand is not coded with the instruction, the 8087 assumes that the next stack element is compared with the top of the stack element.

Table 11–5 illustrates the result of the comparison found in the status register condition code bits C_3 and C_0. These two bits indicate the relative magnitudes of the numbers compared by FCOM. The only exception is the 1,1 condition, which is the result of comparing two numbers that do not exist. How can a number not exist? This happens if no number is loaded into the stack top and/or the operand before the comparison.

FCOMP and FCOMPP both perform the same comparison as FCOM. The FCOMP instruction pops the stack once after comparing the data, and the FCOMPP instruction pops the stack twice after comparing the data.

FICOM and FICOMP both compare the stack top with an integer memory operand that has been converted to a floating-point number. The only difference between these instructions is that the FICOMP instruction pops data from the stack after the comparison and FICOM does not.

FTST tests the stack top data with a 0. This results in the condition listed in Table 11–6.

FXAM examines the stack top and indicates whether the contents are positive or negative, invalid, normalized, unnormalized, 0, or empty. Table 11–7 illustrates the outcome of an FXAM and the result found the condition bits C_3–C_0.

TABLE 11–5 Condition bits after an FCOMP instruction

C_3	C_0	Function
0	0	ST > operand
0	1	ST < operand
1	0	ST = operand
1	1	Invalid operand or ST

TABLE 11−6 Condition bits after an FTST instruction

C_3	C_0	Function
0	0	ST is positive and non-0
0	1	ST is negative and non-0
1	0	ST is 0
1	1	ST invalid

TABLE 11−7 Result after executing an FXAM instruction

C_3	C_2	C_1	C_0	Function
0	0	0	0	Positive unnormalized
0	0	0	1	Positive invalid
0	0	1	0	Negative unnormalized
0	0	1	1	Negative invalid
0	1	0	0	Positive normalized
0	1	0	1	Positive infinity
0	1	1	0	Negative normalized
0	1	1	1	Negative infinity
1	0	0	0	Positive 0
1	0	0	1	Empty
1	0	1	0	Negative 0
1	0	1	1	Empty
1	1	0	0	Positive invalid
1	1	0	1	Empty
1	1	1	0	Negative invalid
1	1	1	1	Empty

Transcendental Operation

The transcendental instructions include FPTAN (partial tangent), FPATAN (partial arctangent), F2XMI ($2^x - 1$), FYL2X ($Y \cdot \log_2 X$), and FYL2XP1 ($Y \cdot \log_2 (X + 1)$).

FPTAN calculates the function $Y/X = $ TAN (0). The range of 0 must be between 0 and $\pi/4$ radians or 0 and 45 degrees for this operation to work correctly. Before executing FPTAN, the value of 0 is placed on the stack top, and after execution the value of Y replaces 0 on the stack, becoming the new stack top.

FPATAN finds the arctangent 0 = ARCTAN (X/Y). X is located at the stack top, and Y is the next element of the stack before execution of FPATAN. After execution the value of 0 is left as the stack top data after a pop. 0 is stored on top of the old value of Y. It is important that the value of Y be greater than 0 and that X be greater than Y. Y must also be less than infinity for this function to work properly.

F2XMI finds $2^x - 1$. X, which is located in the stack top and must be $0 \geq X \leq 0.5$, is used to calculate the result, which is placed back onto the stack top. If the value of 2^x is required, a 1 is added to the result after executing this instruction. Table 11-8 illustrates some common formulas and the method used to obtain the results indicated.

FYL2X calculates $Y \cdot \log_2 X$. Before execution, the values X and Y are found on the stack top and the next stack element, respectively. After FYL2X is executed, X is popped from the stack, and the result replaces the old value of Y at the stack top. This instruction is used to calculate the log to any base other than base 2 ($\log_n \cdot \log_2 X$).

The FYL2XP1 is used to calculate the function $Y \cdot \log_2(X + 1)$. X is located at the stack top and must be $0 < X > (1 - \sqrt{2}/2)$. Y is the next element on the stack and must be $-\infty < Y + \infty$. After execution, the prior value of X is popped from the stack, and the result replaces Y as the new stack top data. This function is most often used to compute the log of a number that is very nearly 1.

Constant Operations

The 8087 instruction set includes instructions that return constant values after execution. Each pushes the constant onto the stack after execution in preparation for use with another instruction. Table 11-9 depicts each instruction and the value that is pushed onto the stack by its execution.

8087 Control Instructions

The 8087 coprocessor has control instructions for initialization, exception handling, and task switching. Many of these instructions have two opcodes. If the letter N is the second letter of the opcode, the assembler executes the instruction as it appears. If no N is

TABLE 11-8 Exponentiation equations

Result	Equation
10^x	$2^x \cdot \log_2 10$
e^x	$2^x \cdot \log_2 e$
y^x	$2^x \cdot \log_2 y$

TABLE 11-9 Constant instructions

Instruction	Constant Pushed
FLDZ	+0.0
FLD1	+1.0
FLDP1	π
FLDL2T	$\log_2 10$
FLDL2E	$\log_2 e$
FLDLG2	$\log_{10} 2$
FLDLN2	$\log_e 2$

present, the assembler places a WAIT instruction before the opcode. This allows the programmer to have the processor wait or not wait for the completion of a previous operation.

Instructions that control the 8087 include FINIT/FNINIT (initialize), FDISI/FNDISI (disable interrupts), FENI/FNENI (enable interrupts), FLDCW (load control word), FSTCW/FNSTCW (store control word), FSTSW/FNSTSW (store status word), FCLEX/FNCLEX (clear exceptions), FSTENV/FNSTENV (store environment), FLDENV (load environment), FSAVE/FNSAVE (save state), FRSTOR (restore state), FINCSTP (increment stack pointer), FDECSTP (decrement stack pointer), FFREE (free register), FNOP (no operation), and FWAIT (8087 wait).

FINIT/FNINIT performs the same operation as a hardware reset, except that it does not affect the instruction fetch synchronization.

FDISI/FNDISI prevents the 8087 from requesting an interrupt through the INT pin by setting the interrupt enable mask in the control word.

FENI/FNENI allows the 8087 to request an interrupt by clearing the interrupt enable mask in the control word.

FLDCW loads the control word from memory. This operation is normally used to establish or change the mode of operation of the 8087. It is important to note that loading a new control word that unmasks the interrupt and exception will generate an immediate interrupt request if any exceptions are pending. For this reason, FLDCW is normally preceded by the *clear exceptions* instruction (FCLEX or FNCLEX).

FSTCW/FNSTCW writes the control word to memory as defined by the instruction.

FSTSW/FNSTCW writes the status word to memory as defined by the instruction.

FCLEX/FNCLEX clears the exception masks (disables them), the interrupt enable mask (disables interrupts), and the busy flag (indicates not busy). The 8087 hardware pins INT and BUSY will also become logic 0 in response to this instruction.

FSAVE/FNSAVE writes the entire internal register set to the memory. This includes registers 7–0, status word, control word, tag word, and the instruction pointer and operand pointer of the exception pointers. Figure 11–11 illustrates the manner in which the internal registers are stored in the memory. After the data are written to the memory, the 8087 initializes itself just as the FINIT instruction does. This instruction is used sparingly in most systems. Its main application lies in processing interrupts that require the use of the 8087 to service the interrupting device.

FRSTOR reloads all 94 bytes of data from memory back into the internal structure of the 8087. FSAVE stores the registers, and FRSTOR restores them.

FSTENV/FNSTENV stores only the first 14 bytes of internal 8087 information, as illustrated in Figure 11–11. Whenever an exception interrupt occurs, the FSTENV instruction stores the exception pointers so that the interrupt service procedure can use them to repair the fault that caused the exception. Unlike FSAVE, the FSTENV instruction does not initialize the 8087.

FLDENV reloads the 14 bytes stored by the FSTENV instruction.

FINCSTP and FDECSTP increment and decrement the stack top pointer. The increment instruction is not equivalent to a pop because it does not indicate that the affected register is empty.

FFREE tags a register as empty. This instruction allows any of the registers 7–0 to be freed or indicated as empty.

FNOP performs no operation.

FIGURE 11–11 Memory format when the 8087 registers are stored by the FSAVE instruction. (Courtesy of Intel Corporation)

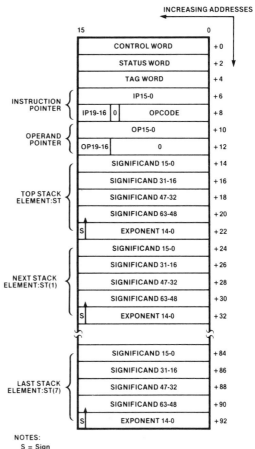

INCREASING ADDRESSES

CONTROL WORD	+0	
STATUS WORD	+2	
TAG WORD	+4	

INSTRUCTION POINTER
| IP15-0 | +6 |
| IP19-16 | 0 | OPCODE | +8 |

OPERAND POINTER
| OP15-0 | +10 |
| OP19-16 | 0 | +12 |

TOP STACK ELEMENT:ST
SIGNIFICAND 15-0	+14
SIGNIFICAND 31-16	+16
SIGNIFICAND 47-32	+18
SIGNIFICAND 63-48	+20
S	EXPONENT 14-0	+22

NEXT STACK ELEMENT:ST(1)
SIGNIFICAND 15-0	+24
SIGNIFICAND 31-16	+26
SIGNIFICAND 47-32	+28
SIGNIFICAND 63-48	+30
S	EXPONENT 14-0	+32

LAST STACK ELEMENT:ST(7)
SIGNIFICAND 15-0	+84
SIGNIFICAND 31-16	+86
SIGNIFICAND 47-32	+88
SIGNIFICAND 63-48	+90
S	EXPONENT 14-0	+92

NOTES:
S = Sign
Bit 0 of each field is rightmost, least significant bit of corresponding register field.
Bit 63 of significand is integer bit (assumed binary point is immediately to the right).

FWAIT is an alternate mnemonic for the WAIT instruction. Recall that the WAIT instruction tests the $\overline{\text{TEST}}$ pin on the 8086/8088 for a logic 0 condition before more instructions are executed.

80387 Instructions

The 8087, 80187, and the 80287 all share essentially the same instruction set. The 80387, which functions with the 80386 and is built into the 80486, has some additional instructions not found in the other versions of the numeric coprocessor. These additional instructions include: FCOS (cosine), FPREM1 (partial remainder), FSIN (sine), FSINCOS (sine and cosine), and FUCOM/FUCOMP/FUCOMPP (unordered compare).

As can be seen from these additions, the 80387 performs additional trigonometric functions that are not present on the earlier versions of the 8087 family. Recall that earlier versions were only capable of finding the tangent or the arctangent. In addition, the 80387 can compare unordered data. Refer to Table 11–10 for a complete listing of all the 80X87

TABLE 11–10　The 80X87 instruction set

Instruction	Function	Coprocessor	Clock Times
F2XM1	$Y = 2^x - 1$ X and Y are both on ST	8087 80287 80387	310–630 310–630 211–476
FABS	Absolute value of ST	8087 80287 80387	10–17 10–17 22
FADD/FADDP/FIADD	Add source to destination and returns result to destination	8087 80287 80387	70–143 70–143 23–72
FBLD	Load ST with BCD	see FLD	
FBSTP	Store BCD from ST and pop	see FST	
FCHS	Change sign of ST	8087 80287 80387	10–17 10–17 24–25
FCLEX/FNCLEX	Clear exceptions	8087 80287 80387	2–8 2–8 11
FCOM/FCOMP/FCOMPP FICOM/FICOMP	Compare operands	8087 80287 80387	40–93 40–93 24–63
FCOS	Converts ST, in radians, to cosine	8087 80287 80387	— — 123–772
FDECSTP	Decrement stack pointer	8087 80287 80387	6–12 6–12 22
FDISI/FNDISI	Disables interrupt (ignored on the 80287 and 80387)	8087 80287 80387	2–8 2 2
FDIV/FDIVP/FIDIV	Division—divides destination by source	8087 80287 80387	191–243 191–243 88–140
FDIVR/FDIVRP/FIDIVR	Divide reversed—divides source by destination	8087 80287 80387	194–245 194–245 88–141
FENI/FNENI	Enable interrupts (ignored on the 80287 and 80387)	8087 80287 80387	2–8 2 2
FFREE	Free a register	8087 80287 80387	9–16 9–16 18

TABLE 11-10 *continued*

Instruction	Function	Coprocessor	Clock Times
FIADD/FISUB/FISUBR FIMUL/FIDIV/FIDIVR	Integer arithmetic	See FADD, FSUB FSUBR, FMUL, FDIV, and FDIVR	
FICOM/FICOMP	Compare integers	See FCOM	
FILD	Load integer	See FLD	
FINCSTP	Increment stack pointer	8087 80287 80387	6-12 6-12 21
FINIT/FNINIT	Initialize coprocessor	8087 80287 80387	2-8 2-8 33
FIST/FISTP	Store integer	See FST	
FLD/FILD/FBLD	Loads the stack top (ST)	8087 80287 80387	17-310 17-310 14-275
FLD1	+1.0 pushed on ST	8087 80287 80387	15-21 15-21 24
FLDZ	+0.0 pushed on ST	8087 80287 80387	11-17 11-17 20
FLDPI	Pi is pushed on ST	8087 80287 80387	16-22 16-22 40
FLDL2E	$\log_2(e)$ pushed on ST	8087 80287 80387	15-21 15-21 40
FLDL2T	$\log_2(10)$ pushed on ST	8087 80287 80387	16-22 16-22 40
FLDLG2	$\log_{10}(2)$ pushed on ST	8087 80287 80387	18-24 18-24 41
FLDLN2	$\log_e(2)$	8087 80287 80387	17-23 17-23 41
FLDCW	Load control word	8087 80287 80387	7-14 7-14 19

TABLE 11–10 *continued*

Instruction	Function	Coprocessor	Clock Times
FLDENV	Load environment	8087	35–45
		80287	25–45
		80387	71
FMUL/FMULP/FIMUL	Multiply	8087	110–168
		80287	110–168
		80387	29–82
FNOP	No operation	8087	10–16
		80287	10–16
		80387	12
FPATAN	ARCTAN(ST(1)/ST)	8087	250–800
		80287	250–800
		80387	314–487
FPREM	Remainder of ST/ST(1)	8087	15–190
		80287	15–190
		80387	74–155
FPREM1	Remainder of ST/ST(1) IEEE	8087	—
	compatible	80287	—
		80387	95–185
FPTAN	Tangent of ST = ST(1)/ST	8087	30–450
		80287	30–450
		80387	191–497
FRNDINT	Round to integer	8087	16–50
		80287	16–50
		80387	66–80
FRSTOR	Restore saved state	8087	197–207
		80287	*
		80387	308
FSAVE/FNSAVE	Save coprocessor state	8087	197–207
		80287	*
		80387	375–376
FSCALE	Scale	8087	32–38
		80287	32–38
		80387	67–86
FSETPM	Set protected mode	8087	—
		80287	2–8
		80387	12
FSIN	Sine in ST	8087	—
		80287	—
		80387	122–771
FSINCOS	Sine and cosine of ST	8087	—
	Sine in ST(1)	80287	—
	Cosine in ST	80387	194–809
FSQRT	Square root of ST	8087	180–186
		80287	180–186
		80387	122–129

TABLE 11–10 *continued*

Instruction	Function	Coprocessor	Clock Times
FST/FSTP/FIST FISTP/FBSTP	Store	8087 80287 80387	15–540 15–540 11–534
FSTCW/FNSTCW	Store control word	8087 80287 80387	12–18 12–18 15
FSTENV/FNSTENV	Store environment	8087 80287 80387	40–50 40–50 103–104
FSTSW/SNSTSW	Store status word	8087 80287 80387	12–18 12–18 15
FSUB/FSUBP/FISUB	Subtract	8087 80287 80387	70–143 70–143 29–82
FSUBR/FSUBRP/FISUBR	Subtract reversed	8087 80287 80387	70–143 70–143 29–82
FTST	Test ST for zero	8087 80287 80387	38–48 38–48 28
FUCOM/FUCOMP/ FUCOMPP	Unordered compare	8087 80287 80387	— — 24–26
FWAIT	Wait	8087 80287 80387	4 3 6
FXAM	Examine ST	8087 80287 80387	12–23 12–23 30–38
FXCH	Exchange registers	8087 80287 80387	10–15 10–15 18
FXTRACT	Extract exponent and fraction $ST(1) = $ exponent $ST = $ fraction	8087 80287 80387	27–55 27–55 70–76
FYL2X	$ST = ST(1) \log_2 ST$	8087 80287 80387	900–1100 900–1100 120–538
FYL2XP1	$ST = ST(1) \log_2(ST + 1)$	8087 80287 80387	700–1000 700–1000 257–547

Note: Cannot determine the exact time for these instructions.

instructions along with their execution times as clocks. If the 80387 is operated with a 25-MHz clock, then the FADD instruction, which requires between 70 and 143 clocks, will take between 2.8 and 5.72 μs to execute. These times were calculated by using a clock time of 40 ns and multiplying it by the number of clocks required to execute the instruction.

11–5   PROGRAMMING THE 80X87

This section of the chapter provides many programming examples for the 80X87 arithmetic coprocessor. Note that the FWAIT instruction is inserted by the assembler before each 80X87 instruction.

Calculating the Area of a Circle

This programming example provides a simple illustration of the method of addressing data on the 80X87 stack. First recall that the equation for calculating the area of a circle is $A = \pi R^2$. A procedure that performs this calculation is listed in Example 11–3.

EXAMPLE 11–3

```
        ;Procedure that calculates the area of a circle
        ;
        ;The radius of the circle must be stored at memory location
        ;RADIUS before calling this procedure as a short floating-
        ;point number.  The result is found in memory location AREA
        ;after this procedure.
        ;
0000                            AREA_CIRCLE  PROC    FAR

0000  9B D9 06 0000 R                        FLD     RADIUS      ;push radius
0005  9B D8 C8                               FMUL    ST,ST(0)    ;square radius
0008  9B D9 EB                               FLDPI               ;push pi
000B  9B D8 C9                               FMUL    ST,ST(1)    ;multiply pi * r²
000E  9B D9 16 0004 R                        FST     AREA        ;store area
0013  9B DE D9                               FCOMPP              ;clear stack
0016  CB                                     RET

0017                            AREA_CIRCLE  ENDP
```

This is a rather simple procedure, but it does illustrate the operation of the stack. To provide a better understanding of the operation of the stack, Figure 11–12 illustrates the data on the stack as this procedure is executed by the 80X87. Here the RADIUS is moved from memory to ST(0), the stack top. Next, ST, the stack top, is multiplied by ST(0), the stack top, which squares the number at the stack top. Notice that ST and ST(0) are both the stack top.

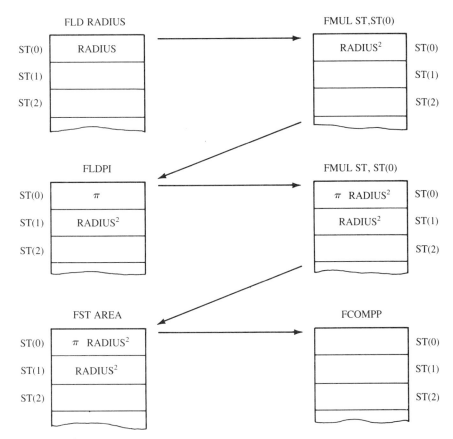

FIGURE 11-12 Operation of the 80X87 stack for the program of Example 11-3.

Next, the value π is pushed onto stack element ST(0). The area is calculated by multiplying ST by ST(1) and stored by the FST AREA instruction. The FCOMPP compares the contents of ST and ST(1), but not for the comparison. This instruction appears in the program because it pops the stack twice, which removes both numbers from the stack to clear it for use by another procedure. If the stack is not cleared, the next operation might not function as expected. The 8087 can be cleared with pops or with the FINIT instruction.

Finding the Resonant Frequency

An equation commonly used in electronics is the formula for determining the resonant frequency of an LC circuit, $Fr = 1/(2 \pi \sqrt{LC})$. This equation is solved by the 8087 in the program illustrated in Example 11-4.

Notice the straightforward manner in which the procedure solves this equation. Very little extra data manipulation is required in this example.

EXAMPLE 11-4

```
        ;Procedure that solves the resonant frequency of an LC circuit
        ;
0000  00000000            RESONANT  DD   ?          ;resonant frequency
0004  00000000            L         DD   ?          ;value of L
0008  00000000            C         DD   ?          ;value of C
000C  40000000            TWO       DD   2.0        ;number 2

0010                      FREQUENCY PROC  FAR

0010  9B 2E: D9 06 0004 R           FLD   L          ;find LC
0016  9B 2E: D8 0E 0008 R           FMUL  C

001C  9B D9 FA                      FSQRT     ;find square root of LC

001F  9B 2E: D8 0E 000C R           FMUL  TWO
0025  9B D9 EB                      FLDPI     ;load pi
0028  9B D8 C9                      FMUL  ST,ST(1)
002B  9B 2E: D9 1E 0000 R           FSTP  RESONANT  ;save denominator

0031  9B D9 E8                      FLD1      ;get 1
0034  9B 2E: D8 36 0000 R           FDIV  RESONANT  ;form frequency
003A  9B 2E: D9 1E 0000 R           FSTP  RESONANT  ;save result
0040  9B D8 D9                      FCOMP     ;clear stack
0043  CB                            RET

0044                      FREQUENCY ENDP
```

Finding the Roots of a Quadratic Equation

This example illustrates how the roots of the quadratic equation $(ax_2 + bx + cx = 0)$ are found by the quadratic formula: $x = (-b \pm \sqrt{b^2 - 4ac})/2a$. Example 11-5 illustrates this process and returns the roots to memory locations R1 and R2. Constants a, b, and c are transferred to the procedure through memory locations A, B, and C.

EXAMPLE 11-5

```
        ;Procedure that solves the roots of the quadratic equation
        ;
0000  00000000            A         DD   ?          ;variable a
0004  00000000            B         DD   ?          ;variable b
0008  00000000            C         DD   ?          ;variable c
000C  00000000            R1        DD   ?          ;root 1
0010  00000000            R2        DD   ?          ;root 2
0014  40000000            TWO       DD   2.0        ;number 2
0018  40800000            FOUR      DD   4.0        ;number 4

001C                      ROOTS     PROC  FAR

001C  9B 2E: D9 06 0014 R           FLD   TWO        ;form 2a
0022  9B 2E: D8 0E 0000 R           FMUL  A
```

```
0028   9B 2E: D9 06 0018 R        FLD       FOUR        ;form 4ac
002E   9B 2E: D8 0E 0000 R        FMUL      A
0034   9B 2E: D8 0E 0008 R        FMUL      C

003A   9B 2E: D9 06 0004 R        FLD       B           ;form b²
0040   9B D8 C8                   FMUL      ST,ST(0)

0043   9B DE E1                   FSUBRP    ST(1),ST    ;form b² - 4ac
0046   9B D9 FA                   FSQRT                 ;find square root

0049   9B 2E: D9 06 0004 R        FLD       B           ;find root 1
004F   9B D9 E0                   FCHS
0052   9B D8 C1                   FADD      ST,ST(1)
0055   9B D8 F2                   FDIV      ST,ST(2)
0058   9B 2E: D9 1E 000C R        FSTP      R1

005E   9B 2E: D9 06 0004 R        FLD       B           ;find root 2
0064   9B D9 E0                   FCHS
0067   9B D8 E1                   FSUB      ST,ST(1)
006A   9B D8 F2                   FDIV      ST,ST(2)
006D   9B 2E: D9 1E 0010 R        FSTP      R2

0073   9B DE D9                   FCOMPP                ;clear stack
0076   CB                         RET

0077                     ROOTS    ENDP
```

Raising X^Y

A fairly common task not directly implemented by the 80X87 is raising any number to any power. This operation appears in many programs and is defined as $X^Y = 2^{Y \cdot \log_2 X}$. The 80X87 is able to perform the FYL2X function that will find $Y \cdot \log_2 X$.

Once the exponent has been calculated, the entire function can be calculated by the F2XM1 instruction. F2XM1 performs the following operation: $2^X - 1$. The only problem with this function is that it requires the value of X to be within 0 and 0.5.

Example 11-6 shows how these functions are used to find X^Y.

The most difficult function to use is the F2XM1, which requires the exponent to be between 0 and 0.5. To accomplish this, the number must be broken into an integer and fractional part. After the fractional part is determined, it is divided by 2 to scale it to between 0 and 0.5, and the F2XM1 instruction is executed. A 1 is then added to the result, which is doubled and saved. The integer portion uses the FSCALE instruction to raise a 1 to the integer power of 2. After this, the complete result is formed by adding both parts.

EXAMPLE 11-6

```
       ;Procedure that finds X^Y.
       ;
       ;The value is left as a short floating-point number in ANSWER
       ;
0000   00000000        X       DD      ?       ;number
0004   00000000        Y       DD      ?       ;power
0008   00000000        ANSWER  DD      ?       ;answer
```

```
000C  00000000            FRAC    DD    ?          ;temporary storage
0010  0FFF                CHOPS   DW    0FFFH      ;select chop-mode
0012  3F800000            ONE     DD    1.0        ;one
0016  40000000            TWO     DD    2.0        ;two

001A                      EXP     PROC  FAR

001A  9B 2E: D9 06 0004 R         FLD   Y          ;find exponent
0020  9B 2E: D9 06 0000 R         FLD   X
0026  9B D9 F1                    FYL2X

0029  9B 2E: D9 16 000C R         FST   FRAC
002F  9B 2E: D9 2E 0010 R         FLDCW CHOPS      ;select truncate
0035  9B D9 FC                    FRNDINT          ;truncate
0038  9B 2E: D9 06 000C R         FLD   FRAC
003E  9B D8 E1                    FSUB  ST,ST(1)
0041  9B 2E: D8 36 0016 R         FDIV  TWO
0047  9B D9 F0                    F2XM1            ;find partial result
004A  9B 2E: D8 06 0012 R         FADD  ONE
0050  9B 2E: D8 0E 0016 R         FMUL  TWO
0056  9B 2E: D9 1E 0008 R         FSTP  ANSWER     ;save parital result

005C  9B D9 E8                    FLD1
005F  9B D9 FD                    FSCALE
0062  9B 2E: D8 06 0008 R         FADD  ANSWER
0068  9B 2E: D9 1E 0008 R         FSTP  ANSWER
006E  9B D8 D9                    FCOMP            ;clear stack
0071  CB                          RET

0072                      EXP     ENDP
```

11–6   SUMMARY

1. The 8087 arithmetic coprocessor functions in parallel to the 8086/8088 microprocessor.
2. The data types manipulated by the 8087 include integer, floating point, and binary coded decimal (BCD).
3. There are three forms of integer for the 8087: word (16 bits), short (32 bits), and long (64 bits). Each integer contains a signed number in true magnitude form for positive numbers and two's complement form for negative numbers.
4. BCD numbers are stored as 18-digit numbers in 10 bytes of memory. The most significant byte contains the sign of the BCD number, and the remaining 9 bytes contain the 18 BCD digits.
5. The 8087 supports three types of floating-point numbers: short (32 bits), long (64 bits), and temporary (80 bits). A floating-point number is formed of two main parts: the exponent and the significand. In the 8087, the exponent is biased with a constant, and the integer bit of the normalized binary number is not stored except in the temporary form.

6. Decimal numbers are converted to floating-point form by converting to binary, normalizing the binary number, adding the bias to the exponent, and storing the number in floating-point form.

7. Floating-point binary numbers are converted to decimal by subtracting the bias from the exponent, denormalizing the number, and then converting it to decimal.

8. The only really new pin connections on the 8087, compared to the 8086/8088, are the INT and BUSY pins. INT is an active-high interrupt output that is normally connected to that 8259A interrupt controller. BUSY is connected to the $\overline{\text{TEST}}$ pin on the 8086/8088 so that software can use the WAIT instruction to test the state of the BUSY pin.

9. The 8087 status word indicates when the 8087 is busy, what conditions follow a compare or test, the location of the stack top address, and the state of the exception bits.

10. The control word of the 8087 directs the 8087 and controls infinity, rounding, precision, interrupts, and exception masks.

11. The following assembler directives are often used with 8087 data: DW (define word), DD (define doubleword), DQ (define quadword), DT (define tenbyte).

12. The 8087 uses a stack to transfer data to and from the memory. Generally, data are loaded *onto* the top of the stack and stored *from* the top of the stack. The actual register number at the top of the stack can vary, but if pushes and pops are correctly used, then the stack and the registers associated with it will be known.

13. All internal 8087 data are in floating-point form. The only time that the data are ever changed to integers or BCD numbers is when they are transferred between the 8087 and the memory.

14. Addressing modes include stack, register, register pop, and memory. Stack addressing is implied, and the data at the top of the stack and the element next to the top of the stack are operated upon. The other modes are self-explanatory.

15. 8087 arithmetic operations include addition, subtraction, multiplication, division, and finding square root.

16. There are function-type transcendental instructions in the 8087 instruction set that will find the partial tangent, the partial arctangent, $2^X - 1$, $Y \log_2 X$, and $Y \log_2(X + 1)$.

17. Constants also available for use with the 8087 include $+0.0$, $+1.0$, π, $\log_2 10$, $\log_2 e$, $\log_{10} 2$, and $\log_e 2$.

11-7 QUESTIONS AND PROBLEMS

1. List the three types of data that are loaded or stored in memory by the 8087.

2. List the three integer data types, the range of the integers stored in them, and the number of bits allotted to each.

3. Explain how the BCD number is stored in memory.

4. List the three types of floating-point numbers used with the 8087 and the number of binary bits assigned to each.

5. Convert the following decimal numbers into short floating-point numbers:
   a. 28.25   d. 0.0
   b. 624   e. − 1000.5
   c. −0.625
6. Convert the following short floating-point numbers into decimal numbers:
   a. 11000000 11110000 00000000 00000000
   b. 00111111 00010000 00000000 00000000
   c. 01000011 10011001 00000000 00000000
   d. 01000000 00000000 00000000 00000000
   e. 01000001 00100000 00000000 00000000
   f. 00000000 00000000 00000000 00000000
7. What operations do the $\overline{S}_2$, $\overline{S}_1$, and $\overline{S}_0$ bits from the 8087 indicate?
8. What is the purpose of the $\overline{RQ/GT}_0$ pin on the 8087?
9. What is the purpose of the $\overline{RQ/GT}_1$ pin on the 8087?
10. Explain how the BUSY pin is used.
11. How many instructions is the 8087 capable of executing?
12. What is the purpose of the ST field in the status register?
13. When do the C_3–C_0 bits of the status word change?
14. How is the type of rounding selected?
15. A mask of 1 will _____ an exception.
16. Whenever the 8087 is reset, the top of the stack register is register number _____ .
17. What does the term *chop* mean in the rounding control bit of the control register?
18. Explain the difference between projective and affine infinity control.
19. What 8086/8088 instruction forms the opcode for the 8087?
20. What do the following pseudo-operations accomplish?
    a. DD
    b. DT
    c. DQ
21. Describe how the FST DATA instruction functions. Assume that DATA is defined as a quadword.
22. What does the FILD DATA instruction accomplish?
23. Form an instruction that will add the contents of register 3 to the top of the stack.
24. Form an instruction that will subtract the contents of the top of the stack from register 2 and store the result in register 2.
25. What is the function of the FBSTP DATA instruction?
26. What is the difference between a forward and a reverse division?
27. What is the difference between the FTST instruction and the FXAM instruction?
28. Explain what the F2XM1 instruction calculates.
29. What instruction pushes the value of π onto the stack?
30. What will FFREE do?
31. What does the FSAVE instruction store in the memory?
32. What instruction stores the environment of the 8087 in the memory?
33. Develop a procedure that finds the area of a rectangle (A = L × W). Memory locations for this procedure are A, L, and W.
34. Write a procedure that finds the inductive reactance (XL = 2πFL). Memory locations for this procedure are XL, F, and L.
35. Develop a procedure that will generate a table of square roots for the integers 2–10.

CHAPTER 12

The 80186/80188 and 80286 Microprocessors

INTRODUCTION

The Intel 80186/80188 and the 80286 are enhanced versions of the 8086/8088. Luckily, they are also very similar to the 8086/8088. For example, the instruction set of the 8086/8088 executes without modification on all the new versions. Even their hardware is similar. This chapter presents an overview of each of these new microprocessors and points out the differences or enhancements that are present in each.

The first portion of the chapter covers the 80186/80188, and the last portion covers the 80286. Get ready to travel into a world of amazing modern technology with these very powerful and sophisticated versions of the popular 8086/8088 microprocessor.

OBJECTIVES

Upon completion of this chapter, you will be able to:

1. Describe the hardware and software enhancements of the 80186/80188 and the 80286 microprocessors as compared to the 8086/8088.
2. Interface the 80186/80188 and the 80286 to memory and I/O.
3. Develop software using the enhancements provided in these microprocessors.
4. Describe the operation of the memory management unit (MMU) within the 80286 microprocessor.

12-1   80186/80188 ARCHITECTURE

The 80186 and 80188, like the 8086 and 8088, are nearly identical. The only difference between the 80186 and the 80188 is the width of their data buses. The 80186 (like the 8086) has a 16-bit data bus, and the 80188 (like the 8088) has an 8-bit data bus. The internal register structures of the 80186/80188 and the 8086/8088 are virtually identical. The only difference is that the 80186/80188 has some additional reserved interrupt vectors that are not used in the 8086/8088 microprocessor and some very powerful built-in I/O features.

80186 Block Diagram

Figure 12-1 provides the block diagram of the 80186 microprocessor. Notice that this microprocessor has a great deal more internal circuitry than the 8086. The block diagrams of the 80186 and the 80188 are identical except that the prefetch queue for the 80188 is 4 bytes and the 80186 is 6 bytes. Like that of the 8086, the 80186 contains a bus interface unit (BIU) and an execution unit (EU), but it also has a great deal more.

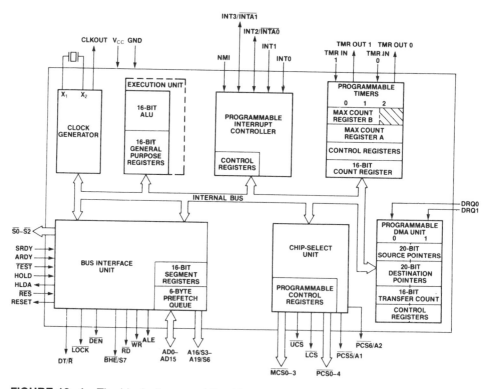

FIGURE 12-1   The block diagram of the 80186 microprocessor. Note that the block diagram of the 80188 is identical except $\overline{BHE}$/S7 is missing and AD15–AD8 are re-labeled A15–A8. (Courtesy of Intel Corporation)

In addition to the BIU and EU, the 80186 contains a clock generator, a programmable interrupt controller, programmable timers, a programmable DMA controller, and a programmable chip selection unit. These enhancements greatly increase the performance of the 80186 and reduce the number of peripheral components required to implement a system. Many subsystems today are constructed using these powerful microprocessors as controllers.

80186/80188 Hardware Enhancements

In this segment of the text, we introduce the enhancements of the 80186/80188, but do not provide an exclusive coverage. More details on the operation of each enhancement are provided later in this chapter.

Clock Generator.   The internal clock generator replaces the external 8284A clock generator that is used with the 8086/8088 microprocessor. This reduces the number of components in a system.

The internal clock generator has three pin connections: X_1, X_2, and CLKOUT. X_1 and X_2 are normally connected to a crystal twice the basic operating frequency of the 80186/80188. In the 8-MHz version of the 80186/80188, a 16-MHz crystal is attached to X_1 and X_2. The 80186/80188 is currently available in two speeds: an 8-MHz version and a 12-MHz version, with higher speed versions soon to come.

The CLKOUT pin is at one half the crystal frequency (the basic operating frequency of the processor) and has a 50 percent duty cycle. CLKOUT drives other devices in the system and, in a parallel-processing environment with multiple microprocessors, it provides a clock for the additional microprocessors or other devices.

In addition to these external pin connections, the clock generator provides internal synchronization for the READY input pin, whereas in the 8086/8088 system, READY synchronization is accomplished in the clock generator (8284A).

Programmable Interrupt Controller.   The programmable interrupt controller (PIC) arbitrates all internal and external interrupts and can control up to two external 8259As. When external 8259A PICs are added, the 80186/80188 functions as the master and the 8259As as the slaves.

If the PIC is operated without external 8259As, it has five interrupt inputs: INT_0–INT_3 and NMI. This is an expansion from the two interrupt inputs available on the 8086/8088. In many systems this, along with the expansion provided by the 8259As, provides adequate interrupt capabilities.

Timers.   The timer section contains three fully independent 16-bit programmable counters/timers. Timers 0 and 1 generate waveforms for external systems and are driven by either the master clock of the 80186/80188 or by an external clock input. They are also used to count external events. The third timer, timer 2, is internal and clocked only by the system clock. The output of this timer generates an interrupt after a specified number of clocks have occurred and provides clocks for the other timers. Timer 2 can be used as a watchdog timer, if required.

Programmable DMA Unit.   The programmable DMA unit is a fully programmable two-channel DMA controller. Each channel can transfer data between memory locations, between memory and I/O, and between I/O devices. This mechanism is similar to the

DMA controller (8237A-5) discussed in an earlier chapter, except that it has only two channels instead of four.

Programmable Chip Selection Unit.   The chip selection unit is actually a built-in, fully programmable memory and I/O decoder. It has six output lines to select memory and seven to select I/O.

The memory output selection lines are split into three groups that are used to address major sections of the 80186/80188 memory: lower memory for the interrupt vectors, mid-memory for program memory, and upper memory for the system reset ROM. The boundary of lower memory begins at location 00000H, and the boundary of the upper memory ends at FFFFFH. The size of these two blocks is programmable. The mid-memory is fully programmable, and the user selects both the size and the boundaries.

Each programmable I/O selection line addresses a 128-byte block of I/O space. Each of the seven blocks begins at a base address that is programmable by the user, and the blocks of I/O space are contiguous to each other.

In addition to selecting memory and I/O, each of the selection areas—lower memory, mid-memory, upper memory, and the seven I/O lines—has a set of internal ready lines connected to a programmable wait state generator that selects 0–3 wait states. The wait state generator allows a preprogrammed number of wait states to be inserted whenever a section of memory or the I/O is selected with the selection lines.

Pinout

Figure 12–2 illustrates the pinout of the 80186 microprocessor. Notice that the 80186 is a 68-pin leadless chip carrier (LCC). This package (illustrated in Figure 12–3 with dimensions) is becoming popular for many integrated circuits that require more than 40 pins.

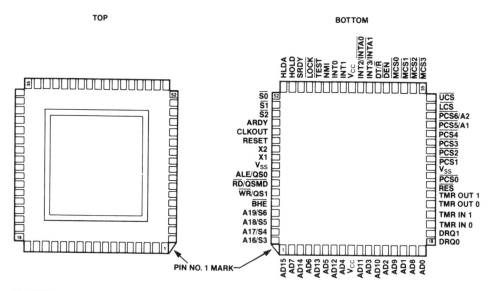

FIGURE 12–2   Pinout of the 80186 microprocessor. (Courtesy of Intel Corporation)

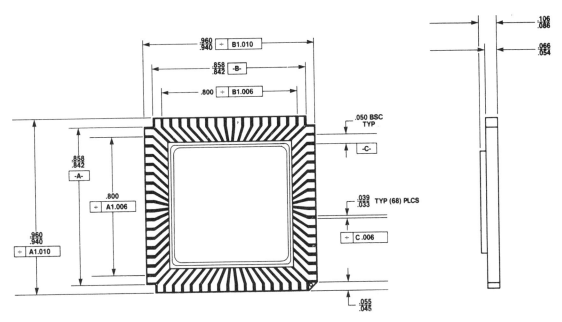

FIGURE 12-3 Leadless chip carrier (LCC) for the 80186/80188 microprocessor. (Courtesy of Intel Corporation)

Pin Definitions. The following list defines each 80186 pin and notes any differences between the 80186 and the 80188 microprocessors.

1. V_{CC} is the system power supply connection for + 5 V.
2. V_{SS} is the system ground.
3. X_1 and X_2 are generally connected to a fundamental-mode parallel resonant crystal that operates the internal crystal-controlled oscillater. X_1 also drives the 80186/80188 with an external source, which is connected to X_1 with its complement connected to X_2. The internal clock generator divides the crystal frequency by a factor of 2.
4. CLKOUT has a 50 percent duty cycle, and its frequency is at one half the crystal frequency.
5. $\overline{RES}$ resets the 80186/80188. It must be held low for 50 ms after power is applied to guarantee proper resetting. This pin is connected to an RC circuit that generates the $\overline{RES}$ signal at the application of system power. The reset location is identical to that of the 8086/8088 and is at location FFFF0H.
6. $\overline{TEST}$ is interrogated by the WAIT instruction. If it is low at that time, no wait occurs. If it is high, the microprocessor waits for it to go low.
7. TMRIN 0 and TMRIN 1 are used as clock inputs or control inputs for internal timers 0 and 1. Their operation is determined when the timers are programmed.
8. TMROUT 0 and TMROUT 1 outputs provide either continuous square waves or single pulses.
9. DRQ_0 and DRQ_1 are active-high DMA request inputs for DMA channels 0 and 1. They are active, level-triggered inputs.

10. NMI is the nonmaskable interrupt input. It is positive-edge-triggered and always active. This input causes an interrupt vector type 2.

11. INT_0, INT_1, $INT_2/INTA_0$, and $INT_3/INTA_1$ are maskable interrupt inputs. They are active-high-programmable as level- or edge-triggered inputs. These pins are either configured as four interrupt inputs or as two interrupt inputs with two interrupt-acknowledge outputs.

12. A_{19}/S_6, A_{18}/S_5, A_{17}/S_4, and A_{16}/S_3 are multiplexed address status outputs that provide address bits $A_{19}-A_{16}$ and status bits S_6-S_3. Status bit S_6 indicates a processor cycle when low and a DMA cycle when high. The remaining status bits are low.

13. $AD_{15}-AD_0$ are multiplexed address/data bus connections. During T_1, the 80186 sends $A_{15}-A_0$ on these pins, and during T_2, T_3, T_W, and T_4, data are transferred between the processor and the memory or I/O. Note that the 80188 has pins $A_{15}-A_8$ and AD_7-AD_0 because its data bus is only 8 bits wide.

14. $\overline{BHE}/S_7$ indicates by its output that valid data have been transferred on the leftmost 8 bits of the data bus. On the 80188, this pin is labeled S_7. Status bit S_7 is always a logic 1 on the 80188. It is the same as $\overline{BHE}$ on the 80186, and, therefore, no latch is required to capture $\overline{BHE}$ on this system.

15. ALE/QS_0 is a multiplexed output pin that contains ALE one-half clock cycle earlier than in the 8086. QS_0 is the queue status bit that is present on this pin during queue status mode.

16. $\overline{WR}/QS_1$ is a signal that causes data to be written from the data bus to either a memory component or an I/O device. $\overline{WR}$ is active during T_3, T_W, and T_4, and QS_1 is active during the queue status mode.

17. $\overline{RD}/QSMD$ is an output pin that is active during T_3, T_W, and T_4 of a read bus cycle. If this pin is grounded, then the queue status mode is selected, and the ALE and $\overline{WR}$ pins present the queue status information.

18. ARDY (asynchronous ready input) informs the 80186/80188 that the memory or I/O is ready for the 80186/80188 to read or write data. If this pin is tied to + 5 V and grounded wait states are entered, then the processor functions normally.

19. SRDY (synchronous ready input) must be synchronized with the system clock to provide a relaxed system timing for the ready input. As with ARDY, if SRDY is tied to + 5 V, no wait states are inserted.

20. $\overline{LOCK}$ is an output pin controlled by the LOCK prefix. If an instruction is prefixed with LOCK, then the $\overline{LOCK}$ pin is a logic 0 for the execution of the locked instruction.

21. $\overline{S}_2$, $\overline{S}_1$, and $\overline{S}_0$ are status bits that provide the system with the type of bus transfer in effect. $\overline{S}_2$ is used as the M/$\overline{I/O}$ signal and $\overline{S}_1$ as DT/$\overline{R}$. $\overline{S}_2$ is even the M/$\overline{IO}$ on the 80188, since there is no IO/$\overline{M}$ signal as in the 8088.

22. HOLD and HLDA are pins used with external DMA devices. HOLD is an input that requests a DMA, and HLDA is a signal that acknowledges that the DMA is in effect. During a DMA, the HOLD pin causes the 80186/80188 to float its address, data, and control buses as in the 8086/8088.

23. $\overline{UCS}$ (upper-memory chip select) is an output pin used to select memory in the upper portion of the system memory map. This output is programmable so that 1K–256K of memory is selected by this pin, ending at location FFFFFH.

24. $\overline{LCS}$ (lower-memory chip select) is used to enable memory beginning at memory location 00000H. This pin is also programmed to select a 1K–256K block of memory.
25. $\overline{MCS_0}$–$\overline{MCS_3}$ are four mid-memory select pins used to enable four different sections of memory. Each is programmable so that different ranges for each pin are selected within an 8K–512K portion of the memory at any beginning boundary.
26. $\overline{PCS_0}$–$\overline{PCS_4}$ are five peripheral section lines, each programmable to select different I/O devices in the 64K-byte I/O space of the 80186/80188.
27. $\overline{PCS_5}/A_1$ and $\overline{PCS_6}/A_2$ are programmed as peripheral select lines or as internally latched A_1 and A_2 address pins.
28. DT/$\overline{R}$ (data transmit/receive) controls the direction of data flows through the external data bus buffers.
29. $\overline{DEN}$ enables the external data bus buffers.

DC Operating Characteristics

It is necessary to know the DC operating characteristics of the 80186/80188 before attempting to interface it to memory or I/O. The amount of power supply current it requires is between 450 mA and 550 mA at + 5 V $\pm$ 10 percent. The 80C186 requires only 10mA of supply current because it is a CMOS device. Each output pin is capable of supplying 2.0 mA at a logic 0 and $-$ 400 μA at a logic 1. The inputs require $\pm$ 10 μA of current each. Note that the CLKOUT pin is capable of supplying 4.0 mA at a logic 0 and the $\overline{S}_2$–$\overline{S}_0$ pins 2.5 mA at a logic 0. These values are comparable to those of the 8086/8088 microprocessor except for the CLKOUT and $\overline{S}_2$–$\overline{S}_0$ pins.

80186/80188 Timing

The timing diagram for the 80186 is provided in Figure 12–4. Timing for the 80188 is identical except for the multiplexed address connections, which are AD_7–AD_0 instead of AD_{15}–AD_0, and the $\overline{BHE}$ signal, which does not exist in the 80188 timing diagram.

The basic timing for the 80186/80188 is composed of four clocking periods just as in the 8086/8088. A bus cycle is either 667 ns for the 6-MHz version of the 80186 or 500 ns for the 8-MHz version.

There are very few differences between 8086/8088 timing and 80186/80188 timing. The most noticeable is that in the 80186/80188, the ALE pulse appears in T_4 about one half clock cycle before it appears in the 8086/8088.

Memory Access Time.   One of the more important points in any microprocessor's timing diagram is memory access time. Access time calculations in the 80186/80188 are identical to those in the 8086/8088. Recall that the access time is the time allotted the memory to access data and extends from the point where the address appears until the data are sampled from the data bus.

As a close examination of the timing reveals, the address appears T_{CLAV} time after the start of T_1. T_{CLAV} time is equal to 63 ns for the 6-MHz version and 44 ns for the 8-MHz version. (Refer to Figure 12–5 for these times.) Data are read from the data bus at the end of T_3, but a setup time is required for the 80186/80188 before this clock. The

FIGURE 12–4
80186/80188 timing. (a)
Read cycle timing and (b)
write cycle timing. (Courtesy
of Intel Corporation)

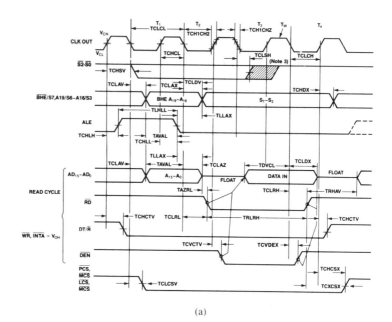

(a)

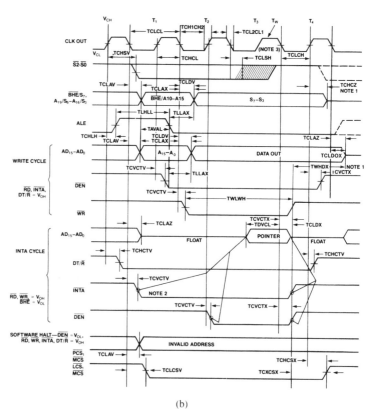

(b)

80186 Master Interface Timing Responses

Symbol	Parameters	80188 (8 MHz) Min.	80188 (8 MHz) Max.	80188-6 (6 MHz) Min.	80188-6 (6 MHz) Max.	Units	Test Conditions
T_{CLAV}	Address Valid Delay	5	44	5	63	ns	C_L = 20-200 pF all outputs
T_{CLAX}	Address Hold	10		10		ns	
T_{CLAZ}	Address Float Delay	T_{CLAX}	35	T_{CLAX}	44	ns	
T_{CHCZ}	Command Lines Float Delay		45		56	ns	
T_{CHCV}	Command Lines Valid Delay (after float)		55		76	ns	
T_{LHLL}	ALE Width	$T_{CLCL-35}$		$T_{CLCL-35}$		ns	
T_{CHLH}	ALE Active Delay		35		44	ns	
T_{CHLL}	ALE Inactive Delay		35		44	ns	
T_{LLAX}	Address Hold to ALE Inactive	$T_{CHCL-25}$		$T_{CHCL-30}$		ns	
T_{CLDV}	Data Valid Delay	10	44	10	55	ns	
T_{CLDOX}	Data Hold Time	10		10		ns	
T_{WHDX}	Data Hold after WR	$T_{CLCL-40}$		$T_{CLCL-50}$		ns	
T_{CVCTV}	Control Active Delay 1	5	70	5	87	ns	
T_{CHCTV}	Control Active Delay 2	10	55	10	76	ns	
T_{CVCTX}	Control Inactive Delay	5	55	5	76	ns	
T_{CVDEX}	$\overline{DEN}$ Inactive Delay (Non-Write Cycle)		70		87	ns	
T_{AZRL}	Address Float to $\overline{RD}$ Active	0		0		ns	
T_{CLRL}	$\overline{RD}$ Active Delay	10	70	10	87	ns	
T_{CLRH}	$\overline{RD}$ Inactive Delay	10	55	10	76	ns	
T_{RHAV}	$\overline{RD}$ Inactive to Address Active	$T_{CLCL-40}$		$T_{CLCL-50}$		ns	
T_{CLHAV}	HLDA Valid Delay	10	50	10	67	ns	
T_{RLRH}	$\overline{RD}$ Width	$2T_{CLCL-50}$		$2T_{CLCL-50}$		ns	
T_{WLWH}	$\overline{WR}$ Width	$2T_{CLCL-40}$		$2T_{CLCL-40}$		ns	
T_{AVAL}	Address Valid to ALE Low	$T_{CLCH-25}$		$T_{CLCH-45}$		ns	
T_{CHSV}	Status Active Delay	10	55	10	76	ns	
T_{CLSH}	Status Inactive Delay	10	55	10	76	ns	
T_{CLTMV}	Timer Output Delay		60		75	ns	100 pF max
T_{CLRO}	Reset Delay		60		75	ns	
T_{CHQSV}	Queue Status Delay		35		44	ns	

80186 Chip-Select Timing Responses

Symbol	Parameter	Min.	Max.	Min.	Max.	Units	Test Conditions
T_{CLCSV}	Chip-Select Active Delay		66		80	ns	
T_{CXCSX}	Chip-Selct Hold from Command Inactive	35		35		ns	
T_{CHCSX}	Chip-Select Inactive Delay	5	35	5	47	ns	

Symbol	Parameter	Min.	Max.	Units	Test Conditions
TDVCL	Data in Setup (A/D)	20		ns	
TCLDX	Data in Hold (A/D)	10		ns	
TARYHCH	Asynchronous Ready (AREADY) active setup time*	20		ns	
TARYLCL	AREADY inactive setup time	35		ns	
TCHARYX	AREADY hold time	15		ns	
TSRYCL	Synchronous Ready (SREADY) transition setup time	35		ns	
TCLSRY	SREADY transition hold time	15		ns	
THVCL	HOLD Setup*	25		ns	
TINVCH	INTR, NMI, TEST, TIMERIN, Setup*	25		ns	
TINVCL	DRQ0, DRQ1, Setup*	25		ns	

*To guarantee recognition at next clock.

FIGURE 12–5 80186 AC characteristics. (Courtesy of Intel Corporation)

setup time is defined as $T_{DVCL}-20$ ns for both speed versions of the 80186/80188. Access time is, therefore, three clocking periods (from the start of T_1 to the end of T_3) minus the T_{CLAV} and T_{DVCL} times. Access time for the 8-MHz version is 375 ns − 66 ns, or 309 ns, and 500 ns − 83 ns, or 417 ns, for the 6-MHz version. In both cases, wait states are required if 450-ns memory is used.

12-2   80186/80188 INSTRUCTIONS

The instruction set of the 80186/80188 includes all the instructions and addressing modes of the 8086/8088, but is enhanced with some additional instructions. This section details the operation of these additional instructions.

Additional Immediate Instructions

The immediate instructions that have been added to the 80186/80188 include push immediate, integer (signed) immediate multiplication (IMUL), and shift-and-rotate with an immediate count.

The push immediate instruction is useful for preloading the stack with information. For example, a PUSH 1233H will push a 1233H onto the stack.

The IMUL instruction allows the contents of any register or memory location to be multiplied by a byte or a word. It has three operands: destination, immediate byte or word, and source. For example, the instruction IMUL BX,2222H,ARRAY[DI] multiples the contents of memory location ARRAY[DI] by 2222H and stores the 16-bit result in BX. The result may be stored in any 16-bit register except the segment registers, and the source may be any memory location or any register except a segment register.

The shift-and-rotate instruction is able to use an immediate count, like the shift/rotate by CL number of places. The number of places to be shifted or rotated, however, is an immediate byte. For example, a SHL BX,4 will shift the contents of the BX register four places to the left.

PUSHA and POPA

In addition to the push immediate, two new stack operations have been added to the 80186/80188 instruction set. The PUSHA instruction pushes the contents of registers AX, BX, CX, DX, SP, BP, DI, and SI onto the stack in the order in which the registers are listed. The value of the SP pushed onto the stack is the same as it was before the execution of the first push (PUSH AX). The POPA instruction removes the data from the stack and places them back into SI, DI, BP, SP, DX, CX, BX, and AX. Both instructions are very useful for saving the contents of all the registers in procedures such as an interrupt service procedure.

String I/O

The 80186/80188 has two new instructions that allow string I/O operations: INS and OUTS. INSB and OUTSB will transfer a byte of data, and INSW and OUTSW will transfer a word of data.

The INS instruction inputs a byte or word of data from an I/O device addressed by the DX register into the memory location addressed by the destination index registers (DI). Recall that DI is in the extra segment for string operations and may *not* be overridden with a segment override prefix. Only DI is incremented or decremented after each input: register DX remains unchanged. The REP prefix may be attached to the INS instructions so that data from one I/O device can be input to a block of memory.

OUTS transfers a byte or word of data from the location addressed by SI to an output device addressed by DX. Recall that SI is in the data segment for string operations and may be overridden with the segment override prefix. As with INS, OUTS may also be prefixed by REP. This allows a block of memory data to be transferred to a single I/O device, because DX does not change and SI is either incremented or decremented.

BOUND Instruction

In a multiuser environment, the BOUND instruction checks the boundaries of a section of memory. Actually, this instruction checks the contents of any register except the segment registers against two words of memory: an upper and a lower boundary. If the value in the register is not between the two words stored in memory, then a type-5 interrupt is generated. If the BOUND SI,DATA instruction is executed, then an interrupt occurs if SI is not greater than the value stored at DATA or less than the value stored at memory word DATA + 2. The memory-to-register comparisons are signed ones.

ENTER and LEAVE

The ENTER and LEAVE instructions are most often used to build and tear down stack frames for higher level languages. ENTER has two operands: the first specifies the displacement subtracted from the stack pointer for local variables, and the second indicates the frame level. The displacement is an unsigned 16-bit number, and the level is an unsigned 8-bit number.

ENTER pushes the contents of the BP register onto the stack and then uses the level to determine how many other pointers to transfer into the frame. Level 2 transfers two pointers from the prior frame, level 3 transfers three pointers, and so forth. Once the pointers are transferred, the value of the stack pointer after the first push is loaded into BP and pushed onto the stack. This sets up linkage so that the current table of pointers is accessible. Next, the displacement is added to the stack pointer for local variable storage.

The LEAVE instruction transfers BP to the SP and then POPs BP so that the address of the pointer table will once again be in BP.

12-3 PROGRAMMING THE 80186/80188 ENHANCEMENTS

This section provides complete details on the programming and operation of the 80186/80188 enhancements. The next section details the use of the 80186/80188 in a system that employs many of the enhancements discussed here. The only new internal component not discussed here is the clock generator, which is discussed completely in the section on architecture.

Peripheral Control Block

All internal peripherals are controlled by a set of registers in the peripheral control block (PCB). The PCB is a set of 256 registers beginning at any 256-byte boundary in the memory or the I/O space.

Whenever the 80186/80188 is reset, the peripheral control block is automatically placed at the top of the I/O space (I/O address FF00H–FFFFH). The PCB may be relocated by changing one of the registers in the PCB called the *relocation register* (illustrated in Figure 12–6).

The relocation register is set to a 20FFH when the 80186/80188 is reset, which locates the PC3 at I/O address FFFEH afterwards. To move the PCB to some other location, the user need only send a word OUT to I/O address FFFEH with a new bit pattern. For example, the PCB can be moved to memory location 20000H–200FFH by sending a 1200II to I/O address FFFEH. Notice that M/$\overline{\text{IO}}$ is a logic 1, and the most significant 12 bits of the address are a 200H.

The PCB itself is illustrated in Figure 12–7. Notice that the control and status of all internal peripherals exist in this block, as does the relocation register. All accesses to the peripheral control registers must be word accesses, or the results are undefined.

Interrupts in the 80186/80188

The interrupts in the 80186/80188 are identical to those in the 8086/8088 except that some additional interrupt vector type numbers are defined. A complete listing of the reserved interrupt vectors appears in Table 12–1. The first five interrupt vectors listed are also present in the 8086/8088. The additional interrupts are present in the 80186/80188.

The array BOUND interrupt is requested if the boundary of an index register is outside the values set up in the memory.

The unused opcode interrupt occurs whenever the 80186/80188 executes any undefined opcode. This is important if a program begins to run at an unknown memory location, because it is bound to execute an unused opcode and cause this type of interrupt.

The ESC opcode interrupt occurs if ESC opcodes D8H–DFH are executed. This occurs only if the ET (escape trap) bit of the relocation register is set. If an ESC-opcoded interrupt does occur, the address that is stored onto the stack during the interrupt points to the ESC opcode or to its segment override prefix if it is attached.

The internal hardware interrupts must be enabled by the I flag bit and must be unmasked to function. The I flag is set (enabled) with the STI instruction and cleared (disabled) with the CLI instruction.

ET = ESC/NO ESC TRAP
RMX = iRM × 86 mode/master mode
M/$\overline{\text{IO}}$ = Memory/IO space
X = Unused

FIGURE 12–6 Peripheral control register.

FIGURE 12-7 Peripheral control block (PCB) of the 80186/80188. (Courtesy of Intel Corporation)

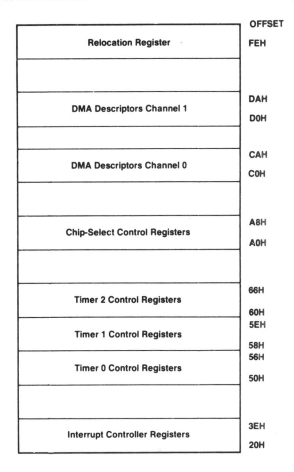

	OFFSET
Relocation Register	FEH
DMA Descriptors Channel 1	DAH
	D0H
DMA Descriptors Channel 0	CAH
	C0H
Chip-Select Control Registers	A8H
	A0H
Timer 2 Control Registers	66H
	60H
Timer 1 Control Registers	5EH
	58H
Timer 0 Control Registers	56H
	50H
Interrupt Controller Registers	3EH
	20H

The remaining internally decoded interrupts are discussed with the timers and the DMA controller.

Interrupt Controller

The interrupt controller inside the 80186/80188 is a fairly sophisticated device. It has many inputs that arrive from the five external interrupt pins, the DMA controller, and the timers. Figure 12–8 provides the block diagram of the interrupt controller.

The interrupt controller operates in two modes: master and iRMX86* mode. In the master mode, the interrupt controller acts as a master for up to two external 8259A programmable interrupt controllers, and in the iRMX86 mode the external interrupt pins cause interrupts.

This portion of the chapter does not cover the interrupt controller programming. Rather, it is limited to a discussion of the internal structure of this section of the 80186/80188. The programming of the interrupt controller is discussed in the sections on timers and the DMA controller.

*iRMX86 is a trademark of Intel Corporation.

TABLE 12–1 Interrupt vector table

Name	Type	Address	Priority
Divide error	0	00000–00003	1
Single-step	1	00004–00007	12
NMI	2	00008–0000B	1
Breakpoint	3	0000C–0000F	1
INTO	4	00010–00013	1
Array BOUNDS	5	00014–00017	1
Unused opcode	6	00018–0001B	1
ESC opcode	7	0001C–0001F	1
Timer 0	8	00020–00023	2A
Timer 1	18	00048–0004B	2B
Timer 2	19	0004C–0004F	2C
Reserved	9	00024–00027	3
DMA 0	10	00028–0002B	4
DMA 1	11	0002C–0002F	5
INT_0	12	00030–00033	6
INT_1	13	00034–00037	7
INT_2	14	00038–0003B	8
INT_3	15	0003C–0003F	9

FIGURE 12–8
80186/80188 programmable interrupt controller. (Courtesy of Intel Corporation)

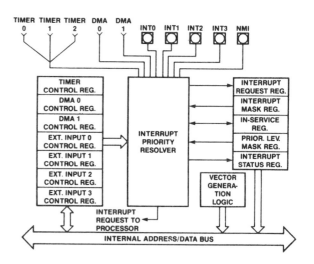

Interrupt Controller Registers. Figure 12–9 illustrates the interrupt controller registers, which are located in the peripheral control block beginning at address 20H. Notice that two completely different sets of registers exist—one for master mode and the other for iRMX86 mode.

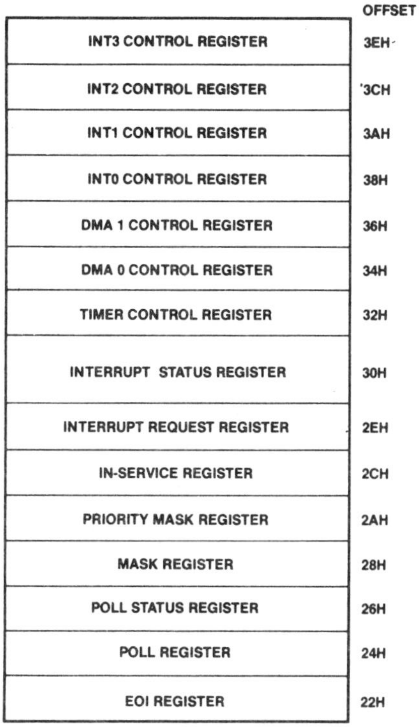

FIGURE 12–9
80186/80188 programmable
interrupt controller registers.
(Courtesy of Intel Corporation)

	OFFSET
INT3 CONTROL REGISTER	3EH
INT2 CONTROL REGISTER	'3CH
INT1 CONTROL REGISTER	3AH
INT0 CONTROL REGISTER	38H
DMA 1 CONTROL REGISTER	36H
DMA 0 CONTROL REGISTER	34H
TIMER CONTROL REGISTER	32H
INTERRUPT STATUS REGISTER	30H
INTERRUPT REQUEST REGISTER	2EH
IN-SERVICE REGISTER	2CH
PRIORITY MASK REGISTER	2AH
MASK REGISTER	28H
POLL STATUS REGISTER	26H
POLL REGISTER	24H
EOI REGISTER	22H

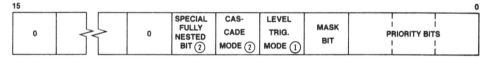

1. This bit present only in INT0-INT3 control registers
2. These bits present only in INT0-INT1 control register

FIGURE 12–10   Interrupt control register. (Courtesy of Intel Corporation)

Interrupt Control Registers.   There are interrupt control registers in both modes of operation that control each source of an interrupt. The master mode has seven interrupt control
registers, and the iRMX86 mode has five. Figure 12–10 illustrates the bit pattern of each
interrupt control register. The mask bit enables (1) or disables (0) the interrupt input
represented by the control word, and the priority bits set the priority level of the source.
The highest priority is a 0, and the lowest is a 7. The remaining three bits are used only
in master mode operation to select special fully nested mode, cascade mode, and level-
trigger mode.

Interrupt Request Register.   The interrupt request register is an image of the interrupt
sources in each mode of operation. Whenever an interrupt is requested for a source, the
corresponding interrupt request bit becomes a logic 1 even if the interrupt is masked. The
request bit is cleared whenever the 80186/80188 acknowledges the interrupt. Figure

12–11 illustrates the binary bit pattern for the interrupt register for both modes of operation.

Mask Register and Priority Mask Register.   The interrupt mask register has the same format as the interrupt request register illustrated in Figure 12–11. If a source is masked, it appears as a logic 1 in this register, and if enabled, it appears as a logic 0. The interrupt mask register is read to determine which interrupt sources are masked. A source is masked by setting the mask bit in the source's interrupt control register.

The priority mask register, illustrated in Figure 12–12, shows the priority of the interrupt currently being serviced by the 80186/80188. The level of the interrupt is indicated by bits P_2, P_1, and P_0. Internally, these bits prevent an interrupt by a lower priority source. These bits are automatically set to the next lower level at the end of an interrupt as issued by the 80186/80188. If no other interrupts are pending, these bits are all set (111) to enable all priority levels of interrupts. This register may be read or written.

In-Service Register.   The in-service register also has the same bit pattern as the request register of Figure 12–11. The bit that corresponds to the interrupt source is set if the 80186/80188 is currently acknowledging the interrupt. The bit is reset at the end of an interrupt.

Poll and Poll Status Registers.   Both the interrupt poll and interrupt poll status registers have the same bit patterns as those illustrated in Figure 12–13. These registers have a bit (INT REQ) that indicates a pending interrupt. This bit is set if an interrupt is received with sufficient priority and cleared when the interrupt is acknowledged. The S bits indicate the interrupt vector type number of the highest priority pending interrupt.

These two registers may appear to be identical because they contain the same information. However, they differ in function. When the interrupt poll register is read, the interrupt is acknowledged. When the interrupt poll status register is read, no acknowledgment is sent. These registers are used only in the master mode and not in the iRMX86 mode.

FIGURE 12–11   Interrupt request register shown for both modes of operation. (Courtesy of Intel Corporation)

FIGURE 12–12   Interrupt priority mask register. (Courtesy of Intel Corporation)

FIGURE 12–13   Interrupt poll and poll status registers. (Courtesy of Intel Corporation)

End-of-Interrupt Register.   The programmer who wishes to end the interrupt request must write to the end-of-interrupt register. Figure 12–14 illustrates the bit pattern of this register for both master and iRMX86 modes of operation.

In the master mode, this procedure ends either a specific interrupt level or whichever level is currently activated (nonspecific). In the nonspecific mode, the SPEC/NSPEC bit must be set before this register is written to. This end-of-interrupt clears the highest level interrupt bit in the in-service register. The specific end-of-interrupt clears the selected interrupt bit in the in-service' register.

In the iRMX86 mode, the level of the interrupt to be ended is written to this register to clear this specific interrupt level. The iRMX86 mode does not allow a nonspecific end-of-interrupt.

Interrupt Status Register.   The format of the interrupt status register is illustrated in Figure 12–15. In the master mode, the T_2, T_1, and T_0 bits indicate which timer is causing an interrupt. These bits are set when a timer requests an interrupt and cleared when it is acknowledged.

The DHLT (DMA halt) bit prevents a DMA action if DHLT is set. This bit is set by writing it to the register or by an NMI interrupt request. DHLT is cleared by writing to the status register or by the IRET instruction.

Interrupt Vector Register.   The interrupt vector register is present only in the iRMX86 mode of operation and is used to specify the most significant 5 bits of the interrupt type number. Figure 12–16 illustrates the format for this register. The lower 3 bits of the vector number are determined by the priority level of the interrupt.

Timers

The 80186/80188 contains three fully programmable 16-bit timers. Each is totally independent of the others. Two of the timers (timer 0 and timer 1) have input and output pins that allow them to count external events or generate waveforms. The third timer (timer 2)

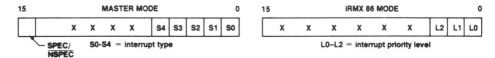

FIGURE 12–14   End of interrupt register shown for both modes of operation. (Courtesy of Intel Corporation)

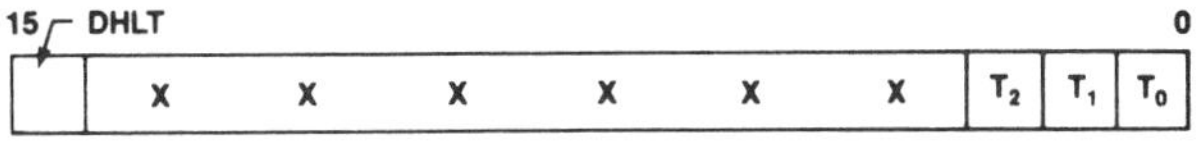

FIGURE 12–15   Interrupt status register. (Courtesy of Intel Corporation)

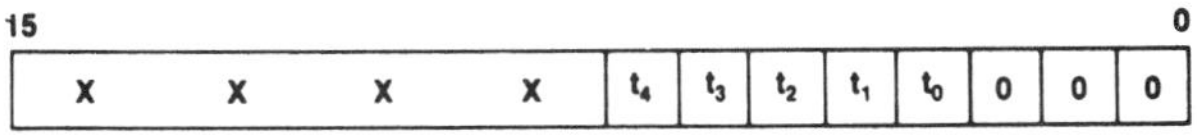

FIGURE 12–16   Interrupt vector register. (Courtesy of Intel Corporation)

is connected to the 80186/80188 clock and is used as a DMA request source or as a prescaler for the other timers.

Figure 12–17 illustrates the internal structure of the timer unit. Notice that the timer unit contains one counting element that is responsible for updating all three counters. Each timer is actually a register that is rewritten from the counting element (a circuit that reads the value from a timer register and increments it before returning it). The counter element is also responsible for generating the outputs through pins T_0 OUT and T_1 OUT, reading the T_0 IN and T_1 IN pins, and causing a DMA request from the terminal count (TC) of timer 2 if timer 2 is programmed.

Timer Register Operation. The timers are controlled by a block of registers in the parameter control block (see Figure 12–18). Each timer has a count register, maximum-count register or registers, and a control register. These registers may all be written or read at any time because the 80186/80188 ensures that the contents are never changed during read, and during a write the information is not entered until the register is free.

The timer count register contains a 16-bit number that is incremented whenever an input to the timer occurs. Timers 0 and 1 are incremented at the positive edge on an external timer input pin, every fourth 80186/80188 clock, or by the output of timer 2. Timer 2 is clocked by the 80186/80188 only on every fourth clock and has no other timing source. Figure 12–19 illustrates these four clocking periods, which are not related to the bus timings states T_1–T_4.

Each timer has at least one maximum-count register (register A for timers 0 and 1) that is compared with the contents of the count register to generate an output. Whenever the count register is equal to the maximum-count register, it is cleared to 0. With a

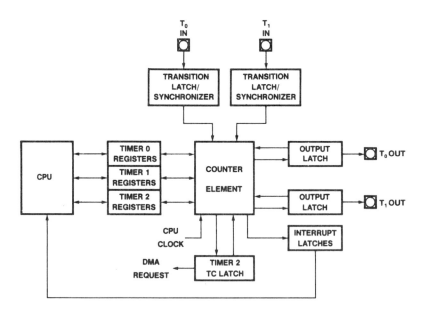

FIGURE 12–17 Internal structure of the 80186/80188 times. (Courtesy of Intel Corporation)

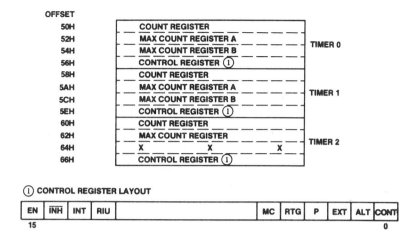

FIGURE 12-18   The timer registers. (Courtesy of Intel Corporation)

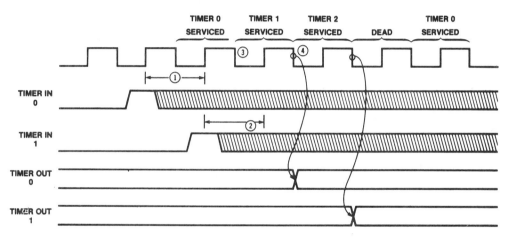

1. Timer in 0 resolution time
2. Timer in 1 resolution time
3. Modified count value written into 80186 timer 0 count register
4. Modified count value written into 80186 timer 1 count register

FIGURE 12-19   Timing for the 80186/80188 timers. (Courtesy of Intel Corporation)

maximum count of 0000H, the counter counts 65,536 times. For any other value, the timer counts the true value of the count. For example, if the maximum count is 0002H, then the counter will count from 0 to 1 and then be cleared to 0 — a modulus 2 counter.

Timers 0 and 1 each have a second maximum-count register (maximum-count register B) that is selected by the control register for the timer. Either maximum-count A or both maximum-counts A and B are used with these timers as programmed by the ALT bit, the control register for the timer. When both maximum-count registers are used, the timer counts up to the value in maximum-count register A, clears to 0, and then counts to the value in maximum-count register B before again clearing. This process is then repeated. Using both maximum-count registers allows the timer to count up to 131,072.

The control register (refer again to Figure 12–18) of each timer is 10 bits wide and is used to specify the operation of the timer. A definition of each control bit follows:

1. EN (enable) allows the timer to start counting. If EN is cleared, the timer will not count. If it is set, the timer counts.
2. $\overline{INH}$ (inhibit) allows the write to the timer control register to affect the enable bit (EN). If $\overline{INH}$ is set, then the EN bit may be set or cleared. If $\overline{INH}$ is cleared, EN is not affected by a write to the control register. This allows other features to be modified without enabling or disabling the counter.
3. INT (interrupt) allows an interrupt to be generated by the timer. If INT is set, an interrupt will occur each time the maximum count is reached in either maximum-count register A or B. If this bit is cleared, no interrupt is generated. When the interrupt request is generated, it remains in force even if the EN bit is cleared after an interrupt request.
4. RIU (register in use) indicates which maximum-count register is currently in use by the timer. If RIU is a logic 0, then maximum-count register A is in use. If it is a 1, then maximum-count register B is in use. This bit is a read-only bit, and a write has no effect on its setting.
5. MC (maximum count) indicates that the timer has reached its maximum count. This bit remains a logic 1 each time the timer reaches its maximum count and is cleared only if a 0 is written to this bit. This allows a maximum count to be detected by software.
6. RTG (retrigger) is active only for internal clocking (EXT = 0) by the 80186/80188. RTG is used only with timers 0 and 1 to select the operation of the timer input pins (T_0 IN and T_1 IN). If RTG is a logic 0, the external input pin will cause the timer to count if it is a 1 and to hold its count (stop counting) if it is a logic 0. If RTG is a logic 1, the external input pin will clear the timer to 0000H each time a positive edge occurs on the input pin.
7. P (prescaler) selects the clock source for timers 0 and 1. If EXT = 0 and the P bit is a logic 0, the source is one fourth of the system clock. If P is a logic 1, then the source is the output of timer 2.
8. EXT (external) selects internal timing (EXT = 0) or external timing (EXT = 1). If EXT = 1, then the timing source is applied to the T_0 IN or T_1 IN pins for timers number 0 and 1. In this mode, the timer is incremented each time a positive edge occurs at the input pin. If EXT = 0, then the clock source for the timer is applied from one of the internal sources.
9. ALT (alternate) selects single maximum-counter register operation (maximum-count register A only) or alternate maximum-counter operation. In alternate operation (ALT = 1), both maximum-count registers A and B are used alternately.
10. CONT (continuous) selects continuous operation if CONT = 1. In continuous operation, the counter automatically continues counting after it reaches its maximum count.

If CONT = 0, the timer will automatically clear the EN bit after reaching the maximum count. This stops the counting.

Whenever the 80186/80188 is reset, the timers are all disabled so that erroneous interrupts or DMA actions do not occur.

Timer Output Pin.   Timers 0 and 1 each have an output pin used to generate either square waves or pulses. To produce pulses at any of these pins, the timer is operated in single maximum-count mode. In this mode, the output pin goes low for one clocking period when the counter reaches its maximum count.

To produce square waves of varying duty cycles, the alternate mode of operation must be selected. In this mode, the output pin becomes a logic 1 while the counter is reaching the maximum count in maximum-count register A and a logic 0 while maximum-count register B is in use.

Almost any duty cycle can be generated in this manner. For example, suppose that a 10 percent duty cycle square wave is required at the output pin. This is achieved by programming maximum-count register A for a count of 10 and maximum-count register B for a count of 90. The output pin is high for 10 counts and low for 90 for a duty cycle of 90 percent.

Real-Time Clock Examples.   Many systems require the time of day to be available to the microprocessor. In our example, this application uses the timers within the 80186/80188 and an interrupt to keep track of the time of day.

The hardware required for this application is illustrated in Figure 12–20. Notice that only a connection to + 5 V is required to implement the clock. In this circuit, the timers are programmed to generate an interrupt once per second. The interrupt is responsible for keeping the time of day in a memory clock.

The software required to program the clock is listed in Example 12–1. Here there are two procedures: one to set up and start the timers and the other, the interrupt service subroutine, to keep the time. There is a third subroutine that the interrupt service procedure uses to increment a BCD modulus counter. None of the software required to set up the interrupt vector is illustrated, and the data segment where the counters are located is not shown.

FIGURE 12–20   Timer hardware for a real-time clock.

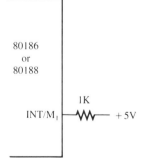

EXAMPLE 12-1

```
        ;Software to control the timers for a real-time clock.
        ;
        ;It is assumed that the peripheral control block (PCB)
        ;is as it is set after a reset at I/O ports FF00H -- FFFFH.
        ;

= FF62          TIM2_MCOUNT     EQU   0FF62H        ;max count Timer 2
= FF66          TIM2_CONTR      EQU   0FF66H        ;control Timer 2
= FF5A          TIM1_MCOUNT     EQU   0FF5AH        ;max count Timer 1
= FF5E          TIM1_CONTR      EQU   0FF5EH        ;control Timer 1

0000            SET_UP          PROC NEAR

0000  B8 07D0                   MOV   AX,2000       ;load count Timer 2
0003  BA FF62                   MOV   DX,TIM2_MCOUNT
0006  EF                        OUT   DX,AX

0007  B8 C001                   MOV   AX,0C001H     ;enable timer 2
000A  BA FF66                   MOV   DX,TIM2_CONTR
000D  EF                        OUT   DX,AX

000E  B8 0064                   MOV   AX,100        ;load count Timer 1
0011  BA FF5A                   MOV   DX,TIM1_MCOUNT
0014  EF                        OUT   DX,AX

0015  B8 E009                   MOV   AX,0E009H     ;enable Timer 1
0018  BA FF5E                   MOV   DX,TIM1_CONTR
001B  EF                        OUT   DX,AX
001C  C3                        RET

001D            SET_UP          ENDP


001D   ·                        INTERRUPT PROC FAR

001D  56                        PUSH SI
001E  50                        PUSH AX

001F  BE 0000 R                 MOV   SI,OFFSET SECONDS
0022  B4 60                     MOV   AH,60H

0024  E8 0038 R                 CALL  UP_COUNT      ;increment seconds
0027  75 0C                     JNZ   ENDI
0029  46                        INC   SI

002A  E8 0038 R                 CALL  UP_COUNT      ;increment minutes
002D  75 06                     JNZ   ENDI
002F  46                        INC   SI
0030  B4 24                     MOV   AH,24H
0032  E8 0038 R                 CALL  UP_COUNT      ;increment hours

0035            ENDI:

0035  58                        POP   AX
```

```
0036  5E                              POP   SI
0037  CF                              IRET

0038                        INTERRUPT  ENDP

0038                        UP_COUNT   PROC  NEAR

0038  8A 04                           MOV   AL,[SI]
003A  04 01                           ADD   AL,1
003C  27                              DAA
003D  88 04                           MOV   [SI],AL
003F  2A C4                           SUB   AL,AH
0041  75 02                           JNZ   UP_END
0043  88 04                           MOV   [SI],AL

0045                                  UP_END:

0045  C3                              RET

0046                        UP_COUNT   ENDP
```

Timer 2 is programmed to divide by a factor of 20,000. This causes its input (2 MHz in the 8-MHz version of the 80186/80188) to be divided down to one pulse every 10 ms. The clock for timer 1 is derived from the timer 2 output. Timer 1 is programmed to count by 100. This produces a maximum count every one hundred 10-ms pulses, or once per second. The control register of timer 1 is programmed so that an interrupt is generated for each maximum count at once per second.

The interrupt service procedure keeps the time. Once per second, this procedure increments the contents of memory location SECONDS. Once every 60 interrupts, it increments the contents of memory location MINUTES, and once per hour it increments the contents of memory location HOUR. The time is stored in these three memory locations in BCD so that it is easy to use by the software in the system.

DMA Controller

The DMA controller location within the 80186/80188 has two fully independent channels. Each has its own set of 20-bit address registers so that any memory or I/O location is accessible for a DMA as either the source or destination for the transfer. In addition, each channel is programmable for auto-increment or auto-decrement to either the source or destination registers.

Figure 12–21 illustrates the internal register layout of the DMA controller. These registers are located in the peripheral control block at offsets COH–DBH.

Notice that the channels are identical. Each channel contains a control word, a source and destination pointer, and a transfer count. The transfer count is a 16-bit number that allows unattended DMA transfers of bytes or words of up to a count of 65,536. Each time a byte or word is transferred, the count is decremented by 1 until it reaches 0000H— the terminal count.

The source and destination pointers each hold a 20-bit address so that DMA transfers can occur to any memory location or I/O address without concern for segment. In the

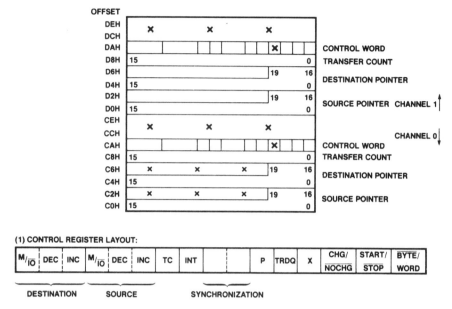

FIGURE 12–21   Register structure of the 80186/80188 DMA controller. (Courtesy of Intel Corporation)

source pointer of channel 0, the least significant 16 bits of the address are located at offset C0H. C2H contains the most significant 4 bits, A_{19}–A_{16}. If the source or destination is an I/O address, A_{19}–A_{16} must be 0s or the I/O port might not be addressed properly.

Channel Control Register.   Each DMA channel has its own control register, which defines its operation. The leftmost 6 bits of the control register specify the operation of the source and destination registers. M/$\overline{IO}$ indicates a memory or I/O location, DEC causes the pointer to be decremented, and INC causes the pointer to be incremented. If both the INC and DEC bits are 1, then the pointer is unchanged after each DMA transfer. Notice that memory-to-memory transfers are possible with the controller.

The TC (terminal count) bit causes the DMA channel to stop transfers when the channel count register is decremented to 0000H. If this bit is a logic 0, then the DMA controller continues transferring data even after a terminal count.

The INT bit enables interrupts to the interrupt control unit. If set, this bit causes an interrupt to be issued when the terminal count for the channel has been reached by the controller.

The SYN bits select the type of synchronization for the channel: 00 = no synchronization, 01 = source synchronization, and 10 = destination synchronization. When either unsynchronized operation or source synchronization is selected, data are transferred at the rate of 2M bytes per second. These two types of synchronization allow transfers to occur without interruption. If destination synchronization is specified, the transfer rate is slower (1.3M bytes per second), and the controller relinquishes control to the 80186/80188 after each DMA transfer.

The P bit selects the channel priority. If P = 1, the channel has a higher priority. If P = 0, it has a lower priority. If both channels have the same priority, then the controller alternates transfers between the channels.

TDRQ enables DMA transfers from timer 2. If this bit is high, the DMA request originates from timer 2. If low, it does not.

The CHG/$\overline{\text{NOCHG}}$ bit determines whether the ST/$\overline{\text{STOP}}$ bit changes for a write to the control register. ST/$\overline{\text{STOP}}$ starts or stops a DMA transfer from the channel. To start a DMA transfer, both the CHG/$\overline{\text{NOCHG}}$ and the ST/$\overline{\text{STOP}}$ bits must be high.

$\overline{\text{B}}$/W selects byte or word transfers. If $\overline{\text{B}}$/W is a 0, then bytes are transferred. If it is a 1, words are transferred.

Sample Memory-to-Memory DMA Transfer. The built-in DMA controller is capable of many types of transfers, but a very useful and often-used type is the memory-to-memory transfer. The procedure used to start this type of transfer is illustrated in Example 12–2.

This procedure transfers CX number of bytes from the location addressed by the SI register in the data segment to the location addressed by the DI register in the extra segment. This operation is identical to a MOVSB instruction except that it executes at a much higher speed.

EXAMPLE 12–2

```
              ;Memory-to-memory DMA transfer procedure
              ;
              ;Source address is DS:SI
              ;Destination address is ES:DI
              ;Count is CX
              ;
              ;Peripheral control block (PCB) is at FF00H -- FFFFH
              ;
0000                      MOVE_BYTES      PROC FAR

0000  8C D8               MOV        AX,DS        ;form source
0002  C1 E0 04            SHL        AX,4
0005  03 C6               ADD        AX,SI
0007  BA FFC0             MOV        DX,0FFC0H
000A  EF                  OUT        DX,AX
000B  9C                  PUSHF
000C  8C D8               MOV        AX,DS
000E  C1 E8 0C            SHR        AX,12
0011  9D                  POPF
0012  05 0000             ADD        AX,0
0015  83 C2 02            ADD        DX,2
0018  EF                  OUT        DX,AX

0019  8C C0               MOV        AX,ES        ;form destination
001B  C1 E0 04            SHL        AX,4
001E  83 C2 02            ADD        DX,2
0021  03 C7               ADD        AX,DI
0023  EF                  OUT        DX,AX
0024  9C                  PUSHF
```

```
0025   8C C0              MOV      AX,ES
0027   C1 E8 0C           SHR      AX,12
002A   9D                 POPF
002B   05 0000            ADD      AX,0
002E   83 C2 02           ADD      DX,2
0031   EF                 OUT      DX,AX

0032   8B C1              MOV      AX,CX        ;program count
0034   83 C2 02           ADD      DX,2
0037   EF                 OUT      DX,AX

0038   B8 B606            MOV      AX,0B606H  ;program control
003B   83 C2 02           ADD      DX,2
003E   EF                 OUT      DX,AX        ;start transfer

003F   CB                 RET

0040        MOVE_BYTES    ENDP
```

Chip Selection Unit

The chip selection unit simplifies the interface of memory because memory address decoders and the I/O port decoders are built into the 80186/80188 microprocessor. In small and medium-sized systems, no additional decoders are necessary. Large systems, however, often require additional external decoders.

Memory Chip Selects.   Six lines are used to select six different external memory components in a small or medium-sized 80186/80188-based system. $\overline{UCS}$ selects the upper portion of the memory where the system ROM is located. This programmable pin allows the size of the ROM to be specified. Note that the ROM ends at address FFFFFH.

The $\overline{LCS}$ output pin is a chip select output that enables the RAM or, on occasion, a ROM that exists at the bottom of the memory. Its starting address is 00000H, and its size is programmable.

The remaining pins select four additional memory devices located in the middle of the system memory map. These four pins are $\overline{MCS_0}$–$\overline{MCS_3}$. Their location can be programmed by specifying the starting address and the size of each block. Note that all four blocks must be the same size in a system.

Peripheral Chip Selects.   The 80186/80188 can address up to seven external peripherals with selection lines $\overline{PCS_0}$–$\overline{PCS_6}$. The base address of these seven peripheral selection lines is programmable at 1K intervals. Once the base address is selected, pins are located at 128-byte intervals from that base address.

Programming the Chip Selection Unit.   The number of wait states in each section of the memory and I/O is programmable. The 80186/80188 has a built-in wait state generator that is able to introduce from 0 to 3 wait states. Table 12–2 illustrates the logic levels required on bits R_2–R_0 in each programmable register to select various numbers of wait states. These three bits can also select whether an external ready signal is required for the waits.

If READY is selected for use with the wait states generator, the READY line is in parallel with the internal wait state generator. For example, if READY is a logic 0 for

TABLE 12–2 Walt state control bits R_2–R_0

R_2	R_1	R_0	Number of Waits	READY Required
0	0	0	0	Yes
0	0	1	1	Yes
0	1	0	2	Yes
0	1	1	3	Yes
1	0	0	0	No
1	0	1	1	No
1	1	0	2	No
1	1	1	3	No

FIGURE 12–22 Register structure for the 80186/80188 chip select unit. (Courtesy of Intel Corporation)

OFFSET:

A0H	UPPER MEMORY SIZE	①	UMCS
A2H	LOWER MEMORY SIZE	②	LMCS
A4H	PERIPHERAL CHIP SELECT BASE ADDRESS	③	PACS
A6H	MID-RANGE MEMORY BASE ADDRESS	④	MMCS
A8H	MID-RANGE MEMORY SIZE E M / X S	⑤	MPCS

⑥

1. Upper memory ready bits
2. Lower memory ready bits
3. PCS0-PCS3 ready bits
4. Mid-range memory ready bits
5. PCS4-PCS6 ready bits
6. MS: 1 = Peripherals active in memory space
     0 = Peripherals active in I/O space
    EX:1 = 7 PCS lines
    0 = PCS5 = A1, PCS6 = A2

Not all bits of every field are used

three states and the internal wait state generator is programmed for two waits, then three will be inserted. If READY is not selected, then it has no effect on the number of wait states inserted.

Suppose that a 4K EPROM is to be located at the top of the memory and it requires two wait states for proper operation. To set up this device and the $\overline{\text{UCS}}$ line that is connected to its $\overline{\text{CE}}$ input, it is necessary to program register A0H. Figure 12–22 illustrates all the control registers for the chip selection unit. These registers are located in the peripheral control block. Notice that address A_0 contains the ready bits (R_2–R_0) and also that address bits A_0–A_{17} are programmable for the $\overline{\text{UCS}}$ line. The starting address of the 4K block of memory is programmed into this register along with the number of waits. A 4K block of memory begins at address FF000H and extends to FFFFFH. In this example, an FF3EH is programmed if two waits with no READY input are required. Table 12–3 illustrates various block sizes programmed into the chip selection unit and also the starting memory addresses. RESET causes a 1K block to be selected for the $\overline{\text{UCS}}$ pin.

TABLE 12-3 Upper-memory programming for register A0H

Starting Address	Block Size	Value for No Waits with Ready
FFC00H	1K	FFF8H
FF800H	2K	FFB8H
FF000H	4K	FF38H
FE000H	8K	FE38H
FC000H	16K	FC38H
F8000H	32K	F838H
F0000H	64K	F038H
E0000H	128K	E038H
C0000H	256K	C038H

TABLE 12-4 Lower-memory programming for register A2H

Upper Address	Block Size	Value for No Waits with Ready
003FFH	1K	0038H
007FFH	2K	0078H
00FFFH	4K	00F8H
01FFFH	8K	01F8H
03FFFH	16K	03F8H
07FFFH	32K	07F8H
0FFFFH	64K	0FF8H
1FFFFH	128K	1FF8H
3FFFFH	256K	3FF8H

Suppose that a 16K RAM that requires no waits and no READY input is located at the bottom of the memory. To program this, register A2H must be loaded in exactly the same manner as register A0H. In this example, a 03FCH is sent to register A2H. Table 12-4 illustrates the programming values for chip selection register A2H.

The central portion of the memory is programmed via two registers: A6H and A8H. Register A6H programs the beginning location of the midrange memory selection lines $\overline{\text{MCS}_0}$–$\overline{\text{MCS}_3}$. Register A8H defines the size of the block size and the individual chip selection size. (Refer to Table 12-5.) In addition to block and select size, the number of wait states can be programmed like the other areas of memory, and EX and MS bits are present. EX and MS specify the peripheral selection lines and will be discussed in the section on programming those lines.

For example, suppose that four 64K DRAM memory devices are to be decoded at address 80000H–BFFFFH with no wait states. The first register programmed is A6H, which sets the block starting address as 80000H. An 81FCH is sent to register A6H. Next, register A8H is programmed with the block size and the number of wait states. (Here EX and MS are assumed to be 0.) An A03CH is sent to register A8H.

TABLE 12–5 Midrange-memory programming for register A8H

Block Size	Select Size	Bits M_6–M_o
8K	2K	0000001
16K	4K	0000010
32K	8K	0000100
64K	16K	0001000
128K	32K	0010000
256K	64K	0100000
512K	128K	1000000

Register A4H programs the peripheral lines $\overline{PCS}_0$–$\overline{PCS}_6$ along with the EX and MS bits in register A8H. Register A4H holds the beginning address of the peripheral selection lines. These lines may be placed in the memory or in the I/O map. If they are placed in the I/O map, A_{19}–A_{16} of the port number must be 0. Once the starting address is programmed, the $\overline{PCS}$ pins are spaced at 128-byte intervals from that address.

For example, if register A4H is programmed with a 00FCH, no wait states are selected, and the memory address begins at location 00C00H or I/O port number 0C00H. If this is the case, then $\overline{PCS}_0$ = 0C00H, $\overline{PCS}_1$ = 0C80H, $\overline{PCS}_2$ = 0D00H, $\overline{PCS}_3$ = 0D80FH, $\overline{PCS}_4$ = 0E00H, $\overline{PCS}_5$ = 0E80H, and $\overline{PCS}_6$ = 0F00H.

The MS bit of A8H selects memory mapping or I/O mapping for the peripheral selection lines. If MS is a logic 1, then the $\overline{PCS}$ lines are in the memory. If it is a 0, they are in the I/O.

The EX bit selects the function of $\overline{PCS}_5$ and $\overline{PCS}_6$. If EX is a logic 1, these two pins are used for selecting I/O devices. If EX is a logic 0, then $\overline{PCS}_5$ and $\overline{PCS}_6$ provide the latches for address bits A_1 and A_2, respectively.

12–4   80186/80188 INTERFACE EXAMPLE

The example in this section illustrates simple memory and I/O attached to the 80188 microprocessor. It also lists the software used to program the 80188 and its internal structure after a system reset. The software to control the system itself is not illustrated.

The 80188 can be interfaced in a small system designed to be used as a micropro-cessor trainer. The trainer itself uses a 2732 EPROM for program storage, three 4016 SRAMs for data storage, an 8279 programmable keyboard/display interface, and an 8251A USART. Figure 12–23 illustrates a small trainer based on the 80188 micropro-cessor.

The $\overline{UCS}$ pin selects the 2732 EPROM, the $\overline{LCS}$ selects one of the SRAMS, and $\overline{MCS}_0$ and $\overline{MCS}_1$ select the other two SRAMs. The $\overline{PCS}_0$ and $\overline{PCS}_1$ pins select the I/O devices, while $\overline{PC}_5$ and $\overline{PCS}_6$ are programmed as address pins A_0 and A_1. $\overline{PCS}_5$ (A_0) is connected to the C/$\overline{D}$ pins of the 8279 and the 8251A.

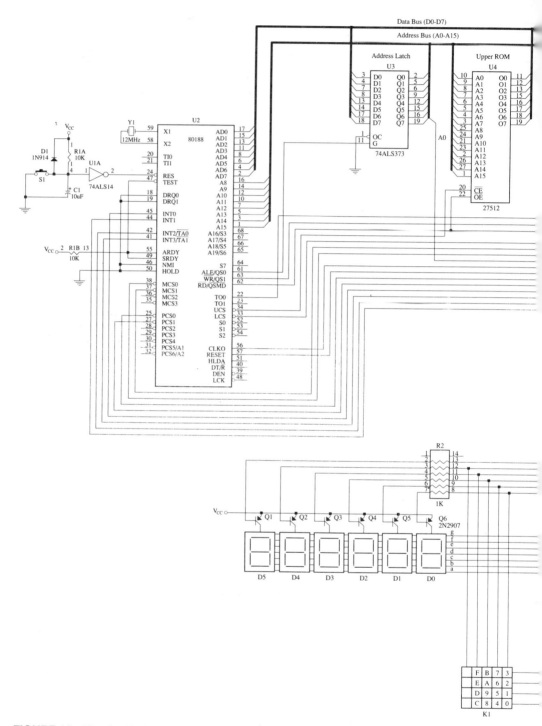

FIGURE 12-23 An 80188-based system that contains a keyboard interface, a six-digit numeric display, and a serial interface.

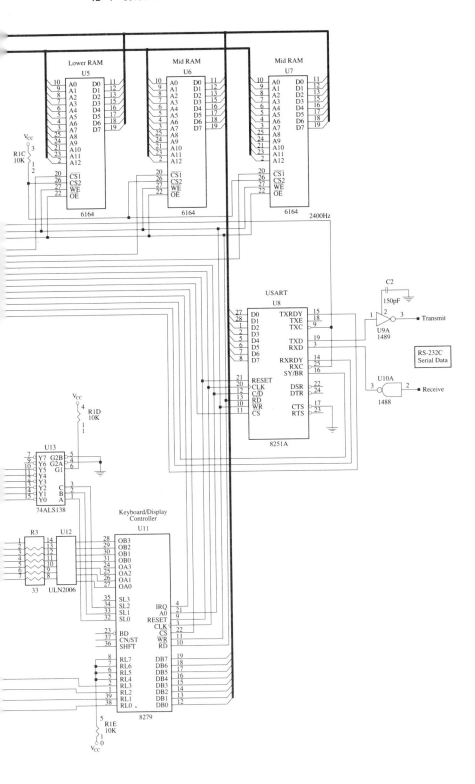

Software locates the EPROM at memory address range FF000H–FFFFFH; the
SRAM at 00000H–07FFH, 80000H–807FFH, and 80800H–80FFFH; the 8279 at I/O
address 1000H–107FH; and the 8251A at I/O address range 1080H–10FFH. In this
example, we do not attempt to modify the address of the peripheral control block, which
resides at I/O address range FF00H–FFFFH.

Example 12–3 lists the initialization software for the 80188. It does not illustrate
the software required to program the 8279 or the 8251A, nor does it show the software
required to operate the trainer. This software is left to the user of this hardware.

EXAMPLE 12–3

```
                        ;Initialization sotware for the 80188 microprocessor
                        ;trainer
FFF0                            ORG       0FFF0H

FFF0   EB 8E                    JMP       SETUP

FF80                            ORG       0FF80H

FF80                    SETUP:

FF80   B8 FF3E                  MOV       AX,0FF3EH ;2 waits, 4K block
FF83   BA FFA0                  MOV       DX,0FFA0H ;address A0H
FF86   EF                       OUT       DX,AX     ;program upper memory

FF87   B8 007C                  MOV       AX,007CH  ;no waits, 2K block
FF8A   83 C2 02                 ADD       DX,2      ;address A2H
FF8D   EF                       OUT       DX,AX     ;program lower memory

FF8E   B8 103E                  MOV       AX,103EH  ;2 waits, address 1000H
FF91   83 C2 02                 ADD       DX,2      ;address A4H
FF94   EF                       OUT       DX,AX     ;program I/O

FF95   B8 81FC                  MOV       AX,81FCH  ;no waits, address 80000H
FF98   83 C2 02                 ADD       DX,2      ;address A6H
FF9B   EF                       OUT       DX,AX     ;program mid memory

FF9C   B8 813C                  MOV       AX,813CH  ;no waits, 2K devices
FF9F   83 C2 02                 ADD       DX,2      ;address A8H
FFA2   EF                       OUT       DX,AX     ;program mod memory

FFA3   E9 F000 R                JMP       SYSTEM    ;go to system

F000                            ORG       0F000H

F000                    SYSTEM:                     ;system program
```

12–5   INTRODUCTION TO THE 80286

The 80286 microprocessor is an advanced version of the 8086 microprocessor that is
designed for multiuser and multitasking environments. The 80286 can address 16M bytes

of physical memory and 1G byte of virtual memory by using the memory-management unit that is located within the microprocessor. This section of the text introduces the 80286 microprocessor, which finds widespread use in AT-type clone machines that flood the computer market. More detail on its memory manager is presented with the coverage of the 80386 microprocessor in Chapter 13. The 80286 is basically an 8086 that has been optimized to execute instructions in fewer clock cycles than the 8086 and also enhanced because it contains the memory manager and the ability to address up to 16M bytes of physical memory and 1G byte of virtual memory.

Hardware Features

Figure 12–24 provides the block diagram of the 80286 microprocessor. Notice that, unlike the 80186/80188, the 80286 does not incorporate internal peripherals; instead it contains a memory-management unit (MMU) that is named the *address unit* in this block diagram.

As a careful examination of the block diagram reveals, address pins A_{23}–A_0, $\overline{BUSY}$, $\overline{ERROR}$, $\overline{PEREQ}$, and $\overline{PEACK}$ are new or additional pins that do not appear on the 8086 microprocessor.

The additional signals are used with the processor extension or coprocessor, of which the 80287 is an example that is often connected to the 80286. Like the 8087, the 80287 performs floating-point arithmetic operations with the microprocessor. The address bus is also wider (24 bits) in the 80286, which allows it to directly address up to 16M bytes of physical memory space instead of 1M byte as in the 8086 system.

The 80286 is operated in two modes: (1) the real mode, and (2) the protected virtual mode. The *real mode* is identical to the 8086, and only address bits A_{19}–A_0 are active and are used to address 1M byte of memory as does the 8086. In the real mode, address connections A_{23}–A_{20} contain logic 0s so that only the first 1M byte of memory is addressable. The real mode is the 80286 mode where all 8086 software will function perfectly without any modification. The *protected virtual mode* is new with the 80286, and it is used to address any location in the 16M-byte address range of this micropro-

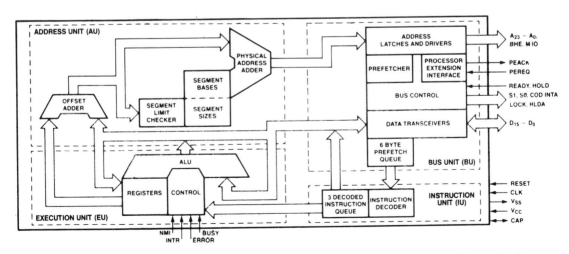

FIGURE 12–24 The block diagram of the 80286 microprocessor. (Courtesy of Intel Corporation)

cessor. The protected virtual mode is controlled by the MMU and addresses a virtual address space of 1G byte, if required. Virtual addressing is accomplished by the MMU because it can address up to 16K different 64K-byte segments that provide a virtual address range of 64K × 16K or 1G byte.

In addition to the changes mentioned there are a few additional registers found in the register set of the 80286 that do not appear in the 8086. Refer to Figure 12–25 for an illustration of the 80286 register set. Notice that it is similar to the 8086, yet different because it contains additional registers. In addition to the standard 8086/8088 registers

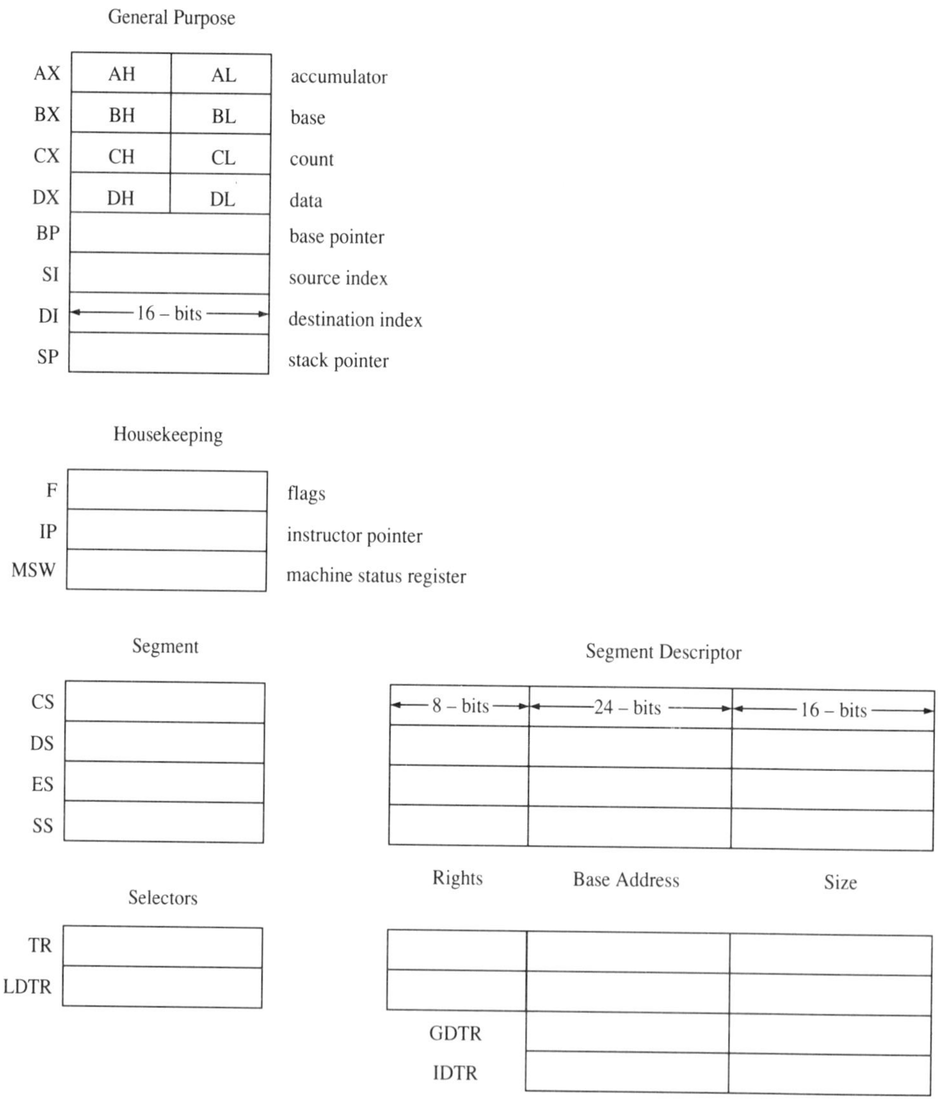

FIGURE 12–25 The register structure of the 80286 microprocessor.

there are additional registers that are used by the memory manager to control memory-addressing operations when the 80286 is operated in the protected mode. These additional registers are discussed under the heading ''Memory Manager.'' The flag register of the 80286 is identical to the 8086/8088 except that the most significant 4 bits of the 80286 flags are always a logic 0, while the most significant 4 flag bits of the 8086 are always a logic 1 when read. This allows software to detect the type of microprocessor found in a system, if so desired. A machine status register has also been added to the 80286 to control, among other things, its entrance into the protected mode of operation.

Figure 12–26 illustrates the predefined interrupt structure of the 80286 micropro-cessor. In the 8086 microprocessor, only the first five interrupts were predefined; in the 80286 many more interrupts are predefined with new functions. The additional interrupts apply mainly to the MMU or the math coprocessor. The new interrupts are as follows:

Type 5 —Occurs for a BOUND instruction as outlined earlier in this chapter for the 80186/80188 microprocessors. An interrupt occurs if the operand in the BOUND instruction is greater than the limit.

Type 6 —This interrupt occurs whenever an instruction not present in the instruction set is executed. This interrupt finds use whenever new software is written and tested, because it tends to find errant behavior as a program randomly runs through the memory when an error occurs.

Type 7 —The coprocessor not present trap occurs whenever the coprocessor is not present in a system when the WAIT or ESC instruction is executed.

Type 8 —Occurs whenever a double fault or exception occurs. An example might be an invalid opcode and a device not available at the same time.

FIGURE 12–26 Interrupt vector register. (Courtesy of Intel Corporation)

Type	Description
0	Divide-error
1	Single-step
2	Nonmaskable
3	Breakpoint
4	INTO
5	BOUND
6	Invalid opcode
7	Processor extension—not present
8	Double protection
9	Processor extension segment overrun
A	Task segment format
B	Segment not present
C	Stack
D	General protection
10	Processor extension error

Type 9—Occurs whenever the segment address, in the protected mode, is in privilege violation, as it appears on the 80287 arithmetic coprocessor.

Type A—Occurs whenever an error in the TSS is detected and can be caused whenever a JMP, CALL, IRET, or INT instruction is executed.

Type B—Caused whenever a segment is used that contains a zero in the P bit of the descriptor used to describe the segment.

Type C—Occurs whenever the SS register is loaded with its descriptor marked as not present.

Type D—Occurs if the protection level is not correct for a given memory reference.

Type 10—Occurs for a floating-point WAIT instruction.

Additional Instructions

The 80286 contains even more instructions than its predecessors. These extra instructions control the virtual memory system through the memory manager of the 80286 microprocessor. Table 12–6 lists the additional 80286 instructions with a comment about each. These instructions control the system only during virtual memory operations and are not used in the real mode. Following are descriptions of several of these instructions that are not described under the memory-management section. The instructions described here are special in nature and only used for the conditions indicated.

CLTS. The clear task-switch flag instruction (CLTS) clears the TS (task-switch) flag bit to a logic 0. If the TS bit is a logic 1 and the 80287 coprocessor is used by a task, an interrupt occurs (type 9). The CLTS instruction is used in system programs and is con-

TABLE 12–6 Additional 80286 instructions

Instruction	Comment
CLTS	Clears the task-switched flag
LDGT	Loads the global descriptor table register
SGDT	Stores the global descriptor table register
LIDT	Loads the interrupt descriptor table register
SIDT	Stores the interrupt descriptor table register
LLDT	Loads the local descriptor table register
SLDT	Stores the local descriptor table register
LMSW	Loads the machine status word
SMSW	Stores the machine status word
LAR	Loads access rights
LSL	Loads segment limit
ARPL	Adjusts requested privilege level
VERR	Verifies read access
VERW	Verifies write access

sidered a privileged instruction because it can only be executed in the protected mode at privilege level zero.

LAR. The load access rights instructions (LAR) reads the segment descriptor and places a copy of the access rights into a 16-bit register. An example of this instruction is LAR AX,BX loads AX with the access rights from the segment selector indicated by BX. This instruction can be used to test the access rights of a segment before it is used in a program.

LSL. The load segment limit instruction (LSL) loads a user-specified register with a segment limit. The second register indicates the segment selector that addresses a descriptor whose limit is loaded into the first register. The example instruction LSL AX,BX will load the segment limit from the descriptor addressed by BX into AX. This instruction is used to test the limit of a segment.

ARPL. The adjust requested privilege level instruction (ARPL) is used to test a selector so that the privilege level of the requested selector is not violated. If the ARPL instruction is executed, the first register/memory location contains the value of the requested selector. The second register contains the selector value of the caller's code segment. The ARPL instruction checks the requested privilege level of the first operand against the level of the second operand. If the requested privilege level of the first operand is less than the second the Z flag bit is set. An example is ARPL AX,CX, where AX contains the requested privilege and CX contains the selector value to be tested.

VERR. The verify for read access instruction (VERR) is used to verify whether a segment that is indicated by its operand can be read. An example instruction is VERR CODE_SEG where memory location CODE_SEG contains a selector that accesses a code segment that is to be checked for reading. If the code segment can be read, the Z flag bit is set.

VERW. The verify for write access instruction (VERW) is used to verify whether a segment that is indicated by its operand can be written. An example instruction is VERW DATA_SEG, which tests the selector stored in memory location DATA_SEG to see whether the segment that it describes can be written. If the segment is writable, then the Z flag bit is set.

The Virtual Memory Machine

A *virtual memory machine* is a system that maps a larger memory space (1G byte in the case of the 80286) into a much smaller physical space (16M bytes on the 80286). This allows very large systems to be operated in smaller physical memory spaces. Only 16M bytes of the system may be present at any instant. The remaining portion is spooled between the physical memory and the disk memory system. Addressing 1G byte of memory is accomplished in the 80286 by the use of descriptors that each define a 64K-byte segment of physical memory. Because the 80286 allows 16K different segments to be defined with descriptors, this allows a virtual memory address range of 1G byte.

Descriptors define the use of the memory space. The 80286 has descriptors that define global tasks that are shared by all programs, local tasks that are used in the local tasks only, and interrupt tasks that are used for the system's interrupt structure. It also has descriptors that define new environments or tasks. Descriptor accesses are performed as the bus is locked to ensure descriptor integrity in multiuser environments. Figure 12–27 illustrates how memory is addressed via a selector. The selector is used to address a 64K-byte memory segment in the protected mode of operation. A *selector* is a segment register that holds the descriptor number of the current descriptor. The selector selects a descriptor from the local or global descriptor table and also sets the requested privilege level of the access. The selector is a 13-bit number (leftmost 13 bits of the segment register) that is used to select from any of 8,192 different descriptors stored in a descriptor table. One bit of the segment register (TI or *table indicator*) selects from either a local or global descriptor table. The rightmost 2 bits of the segment register select the requested privilege level of the access. More detail on these registers, descriptors, and descriptor tables follows under the heading "Memory Manager."

In addition to addressing much more memory than the 8086, the 80286 has access to segments restricted by privilege levels when operated in the protected mode. There are four privilege levels in the 80286 system, (PL0–PL3). Level PL0 is the most trusted

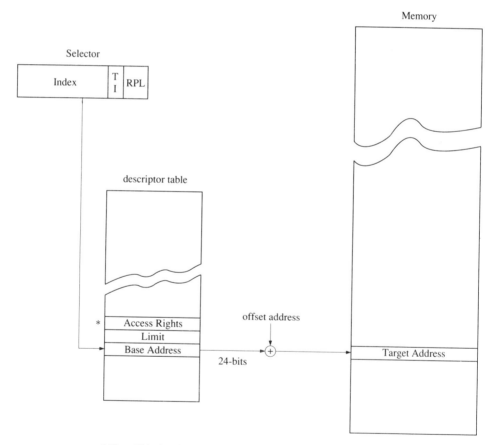

* Note: This descriptor is also loaded into
  the segment descriptor register.

FIGURE 12–27   Addressing memory data in the protected mode.

privilege level and also the highest. Figure 12–28 illustrates the privilege levels as well as the most common types of software found at each level. Each *kernel* or privilege level can only access data or code at the same or lower privilege levels. Any breach of this scheme is called a *privilege violation*. This prevents low-level software from gaining access to system-level software, which normally has a higher privilege level. These kernels are primarily designed for multiuser systems to prevent the end user from access- ing critical system software and also to prevent one user from accessing another user's memory space. An access to a higher level kernel causes an interrupt so that the protection scheme, created by the protection levels, functions correctly. Both software (code) and memory (data) segments are protected by privilege. If a privilege violation occurs, an interrupt ensues (type D) so that the system software can take the appropriate action. This action usually blocks the access and informs the offender of a privilege violation. This denies access to the protected segment.

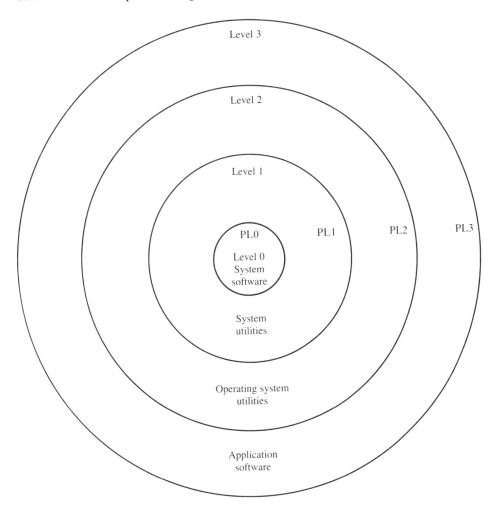

FIGURE 12–28 Privilege levels for the 80286 microprocessor.

Memory Manager

The memory-management unit (MMU) is used only in the protected virtual mode of operation. If the 80286 is operated in the 8086 real mode, only 1M byte of memory exists and there is no need for memory management, because the memory is managed through the segment and offset pointer or index registers as it was in the 8086 microprocessor. The purpose of the MMU is to allocate memory to each user or task through a series of descriptors. The 80286 is operated in the 8086 real mode when it is reset with the system hardware. If more than 1M byte of memory is required, and the system is to run in the protected mode, then the LMSW (load machine status word) instruction is executed. If the protection enable bit (PE), in machine status register, is loaded with a 1 by this instruction, the 80286 enters the protected mode. The PE bit is the rightmost bit of the MSW. Once the 80286 is in the protected mode, the only possible way to switch back to the 8086 real mode is by a hardware reset. This is a problem in many system designs that need to switch back and forth between modes. In the AT clone, a switch back to the real mode is accomplished by actually causing a hardware reset. This takes a considerable amount of time in the 80286-based computer.

A *descriptor* is a series of data in a memory table that defines the physical address of a segment and the privilege level of the segment. It is through descriptors that the MMU keeps track of the physical address space allocated to a given task. The *descriptor table* defines all of the types of segments in use in the 80286. Three types of descriptor tables are used for segment description: (1) global descriptor table (GDT), (2) local descriptor table (LDT), and (3) interrupt descriptor table (IDT).

Global Descriptor Table. The GDT holds descriptors that are available to all tasks in a system. Except for interrupts, the GDT contains descriptors for data and code segments that are used by the operating system. It also contains descriptors that allow task switches. Each table entry is 8 bytes in length (64 bits) and contains the descriptors. The first entry in the GDT is called a null descriptor and is not used because it contains a null pointer (all zeros). The GDT, which is stored in the memory, is addressed by the GDTR (global descriptor table register). The GDTR contains a 24-bit physical address that is used by the 80286 to locate the GDT. The GDTR is loaded with the LGDT instruction. The LGDT instruction loads a 48-bit number into the GDTR from memory. The low-order word in memory contains the limit and the high-order double word contains the base address of the descriptor table. The *base address* is where the descriptor table is stored in the memory and 24 of its 32 bits are used to address a location within the 16M bounds of the 80286 memory system. The *limit* indicates the length of the segment in bytes from 1 byte up to 64K bytes in length.

Local Descriptor Table. The LDT holds descriptors that are available to a given task rather than to the entire system as do the descriptors found in the GDT. The GDT contains the descriptors for segments that are common to all tasks in a system, while the LDT holds descriptors of segments that are local in nature and only used by the current task. A segment cannot be accessed by a task unless the segment descriptor appears in either the GDT or the LDT. The LDT is addressed by the LDTR (local descriptor table register), which is a 16-bit register that holds a 16-bit selector. This selector points to the LDT descriptor, which is found in the GDT. This is different from the GDTR, which holds a memory address where the GDT is stored. The local descriptor is selected by the TI bit in the selector. The LDTR is loaded with the LLDT instruction.

Interrupt Descriptor Table. The IDT holds descriptors that contain the addresses (vectors) of any of the 256 different interrupt levels. The IDT should contain descriptors, in the form of interrupt gates, for all interrupts in use in a system. If all 256 interrupt vectors are stored in this descriptor table, the table must be 2048 bytes in length. This table must be at least 256 bytes in length, describing the Intel reserved interrupt vectors 00H–1FH. Each descriptor is 8 bytes in length, as they are for the local or global descriptors. The IDTR (interrupt descriptor table register) is like the GDTR, because it is used by the microprocessor to locate the IDT. The IDTR holds the 24-bit address of the IDT and the limit of the interrupt descriptor table. The contents of the IDTR are loaded by the LIDT instruction, which functions in the same manner as the LGDT instruction described earlier.

Descriptors

Figure 12–29 illustrates the basic forms of the descriptors allowed in the 80286 micro-processor. Notice that the descriptor is 8 bytes in length and is used by the 80286 in the protected mode to locate a data or code segment in the memory system. The descriptor contains a 24-bit base address that is used to locate the segment at any location within the 16M-byte boundary of the 80286 microprocessor's physical memory system. It also contains a 16-bit limit that indicates the length of the segment described by the descriptor. The remaining bits are used to describe the type of segment being described by the descriptor and also the privilege level of the segment. The descriptor is selected by the contents of a segment register that contains the descriptor number. The segment register, as mentioned before, used in this manner is called a *selector*. The most significant 13 bits of the segment register index the descriptor through the global descriptor table or the local descriptor table. This allows the microprocessor to access up to 16K different descriptors or 16K different segments in the memory. The selector also indicates the requested privilege level of the desired segment. Each of these segments can be 64K bytes in length. Figure 12–30 illustrates the binary bit pattern of the selector (segment register).

FIGURE 12–29 Eight-byte segment descriptor for the 80286 microprocessor.

Descriptor

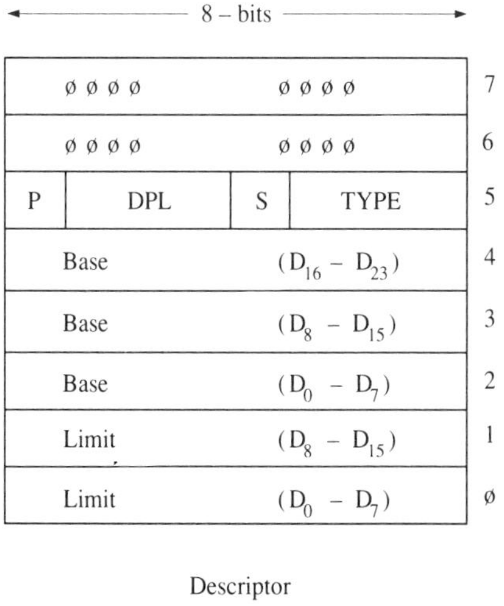

FIGURE 12–30 The binary bit pattern of the selector.

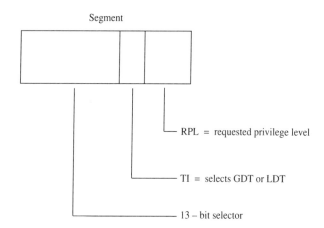

Types of Descriptors

There are different types of descriptors, as mentioned earlier. These types include system and segment descriptors. The *segment descriptors* are used to locate segments in the memory, while the *system descriptors* are used to describe information about the operating system. These system descriptors include the LDT descriptor, TSS (task state segment) descriptor, and gate descriptors.

Local Descriptor Table Descriptor. The local descriptor table (LDT) descriptor has a logic 0 in the S bit, and is type number 2. The LDT descriptors contain information about LDTs. LDTs contain a table of segment descriptors that are unique to a given task and cannot be shared with other tasks.

Task State Segment Descriptor. The task state segment (TSS) descriptor has a zero in the S bit, and is type 1 or 3. Type 1 indicates that the TSS is available, while type 3 indicates that it is busy. A TSS descriptor contains information about the location, size, and privilege level of a TSS. A TSS is a fixed-format segment that contains all the state information for a task and a linkage field to permit nesting tasks. Figure 12–31 illustrates the structure of the TSS. The task register (TR) is used to address the TSS in memory. Each task operating in the protected mode must have a TSS associated with it. The TSS is where the entire state of the machine is loaded from when the task is entered and where the state of the machine is stored when the task is exited. This allows the 80286 to automatically store the state of the machine when tasks are switched.

Gate Descriptors. Gate descriptors are used to control access to entry points within the target code. The types of gate descriptors are called: call gates, task gates, interrupt gates, and trap gates. Gates are used to provide a level of interdiction between the source and destination of a control transfer. This interdiction allows the microprocessor to automatically perform protection checks. Call gates are used to change privilege levels, task gates are used to perform a task switch, and interrupt and trap gates are used to perform interrupt service subroutines.

Call gates provide protected indirect calls and are accessed by using the CALL instruction. Whenever a CALL instruction is executed in the protected mode, the call gate

FIGURE 12–31 The task
state segment (TSS) for the
80286 microprocessor.

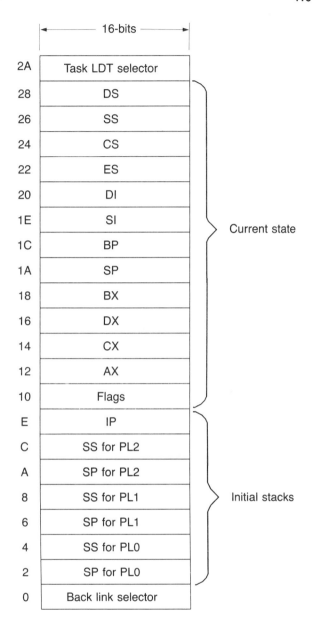

is first tested for validity, then the contents of SS and SP registers are pushed on the stack. The word count is next copied from the old stack to the new stack, followed by the contents of the CS:IP register, which are next placed in the stack as a return address. The interrupt and trap gates work as a call gate, except there is no parameter passing between the old and new stack area as with the call gate.

Task gates are used to switch tasks and specify the TSS for the task. The task gate is accessed by executing a far jump or far call, which refers to a TSS through the task gate. The TR is loaded from the task gate to specify a new TSS.

Transition to the Protected Mode

Before a transition can be made from the real mode, which is active upon a hardware reset, to the protected mode, the GDTR and IDTR registers must be initialized. This initialization must occur prior to switching to the protected mode. The global descriptor table must contain valid descriptors for all data and code segments used by the operating system before the switch is made, and the interrupt descriptor table must contain descriptors for all of the interrupts. After these registers are initialized, using the LGDT and LIDT instructions, and after constructing the descriptor tables, the LMSW instruction is executed in order to place a logic 1 in the protected mode control (PE) bit in the machine status register. This places the 80286 into the protected mode, allowing access to all 16M bytes of memory space. Immediately after placing the 80286 into the protected mode, the user must execute an intersegment (far) jump to load CS and to flush the instruction queue. The final step initializes all data and code selectors so that the task may continue in the protected mode. Once the system is in the protected mode it can access any system memory location, but it must remain in this mode until the 80286 is reset via the hardware system.

Example 12–4 illustrates how to switch from the real mode to the protected mode via a software switch. Here the GDT and IDT are first set up so that the task switch to the protected mode can be accomplished. Loading of these registers is accomplished via the LGDT and LIDT instructions. The actual switch occurs with the LMSW instruction followed by the intersegment jump. From the jump instruction forward, the system will operate in the protected mode. Notice that only the bare minimum has been initialized to reduce the length of this software. In an actual system many more entries in the GDT would be initialized before the switch to protected mode would be accomplished.

Since the 80386SX and 80386DX are replacing the 80286, and soon the 80486 will also command a respectable place in the microprocessor world, we have decided to cut short this presentation of the 80286 by not illustrating more examples of its operation. The same memory management mechanisms apply to the new 80386 and 80486 microprocessors, which are covered in much more detail in the next chapter. Please entrust most of your time to learning these newer upward compatible microprocessors. The coverage of the 80386 and 80486 details their differences from the 80286 and the earlier 8086 microprocessors.

EXAMPLE 12–4

```
.286P
;This software causes the 80286 to enter the protected mode of
;operation.  It does not illustrate or load the interrupt descriptors
;or any software that will be executed by the system.

0000                    DATA    SEGMENT  AT  0        ;segment at 0000H

0100                    ORG  100H                     ;offset at 100H

                        ;
                        ;The Global Descriptor Table
                        ;
```

```
0100   0000000000000000      ENTRY0      DQ    0              ;null descriptor
                             ;
                             ;Code segment descriptor
                             ;
0108   FFFF                  ENTRY1      DW    0FFFFH         ;limit 64K
010A   0000                              DW    0    ;base address = 100000H
010C   01                                DB    01H
010D   9E                                DB    9EH            ;code segment
010E   0000                              DW    0
                             ;
                             ;Data segment descriptor
                             ;
0110   FFFF                  ENTRY2      DW    0FFFFH         ;limit 64K
0112   0000                              DW    0    ;base address = 200000H
0114   02                                DB    02H
0115   92                                DB    92H            ;data segment
0116   0000                              DW    0

0118   00FF                  IDT_TABLE   DW    0FFH           ;set limit to FFH
011A   00000000                          DD    0    ;base set to 00000000H

011E   0017                  GDT_TABLE   DW    17H            ;set limit to 17H
0120   00000100                          DD    100H   ;base set to 00000100H

0124                         DATA      ENDS

0000                         CODE      SEGMENT
                             ASSUME    CS:CODE,DS:DATA


0000   B8 ---- R             START:      MOV   AX,DATA        ;load DS
0003   8E D8                             MOV   DS,AX

0005   0F 01 1E 0118 R             LIDT    FWORD PTR IDT_TABLE;address IDT

000A   0F 01 16 011E R             LGDT    FWORD PTR GDT_TABLE     ;address GDT

000F   0F 01 E0                            SMSW AX            ;get MSW
0012   0D 0001                             OR    AX,1         ;set PE bit
0015   0F 01 F0                            LMSW AX            ;set protected
mode

0018   B8 0010                             MOV   AX,10H       ;selector 2
001B   8E D8                               MOV   DS,AX        ;load selectors
001D   8E C0                               MOV   ES,AX
001F   8E D0                               MOV   SS,AX
                             ;at this point we are now in the protected mode.
                             ;A switch to the code segment addressed by GDT entry
                             ;1 can now be accomplished or additional software
                             ;may follow.

0021                         CODE      ENDS

                                   END
```

___

12–6   SUMMARY

1. The 80186/80188 is identical to the 8086/8088 in software, except that some additional instructions increase its effectiveness. It is thus an enhanced version of the 8086/8088.
2. Hardware enhancements for the 80186/80188 include a clock generator, a programmable interrupt controller, programmable timers, a programmable DMA controller, and a programmable chip select unit.
3. The clock generator allows the 80186/80188 to be operated from an external TTL-level clocking source or from a crystal attached to the X_1 and X_2 pins. The frequency of the crystal is divided by a factor of 2 to generate the basic 80186/80188 timing.
4. The programmable interrupt controller arbitrates all internal and external interrupt requests. It is also capable of operating as a master for two external 8259A programmable interrupt controllers.
5. There are three programmable timers located within the 80186/80188. Each timer is a fully programmable 16-bit counter used to generate waveforms or to count events. Two of the timers, timer 0 and timer 1, have external inputs and outputs. The third timer, timer 2, is clocked from the system clock.
6. The programmable DMA controller is a fully programmable two-channel controller. DMA transfers are made between memory and I/O, memory and memory, and I/O and I/O. DMA requests can occur from the software or the output of timer 2.
7. The programmable chip select unit is an internal decoder that provides up to 13 output pins used to select different areas of memory or I/O. In a small or medium-sized system, no external memory address or I/O port decoders are required.
8. The 80186/80188 microprocessor is available in two speeds: a 6-MHz version and an 8-MHz version. The only difference in the timing between the 8086/8088 and the 80186/80188 is that the ALE pulse appears one-half clock cycle earlier in the 80186/80188.
9. The 6-MHz version of the 80186/80188 allows the memory 417 ns to access data, and the 8-MHz version allows 309 ns.
10. Additional 80186/80188 instructions include push immediate, immediate integer multiplication, shift and rotate with immediate counts, push and pop all registers, string input and output, boundary, and enter and leave.
11. The internal 80186/80188 peripherals are programmed through a peripheral control block (PCB) initialized at I/O port addresses FF00H–FFFFH. The contents of the PCB are the registers associated with the internal peripherals. The peripheral control block may be located anywhere in the memory or the I/O by changing the contents of the relocation register, which is initially the word at I/O port FFFEH.
12. The 80286 microprocessor is an 8086 that has been enhanced to include a memory management unit. The 80286 is able to address 16M bytes of memory directly. Through the memory-management unit it is possible to have a virtual memory of 1G byte.
13. The 80286 is designed to be used in multiuser and multitask environments. For this reason, it is structured with four privilege levels, which provide security for the system software and data while allowing user tasks within the system.

14. Real mode operation is entered upon a hardware reset of the 80286 microprocessor. Protected mode operation is attained by placing a logic 1 into the PE bit of the machine status register.

15. The memory management unit (MMU) accesses memory through a series of selectors and descriptors. The selector is a segment register that contains a 13-bit selector index number. The selector index addresses a descriptor in the descriptor table. The descriptor table contains the actual base address of the memory segment selected by the selector.

12-7   QUESTIONS AND PROBLEMS

1. List the differences between the 8086/8088 and the 80186/80188 microprocessors.
2. What hardware enhancements are added to the 80186/80188 that are not present in the 8086/8088?
3. What type of integrated circuit package is found in the 80186/80188?
4. Describe the signal available at the CLKOUT pin.
5. How is the queue status made available on the ALE and $\overline{WR}$ pins?
6. The fanout from any 80186/80188 pin except CLKOUT and $\overline{S_2}$–$\overline{S_0}$ is _____ for a logic 0.
7. How many clocking periods are found in a bus cycle?
8. What is the main difference between the 8086/8088 and 80186/80188 timing diagrams?
9. What is the importance of memory access time?
10. How much access time is allowed by the 80186/80188 if operated with a 6-MHz clock?
11. Explain how the IMUL immediate instruction differs from the normal IMUL instruction.
12. A PUSHA instruction will place what registers on the stack? In what order are these registers pushed onto the stack?
13. Explain how the INSB instruction operates.
14. Explain how the OUTSW instruction operates.
15. Describe the operation of the BOUND DI,NUMBER instruction.
16. Internal peripherals are always accessed through the peripheral control block. Where is the peripheral control block located after a reset?
17. Write the software required to move the peripheral control block to memory locations 10000H–100FFH.
18. The interrupt vector table of the 80186/80188 is expanded from that of the 8086/8088. What vector is used for the timer 1 interrupt?
19. How many interrupt inputs are available to the interrupt controller located within the 80186/80188?
20. What two modes of operation are available to the interrupt controller?
21. What is the purpose of the interrupt control register?
22. Whenever a source is masked, the mask bit in the interrupt mask register is a logic _____ .

23. What is the difference between the interrupt poll and poll status registers?
24. What is the purpose of the end-of-interrupt register?
25. What is the interrupt vector register used for in the iRMX86 mode of operation?
26. How many 16-bit timers are available in the 80186/80188?
27. Which timers are able to have external inputs?
28. Which timer may be connected only to the system clock?
29. If two maximum-count registers are used with a timer, explain their operation.
30. What is the purpose of the $\overline{\text{INH}}$ control register bit?
31. What is the purpose of the P control register bit of the timers?
32. ALT selects what type of operation for timers 0 and 1?
33. Explain how the timer output pins are used.
34. Develop a short program that will divide an external clock signal by 100. The output waveform to be available at the output pin must be high for 25 counts and low for 75 counts. (Any of the timers may be used for this program.)
35. How many DMA channels are controlled by the internal DMA controller?
36. The DMA controller's source and destination registers are each _____ bits wide.
37. How is a DMA channel started with software?
38. The chip selection unit has _____ pins that select memory devices.
39. The chip selection unit has _____ pins that select peripheral components.
40. When the 80186/80188 is reset, what is the starting address for the $\overline{\text{UCS}}$ output pin?
41. Where does the $\overline{\text{LCS}}$ memory address range begin?
42. The mid-memory chip selection outputs may be programmed for memory chip sizes of _____ to _____ .
43. The internal wait state generator is capable of automatically inserting between _____ and _____ wait states.
44. Set up register A8H so that the midrange memory block size is 128K bytes.
45. What is the purpose of the EX bit in register A8H?
46. The 80286 is capable of directly addressing _____ bytes of memory.
47. With the internal memory manager, the 80286 is capable of addressing _____ virtual bytes of memory.
48. What two modes of operation are available for the 80286? How much memory is addressable in each mode?
49. What are descriptors used for in the 80286?
50. What is the purpose of the LDTR?
51. Explain where the LGTR instruction would be used.
52. How many descriptors can be referenced with a selector?
53. Describe the contents of a descriptor.
54. How is the real mode of operation entered in the 80286 microprocessor?
55. How is the protected mode of operation entered in the 80286 microprocessor?
56. Which 80286 kernel has the highest priority level?

CHAPTER 13

The 80386 and 80486 Microprocessors

INTRODUCTION

The 80386 is a full 32-bit version of the 8086/8088 microprocessor, just as the 80286 was an updated 16-bit version. The 80386 features multitasking, memory management, virtual memory with or without paging, software protection, and a large memory system. All software written for the 8086/8088, 80186/80188, and 80286 functions on the 80386, making this microprocessor upward compatible with these earlier versions. In the case of the 80386, the amount of memory that is addressable by the microprocessor has been increased from 1M byte on the 8086/8088 and 80186/80188, 16M bytes on the 80286 to a huge 4G bytes on the 80386. This 4G-byte (1G byte = 1024M bytes) range of physical memory can be addressed so that up to 64T bytes (1T byte = 1024G bytes) of virtual memory are available. A 4G-byte memory can hold approximately 1,000,000 typewritten pages (4K bytes per page) of information. Please note that no one has ever assembled a memory system containing 64T bytes, so this is an expansive amount of memory. The 80286 could not return to 8086 real mode, as described in the last chapter, without a hardware reset. The 80386 can switch between real and protected modes via software that is a tremendous improvement to what many claimed as a major fault in the 80286 microprocessor.

The 80486 microprocessor is basically an 80386 that contains an 80387 math coprocessor, and an internal 8K-byte cache memory. This higher level of integration will cause the 80486 to eventually take the leading position in the 8086 class of microprocessors. Other than the higher level of integration, the 80486 is redesigned so that it executes many instructions in one clock rather than the two clocks used by the 80386. This represents a significant speed and performance increase over the 80386.

OBJECTIVES

Upon completion of this chapter, you will be able to:

1. Contrast the differences between the 8086/8088, 80186/80188, 80286, 80386, and the 80486 microprocessors.
2. Describe the organization of a 32-bit memory system and interface memory components in that system.
3. Describe the operation of the 80386 memory-management unit and the paging unit.
4. Switch between the real and protected modes of operation of the 80386 microprocessor.
5. Explain the operation of the 80386 in the virtual 8086 mode of operation.
6. Define the operation of the additional 80386 instructions.
7. Explain the operation of a discrete cache memory and pipelining as they apply to the 80386 microprocessor.
8. Detail the operation of the interrupt structure and direct memory access structure of the 80386 microprocessor.
9. Contrast the 80486 with the 80386 and earlier family members.

13–1   INTRODUCTION TO THE 80386

Before this microprocessor can be used in a system, the function of each pin must be understood. This section of the chapter details the operation of each pin connection along with the internal register structure and external memory and I/O structures of the 80386. Figure 13–1 illustrates the pinout of the 80386 that is packaged in a 132-pin PGA circuit. (A PGA is a pin grid array.) Two versions of the 80386 are currently available. The 80386DX is illustrated and described in this chapter and is the full version of this powerful microprocessor. A reduced data bus version (16-bit data bus), the 80386SX, is available, but is not illustrated in this chapter. Its main differences are that it contains a 16-bit data bus and is designed to be a replacement for the 80286 microprocessor. The 16-bit data bus allows designers to incorporate the 80386SX microprocessor into an older 80286 design with a minimum of changes to the main circuit board. It also allows the reworked system board to execute software written for the 80386.

As with the 8086/80286, the 80386 requires a +5-V power supply at a moderate amount of power supply current averaging 550 mA for the 25-MHz version, 500 mA for the 20-MHz version, and 450 mA for the 16-MHz version. During normal operation, the 80386 might require surge currents in excess of 1.0 A. This means that the power supply and power distribution network must be capable of supplying these surge currents. Note that this device contains many V_{cc} connections for +5 V and many V_{ss} connections for ground. In all cases each of these must be attached to the power supply for proper operation. Some connections are labeled *N/C*, which is used to denote no external connection. The N/C pins must be left unconnected or the microprocessor will not function properly due to external noise that is introduced through these pins. Each 80386 output pin connection is capable of driving 4.0 mA (address and data connections) or 5.0 mA (other

FIGURE 13-1 Pinout of the 80386 microprocessor. (Courtesy of Intel Corporation)

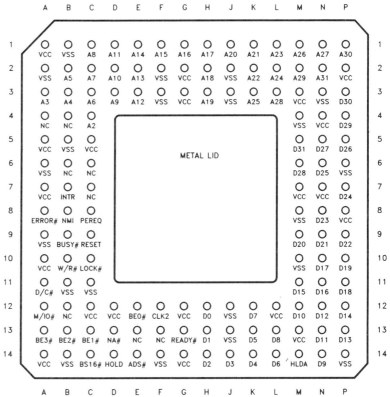

connections) of current, and each input connection requires only a small ± 10 μA of current. In most systems, except for very small systems, these output current levels require that the microprocessor be buffered to drive most systems.

Memory System

The physical memory system in the 80386 is 4G bytes in size and can be addressed as such, or if virtual addressing is used, 64T bytes are mapped into the 4G-byte address space by the memory management unit. Figure 13–2 illustrates the organization of the 80386 physical memory system. Notice that the memory is divided into four banks of memory, with each bank containing 1G byte for a total memory system capacity of 4G bytes. The reason that the memory is this width (32 bits) is that the data bus path between the microprocessor and its memory is 32 bits. This width allows bytes, words, or doubleword of memory to be addressed with one memory cycle. For comparison, the 8088 requires four memory cycles to transfer a doubleword between itself and memory because its data bus width is only 8 bits. Each byte of the memory system is numbered in hexadecimal as it was in all prior versions of the 8086 family of microprocessors, but in this case there are many more memory locations and there are four 8-bit memory banks instead of one (as in the 8088/80188) or two (as in the (8086/80186/80286). The memory banks are individually selected or enabled with the $\overline{BE0}$–$\overline{BE3}$ (bus enable) control sig-

FIGURE 13–2 The memory system for the 80386 microprocessor. Notice that the memory is organized as 4 banks with each containing 1G bytes. Memory is accessed as 8, 16, or 32-bit data.

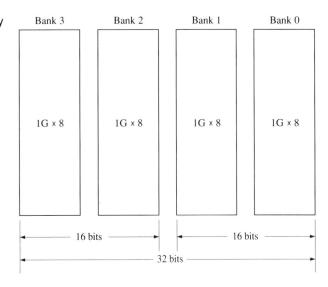

nals. This arrangement allows any single bank to be selected for an 8-bit transfer, banks $\overline{BE3}$ and $\overline{BE2}$ or $\overline{BE1}$ and $\overline{BE0}$ to be selected for a 16-bit transfer, and all four banks for a 32-bit transfer.

As with this microprocessor and all of its 8086 family member predecessors, the memory is numbered in bytes so that each 32-bit memory location contains four consecutively numbered bytes of memory. For example, the very first 32-bit memory location contains bytes 00000000H, 00000001H, 00000002H, and 00000003H. Also notice that the address used to select a memory location is 32 bits wide or an 8-digit hexadecimal address numbered from 00000000H to FFFFFFFFH. In contrast, the 8086/8088 and 80186/80188 have memory numbered from 00000H to FFFFFH and the 80286 has memory numbered from 000000H to FFFFFFH. Notice that the 80386 does not have address connections A_0 or A_1. These two address signals are encoded in the $\overline{BE}$ signals.

Figure 13–3 illustrates a small, buffered 80386 system with a small amount of memory attached in the form of EPROM and also DRAM. Although much more memory is normally attached, this allows us to look at the structure of the decoder and also the buffers found in a 80386-based system. When you compare this buffered system with the buffered 8086 system presented much earlier in the text, notice that this system uses separate write signals in the DRAM section and a common decoder rather than an individual decoder for each bank of memory. In this system the EPROM is decoded at memory locations FFFFF000H–FFFFFFFFH. After a reset the 80386 begins operation at memory location FFFFFFF0H with its CS register = 0000H and its IP = FFF0H. The reason that the address is FFFFFFF0H after a reset is that the upper address connections A_{31}–A_{21} are locked at a logic one level until a far jump or fall call occurs that causes these lines to drop low. The 80386 is started in the real mode so that it only normally addresses memory locations 00000000H–000FFFFFFH until it is switched from the real mode to the protected mode. A near jump instruction is stored at location FFFFFFF0H to location FFFFF000H so that the system can be initialized from the EPROM before a far jump occurs, switching the address lines low. The DRAM located in this diagram begins at memory location 00000000H and extends to location 001FFFFFH.

Pipelines and Cache Memory.   The cache memory is a buffer that allows the 80386 to function more efficiently with lower speed DRAM memory. A pipeline is a special way of handling memory addresses so that the memory has additional time to address data. A 16 MHz 80386 microprocessor allows memory with access times of 50 ns or less to operate at full speed. Obviously there is no DRAM available at this speed. In fact, the fastest devices have an access time of 70 ns, which means that another technique for connecting the memory must be realized. Two techniques are available. Caching, which uses a buffer memory of high-speed TTL memory (access times of 70 ns or less), or a pipeline.

The pipeline is the preferred technique with a 16 MHz 80386, because the microprocessor supports pipelines. Pipelining in the 80386 allows the memory one extra clock to access the data. That extra clock extends the memory access time from 50 ns, to 100 ns, which is acceptable for most 16 MHz 80386s. The pipeline is set up by the microprocessor. When an instruction is fetched from the memory, the microprocessor has extra time before the next instruction is fetched. During this extra time it sends out the address of the next instruction ahead of the time where it actually requires the next instruction. This extra time (one clock period) is used to access slower memory, and the act of sending the address out for the data before it is needed is called *pipelining*. Not all memory references can take advantage of the pipeline, so there are some bus cycles that are not pipelined. These non-pipelined cycles require one wait state if the normal pipeline cycle requires no wait states. Overall pipelines are a great cost saving feature in lower speed microprocessors.

Not all systems can take advantage of the pipeline. Those systems that cannot are typically systems that operate at 20, 25, 33 MHz, or higher speeds. In these higher speed systems, another technique must be used to increase the speed of the memory system as seen from the microprocessor. This additional technique uses a cache memory system. The cache is a high-speed memory that is placed between the 80386 and the normal memory system. Intel provides the 80385 cache controller, which can use up to a 32K × 8 cache memory. The term *cache* refers to the fact that the cache memory appears transparent to the microprocessor and that it is a storehouse or stockpile of memory data. Cache memory speeds the process of memory reference because the microprocessor spends most of its time reading basically the same data from the memory with only occasional writes to the memory. If the data that are read often are kept in a high-speed cache memory, the microprocessor can access it without any wait states. In many cases, today, the cache memory varies in size from 32K bytes to 256K bytes. Cache memory reduces the number of wait states required by a large percentage.

The cache operates in the following manner. Whenever the microprocessor requests data from the memory, the cache is first tested to see if the data are stored in the cache. If the data are in the cache, we have a *cache hit*. Whenever a cache hit occurs, the data are read from the cache without any reference to the main memory. This cache hit read operation is performed without wait states because the cache memory is high-speed memory. If a *cache miss* occurs, the data are read from the main memory into both the microprocessor and the cache. This requires up to four wait states in many cache systems. This means that if the data are accessed again, they are in the cache making its access quicker. When data are written, the cache receives a copy, as does the memory location addressed by the transfer. This is called a *write-through* because the data are written through the cache and also into the cache.

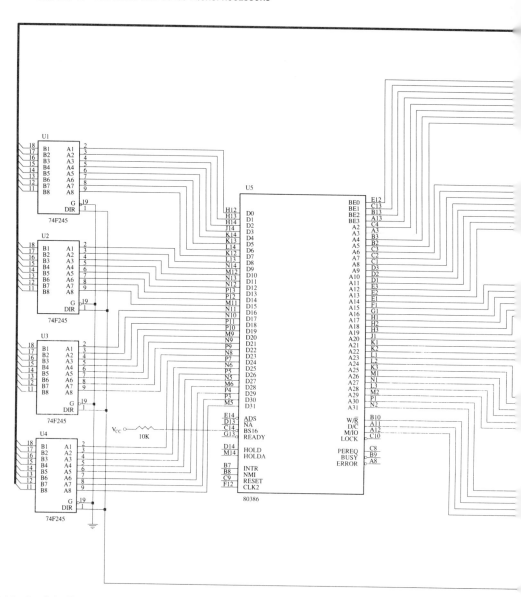

FIGURE 13–3 A buffered 80386 operated in the non-pipeline mode. The decoder illustrated uses programmable array logic (PAL) to decode an area or memory for EPROM and also a 28M-byte area of memory (divided into seven sections of 4M bytes) for DRAM.

In cache memory systems the cache is usually organized in blocks. Blocks are typically 2 to 16 bytes in length for 32-bit microprocessors. What this means is that each time that there is a cache miss, the cache controller fetches a block of memory from the main memory into the cache. This block fetch can acquire the data long before it is needed by the microprocessor. If the byte fetched is before the data in the memory, it is called *lookbehind* cache and if it follows the data, it is called *lookahead* cache. Most cache

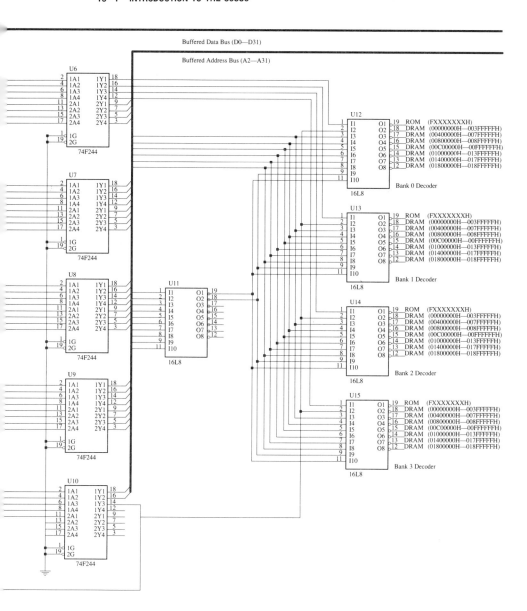

memories are lookahead caches because of the way that the microprocessor normally accesses memory data. The microprocessor normally progresses through a program from a lower memory location to a higher memory location, making the lookahead cache the better choice. This allows the next bytes of memory data to be fetched into the cache before they are needed by the microprocessor.

Figure 13–4 illustrates a typical 32K-byte cache memory system. The cache memory is organized as a 8K × 48 memory. This means that there are 8K locations with each location containing 48 bits. The 48-bit memory locations are divided into two sections; one section is 32 bits in width and stores the data, and the other section is 16 bits in width

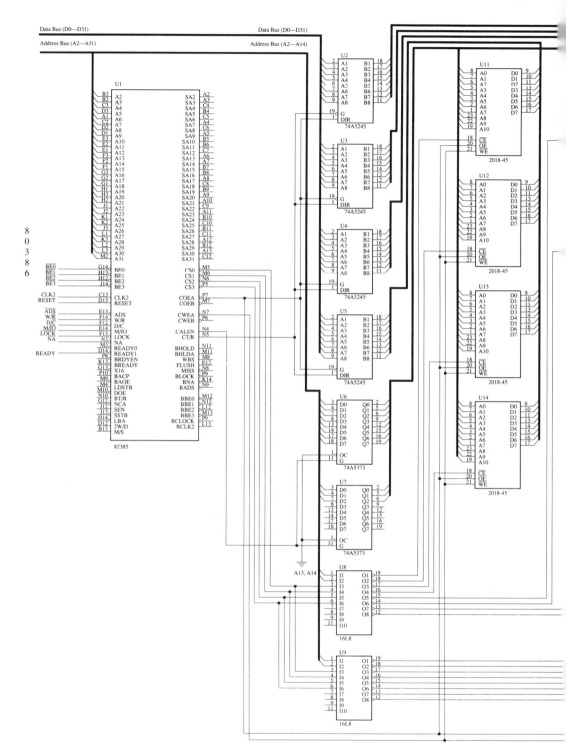

FIGURE 13–4 A 32K-byte cache memory system controlled by the 82385 cache controller. The memory consists of 2K × 8 high-speed stack RAM that has an access time of 45 ns.

432

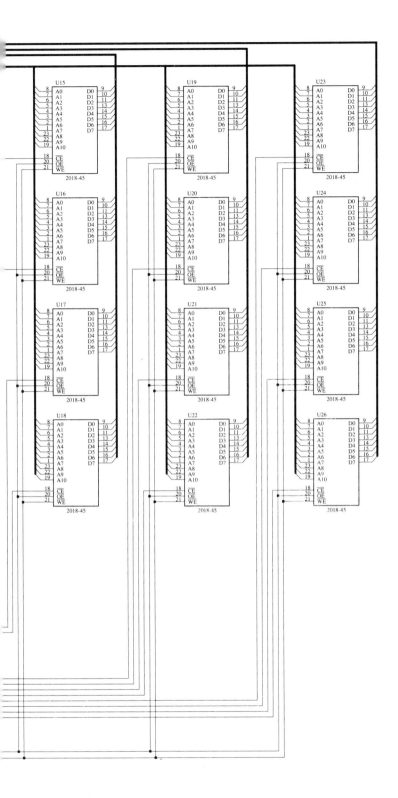

433

and stores a tag. The tag is actually a portion of the memory address, bits A_{31}–A_{16}. This means that there are 32K bytes for data and 8K bytes for tag information. The tag information is not included in the cache memory size calculation of 32K bytes. This is a direct-mapped cache because only the most significant 16 bits of the address are actually stored in the tag field. The remaining 13 bits (A_{14}–A_2) are used to address a location in the cache because it takes a 13-bit address to address any of the 8K memory locations.

Each time that the microprocessor reads a doubleword of data, the cache controller checks the tag (A_{31}–A_{15}) to determine whether the location address by A_{14}–A_2 is stored in the cache. If it is in the cache, the microprocessor fetches it from the cache without a wait state. If it is not, the cache controller generates the necessary memory signals to read the doubleword from the memory and place it into the cache and the microprocessor. This requires up to four wait states. If data are written to memory, the cache controller writes them into a cache location at the same time that it writes them to the memory. This typically takes one wait state.

Some cache controllers are designed to automatically fetch more than one double-word from the memory each time that a cache miss occurs. This is usually called a *burst cycle,* and it will often fetch up to eight doublewords while the microprocessor is busy with other data in the cache. This is advantageous in most cases because programs are stored in ascending memory locations just as data are often stored.

Suppose that the microprocessor has read data from memory location 01007FF0H. The data from this location are stored in cache memory location 7FF0H (the least significant 13 bits of this address less A_1 and A_0). The tag that is stored for this access, with the data from this address, is 0100H. If this same address is again requested by the microprocessor, the cache controller would find that the tag matches the request, and the data are read from this location. On the other hand, if the microprocessor requests a read from memory location 0200FF0H, the tags will not match and the old information is replaced with the new tag (0200H) and the data from the new memory location. Luckily, memory accesses are usually sequential, so this type of miss rarely happens. Think of a procedure that contains some form of loop. This is very common in most programs. The entire instruction sequence of the loop is loaded into the cache and as it executes, the microprocessor runs the program completely from the cache, increasing execution speed markedly.

The I/O System

The I/O system of the 80386 is basically the same as the system found in all 8086 family members. There are 64K bytes of I/O space available if isolated I/O is implemented in a system. The I/O port number or address appears on address connections A_{15}–A_2, with $\overline{BE3}$–$\overline{BE0}$ used to select a byte, word, or doubleword as addressed by an I/O instruction. If memory-mapped I/O is implemented, then the number of I/O spaces may be any number up to the total amount of available memory. With memory-mapped I/O, the $\overline{M/IO}$ signal is not used for decoding, and with isolated I/O, the $\overline{M/IO}$ signal is used to select the I/O or the memory in a system. The main disadvantage of memory-mapped I/O is that some of the memory space is lost to I/O devices, while in the isolated I/O system, none of the memory spaces are forfeited to I/O. The main disadvantage of isolated I/O is that only the IN (INS) or OUT (OUTS) instructions are used to transfer I/O data, while memory-mapped I/O allows all instructions that reference memory to be used to access

I/O devices. Most systems use isolated I/O because there cannot be a memory conflict as may occur with memory-mapped I/O.

Figure 13–5 illustrates the isolated I/O map for the 80386 microprocessor. Notice that it, like the memory, is divided into four banks that are selected with the $\overline{BE}$ signals. This means that I/O devices can be 8, 16, or 32 bits in width. As with the other microprocessors within the family, most I/O operations tend to be 8-bit transfers, so that often most or all of the I/O will be located in just one of the I/O banks. More recently some of the peripherals, such as disk memory driver interfaces and video graphics interfaces are 16-bits in width. With isolated I/O, I/O devices are numbered in hexadecimal from 0000H to FFFFH, with the I/O port address appearing on the least significant bits of the address bus. In systems that use many 8-bit I/O devices these devices might be assigned to one of the four banks to simplify interfacing and programming. Also notice from the I/O map illustrated that a portion is designated for use with the 80387 numeric coprocessor. I/O port numbers 800000F8H–800000FFH are used for communications between the 80386 and the 80387 and are well above the normal I/O ports.

The only new feature added to the 80386 with respect to I/O is the I/O privilege information added to the tail end of the TSS when the 80386 is operated in the protected mode. In the protected mode, as described in the section under 80386 memory management, an I/O location can be blocked or inhibited. If the blocked I/O port is accessed by the software, an interrupt-type number 13 (0DH) is generated. This scheme is added to the 80386 so that accesses to I/O can be prohibited in multiuser systems. Blocking is an extension of the protected mode of operation for the memory system, as are the privilege levels.

Memory and I/O Control Signals

As with the other family members, the memory and I/O are controlled with three signals if isolated I/O is in use. The $M/\overline{IO}$ signal is used to indicate whether the bus cycle will transfer a memory datum or an I/O datum. In addition to $M/\overline{IO}$, the memory and I/O systems must be commanded to read or write data. The $W/\overline{R}$ signal is a logic 0 to indicate a read operation and a logic 1 to indicate a write operation. The $\overline{ADS}$ signal is used to

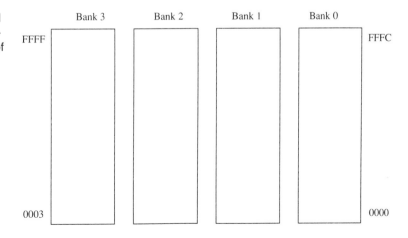

FIGURE 13–5 The isolated I/O map for the 80386 microprocessor. Here four banks of 8 bits each are used to address 64K different I/O locations. I/O is numbered from location 0000H to FFFFH.

qualify these two control signals. This is a deviation from the prior Intel microprocessors that used a separate read and a separate write signal. In a system that uses memory-mapped I/O, the M/$\overline{\text{IO}}$ signal is not connected because it has no function.

Pin Functions

Group	Description
A_2–A_{31}	The address connections (A_2–A_{31}) are used to address any of the 1G bytes of 32-bit memory found in the 80386 system. Note that A_0 and A_1 are encoded in the $\overline{\text{BE3}}$–$\overline{\text{BE0}}$ signals described elsewhere. Also notice that these connections are not multiplexed as in the 8086/8088 microprocessor.
D_0–D_{31}	The data connections D_0–D_{31} are used to carry a 32-bit number between the microprocessor and its memory and I/O system. Notice that these signals comprise the data bus and are bidirectional. Unlike these same connections in the 8086/8088, they are not multiplexed with address information in the 80386.
$\overline{\text{BE0}}$–$\overline{\text{BE3}}$	The bank enable signals are used to select the appropriate memory banks within a 32-bit datum. These signals allow 8-, 16-, and 32-bit data to be addressed by the 80386.
M/$\overline{\text{IO}}$	The M/$\overline{\text{IO}}$ signal indicates that the current bus cycle is a memory cycle when this pin is a logic one, or an I/O cycle when this pin is a logic zero. During an I/O operation the address bus contains the 16-bit I/O address.
W/$\overline{\text{R}}$	The write/read signal indicates that the current bus cycle is either a write cycle when this pin is a logic 1 or a read cycle when this pin is a logic 0. Note that this is different from the read/write control signals present on the 8086/8088 microprocessor.
$\overline{\text{ADS}}$	The address status signal becomes active (logic 0) whenever the microprocessor has issued a valid memory or I/O address on its address connections. This signal is usually combined with the W/R signal to generate separate read and write signals similar to the 8086/8088.
RESET	The RESET input is used to initialize the 80386, causing it to begin executing software at memory location FFFFFFF0H after a reset. The 80386 is reset to the real mode and the most significant 12 address lines will remain high until a far jump or a far call is executed.
CLK2	The clock input must be driven with a clock signal that is twice the operating frequency of the 80386. For example, if you are using a 16-MHz 80386, a 32-MHz clock signal is required for the CLK2 input.
$\overline{\text{READY}}$	The $\overline{\text{READY}}$ input is an active low input that is used to control the number of wait states inserted in the timing for memory access.
$\overline{\text{LOCK}}$	The $\overline{\text{LOCK}}$ output is used in some systems to lock out external DMA controllers or even additional microprocessors that may be present in the system. If the LOCK prefix is added to an instruction, the $\overline{\text{LOCK}}$ pin will become a logic 0 for the duration of the locked instruction.

D/C̄   The data/control (D/C̄) signal is an output that indicates that the data bus contains data for the memory or I/O when it is a logic 1 and that a control instruction such as HALT or an interrupt acknowledge is being executed when D/C̄ is a logic 0.

BS16   This input allows the size of the 80386 bus to be changed from a 32-bit bus (BS16 = 1) to a 16-bit bus (BS16 = 0), which might be advantageous in some systems. In other systems the designer might elect to use the 16-bit bus version of the 80386, the 80386SX.

NA   The next address input is used to cause the microprocessor to output the next address during the current bus cycle so that the memory can be organized to pipeline data.

HOLD   The HOLD input is used to request a DMA action as with the other family members.

HLDA   The HOLD companion output signal that indicates the 80386 has relinquished control of the system bus.

PEREQ   The input allows the 80387 coprocessor to request data from the 80386.

BUSY   This input is used to cause the 80386 to wait for the 80387 if it is busy executing a numeric instruction. The only time that the 80386 will wait for the 80387 is when the 80386 is ready to execute another 80387 instruction; otherwise, processing continues at full speed.

ERROR   This input to the 80386 is used by the coprocessor to indicate that an error has occurred.

INTR   The INTR input is used by external circuitry to request an interrupt. INTR is maskable through the I flag bit.

NMI   The NMI input is used to request a non-maskable input. As with other family members, this input uses interrupt vector 2 for this request.

80386 Register Structure

The register structure of the 80386 is a much expanded version of the registers found in the 8086/8088, and all subsequent versions of the 8086 including the 80286. Figure 13–6 illustrates the basic register structure of the 80386 microprocessor. Notice that this set of registers is divided into three sections: (1) general purpose, (2) segment (selector) registers, and (3) internal housekeeping.

    The general-purpose registers are accessed through most instructions and are designed to hold 8-, 16-, or 32-bit data for use by programs. The main difference between this set and the set found in the 8086/8088 is that all of the registers can be addressed as 32-bit registers by appending the letter E to the front of the normal 16-bit register. For example, EAX is used (*extended AX*) instead of AX, which is the 16-bit accumulator found in the 8086/8088, to address the 32-bit extended AX or EAX register.

    The segment or selector registers are also similar to the 8086/8088 except that two additional data segment or selector registers are present, FS and GS. The segment registers are used to address a 64K-byte segment of the memory whenever the 80386 is operated real mode, which allows the 80386 to act as a very fast 8086/8088. Segment

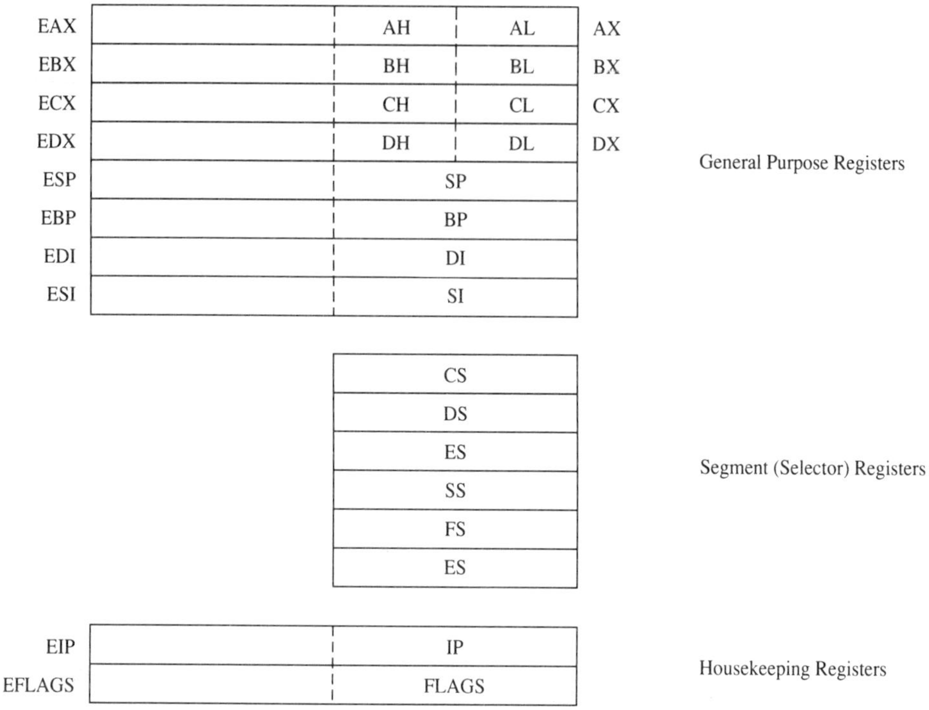

EAX		AH	AL	AX
EBX		BH	BL	BX
ECX		CH	CL	CX
EDX		DH	DL	DX
ESP		SP		
EBP		BP		
EDI		DI		
ESI		SI		

General Purpose Registers

CS
DS
ES
SS
FS
ES

Segment (Selector) Registers

EIP		IP
EFLAGS		FLAGS

Housekeeping Registers

FIGURE 13-6 The internal structure of the 80386 microprocessor illustrating the general, segment, and housekeeping registers.

registers hold the segment address that is combined with an offset address to address a location in the physical address space between locations 00000000H and 000FFFFFH in the real mode. Segment registers are also used in protected mode, except they are called selectors and are combined with a 32-bit offset address instead of a 16-bit offset address. Segment registers are used as selectors for the memory-management unit, as described in Chapter 12, with the 80286 microprocessor and later, in much more detail, in this chapter. Associated with each segment register is an invisible (to the programmer) cache that contains the descriptor addressed by the segment register in the protected mode. This invisible portion of the selector contains three fields of information: (1) access rights, base address, and limit. Each time that a new selector is loaded into a segment register during protected mode operation, the descriptor is looked up in the descriptor table and automatically loaded into this invisible cache portion of the segment selector register.

The housekeeping registers consist of a 32-bit instruction pointer (EIP) and a flag register called EFLAGS. The instruction pointer is a 32-bit register designated EIP. During real mode operation of the 80386, the least significant 16 bits of EIP are combined with the segment register CS to address a memory location for the next instruction in the program. During protected mode operation, all 32-bits of EIP are used to address memory data within the entire 4G-byte address range of the 80386.

Example 13-1 illustrates a variety of instructions that use the 32-bit registers, but not all of the instructions, because the listing would be far too expansive for inclusion in the text. Basically, any instruction can use an extended 32-bit register. Notice that the directive .386 is used to indicate to the assembler that the program is written for a 80386 microprocessor. Also notice that USE16 indicates that the code segment is to be set up as a standard segment with 16-bit offset addresses. This is the case for systems that operate in the real mode. In a protected mode system the directive USE32 is found to allow 32-bit addressing and register without a prefix.

EXAMPLE 13-1

```
                           .386

                           ;example 80386 instructions using a variety of
                           ;addressing modes

0000                       PROGRAM   SEGMENT    USE16

0000   66¦ B8 22223333         MOV    EAX,22223333H
0006   66¦ BB 44445555         MOV    EBX,44445555H
000C   BF 1000                 MOV    DI,1000H
000F   BD 2000                 MOV    BP,2000H
0012   8A 0D                   MOV    CL,[DI]
0014   3E: 8A 6E 00            MOV    CH,DS:[BP]
0018   66¦ 03 D8               ADD    EBX,EAX
001B   66¦ 8B F3               MOV    ESI,EBX
001E   66¦ F7 E6               MUL    ESI
0021   67¦ 66¦ 89 01           MOV    [ECX],EAX
0025   64: 67¦ 88 0403         MOV    FS:[EBX+EAX],AL
002A   65: 67¦ 8B 07           MOV    AX,GS:[EDI]


002E                       PROGRAM   ENDS

                           END
```

Figure 13–7 illustrates the contents of the EFLAG register for the 80386 microprocessor. The rightmost 8-flag bits are identical to the 8-flag bits found in the 8085 microprocessor. The rightmost 12-flag bits are identical to those found in the 8086/8088 microprocessor. The rightmost 16-flag bits are identical to those found in the 80286 microprocessor. In the 80386, two additional flag bits are added to the upper 16 bits of EFLAGS, R (resume) and VM (virtual 8086 mode).

The flag bits each indicate the following:

C   Carry flag is used to indicate a carry after addition, a borrow after a subtraction, and also indicate whether the product's most significant portion is zero or not zero after a multiplication.

P   Parity flag indicates whether the outcome of an arithmetic or logic operation contained even (P = 1) or odd (P = 0) parity.

A   Auxiliary carry is used with DAS and DAA to adjust the result after a BCD addition or subtraction.

Z   Zero flag indicates that the outcome of an arithmetic or logic operation is zero (Z = 1) or not zero (Z = 0).

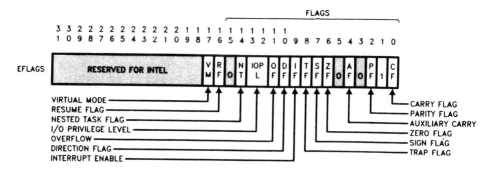

FIGURE 13–7   The EFLAG register. (Courtesy of Intel Corporation)

S   Sign flag indicates the arithmetic sign of the result after an arithmetic or logic operation. If the result is positive $S = 0$, and if the result is negative, $Z = 1$.

T   Trap flag is used to select normal or single-step operation of the 80386. If T $= 1$, then single-step operation is selected.

I   Interrupt flag enables or disables the INTR interrupt input pin. If I is set, then the interrupt pin will function.

D   Direction flag is used to select auto-increment $(D = 0)$ or auto-decrement $(D = 1)$ operation for the string instructions.

O   Overflow flag indicates that the result of a signed arithmetic operation overflowed the capacity of the result register or memory location.

IOP   These protected mode I/O privilege flag bits are used to indicate the maximum current privilege level value allowed before I/O instructions begin generating privilege violation exception 13 or without consulting the I/O permission bit map.

NT   The protected mode, nested task flag is used to indicate that the current nested task has a valid back-link to the previous task's TSS. On a return from a task, the value of NT is tested to determine whether an intra- or intertask return shall occur.

R   Resume flag temporarily disables the debug exception for the next instruction.

VM   Virtual 8086 mode flag selects the virtual 8086 mode while the 80386 is operating in the protected mode.

In addition to the EFLAGS and EIP there are other registers that are used during either the protected mode operation of the 80386 or during special operations. These include the system address registers, the control registers, test registers, and also the debug registers.

System Address Registers.   The system address registers are: GDTR (global descriptor table register), LDTR (local descriptor table register), IDTR (interrupt descriptor table register), and TR (task register). The first three registers are used to address tables that are used in the operation of the global, local, and interrupt structures. The task register (TR) is used to address information used by the processor to define the current task. This information is in the form of the task state segment (TSS). These registers perform the same function as comparable registers on the 80286, except the base addresses used in the 80386 are 32 bits in width, while they were 24 bits in width on the 80286.

Control Registers. In addition to the EFLAGS and EIP as described earlier, there are other control registers found in the 80386. Control register 0 (CR0) is identical to the machine status register (MSR) found in the 80286 except that it is 32 bits in width in the 80386. The most significant 24 bits of CR0 are not used. The flag register is also expanded from 16 bits in the 8086/80186/80286 to a full 32 bits in the 80386. Additional control registers have also been added (CR1–CR3). CR1 is not used in the 80386, but CR2 and CR3 are used with the paging unit that will be discussed later. Figure 13–8 illustrates the contents of the control registers. Control register 0 contains a number of special control bits that control the following 80386 events.

> PG—This bit controls whether the 80386 uses page tables in determining the physical address for each instruction.

> ET—Extension type indicates which type of numeric coprocessor is present in the system. If this bit is set, the 80386 will function with the 80387, and if it is reset, the 80386 will function with the 80287.

> TS—Task switched bit indicates that the 80386 has switched tasks and is read to determine whether a task switch has occurred. If TS is set, a numeric coprocessor escape sequence will cause a coprocessor not available fault (interrupt type 7).

> EM—Emulation indicates whether the function of the coprocessor is to be emulated with software. If EM is set, any coprocessor escape instruction will cause a coprocessor not available interrupt.

> MP—This bit is set if the math coprocessor is present in the system and controls the way that the WAIT instruction functions.

> PE—This bit is set to enter the protected mode and cleared to reenter the real mode. This bit could only be set on the 80286.

Control register 1 is not used in the 80386 microprocessor, but it is reserved for use in some future product. Control register 2 is used with paging and holds the page fault address of the last page fault after a page fault interrupt. Finally, control register 3 is used

FIGURE 13–8 The control-register structure of the 80386 microprocessor.

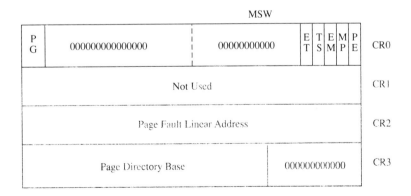

with paging to hold the base address of the page table. Note that the lowest 12 bits of the 32-bit page table base address are ignored and are always logic 0s. Page tables are always stored on 4K-byte boundaries for this reason.

Debug and Test Registers. A new series of registers not present in earlier versions of the 8086 has been added to facilitate debugging and testing. There are two test registers, TR6 and TR7, that are used to verify that paging and caching are functioning correctly. The debug registers (DR0–DR7) are used to allow software debugging with breakpoints.

Figure 13–9 illustrates the contents of the eight debug registers, DR0–DR7, and also the two test registers, TR6 and TR7. The first four debug registers contain 32-bit linear breakpoint addresses. (A *linear address* is a 32-bit address generated by the microprocessor that may or may not address the same physical address.) These addresses are constantly compared with the addresses generated by the microprocessor. If a match address occurs, the 80386 will, if directed to do so by DR6 and DR7, cause a type-1 interrupt (TRAP interrupt) to occur. These breakpoints are very useful in debugging faulty software. The control bits in DR6 and DR7 are defined as follows.

BT—If this bit is set, then the debug trap was invoked by a task switch.

BS—If this bit is set, then the debug trap was due to the trap flag bit in the flag register being set.

BD—If this bit is set, then the debug trap was due to an attempt to read or write the debug registers with the GD bit set.

B3–B0—These bits indicate which of the four DR registers breakpoint addresses caused the debug trap. If DR0 caused the trap, then a logic 1 is found in bit B0.

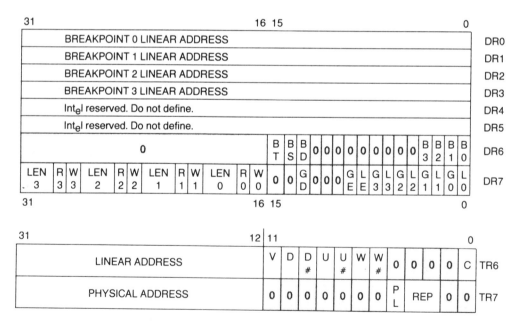

FIGURE 13–9 The debug and test registers of the 80386. (Courtesy of Intel Corporation)

LEN—There are four LEN fields listed in DR7. Each field corresponds to one of the breakpoint addresses stored in DR0--DR3. 00 in length specifies a byte reference address, 01 a word, and 11 a doubleword access.

RW—There are four RW fields listed in DR7. Each breakpoint register has a corresponding RW field. The RW field indicates the cause of the breakpoint as follows: 00 = instruction access, 01 = data writes, 10 = not used, and 11 = data reads and writes.

GD—If the GD bit is set, any attempt to read or write a debug register will cause a debug trap interrupt, thus preventing the read or write attempt. Note that GD is automatically cleared for the debug interrupt.

GE—Set for a global data breakpoint for any of the four breakpoint address registers.

LE—Set for a local data breakpoint for any of the four breakpoint address registers.

The test registers, TR6 and TR7, are used to test the translation lookaside buffer (TLB). The TLB is used with the paging unit located within the 80386. The TLB holds the most commonly used page table entries. This reduces the number of memory reads required for looking up a page table entry. The TLB holds the most common 32 entries from the page table, and it is tested with the TR6 and TR7 test registers.

TR6 holds the tag field (linear address) of the TLB, and TR7 holds the physical address of the TLB. To write a TLB entry perform the following steps.

1. Write TR7 for the desired physical address, PL and REP values.
2. Write TR6 with the linear address making sure that C = 0.

To read a TLB entry:

1. Write TR6 with the linear address making sure that C = 1.
2. Read both TR6 and TR7. If PL indicates a hit, then the values in TR6 and TR7 indicate the contents of the TLB.

The bits found in TR6 and TR7 are used to indicate the following.

V	The valid bit for the TLB entry.
D	The dirty bit for the TLB entry.
U	The user bit for the TLB entry.
W	The writable bit for the TLB entry.
C	The command bit causes a write (0) or an immediate lookup (1).
PL	The PL bit indicates a hit on a TLB lookup if it is a logic 1 and on a write to the TLB, PL = 0 allows the internal pointer in the paging unit to select which TLB block is written. If PL = 1 on a TLB write, the REP field is used to select which four blocks of the TLB are written.

Refer to the later section that deals with the memory-management unit and in specific the paging unit for a fuller description of the paging mechanism and also the TLB.

The Instruction Set

The instruction set of the 80386 contains all of the instructions discussed for the 8086/8088, 80186/80188, and the 80286 plus a vast number of additional instruction variations. These variations are in part due to the fact that in addition the 8-bit registers (AH, AL, BH, BL, CH, CL, DH, and DL), and the 16-bit registers (AX, BX, CX, DX, SP, BP, DI, and SI), and the 16-bit segment registers (CS, DS, ES, and SS) we now have the 32-bit registers (EAX, EBX, ECX, EDX, ESP, EBP, EDI, and ESI) along with two new segment (selector) registers FS and GS to contend with. These additional registers increase the number of valid instructions that occur in the 80386 instruction set. The 32-bit registers are used just as the 8- and 16-bit registers are used with the earlier versions of the microprocessor. The 32-bit registers may be addressed in *either* real or protected mode. Appendix B, which covers the instruction set, includes a listing of all of the instructions for all family members (8086/8088, 80286, 80386, and 80486), with many examples of their usage. In addition to just using the new segment registers and 32-bit registers there are 14 new instructions added to the 80386 instruction set. These new instructions are listed in Table 13–1 along with a brief description of their function.

BSF and BSR.   The bit scan forward and reverse instructions are similar so they are covered together. The bit scan forward (BSF) instruction scans a word or a doubleword from the rightmost bit to the leftmost bit, and the bit scan reverse (BSR) instruction scans a word or doubleword from the leftmost to the rightmost bit. If a bit is found that is set to a logic 1, the scanning ceases. If a logic 1 is found, the number of the bit position containing the logic 1 is stored in the destination register. If no set bit is found, the contents of the destination register are unknown, but the zero flag is set to indicate a zero condition. Suppose that the contents of register EAX are to be scanned for a logic 1. The

TABLE 13–1   The new 80386 instructions

Instruction	Comment	Example
BSF	Bit scan forward	BSF EAX,DATA
BSR	Bit scan reverse	BSR EAX,LIST
BT	Bit test	BT DATA,EAX
BTC	Bit test and complement	BTC AX,WATER
BTR	Bit test and reset	BTR EAX,4
BTS	Bit test and set	BTS ECX,8
LFS	Load FS	LFS DI,DATA
LGS	Load GS	LGS SI,FIELD
LSS	Load SS	LSS SP,STACK
MOVSX	Move with sign extension	MOVSX ECX,DL
MOVCZ	Move with zero extend	MOVCZ EAX,CX
SET	Set byte on condition	SETNC AL
SHLD	Double precision shift left	SHLD AX,BX,8
SHRD	Double precision shift right SHRD	AX,BX,4

following instruction is used to scan this register and store the resultant set bit position number in register ECX (BSF ECX,EAX). If bit position 6, 9, and 12 contain logic 1s, the prior instruction will return with a 6 in register ECX. If none of the bits is a logic 1, then the zero flag is set indicating a zero condition. These instructions can be extremely useful in converting numbers to floating-point form if a numeric coprocessor is not available for this task.

Bit Test Instructions (BT, BTC, BTR, BTS).   The bit test instructions each test a bit in a register or memory location. In addition to testing a bit, some of these instructions also affect the bit under test. The bit test (BT) instruction merely tests the bit under test without changing it. The bit test and complement (BTC) instruction tests the bit and then complements it. The bit test and reset (BTR) instruction tests the bit and then resets it or clears it to a zero. The bit test and set (BTS) instruction tests the bit and then sets it to a logic 1. These instructions give the 80386 user complete control over all bit positions in every memory location and register.

In all four instructions, the bit tested changes the carry flag to the value of the bit under test. The destination operand, leftmost, is the location in memory or in a register of the bit under test. The source operand, rightmost, is a register that contains the bit number to be tested or an 8-bit immediate data that contains the bit number to be tested. For example, suppose that you wish to test bit position 4 of memory location DATA and then clear it to a zero after the test. This is accomplished by using the BTR DATA,4 instruction. The state of bit position 4 before it is cleared to zero is found in the carry flag. Carry is set if bit 4 was a one prior to the execution of the BTR instruction in this example.

Load Segment Register and Pointer Instructions (LFS, LGS, and LSS).   The load segment register and pointer instructions LFS, LGS, and LSS function in the same manner as the LDS and LES instructions listed and explained with the 8086/8088 microprocessor data movement instructions. These instructions load a segment register and a pointer from a doubleword in memory. For example, suppose that an LSS SP,DATA instruction is executed. This instruction loads both the SS and SP registers from memory, beginning at location DATA. The first 2 bytes beginning at memory location DATA are loaded into the SP register, and the last 2 bytes are loaded into the SS segment register. The LFS and LGS instructions behave in the same manner, except the FS or GS registers are loaded in place of the SS register. These instructions are ideal for loading offset and segment selector addresses into a pointer and a segment register.

MOVSX and MOVCZ Instructions.   These instructions are used to either sign extend or zero extend a number from an 8- to 16-bit, 8- to 32-bit, or 16- to 32-bit operand. These instructions replace the CBW and CWD instructions found in the 8086. For example, suppose that you are required to sign extend an 8-bit number in AL into a 32-bit number in EAX. This is accomplished with the MOVSX EAX,AL instruction. Likewise you could zero extend the same number with the MOVCZ EAX,AL instruction. Numbers are sign extended to convert them to wider signed numbers and zero extended to convert them to wider unsigned numbers. Numbers are often extended before a division. Take the example of an 8-bit division. The dividend must be a 16-bit number before the division can take place. To convert the 8-bit dividend into a 16-bit dividend, the MOVSX instruction is used to convert signed numbers and the MOVCZ instruction is convert for unsigned numbers.

Set Byte on Condition.   The set byte on condition instruction comes in many forms. Each form tests a condition and then sets the destination byte (byte only) to 01H if the condition is true or to a 00H if the condition is false. The conditions tested are all of those allowed with the conditional jump instructions. For example, SETZ AL will test the zero flag and if the condition indicated is zero, AL will be set to a 01H, but if the condition is not zero, AL will be cleared to a 00H. Other set byte on condition instructions include: SETNZ, SETE, SETC, SETNC. These instructions are useful when a memory flag is required as an indicator. The contents of the memory location are either cleared to zero if the condition is false or set to a 01H if the condition is true.

Double Precision Shifts.   The 80386 has added two double precision shift instructions to the instruction set: SHLD and SHRD. These instructions shift left (SHLD) or right (SHRD) either a pair of words or a pair of doublewords. For example, suppose that the following instruction is executed, SHLD AX,BX,8. This instruction shifts the 32-bit number located in AX and BX to the left 8 binary places. If AX = 1234H and BX = 5678H before the instruction, they are AX = 3456H and BX = 7800H after the instruction. Thirty-two bit operands may also be used, such as the SHRD EAX,ECX,19 instruction, which shifts EAX into ECX for 19 bit positions. In all cases the vacated bit positions are filled by logic 0s after the shift.

Notes about Older Instructions.   On the 80286 microprocessor, the LMSW instruction is used to load the machine status word. This register is CR0 on the 80386. If you plan to change the contents of CR0, do not use a LMSW instruction. Instead use the MOV EAX,CRO instruction to copy the contents of CR0 into the EAX register. Now use the OR or AND instruction to set or clear specific bits of CR0 before using the MOV CR0,EAX instruction to change CR0. The SMSW instruction should also not be used with the 80386.

In general, most of the older 8086/8088 instructions can be adjusted to use 32-bit registers by using the registers. For example, if you wish to load EAX with a 12H, use MOV EAX,12H. If adding EAX to EBX is desirable, just use ADD EBX,EAX. Refer to Appendix B for a multitude of programming examples. Almost any instruction that uses an 8- or 16-bit register or pointer can use a 32-bit register or pointer.

New Addressing Modes.   The number of addressing modes has been increased from the modes covered with the 8086/8088 microprocessor. These modes include using the extended (32-bit) registers as 32-bit offset addresses. Also some additional forms of indexing have been added. These new forms make the number of addressing modes available greater than for most other microprocessors.

The most obvious of these new modes is the addition of the two new segment registers and prefixes that accompany them. Both the FS and GS segment registers address data in their respective segments. To use these new segments requires a segment override prefix, because no instruction uses these new segments by default. For example, if you wish to address memory location DATA within the GS segment, then the instruction might appear as follows: MOV AX,GS:DATA or as MOV EAX,GS:[BX] or any number of other forms. Like GS, FS is also a segment override prefix that allows an instruction to access data in the FS segment. (Refer to Example 13–1 for examples.)

In addition to the indirect modes of addressing used in the 8086 family thus far, there are additional indirect modes as listed in Table 13–2. Notice that quite a few

TABLE 13-2 Additional indirect addressing modes on the 80386 microprocessor

Mode	Example
DS:[EAX]	ADD ECX,[EAX]
DS:[EBX]	SUB DATA,[EBX]
DS:[ECX]	MOV AL,[EAX]
DS:[EDX]	MOV AX,[EDX]
DS:d32	MOV AL,DATA (where DATA are a 32-bit offset address)
DS:[ESI]	MOV [ESI],AL
DS:[EDI]	MOV ECX,[EDI]
DS:[EAX + d8]	MOV EBP,[EAX + 4]
DS:[EBX + d8]	MOV [EBX − 3],AL
DS:[ECX + d8]	MOV EAX,[ECX + 80H]
DS:[EDX + d8]	MOV [EDX + 1],SP
SS:[EBP + d8]	MOV [EBP + 1FH],AL
DS:[ESI + d8]	AND AL,[ESI + 3]
DS:[EDI + d8]	OR CL,[EDI + 22]
DS:[EAX + d32]	ADD EBX,[EAX + 1A0000H]
DS:[EBX + d32]	SUB EAX,TABLE[EBX]
DS:[ECX + d32]	MOV DATA[ECX],EAX
DS:[EDX + d32]	MOV EAX,LIST[EDX + 10]
SS:[EBP + d32]	MOV EAX,STACK[EBP]
DS:[ESI + d32]	TEST BYTE PTR [ESI + 2000H],2
DS:[EDI + d32]	MOV EAX,LABELS[EDI]

Notes: d8 = 8-bit signed displacement and d32 = 32-bit displacement.

additional addressing modes have been added to the instruction set in comparison to the modes covered earlier in the text. Notice also that the restriction of using only SI, DI, BX, or BP has disappeared form the 80386 instruction set if 32-bit index registers are employed. If machine language programming is attempted for this microprocessor, these additional addressing modes require a prefix to indicate that this form of addressing is used with the opcode. The prefixes are added automatically by the assembler, as indicated in Example 13-1, if 16-bit segment offset addresses are used. If 32-bit segment addresses are used, no prefix is required.

These new modes of addressing memory data, which function in either the real or the protected mode, allow the software developer a much wider variety of instructions to solve a problem. In addition to the many new addressing modes already presented, there is also a set of scaled addressing modes available for use with the 80386 microprocessor. Scaled addressing modes allow the use of two pointer registers with one containing a scaling factor. The 8086 had a few addressing modes that allowed two pointer registers to be added, for example, [BS + DI]. The same is true for the 80386 except the second register or pointer can be scaled by a factor of ×1, ×2, ×4, or ×8. The scaled index register can be EAX, EBX, ECX, EDX, EBP, EDI, or ESI. The scale factor is indicated as in the following examples: 2*EAX (a scaling factor of 2), 4*ECX (a scaling factor of 4), and 8*EDI (a scaling factor of 8). Table 13–3 illustrates all of the forms of the scaled index instructions. Keep in mind that the (scaled index) listed in this table can be the registers previously listed scaled by factors of ×1, ×2, ×4, or ×8. As you can see by the examples listed in this table, it is often difficult to locate a need for such involved addressing modes. If the need arises, the addressing modes are certainly in place in this microprocessor. A *scaled index register* is a register whose contents are multiplied by a scaling factor. Note that the scaling factor is used to determine the address, but it doesn't change the contents of the index register when it is used in an instruction. For example,

TABLE 13–3   Scaled index instructions

Mode	Example
DS:[EAX + (scaled index)]	MOV ECX,[EAX + 2*EBX]
DS:[EBX + (scaled index)]	ADD AL,[EBX + EAX] (Note scale = 1)
DS:[ECX + (scaled index)]	INC BYTE PTR [ECX + 1*EAX]
DS:[EDX + (scaled index)]	MOV [EDX + 8*EAX],SP
SS:[ESP + (scaled index)]	MOV [ESP + 4*EAX],SP
DS:[d32 + (scaled index)]	ADD AL,[DATA + 2*ECX]
DS:[ESI + (scaled index)]	MOV BL,[ESI + EAX]
DS:[EDI + (scaled index)]	MOV [EDI + 8*EAX]DL
DS:[EAX + (scaled index) + d8]	MOV ECX,[EAX + 2*EBX + 16]
DS:[EBX + (scaled index) + d8]	ADD AL,[EBX + EAX − 20H]
DS:[ECX + (scaled index) + d8]	INC BYTE PTR [ECX + 1*EAX + 2]
DS:[EDX + (scaled index) + d8]	MOV [EDX + 8*EAX + 1],SP
SS:[ESP + (scaled index) + d8]	MOV [ESP + 4*EAX + OAH],SP
SS:[EBP + (scaled index) + d8]	ADD AL,[EBP + 2*ECX − 33]
DS:[ESI + (scaled index) + d8]	MOV BL,[ESI + EAX + 100]
DS:[EDI + (scaled index) + d8]	MOV [EDI + 8*EAX − 2],DL
DS:[EAX + (scaled index) + d32]	MOV ECX,[EAX + 2*EBX + 1000AH]
DS:[EBX + (scaled index) + d32]	ADD AL,DATA[EBX + EAX]
DS:[ECX + (scaled index) + d32]	INC BYTE PTR ARRAY[ECX + 1*EAX]
DS:[EDX + (scaled index) + d32]	MOV NUMBER[EDX + 8*EAX],SP
SS:[ESP + (scaled index) + d32]	MOV [ESP + 4*EAX + 0AFFFFH],SP
SS:[EBP + (scaled index) + d32]	ADD AL,DATA[EBP + 2*ECX]
DS:[ESI + (scaled index) + d32]	MOV BL,LIST[ESI + EAX]
DS:[EDI + (scaled index) + d32]	MOV [EDI + 8*EAX − 2000],DL

Note: d8 = 8-bit signed displacement, d32 = 32-bit displacement, and scaled index = EAX, EBX, ECX, EDX, EBP, ESI, or EDI with a scale factor of ×1, ×2, ×4, or ×8.

if EBX = 00000100H and ECX = 00000200H and the MOV AL,[ECX+4*EBX] instruction is executed, the 80386 will access memory address 200H + 400H or 600H. If you are operating in the real mode, this will actually address data at offset location 600H in the data segment. If in the real mode, you are limited to operating with data that are in a 64K-byte segment and within address range 00000000H–000FFFFFH. If in the protected mode, then the instruction can access data at any location within the data selector as described by the descriptor. Scaling is used to access data within an array without requiring additional memory to store a small offset such as 2, 4, or 8.

Interrupts

Figure 13–10 illustrates the predefined interrupts for the 80386. Notice that these are the same as those described for the 80286 listed in Chapter 12 except for interrupt type number E, which is not found in the 80286. Please refer to the following Table (Table 13–4) and its description of all of the predefined interrupt types for the 80386 micropro-

Function	Interrupt Number	Instruction Which Can Cause Exception	Return Address Points to Faulting Instruction	Type
Divide Error	0	DIV, IDIV	YES	FAULT
Debug Exception	1	any instruction	YES	TRAP*
NMI Interrupt	2	INT 2 or NMI	NO	NMI
One Byte Interrupt	3	INT	NO	TRAP
Interrupt on Overflow	4	INTO	NO	TRAP
Array Bounds Check	5	BOUND	YES	FAULT
Invalid OP-Code	6	Any Illegal Instruction	YES	FAULT
Device Not Available	7	ESC, WAIT	YES	FAULT
Double Fault	8	Any Instruction That Can Generate an Exception		ABORT
Coprocessor Segment Overrun	9	ESC	NO	ABORT
Invalid TSS	10	JMP, CALL, IRET, INT	YES	FAULT
Segment Not Present	11	Segment Register Instructions	YES	FAULT
Stack Fault	12	Stack References	YES	FAULT
General Protection Fault	13	Any Memory Reference	YES	FAULT
Page Fault	14	Any Memory Access or Code Fetch	YES	FAULT
Coprocessor Error	16	ESC, WAIT	YES	FAULT
Intel Reserved	17–32			
Two Byte Interrupt	0–255	INT n	NO	TRAP

* Some debug exceptions may report both traps on the previous instruction, and faults on the next instruction.

FIGURE 13–10 The predefined interrupt vectors for the 80386 microprocessor. (Courtesy of Intel Corporation)

TABLE 13–4 The predefined 80386 interrupts (exceptions)

Type	Description
0	Divide error for IDIV and DIV
1	Debug interrupt
2	Nonmaskable interrupt input pin
3	One-byte interrupt
4	Interrupt on overflow (INTO)
5	BOUND instruction exception
6	Illegal instruction exception
7	ESCape or WAIT for coprocessor emulation (see CR0)
8	Double fault
9	Coprocessor segment overrun
A	Invalid TSS
B	Segment not present
C	Stack fault
D	General protection fault
E	Page mechanism fault
F	Not defined
10	Coprocessor error
11–1F	Reserved by Intel for future products

cessor. Note that *interrupts* are generated by the hardware through the INTR and NMI connections and *exceptions* are generated by internal events.

The predefined exceptions above type number 5 have the following functions.

Type 6 —This exception occurs whenever an illegal instruction that is not defined in the instruction set is executed.

Type 7 —If the EM bit of CR0 is set, the type 7 interrupt will occur for any coprocessor ESCape instruction. If the MP bit of CR0 is set and TS is set by a task switch, the WAIT instruction will also cause a type 7 interrupt.

Type 8 —A double fault occurs whenever the 80386 detects a type 10, 11, 12, or 13 interrupt at the same time that an interrupt other than a type 14 is detected.

Type 9 —This exception occurs if the operand address wraps around from location FFFFH to 0000H in the virtual 8086 mode or the real mode or if the operand address wraps around from FFFFFFFFH to 00000000H in the protected mode.

Type A—If an invalid TSS is accessed, the type A exception will occur. An invalid TSS occurs whenever the selector is outside of the table limit, if a code or stack segment is outside of the table limit, if a stack is not writable, or if the requested privilege level is not equal to the current privilege level of the accessed TSS.

Type B—The segment not present exception occurs if the P bit of the descriptor indicates that the segment is not present.

Type C—The stack fault exception occurs if the SS descriptor addresses a segment that is not present or if any stack operation causes a limit violation.

Type D—This exception occurs for the following reasons: exceeding segment limit, writing to a read-only data segment or code segment, loading a selector with a system descriptor, reading an execute-only code segment, switching to a busy task, violating privilege level for a data segment, and loading CR0 with PG = 1 and PE = 0.

Type E—The page fault exception occurs if PG = 1 and the privilege level is incorrect or the page table or directory contains a zero.

Type 10—If the ERROR pin on the 80387 indicates an error, the 80386 issues the type-10H exception.

As far as hardware interrupt circuitry is concerned it remains the same for the 80386 as for the 8086 microprocessor. You might wish to refer to the chapter on Interrupts at this point to review interrupt hardware. The hardware interrupt inputs pins on the 80386 are INTR and NMI as they are on the 8086.

When the 80386 is operated in the protected mode, the interrupt vectors are fetched from the memory defined by the IDT. For example, if interrupt type number 3 occurs in the protected mode, the 80386 will reference the interrupt descriptor table for the descriptor that applies to this interrupt (entry 3). This descriptor is fetched and the task accessed by the interrupt descriptor is executed. This is similar to the vector table found in the 8086, but different because the interrupt descriptor table can be located anywhere in the memory system. More detail on protected mode interrupts is provided in the next section of this chapter.

13-2   80386 MEMORY MANAGEMENT

The memory-management unit (MMU) located within the 80386 is similar to the MMU inside the 80286, except one additional major component (a paging unit) is added to the 80386. The *task* performed by the MMU is to convert logical memory addresses into linear addresses and ultimately physical addresses. The 80386 can use memory paging to allocate its physical memory to any logical memory address. What this means is that even though the program may address memory location A0000H, the actual physical memory can be at location 100000H, or any other memory location, as relocated by the paging unit. This allows a great deal of flexibility in software design that was not allowed with the 80286.

Descriptors and Selectors

Before the paging unit can be discussed, the descriptor and selector is discussed for the 80386. The 80386 uses descriptors and selectors in much the same fashion as did the 80286. A *descriptor* is a series of 8 bytes that are employed to locate and indicate the length of and also the access rights of a segment of the memory. A *selector* is used to index a descriptor from a table of descriptors. The main difference between the 80286 and 80386 is that there are two additional selectors (FS and GS). The descriptors also use a 32-bit base address and a 20-bit limit. This allows the 80386 descriptor to address any physical memory location within the 4G bytes of the memory, with each segment having a limit of 1M byte if the granularity (G) bit = 0. If the G bit = 1, then the limit of the segment is 4G bytes. The granularity bit allows the software to select a multiplier of 1 (G = 0) or a multiplier of 4K (G = 1) for the limit. The granularity bit is found in the descriptor. The 80286 allowed a segment to be located at any location within its 16M bytes with a limit of 64K bytes per segment. This increase in size (1M or 4G bytes) on the 80386 actually allows the entire DOS environment to be placed in one protected mode segment in the 80386 system. This allows multitasking of DOS environments by merely switching from one segment to another with a task switch. Each task segment can be running a different application. Time-sharing can be accomplished by timing the task switches between segment tasks so that it appears that the microprocessor is simultaneously executing more than one task at a time. This is often called *time-slicing*.

Figure 13–11 illustrates the way that a segment is addressed in the protected mode, using a selector and a descriptor. Notice that this is very similar to the way that the 80286 addressed a segment. In fact, the only difference is the size of the memory and the size of the segment. The selector uses its leftmost 13 bits to choose a descriptor from either the GDT or the LDT. The TI bit indicates which descriptor table to use for the reference, and the rightmost two bits indicate the desired privilege level of the reference. If TI is a logic 1, the local descriptor table is selected, and if TI is a logic 0, the global descriptor table is selected. Since the selector is a 13-bit code, there can be up to 8,192 different local and 8,192 different global segments accessed through these two tables. Since each segment can be up to 4G bytes in length, this means that the GDT can access 32T bytes (8K × 4G) of memory and the LDT can access another 32T bytes for a total of 64T bytes of *virtual* memory. Of course only 4G bytes of memory can actually exist in the memory system. (Note that *1T byte* of memory is 1,024 G bytes.)

As with the 80286, the 80386 uses a table for both global (GDT) and local (LDT) descriptors. It also uses a table for interrupt descriptors (IDT). The descriptors themselves, as mentioned earlier, are different because the base address for an 80386 descriptor is 32 bits rather than 24 bits. The limit is also changed from 16 bits to 20 bits for a segment limit of 1M byte or 4G bytes (as selected by G) instead of 64K bytes.

Figure 13–12 illustrates the general descriptor format for the 80386 microprocessor. The fields found in the descriptor are as follows.

FIGURE 13–11 Protected mode addressing using a segment register as a selector. (Courtesy of Intel Corporation)

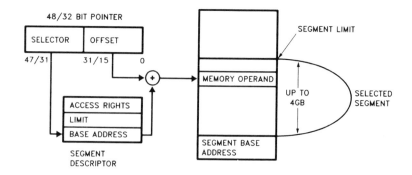

FIGURE 13-12 The basic format for a descriptor in the 80386 microprocessor. The access rights byte is used to further define the descriptor.

Base (B24-B31)	G	D	O	A V L	Limit (L16-L23)	Access Rights	Base (B16-B23)	4
Segment Base (B0-B15)						Segment Limit (L0-L15)		0

Base—Defines the starting 32-bit address of the segment within the 4G-byte physical address space of the 80386 microprocessor.

Limit—Defines the length of the segment in units of bytes if the G bit $= 0$, or in units of 4K bytes if the G bit $= 1$. This allows a segment to be of any length from 1 byte to 1M byte if G $= 0$ and from 4K bytes to 4G bytes if G $= 1$.

Descriptor privilege level (DPL)—These bits are used to set the privilege level of the descriptor.

Granularity bit (G)—Determines whether the limit is in units (G $= 0$) or in 4K-byte pages (G $= 1$).

Segment bit (S)—The segment bit specifies whether the descriptor defines a system segment or gate descriptor (S $= 0$) or a data or code segment (S $= 1$).

Type—The type field specifies the type of descriptor. Refer to the illustration for the different types of descriptors allowed by the 80386 microprocessor.

Segment present bit (P)—If P $= 0$, the segment is mapped into the physical address space, and if P $= 1$, no mapping to physical memory exists and base and limit are not used for the descriptor. This is used in some operating systems to swap segments from physical memory to disk memory so that 64T bytes of memory can actually be used by a program.

Accessed bit (A)—This bit is set to a logic 1 whenever the descriptor and the segment it describes are accessed. This bit is used to test descriptors for activity in some operating systems.

Default size (D)—Indicates the default size of a code segment. If D $= 0$, the code segment default width is 16 bits, and if D $= 1$, the default size is 32 bits. This is used to differentiate between 80286 and 80386 descriptors. This bit determines whether prefixes are required for 32-bit registers and index registers.

Available field (AVL)—This field is available for the operating system or the user.

Descriptors appears in two basic forms in the 80386 microprocessor: (1) the segment descriptor and (2) the system descriptor. The segment descriptor is used to define data and code segments; the system descriptor is used to define information about the system's tables, tasks, and gates.

Segment Descriptors. Figure 13-13 illustrates the segment descriptor. Notice that this descriptor fits the general form of Figure 13-12, but additional bits are defined that indicate how the code or data segment is treated. Notice that bit position 4 of the access rights byte is a logic 1 defining the descriptor as a code or data segment descriptor. A zero defines it as a system descriptor. Bit position 3 is labeled E (executable), which defines the segment as either executable (code) if E $= 1$ or as a data segment if E $= 0$. Bit

FIGURE 13–13 The segment descriptor that is used to define a segment in the 80386.

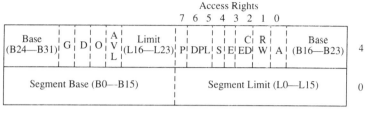

Name	Function
P = Present	P = 1 Segment present
DPL	Descriptor privilege level
S = Segment	S = 0 Code or data segment S = 1 System or gate descriptor
E = Executable	E = 0 Data descriptor E = 1 Code descriptor
C = Code Segment	C = 0 priority ignored for code segment C = 1 priority observed for code segment
ED = Direction	ED = 0 Data segment expands upward ED = 1 Data Segment expands downward
W = Write	W = 0 Data segment may not be written W = 1 Data segment may be written
R = Read	R = 0 Code segment may not be read R = 1 Code segment may be read
A = Accessed	A = 0 Segment has not been accessed A = 1 Segment has been accessed

position 2 has two meanings. If E = 0, then bit position 2 indicates whether the segment will grow upward (data) in the memory or downward (stack). If bit position 2 = 0, the segment expands upward as a data segment. If E = 1, then bit position 2 indicates whether the code segment conforms to privilege. If bit position 2 is a 1, then privilege is conformed to and if it is a 0, privilege is ignored. Bit position 1 indicates that the code segment is readable or that the data segment can be written. E = 0 and bit position = 1 allows the data segment to be written and if E = 1 and bit position 1 = 1 then the code segment may be read. You can quite specifically define how the data or code segment is to respond in the protected mode system with the segment descriptor. This includes priority levels and also types of segments.

System Descriptors. The system descriptor is illustrated in Figure 13–14. Notice that there are 16 possible types of system descriptors, not all are in use for the 80386. Some of these types are defined for the 80286 so that 80286 software is compatible with the 80386, and some are new and unique to the 80386, while some are yet undefined and their definition is reserved for future products.

Descriptor Tables. The descriptor tables define all segments that are used in the 80386 when operated in the protected mode. There are three types of descriptor tables: (1) the global descriptor table (GDT), (2) the local descriptor table (LDT), and (3) the interrupt

FIGURE 13–14 80286 and
80386 system segment de-
scriptors.

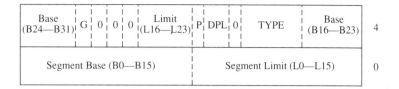

Type	Description
0	Invalid
1	Available 80286 TSS
2	LDT
3	Busy 80286 TSS
4	80286 task gate
5	Task gate
6	80286 interrupt gate
7	80286 trap gate
8	Invalid
9	Available 80386 TSS
A	Undefined
B	Busy 80386 TSS
C	80386 call gate
D	Undefined
E	80386 interrupt gate
F	80386 trap gate

descriptor table (IDT). The registers used by the 80386 to address these three tables are called the global descriptor table register (GDTR), the local descriptor table register (LDTR), and the interrupt descriptor table register (IDTR). These registers are loaded, respectively, with the LGDT, LLDT, and LIDT instructions.

The *descriptor table* is a variable-length array of data with each entry containing 8 bytes of information in the form of a descriptor. Each table holds up to 8,192 different descriptors as addressed by the selector. The selector is located in a segment register and has the form illustrated in Figure 13–15. Notice that 13 of the 16 bits are used to select or address a descriptor. The TI bit is used to single out the local or the global descriptor table. The rightmost two bits are used to indicate the requested privilege level.

Whenever a new descriptor is placed into one of the segment (selector) registers, the 80386 will access one of the descriptor tables and automatically load the addressed descriptor into a 64-bit invisible cache portion, as illustrated earlier in the register model of the 80386. As long as the selector remains the same, no additional accesses are required to the descriptor table. The operation of the selector and the descriptor that it fetches from the descriptor table is invisible to the program that is being executed because the descrip-

FIGURE 13–15 The segment register that contains a selector, TI bit, and requested privilege level (RPL). The TI bit is a logic 1. It selects the local descriptor table and logic 0 selects the global descriptor table.

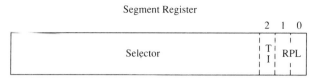

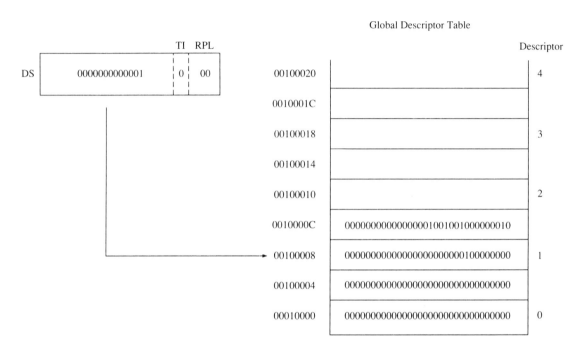

FIGURE 13–16 The data segment used to hold a selector that addresses global descriptor entry 1.

tor is accessed automatically without program intervention once the descriptor table registers are loaded.

Figure 13–16 illustrates a sample global descriptor table (GDT) that is stored at linear memory address 00010000H, which is just above the 1M-byte boundary. This table contains four descriptors, with the first containing a null (0) descriptor because descriptor zero may not be used. Notice that the selector indicated (DS) contains a 0008H, which means that the privilege level request is a 00, the TI bit = 0, meaning that the GDT table is selected, and the actual descriptor number selected is 1. Descriptor 1 is located 8 bytes above the base address of the descriptor table (00010008H) and contains a descriptor with a base address of 00020000H and a limit of 100H bytes. This means that the actual location of this data segment (DS) is at location 00020000H and it occupies memory locations 00020000H–00200FFH.

The local descriptor table (LDT) is accessed in the same manner as the GDT except that the base address of the LDT is not loaded into the local descriptor table register (LDTR) as it is for the GDTR. Instead the LDTR contains a selector number just like the data segment register did in the prior example. The only difference is that the local descriptor table base address is stored in the GDT instead of in the LDTR.

The interrupt descriptor table (IDT) is addressed as is the GDT by storing the base address and limit in its interrupt descriptor table register (IDTR). The main difference between the IDT and the GDT and LDT is that the IDT contains interrupt gates rather than segment descriptors as do the GDT and LDTs. Figure 13–17 illustrates the gate descriptor. Notice that the gate descriptor is different from the segment descriptors discussed previously. The gate descriptor contains a 32-bit offset address, a word count, and a selector. The 32-bit address points to the location of the interrupt service subroutine. The word count indicates how many words are to be transferred from the caller's stack to the stack of the called subroutine. This field is not used for an interrupt gate, only for a call gate. Finally, the selector indicates the location of the task state segment (TSS) in the GDT. The contents of the selector are loaded into the task register (TR) when the interrupt is accepted by the 80386. This acceptance depends on privilege and priority levels. In order to return from the interrupt service procedure, the procedure ends with an IRET instruction just as it did in the 8086 microprocessor. The only difference is that in protected mode the interrupt vector table, as we knew it, now becomes the IDT. The IDT has up to 256, 8-byte descriptors, each corresponding to an interrupt type number. This means that interrupt type number 2 would be located at IDT gate descriptor number 2 at 16 locations above the start of the IDT.

The Task State Segment. The task state segment (TSS) descriptor contains information about the location, size, and privilege level of the task state segment, just as any segment descriptor contains the same information. The difference is that the task state segment does not contain code or data. It contains the state of the task and linkage so that tasks can be nested. The TSS descriptor is addressed by the TR selector. The contents of the TR selector are changed by the LTR instruction or whenever a far CALL or far JMP instruction is executed in the protected mode. The LTR instruction is only used during system initialization. After initialization, the far CALL or far JMP is used to switch tasks. The actual TSS is illustrated in Figure 13–18. As can be seen from this illustration the TSS

FIGURE 13–17 The format for a gate descriptor.

Selector	Offset (D0—D15)						4
Offset (D16—D31)	P	DPL	0	TYPE	0 0 0	Word Count (B0—B4)	0

Type	Function
4	80286 Call gate
5	Task gate
6	80286 Interrupt gate
7	80286 Trap gate
C	80386 Call gate
E	80386 Interrupt gate
F	80386 Trap gate

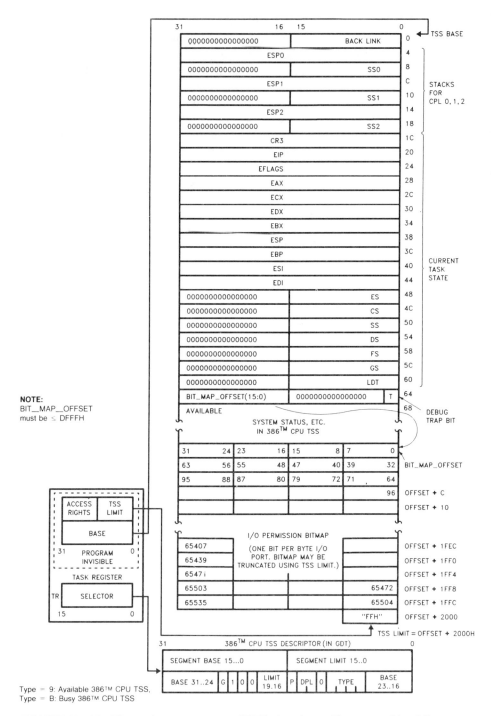

FIGURE 13–18   The task state segment (TSS) descriptor. (Courtesy of Intel Corporation)

is quite a formidable segment containing many pieces of of information. The first word in the TSS is labeled back-link. This is the selector that is used, on a return, to link back to the prior TSS by loading the back-link selector into the TR register. The following word contains a 0. The second through the seventh doublewords contain the ESP and ESS values for privilege levels 0–2. These are required in case that the current task is interrupted so that these privilege level (PL) stacks can be addressed. The eighth word contains the contents of control register 3 (CR3). CR3 contains the prior states page directory base register that must be restored upon return if paging is in use. The contents of the next 17 doublewords are loaded into the registers indicated. When a return is made the contents of all of these registers are stored in these same 17 words so that they can again be made available if the task is again called. The last word contains the I/O permission bit map base address.

The I/O permission bit map allows the TSS to block I/O operations to inhibited I/I port addresses via an I/O bit permission denial interrupt. This permission denial interrupt is type 13, the general protection fault interrupt. The I/O permission bit map base addresses contain an offset from the start of the TSS that locates the I/O permission bit map. The I/O permission bit map begins at the bit of memory addressed by this offset. The bit map continues for 64K bits. This amounts to 8,192 bytes of memory. The very first byte, the rightmost bit, contains the I/O permission bit for I/O port 0000H. The next bit in that very first byte contains the I/O permission bit for I/O port 0001H. This sequence continues through the very last byte and its leftmost bit for I/O port number FFFFH. The byte beyond the end of the I/O bit map must be an FFH or the scheme will not function properly. If a logic 0 is placed in the I/O bit, the I/O operation to the specified port will be allowed. If the I/O bit is a logic 1, the I/O operation is prevented and a type-13 interrupt occurs.

In review of the operation of a task switch: (1) the gate contains the address of the subroutine or the location jumped to by the task switch, it also contains the selector number of the TSS descriptor, and also the number of words to be transferred from the stack of the caller to the stack of the destination for parameter passing; (2) the selector is loaded into the TR register from the gate; (3) the TR register selects the TSS; and (4) the state of the current task is stored in its TSS and the new TSS is accessed with the state of the new task loaded to all of the internal registers. On a return from a task: (1) the current state is saved in the TSS, and (2) the back-link word is loaded into the TR selector so a return can be made to the prior task through the prior TSS. This entire process requires only 17 μs in the 80386 microprocessor.

Moving to Protected Mode from Real Mode

In order to change operation of the 80386 from the real mode, which is where a hardware reset places the 80386 after a reset, to the protected mode, the following steps must be followed.

1. Initialize the interrupt descriptor table so that it refers to valid interrupt descriptors with at least 32 descriptors and up to 256 descriptors in the IDT.
2. Initialize the global descriptor table so that it contains valid descriptors for the initial code and data segments.
3. Switch to protected mode by setting the PE bit in CR0.
4. Perform an intersegment (near) jump to flush the internal instruction queue.

FIGURE 13–19 The memory map for Example 13–2.

5. Load all the data selectors (segment registers) with their initial selector values.
6. The 80386 is now operating in the protected mode using the segment descriptors that are defined in the GDT and IDT.

Figure 13–19 illustrates the protected system that is set up using steps 1–5 and the software listed in Example 13–2. Here the system is set up so that there is one data segment and one code segment with each segment 4G bytes in length. This is the simplest protected mode system possible. This protected system is initialized in protected privilege level 0, the highest. This type of system is used where only one user exists that has access to all hardware and software in the system.

EXAMPLE 13–2

```
        .386P
                        ;This software causes the 80386 to enter the
                        ;protected mode of operation.  It does not
                        ;illustrate or load the interrupt descriptors or
                        ;any software that will be executed by the
                        ;system.
0000            DATA    SEGMENT    AT  0        ;segment at0000H
0000                    ORG   0     ;first 32 interrupt descriptors

                        ;interrupt vectors not shown in this example
```

```
0100                                        ORG    100H                    ;offset at 100H

                                ;
                                ;The Global Descriptor Table
                                ;
0100  0000000000000000  ENTRY0  DQ     0                       ;null descriptor
                                ;
                                ;Code segment descriptor
                                ;
0108  FFFF              ENTRY1  DW     0FFFFH                  ;limit 4G
010A  0000                      DW     0            ;base address = 00000000H
010C  00                        DB     0
010D  9E                        DB     9EH                     ;code segment
010E  8F                        DB     8FH                     ;G = 1 (4K page)
010F  00                        DB     0
                                ;
                                ;Data segment descriptor
                                ;
0110  FFFF               ENTRY2 DW     0FFFFH                  ;limit 4G
0112  0000                      DW     0            ;base address = 00000000H
0114  00                        DB     0
0115  92                        DB     92H                     ;data segment
0116  8F                        DB     8FH                     ;G = 1 (4K page)
0117  00                        DB     0

0118  00FF      IDT_TABLE       DW     0FFH         ;set limit to FFH
011A  00000000                  DD     0            ;base set to 00000000H

011E  0017      GDT_TABLE       DW     17H          ;set limit to 17H
0120  00000100                  DD     100H         ;base set to 00000100H

0124                    DATA    ENDS

0000                    CODE    SEGMENT      USE16

                        ASSUME CS:CODE,DS:DATA

0000  B8 ---- R         START: MOV     AX,DATA                 ;load DS
0003  8E D8                    MOV     DS,AX

0005  67¦ 0F 01 1D 00000118 R  LIDT    FWORD PTR IDT_TABLE ;address IDT

000D  67¦ 0F 01 15 0000011E R  LGDT    FWORD PTR GDT_TABLE ;address GDT

0015  0F 20 C0                 MOV     EAX,CR0                 ;get CR0
0018  0C 01                    OR      AL,1                    ;set PE bit
001A  0F 22 C0                 MOV     CR0,EAX     ;set protected mode

001D  EB 01 90                 JMP     START1                  ;clear pipeline

0020  B8 0010          START1:MOV      AX,10H                  ;selector 2
0023  8E D8                    MOV     DS,AX                   ;load selectors
0025  8E C0                    MOV     ES,AX
0027  8E D0                    MOV     SS,AX
0029  8E E8                    MOV     GS,AX
002B  8E E0                    MOV     FS,AX
```

```
                    ;at this point we are now in the protected mode.

002D                        CODE      ENDS
                                      END
```

In more complex systems, the steps required to initialize the system in protected mode is more involved. For complex systems that are often multiuser systems, the registers are all loaded using the TSS. The steps required to place the 80386 in the protected mode for a more complex system that will use privilege levels follow.

1. Initialize the interrupt descriptor table so that it refers to valid interrupt descriptors with at least 32 descriptors in the IDT.
2. Initialize the global descriptor table so that it contains at least two task state segment (TSS) descriptors and the initial code and data segments required for the initial task.
3. Initialize task register (TR) so that it points to a valid TSS because when the task switch occurs and accesses a new TSS, the current registers will be stored in the initial TSS.
4. Switch to protected mode using an intersegment (near) jump to the TSS, which causes a task switch loading the registers from the TSS.
5. The 80386 is now operating in the protected mode.

Example 13–3 illustrates the software required to initialize the system and switch to the system task. It does not illustrate the system task. This initial system task is the highest priority kernel that controls the entire operating system. In many cases it is used to boot (load) software that will allow many users to access the system.

EXAMPLE 13–3

```
                             .MODEL SMALL
                             .386P

    ;This software is used to switch to protected mode operation.   It
    ;does this by switching to a new task from the intial task after
    ;the system is first powered.   This technique is normally found
    ;in more complicated ;systems that are often multi-user.   A
    ;return to real-mode is handled by ;jumping to TASK1 at program
    ;location RESUME from the protected mode as illustrated.

    ;Structures are set up so that descriptors and the TSS segments
    ;can easily be created.

    ;All descriptors

                       DESCRIPTOR   STRUC

0000  0000            LIMIT        DW     0        ;limit
0002  0000            BASE_L       DW     0        ;low 16-bits of base
0004  00              BASE_M       DB     0        ;base bits 16--23
0005  00              ACCESS       DB     0        ;access byte
```

```
0006    00                      GRAN            DB      0                       ;granularity and limit
0007    00                      BASE_H                  DB      0               ;base bits 24--31

0008                            DESCRIPTOR      ENDS

                                ;All task state segments (TSS)

                                TSS             STRUC

0000    0000                    BACK            DW      0                       ;back link
0002    0000                                    DW      0                       ;reserved
0004    00000000                ESP0            DD      0                       ;SP for level 0
0008    0000                    SS0             DW      0                       ;SS for level 0
000A    0000                                    DW      0
000C    00000000                ESP1            DD      0                       ;SP for level 1
0010    0000                    SS1             DW      0                       ;SS for level 1
0012    0000                                    DW      0
0014    00000000                ESP2            DD      0                       ;SP for level 2
0018    0000                    SS2             DW      0                       ;SS for level 2
001A    0000                                    DW      0
001C    00000000                T_CR3           DD      0                       ;CR3
0020    00000000                T_EIP           DD      0                       ;EIP
0024    00020000                T_EFLAGS                DD      20000H          ;EFLAGS
0028    00000000                T_EAX           DD      0                       ;EAX
002C    00000000                T_ECX           DD      0                       ;ECX
0030    00000000                T_EDX           DD      0                       ;EDX
0034    00000000                T_EBX           DD      0                       ;EBX
0038    00000000                T_ESP           DD      0                       ;ESP
003C    00000000                T_EBP           DD      0                       ;EBP
0040    00000000                T_ESI           DD      0                       ;ESI
0044    00000000                T_EDI           DD      0                       ;EDI
0048    0000                    T_ES            DW      0                       ;ES
004A    0000                                    DW      0
004C    0000                    T_CS            DW      0                       ;CS
004E    0000                                    DW      0
0050    0000                    T_SS            DW      0                       ;SS
0052    0000                                    DW      0
0054    0000                    T_DS            DW      0                       ;DS
0056    0000                                    DW      0
0058    0000                    T_FS            DW      0                       ;FS
005A    0000                                    DW      0
005C    0000                    T_GS            DW      0                       ;GS
005E    0000                                    DW      0
0060    0000                    T_LDT           DW      0                       ;LDT
0062    0000                                    DW      0
0064    0000                                    DW      0
0066    0068                    IOMAP           DW      104

0068                            TSS             ENDS

                                ;MACRO definitions

                                ;MACRO GET_LIN is used to convert the segment address in SREG
                                ;to a 32-bit linear address in EAX.
```

```
        GET_LIN                 MACRO    SREG

               XOR      EAX,EAX  ;clear EAX
               MOV      AX,&SREG ;get segment register
               SHL      EAX,4    ;convert to linear address
               ENDM
```

;MACRO SEG_ADR is used to convert the segment address in REG
;to a 32-bit linear address stored in the base address portion
;of a descriptor in DESC.

```
        SEG_ADR         MACRO    REG,DESC

               GET_LIN &REG
               MOV      DESC&.BASE_L,AX    ;save low address
               SHR      EAX,8
               MOV      DESC&.BASE_M,AH    ;save mid address
               ENDM
```

;MACRO TSS_ADR is used to place the address of the TSS into
;the TSS descriptor. Where TSS is the selected TSS and SEG
;the task descriptor. This macro assumes that the linear
;address is already in EAX.

```
         TSS_ADR                 MACRO    TSS,SEG

                LEA      EBX,&TSS         ;get TSS displacement
                ADD      EBX,EAX          ;get linear address
                MOV      SEG&.BASE_L,BX   ;set low address
                SHR      EBX,8
                MOV      SEG&.BASE_M,BH   ;set mid address
                ENDM
```

;System code segment begins at this point.

```
                .CODE
                ASSUME   SS:_TEXT,DS:_TEXT,ES:_TEXT

                .SALL                     ;don't expand macros
```

```
0000  1000[          DW       1000H DUP (?)  ;stack area
      ????
           ]
```

;Global Descriptor Table

```
2000  0000      GDT_TABLE    DESCRIPTOR <0,0,0,0,0,0>  ;null descriptor
2002  0000
2004  00
2005  00
2006  00
2007  00
```

```
2008  FFFF          CODE_SEG     DESCRIPTOR <0FFFFH,0,0,9AH,0FH,0>  ;4G code
```

```
200A  0000
200C  00
200D  9A
200E  0F
200F  00


2010  FFFF          DATA_SEG    DESCRIPTOR <0FFFFH,0,0,92H,0FH,0> ;4G data
2012  0000
2014  00
2015  92
2016  0F
2017  00


2018  0000          STACK_SEG   DESCRIPTOR <0,0,0,96H,0,0>          ;stack
201A  0000
201C  00
201D  96
201E  00
201F  00


2020  0700          LOCAL1      DESCRIPTOR <7,0,0,0E2H,0,0>
2022  0000
2024  00
2025  E2
2026  00
2027  00


2028  0700          LOCAL2      DESCRIPTOR <7,0,0,082H,0,0>
202A  0000
202C  00
202D  82
202E  00
202F  00


2030  6820          TASK1_D     DESCRIPTOR <2068H,0,0,0EBH,0,0> ;task gate
2032  0000
2034  00
2035  EB
2036  00
2037  00

                    ;Interrupt Descriptor Table (This must be filled with the
                    ;locations of the interrupt service procedures.  Filling is
                    ;not illustrated in this example because the interrupts vary
                    ;from one system to another.  Software is normally to fill
                    ;each interrupt gate.

= 2038              IDT_TABLE   EQU     $

                                REPT    256
```

```
                            DESCRIPTOR <0,8,0,8EH,0,0>

                            ENDM

            ;Setup two TSS segments

2838   0000        TASK1       TSS     <>
283A   0000
283C   00000000
2840   0000
2842   0000
2844   00000000
2848   0000
284A   0000
284C   00000000
2850   0000
2852   0000
2854   00000000
2858   00000000
285C   00000200
2860   00000000
2864   00000000
2868   00000000
286C   00000000
2870   00000000
2874   00000000
2878   00000000
287C   00000000
2880   0000
2882   0000
2884   0000
2886   0000
2888   0000
288A   0000
288C   0000
288E   0000
2890   0000
2892   0000
2894   0000
2896   0000
2898   0000
289A   0000
289C   0000
289E   6800


28A0   1000[                   DW      4096 DUP (0)   ;I/O bit map
          0000
              ]

48A0   FFFF                    DW      -1

48A2   0000        TEMP2       DW      ?              ;temporary storage
48A4   00000000    TEMP1       DD      ?
```

```
                        ;;;;;;;;;;;;;;;;;;;;;;;;;;;;;;;;;;;;;;;;;;;;;;;;;;.
                        ;;;;;Start system here in the real mode;;;;;
                        ;;;;;;;;;;;;;;;;;;;;;;;;;;;;;;;;;;;;;;;;;;;;;;;;;;

48A8                    start:
48A8   8C C8                    MOV      AX,CS ;load segment registers
48AA   8E D8                    MOV      DS,AX
48AC   8E C0                    MOV      ES,AX
48AE   8E D0                    MOV      SS,AX
48B0   BC 2000                  MOV      SP,2000H
48B3   FC                       CLD
48B4   FA                       CLI

                   ;Setup descriptor base addresses using the SEG_ADR macro

                            SEG_ADR   DS,DATA_SEG ;setup data descriptor
                            SEG_ADR   CS,CODE_SEG ;setup code descriptor
                            SEG_ADR   SS,STACK_SEG ;setup stack

                   ;Setup TASK1 to duplicate the current real mode.

48F1   8C D8                    MOV      AX,DS           ;save segments
48F3   A3 288C R                MOV      TASK1.T_DS,AX
48F6   A3 2880 R                MOV      TASK1.T_ES,AX
48F9   A3 2890 R                MOV      TASK1.T_FS,AX
48FC   A3 2894 R                MOV      TASK1.T_GS,AX
48FF   8C D0                    MOV      AX,SS
4901   A3 2888 R                MOV      TASK1.T_SS,AX
4904   8C C8                    MOV      AX,CS
4906   A3 2884 R                MOV      TASK1.T_CS,AX

4909   C7 06 2840 R 0018        MOV      TASK1.SS0,24        ;stack selector

490F   66¦ Ç7 06 283C R 00001800 MOV TASK1.ESP0,1800H        ;stack pointer

4918   66¦ 33 C0                XOR      EAX,EAX
491B   B8 49C2 R                MOV      AX,OFFSET RESUME  ;get resume address
491E   66¦ A3 2858 R            MOV      TASK1.T_EIP,EAX

4922   8B C4                    MOV      AX,SP
4924   66¦ A3 2870 R            MOV      TASK1.T_ESP,EAX

4928   66¦ C7 06 285C R 00023202 MOV    TASK1.T_EFLAGS,23202H ;set eflags
4931   C7 06 289E R 0068        MOV      TASK1.IOMAP,68H

4937   C7 06 2898 R 0023        MOV      TASK1.T_LDT,35     ;select LOCAL

                   ;Setup TSS descriptor, GDTR and IDTR

                            GET_LIN DS    ;get DS linear address

                            TSS_ADR TASK1,TASK1_D       ;load TASK1

495A   66¦ 8D 1E 2000 R         LEA      EBX,GDT_TABLE       ;get GDT_TABLE
495F   66¦ 03 D8                ADD      EBX,EAX
```

```
4962   66¦ 89 1E 48A4 R            MOV      TEMP1,EBX
4967   C7 06 48A2 R 0037           MOV      TEMP2,55

496D   0F 01 16 48A2 R             LGDT     FWORD PTR TEMP2

4972   66¦ 8D 1E 2038 R            LEA      EBX,IDT_TABLE      ;get IDT_TABLE
4977   66¦ 03 D8                   ADD      EBX,EAX
497A   66¦ 89 1E 48A4 R            MOV      TEMP1,EBX
497F   C7 06 48A2 R 07FF           MOV      TEMP2,7FFH

4985   0F 01 1E 48A2 R             LIDT     FWORD PTR TEMP2


                       ;Transfer to protected mode.

498A   0F 20 C0                    MOV      EAX,CR0            ;set protected mo
498D   0C 01                       OR       AL,1
498F   0F 22 C0                    MOV      CR0,EAX
4992   EB 01 90                    JMP      FLUSH              ;jump to flush p

4995                      FLUSH:

                       ;System is now running in the protected mode of
                       ;operation.

4995   B8 0028                     MOV      AX,40              ;load LDT
4998   0F 00 D0                    LLDT     AX

                   ;load data descriptors

499B   B8 0010                     MOV      AX,16
499E   8E D8                       MOV      DS,AX
49A0   8E C0                       MOV      ES,AX
49A2   8E E8                       MOV      GS,AX
49A4   8E E0                       MOV      FS,AX

                   ;load stack descriptor

49A6   B8 0018                     MOV      AX,24
49A9   8E D0                       MOV      SS,AX

                   ;load code descriptor

49AB   EA                          DB       0EAH               ;far jump to set CS
49AC   49B0 0008                   DW       NEXT1-_TEXT,8

49B0                      NEXT1:

                   ;at this point we now have a system which is
                   ;operating in the protected mode with descriptors
                   ;that allow 4G bytes of memory in the DATA,
                   ;CODE, and STACK segments.

           ;;;;;;;;;;;;;;;;;;;;;;;;;;;;;;;;;;;;;;;;;;;;;;;;;;;;;;;;;;;;;;
           ;;;;;;Software at this point uses the entire memory;;;;;;
```

```
                          ;;;;;space.  This software is not illustrated here;;;;;
                          ;;;;;;;;;;;;;;;;;;;;;;;;;;;;;;;;;;;;;;;;;;;;;;;;;;;;;;;;;

                          ;Whenever a need arrises to switch back to the real
                          ;mode is required the following sequence of
                          ;instructions is used to effect the switch back to
                          ;the real mode as saved in TASK1 at program address
                          ;RESUME.

49B0  B9 0030                          MOV     CX,48         ;get task descriptor
(TASK1_D)
49B3  0F 00 D9                         LTR     CX            ;load task register
49B6  66| 9C                           PUSHFD
49B8  66| 58                           POP     EAX
49BA  80 CC 40                         OR      AH,40H        ;set nested task
49BD  66| 50                           PUSH    EAX
49BF  66| 9D                           POPFD

                          ;transfer to TASK1 at memory address RESUME.


49C1  CF                               IRET


49C2                         RESUME:


                          ;;;;;;;;;;;;;;;;;;;;;;;;;;;;;;;;;;;;;;;;;;;;;;;;;;;;;;;;;
                          ;;;;;We are now operating in the original real mode;;;;;;
                          ;;;;;No software for this is illustrated;;;;;;;;;;;;;;;;;;
                          ;;;;;;;;;;;;;;;;;;;;;;;;;;;;;;;;;;;;;;;;;;;;;;;;;;;;;;;;;


                                    END     START
```

Virtual 8086 Mode

One special mode of operation not discussed so far is the virtual 8086 mode. This special mode of operation is designed so that multiple 8086 software can be executed at one time. Figure 13–20 illustrates many 8086 software applications mapped into the 80386 using the virtual 8086 mode. If the operating system allows multiple software to function in this way it is usually called *time-slicing*. The operating system allocates a set amount of time to each task. For example, if three tasks are executing, the operating system can allocate 1 ms to each task. This means that after each millisecond a task switch occurs to the next task. These times can typically be adjusted to give any task any percentage of the system operating time.

The main difference between 80386 protected and the virtual 8086 mode is the way that the segment registers are interpreted by the microprocessor. In the virtual 8086 mode the segment registers are used as they are in the 80386 real mode. The 80386 allows any task to be operated in protected mode or in the virtual 8086 real mode. Access to many

FIGURE 13–20 Two tasks resident to an 80386 operated in the virtual 8086 mode.

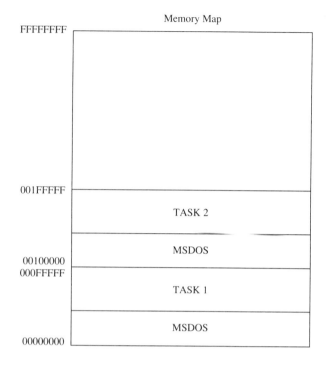

8086 virtual mode systems is made possible by the paging unit. Virtual 8086 mode is entered by changing the VM bit in the EFLAG register to a logic 1. This is only accomplished when a task switch occurs via an IRET instruction if the privilege level is zero. This bit cannot be set in any other manner. Any attempt to access a memory address above the 1M-byte boundary will cause a type-13 (D) interrupt to occur.

The Memory Paging Mechanism

The paging mechanism allows any physical page in the memory system to be placed into any logical page. A *logical memory page* is a page that is addressed with a selector and an offset. A *physical memory page* is a page that exists at some actual physical memory location. Each page in the 80386 paging scheme is 4K bytes in length. Paging allows the system software to be placed at any physical memory location by the paging mechanism. Three components are used in page translation from a logical address to a physical address: (1) the page directory, (2) the page table, and (3) the actual physical memory page.

The Page Directory.   The page directory is stored in the memory and addressed by the page descriptor address register that is actually control register 3 (CR3). CR3 holds the base address of the page directory, which starts on any 4K-byte page boundary in the memory system. CR3 is loaded with a MOV CR3,reg instruction. For example, MOV CR3,EAX would be used to load the page directory base address from EAX into the page directory base address register, CR3. The page directory contains up to 1,024 entries that are each 4 bytes in length. The page directory itself occupies one 4K-byte memory page. Each entry in the page directory (refer to Figure 13–21) contains the 10-bit address of the page

FIGURE 13–21 The page table directory entry.

31		12	11 10 9 8 7 6 5 4 3 2 1 0
	Page Table Address (A31—A12)		Reserved 0 0 D A 0 0 U/S R/W P

table entry and some control bits. This 10-bit address is used to locate different page tables for different page directory entries. The 10-bit address points to a 4K-byte page. This allows 4K different page tables to coexist with the page directory. Because multiple page tables can exist, each application can use its own page table. The page directory entry control bits are as follows.

> D—The dirty bit in the directory entry is undefined for the 80386 microprocessor.

> A—The accessed bit is set to a logic 1 whenever the microprocessor accesses the page directory entry and subsequent page table.

> R/W—The read/wrote bit is placed at a logic 0 if the page directory entry is to be read-only and at a logic 1 level if it is a read and write directory entry.

> U/S—The user/supervisor bit allows read-only access to the page directory entry if this bit is a logic 0 and the R/W bit is a logic 0. If this bit is a logic 1, then the 80386 can write to the page directory entry even though it is marked as read-only with the R/W bit.

> P—The present bit indicates whether the page directory entry can be used. If this bit is a logic 1, then the page directory entry is present. If this bit is a logic 0, then the page directory and its page table reference are not present.

The Page Tables. The page table contains the physical page addresses of the actual physical pages mapped to the page table entry. The format for the page table entry is identical to the format for the page directory entry as illustrated in Figure 13–21. Figure 13–22 illustrates the entire paging mechanism in the 80386 microprocessor. Notice how the address is used to select a page directory entry, a page table entry, and finally the actual byte of data in the active page in the memory system. The paging mechanism functions in the following manner.

1. The 4K-byte-long page directory is stored at the address pointed to by CR3. There is only one page directory possible for a system.
2. The upper 10 bits of the address, as determined by the descriptors described earlier in this section, are applied to the paging mechanism to select an entry in the page directory. This maps a page directory entry to the 10 leftmost bits of the address.
3. The page table is addressed by the 10 leftmost bits in the page directory entry. This allows for different page tables because these 10 bits can contain any address that the software designer requires. In other words the leftmost 10 bits of the address have been exchanged for the leftmost 10 bits in the page directory entry.
4. An entry in the page table is addressed by the next 10 bits of the address as it comes from the descriptor (A_{21}–A_{12}).
5. The entry in the page table contains the actual physical address of the 4K-byte page frame. The desired memory location is obtained from the page by using the least significant 12 bits of the address to locate the byte, word, or doubleword within the selected page.

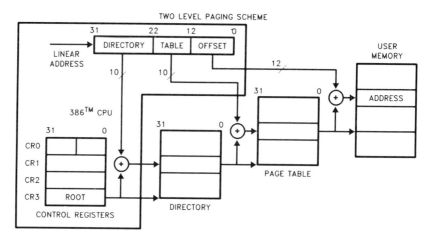

FIGURE 13–22   The paging mechanism in the 80386 microprocessor. (Courtesy of Intel Corporation)

The paging mechanism allows the physical memory to be assigned to any logic memory location through this paging mechanism. For example, suppose that the address output by the descriptor is location 20000000H, but this location does not actually exist in the physical memory. The paging mechanism is used to map this location to an existing physical location in the memory. This address (refer to Figure 13–23) will address an entry in the page directory that points to the page table. In the page table illustrated, the first entry is selected. This first entry contains a 20-bit address equal to 00012H. This is the 20 moŝt significant bits of the actual memory address, which begin at memory location 00012000H. Because the rightmost 12 bits of the original address are 000H, the actual byte of memory addressed is at physical memory location 00012000H. This means that logical memory locations 20000000H–20000FFFH will access physical memory locations 00012000H–00012FFFH in this example. Notice in this example that the next page directory entry contains a reference to a different page table. The next page table entry in this new table contains a 00015000H. This means that logical addresses 20001000H–20001FFFH are mapped to physical addresses 00015000H–0015FFFH. In this manner any logical address can be mapped to any physical address through as many page tables as are required for a given application.

Take for example a typical DOS-base AT clone computer system. The memory map for the system appears in Figure 13–24. Notice from this map that there are unused areas in the map that could be paged to a different location, giving a DOS program more memory to operate with. The normal DOS memory begins at location 00000H and extends to location 9FFFFH, which is 640K bytes of memory. Above this location we normally find other devices such as video cards and system ROM. Notice in the illustration that there is no actual memory located at location A0000H–AFFFFH. This section could be used to extend DOS by an additional 64K bytes so that DOS will have a total of memory of 704K. This is accomplished by paging this section of the memory (A0000H–AFFFFH) into extended memory that begins at location 100000H. This is accomplished by loading the page table directory at memory location 100000H and storing a page table

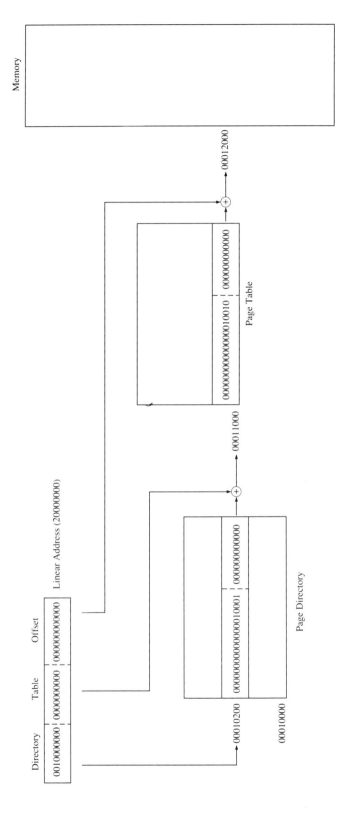

FIGURE 13–23 Mapping linear address 20000000 to physical address 00012000 through the paging mechanism.

Linear Address (20000000)

| Directory | Table | Offset |

0010000000 | 0000000000 | 0000000000

Page Directory

00010200

00010000

0000000000000010001 | 000000000000

00011000

Page Table

0000000000000010010 | 000000000000

00012000

Memory

473

FIGURE 13–24   Memory map for an AT-style clone.

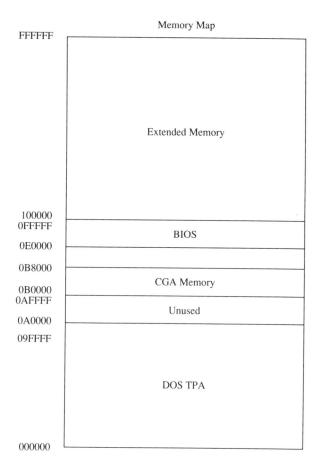

at location 101000H. The entries in the page table can map locations A0000H–AFFFFH to locations 102000H–11FFFFH. Any time that DOS accesses location A0000H–AFFFFH it will see memory, although not at these locations. Actually the memory will be located at 10200H–11FFFFH, but as far as DOS is concerned it is at location A0000H–AFFFFH. This same technique is used at times to remap the BIOS ROM into a RAM section of the memory located above 100000H. Once the BIOS ROM is remapped, it is copied to these new locations so that the DOS BIOS subroutines operate at a much higher rate of speed. (ROM usually requires wait states and RAM does not.) Example 13–4 illustrates how the remapping of locations A0000H–AFFFFH to 102000H–11FFFFH is accomplished via software.

EXAMPLE 13–4

```
0000                    DATA        SEGMENT     AT   800H

                        ;page directory needs only one entry for locations
                        ;A0000H--AFFFFH
```

```
= 0000                    PAGE_DIRECTORY   EQU    $

0000   00000000          TAB1_PNT  DD       ?  ;entry for 00000000-003FFFFF
0004   00000000          TAB2_PNT  DD       0  ;entry for 00400000-007FFFFF
0008   03FE[                       DD       1022 DUP (0)
       00000000
                 ]


                         ;
                         ;additional enteries follow as needed.
                         ;

1000   0400[             PAGE_TABLE1 DD     1024 DUP (?) ;allocate page table
       ????????
                 ]

2000                     DATA ENDS

0000                     CODE SEGMENT

                                 .386P

                         ASSUME CS:CODE,DS:DATA

                 ;This softzware (PAGES) is written to run in so the
                 ;real-mode linear addresses are calculated and
                 ;used in the page procedure to remap locations
                 ;A0000H--AFFFFFH to locations 100000H--10FFFFH.
                 ;
                 ;This software does not change the page enable bit
                 ;in CR0. This is changed when the system is
                 ;switched from the current real mode of operation
                 ;to the protected mode.

0000                     PAGES     PROC     FAR

0000   1E                          PUSH     DS
0001   06                          PUSH     ES
0002   FC                          CLD
0003   66¦ 33 C0                   XOR      EAX,EAX
0006   B8 ---- R                   MOV      AX,DATA ;load DS
0009   8E D8                       MOV      DS,AX
000B   8E C0                       MOV      ES,AX
000D   C1 E0 04                    SHL      AX,4 ;linear address for page directory
0010   0F 22 D8                    MOV      CR3,EAX

             ;load page directory entry 1 for this example

0013   66¦ 33 C0                   XOR      EAX,EAX ;get address of page table1
0016   66¦ 8B D8                   MOV      EBX,EAX
0019   8C D8                       MOV      AX,DS
001B   66¦ C1 E0 04                SHL      EAX,4
001F   BB 1000 R                   MOV      BX,OFFSET PAGE_TABLE1
0022   66¦ 03 C3                   ADD      EAX,EBX
0025   66¦ 25 FFFFF000             AND      EAX,0FFFFF000H ;mask off right 12 bits
```

```
002B  66¦ 83 C0 07              ADD     EAX,7                    ;enable read/write
002F  66¦ A3 0000 R             MOV     TAB1_PNT,EAX
```

;fill page table 1 so that access occurs to normal addresses

```
0033  66¦ 33 FF                 XOR     EDI,EDI
0036  BF 1000 R                 MOV     DI,OFFSET PAGE_TABLE1   ;address table1
0039  66¦ 33 C0                 XOR     EAX,EAX                 ;clear EAX
003C  05 0007                   ADD     AX,7                    ;enable read/write
003F  B9 0400                   MOV     CX,1024                 ;load count

0042                    LOOP1:

0042  66¦ AB                    STOSD
0044  66¦ 05 00001000           ADD     EAX,1000H               ;adjust address by 4K
004A  E2 F6                     LOOP    LOOP1
```

;adjust page table entries for A0000H--AFFFFH

```
004C  BF 1280 R                 MOV     DI,OFFSET PAGE_TABLE1+4*0A0H
004F  66¦ 33 C0                 XOR     EAX,EAX
0052  66¦ 05 00100007           ADD     EAX,00100007H           ;add bias to EAX
0058  B9 0010                   MOV     CX,16

005B                    LOOP2:

005B  66¦ AB                    STOSD
005D  66¦ 05 00001000           ADD     EAX,1000H               ;adjust address by 4K
0063  E2 F6                     LOOP    LOOP2

0065  07                        POP     ES
0066  1F                        POP     DS
0067  CB                        RET

0068           PAGES            ENDP

0068           CODE             ENDS

               END
```

13-3   THE 80486 MICROPROCESSOR

The 80486 microprocessor is a highly integrated device containing well over 1,000,000 transistors. Located within this omnipotent integrated circuit are a memory-management unit (MMU); a complete numeric coprocessor that is compatible with the 80X87 series, a high-speed cache memory that contains 8K bytes of memory; and a full 32-bit microprocessor that is fully upward compatible with the earlier family members. The 80486 is currently available in either a 25-MHz version or a 33-MHz version, with higher speed versions available in the near term. The 80486 is able to execute software written for the

8088 microprocessor as well as all other family members, including the 80X87 numeric coprocessor, without any modification. Of course this microprocessor contains a few additional instructions not present on its predecessors.

Figure 13-25 illustrates the internal structure of the 80486 microprocessor. Notice the degree of integration present in this complex device. RISC (*reduced instruction set computer*) design of the 80486 reduces the amount of time required to execute many of the instructions to just one clock cycle. This provides a tremendous improvement in execution speed for many programs. This, combined with the on-chip cache memory system, allows the 80486 to perform software at twice the speed of the 80386 in many instances. The MMU allows the 80486 to access segments in any size up to 4G bytes in length. Any application may contain up to 16,381 segments, with each containing up to 4G bytes of memory. This allows any task to have a virtual memory size of up to 64T bytes. The MMU also provides four levels of protection numbered PL0 to PL3, with PL0 having the most privileged level of protection. These software shells are often used in multiuser environments and are provided for this application.

Figure 13-26 illustrates the pinout of the 80486 microprocessor. Notice that this device is packaged in a 168 pin, pin grid array (PGA) carrier. For this device to function correctly at high frequencies all 24 V_{cc} and 28 V_{ss} connections to the power supply must be attached. The power supply itself must be capable of supplying 5.0 V ± 10 percent, with up to 1.2 A of current of the 33-MHz version. The average supply current is approximately 650 mA at 33 MHz. Logic 0 outputs allow up to 4.0 mA of current and logic 1 outputs allow up to 1.0 mA of current flow. If larger currents are required, as they most likely will be, then the output pins must be buffered to provide larger currents.

i486™ Microprocessor Pipelined 32-Bit Microarchitecture

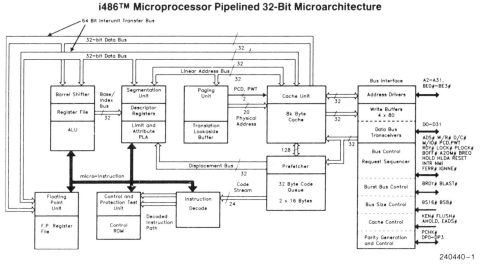

240440-1

iRMX, iRMK, 386, 387, 486, i486 are trademarks of Intel Corporation.
*MS-DOS® is a registered trademark of Microsoft Corporation.
**OS/2™ is a trademark of Microsoft Corporation.
***UNIX™ is a trademark of AT&T.

FIGURE 13-25   The internal structure of the 80486. (Courtesy of Intel Corporation)

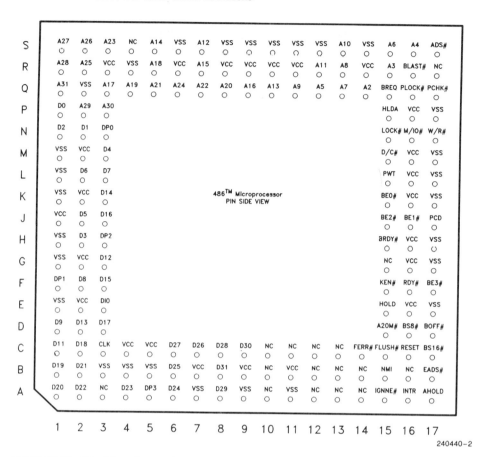

FIGURE 13-26   The pinout of the 80486. (Courtesy of Intel Corporation)

Pin Definitions

Following is a list of the description of each pin connection on the 80486.

1. A_{31}–A_2—The address connections are used to select a memory or I/O location during normal operation and during a cache line invalidation, A_{31}–A_4 are used to drive the microprocessor.

2. $\overline{BE3}$–$\overline{BE0}$—The byte enable signals are used to select the appropriate byte of information whenever less than 32 bits of data are transferred between the microprocessor and the memory or I/O. $\overline{BE3}$ enables data bus connections D31–D24, $\overline{BE2}$ enables D23–D16, $\overline{BE1}$ enables D15–D8, and $\overline{BE0}$ enables D7–D0.

3. CLK—The clock input provides the timing required by the 80486 to function correctly. This signal may be either 25 or 33 MHz, depending on which version of the 80486 is in application.

4. D31–D0—The data bus is a full 32 bits in width and is used to transfer information between the 80486 and its memory and I/O system.

5. DP3–DP0—There are even-parity-generation/parity-detection I/O pins. These pins provide a parity bit for each byte on the data bus whenever data are written and are

used to detect a parity error for each byte when data are read. In a system that does not incorporate parity checks, these connections must be pulled up to a logic 1 level for the 80486 to function correctly.

6. $\overline{PCHK}$ — The parity check output indicates that a parity error has occurred through the parity check inputs.

7. M/$\overline{IO}$ — The memory/I/O output pin defines the information present on the address bus as either a memory address or an I/O port number. It is also used to delineate whether the system is to perform a memory operation or an I/O operation.

8. D/$\overline{C}$ — The data/control signal is used to indicate whether the current bus operation is a data operation or a control operation. Refer to Table 13–5 for the function of this signal along with the M/$\overline{IO}$ and W/$\overline{R}$ signal.

9. W/$\overline{R}$ — The write/read signal is used to signal the memory and I/O that a read or a write operation is to be performed.

10. $\overline{LOCK}$ — The *bus lock* output is controlled by the lock prefix that can be added to any instruction. The $\overline{LOCK}$ pin becomes a logic 0 for the duration of any locked instruction.

11. $\overline{PLOCK}$ — The *pseudo-lock* output indicates that the current operation requires more than one bus cycle to perform. This signal becomes a logic 0 for arithmetic operations that require access to 64-bit-long floating-point numbers.

12. $\overline{ADS}$ — This active low output signal, address status, indicates that a valid address appears on the address bus of the 80486.

13. $\overline{RDY}$ — The non-burst ready input indicates that the current bus cycle is complete. If $\overline{RDY}$ is not returned, the microprocessor will enter wait states into its timing, lengthening access times.

14. $\overline{BRDY}$ — The burst ready input performs the same function as the $\overline{RDY}$ input, except that $\overline{BRDY}$ is used during a burst cycle.

15. $\overline{BLAST}$ — The burst last output indicates that the next time that the $\overline{BRDY}$ signal is activated the burst bus cycle is complete.

16. RESET — The RESET input is used to initialize the 80486 as it does on all other versions of the 80X86 family.

17. INTR — The interrupt request input is a maskable interrupt input that is controlled by the interrupt enable flag bit.

18. NMI — The non-maskable interrupt input is similar to the maskable interrupt input (INTR), except that it always remains active. One other difference is that the NMI interrupt input is edge triggered, while the INTR input is level sensitive.

TABLE 13–5 Bus cycle identification

M/$\overline{IO}$	D/$\overline{C}$	W/$\overline{R}$	Bus Cycle Type
0	0	0	Interrupt acknowledge
0	0	1	Halt/special
0	1	0	I/O read
0	1	1	I/O write
1	0	0	Code cycle
1	0	1	Reserved
1	1	0	Memory read
1	1	1	Memory write

19. BREQ—This output indicates that the 40486 has generated an internal bus request.
20. HOLD—The HOLD input is used to request a DMA action that causes all of the address, data, and control bus connections to three-state when accepted by the microprocessor.
21. HLDA—The hold acknowledge output indicates that the 80486 has relinquished control of the buses in response to a HOLD request.
22. BOFF—The backoff input forces in the 80486 to float its buses during the next clock and is similar in function to the RDY input, except BOFF has a higher priority.
23. AHOLD—The address hold input allows another microprocessor to access the address bus.
24. EADS—This input indicates that an external address that is to be used to perform an internal cache invalidation cycle is applied to the 80486 address pins.
25. KEN—The cache enable input is used to determine whether the current bus cycle is cachcable.
26. FLUSH—The flush input is used to flush (erase) its entire internal 8K-byte cache memory.
27. PWT—The page write through output reflects the state of the PWT attribute bit in the page table entry or the page directory entry.
28. PCD—The page cache disable output reflects the state of thc PCD attribute bit in the page table entry or the page directory entry.
29. FERR—The floating-point error output indicates that the 80387 has detected an error in its floating-point operation.
30. IGNNE—The ignore numeric error input is used to ignore a floating-point error when it is placed at its logic 0 level.
31. BS16—The bus size 16 input is used to cause the 80486 to use its data bus as a 16-bit data bus.
32. BS8—The bus size 8 input is used to cause the 80486 to use its data bus as an 8-bit data bus.
33. A20M—The address bit 20 mask bit is used to cause the 80486 to wrap its address around, as does the 8086 at the 1M-byte address boundary.

Basic 80486 Architecture

As mentioned, the architecture of the 80486 is almost identical to the 80386 with the 80387 math coprocessor. Refer to Figure 13–27 for the internal basic register set of the 80486. From this illustration, notice that this architecture is identical to that of the 80386 microprocessor. As with the 80386 there are eight general-purpose 32-bit registers EAX, EBX, ECX, EDX, EBP, EDI, ESI, and ESP. These registers may be used as 16-bit registers with the following designations: AX, BX, CX, DX, BP, DI, SI, and SP, or as 8-bit registers with the following designations: AH, AL, BH, BL, CH, CL, DH, or DL.

In addition to the general-purpose register there also exist six segment registers that are used to form addresses along with one of the index registers or pointers. These registers include: CS (code segment), DS (data segment), ES (extra segment), SS (stack segment), FS, and GS. Each of these registers is 16 bits in width.

The IP register is the instruction pointer that is used to address memory data within the first 1M of address space in combination with the CS register, or as an EIP linear address, allowing access to any location within the 4G bytes of memory space.

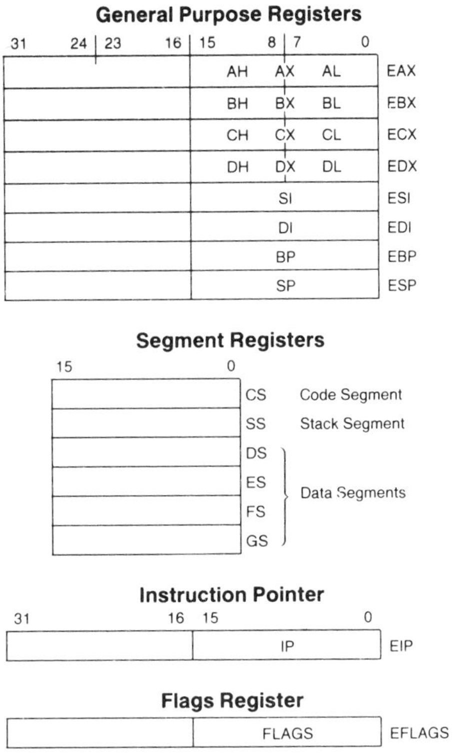

FIGURE 13-27 The internal programming model of the 80486. (Courtesy of Intel Corporation)

General Purpose Registers

31	24	23	16	15	8	7	0	
				AH	AX	AL		EAX
				BH	BX	BL		EBX
				CH	CX	CL		ECX
				DH	DX	DL		EDX
					SI			ESI
					DI			EDI
					BP			EBP
					SP			ESP

Segment Registers

15	0		
		CS	Code Segment
		SS	Stack Segment
		DS	
		ES	Data Segments
		FS	
		GS	

Instruction Pointer

31	16	15	0	
		IP		EIP

Flags Register

	FLAGS	EFLAGS

The flag register, as illustrated in more detail in Figure 13–28, is used to indicate various functions in the 80486 microprocessor. As with all other 80X86 family members, the rightmost 8 bits of this register contain the 8085A-like flags, such as carry and zero. The remaining bits indicate other information about the operation of the microprocessor. Listed below are each of the flag bits along with a brief description of their functions.

1. AC—The *alignment check* flag is new to the 80486 microprocessor, and it indicates that the microprocessor has accessed a word stored at an odd address or a doubleword that is stored at a non-doubleword boundary.

2. VM—*Virtual mode* is entered by setting this flag bit while the 80486 is operating in the protected mode. Note that this bit is always cleared when a PUSHF instruction is executed, even if the 80486 is operating in the virtual mode.

3. RF—The *resume flag* is used in conjunction with the debug register breakpoints.

4. NT—The *nested task* flag is set to indicate that a task is nested within another task.

5. IOPL—The *input/output privilege level* flags indicate the current maximum privilege level permitted to execute.

6. OF—The *overflow flag* indicates that the result of a signed arithmetic operation has resulted in an overflow condition.

7. DF—The *direction flag* is set to select auto-decrement and cleared to select auto-increment modes of operation of the pointers with the string instructions.

8. IF—The *interrupt enable flag* is set to enable the INTR interrupt input pin and cleared to disable it.

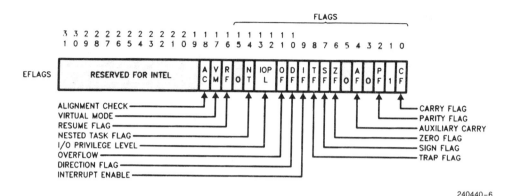

NOTE:
0 indicates Intel Reserved: do not define; see Section 2.1.6.

FIGURE 13–28   The EFLAG register of the 80486. (Courtesy of Intel Corporation)

9. TF—The *trap flag,* if set, is used to cause the microprocessor to interrupt the current program after each instruction is executed.
10. SF—The *sign flag* bit indicates that the sign of an arithmetic or logic operation is positive if it is cleared and negative if it is set.
11. ZF—The *zero flag* indicates that the result after an arithmetic or logic operation is zero if this flag bit is set to a logic 1.
12. AF—The *auxiliary flag* is used with the DAA and DAS instructions to perform BCD corrections after addition or subtraction.
13. PF—The *parity flag* bit indicates that the result of an arithmetic or logic operation has even parity when this bit is set.
14. CF—The *carry flag* bit indicates a carry from the most significant bit of the result after and arithmetic operation and also is used with the shift and rotate instructions to hold any bit that leaves the target register or memory location.

80486 Instructions

The 80486 contains all of the instructions listed for the 80386 and the 80387 coprocessor plus six new instructions not present on these earlier machines. Table 13–6 illustrates these six new instructions along with a brief comment about each.

The first three instructions in Table 13–6 reverse the way that a number is stored by exchanging the least with the most significant bytes for a word or by completely reordering a doubleword. BSWAP causes a number to be reordered so that the number is stored from the least to the most significant byte or the most to the least. For example, if EAX contains a 01234567H before the BSWAP EAX instruction, it will contain a 67542301H after the swap.

The INVD and WBINVD instructions are both used to flush (empty) the internal cache memory system. The difference is that INVD flushes the cache without regard to any data that may need to be stored in the memory before the flush occurs. This can result in lost data. The WBINVD instruction prevents the loss of these data because it first writes unwritten data to the memory before the cache is flushed. The INVLPG allows a page entry in the translation lookaside buffer to be erased or flushed.

Resident Cache Memory

The 80486 microprocessor is unique because it contains an 8K-byte cache memory that is used to cache data and also instructions. The cache is organized as a 4-way set associative cache with each line 16 bytes in width. The 8K bytes of memory are organized as 128 sets each containing four lines.

The cache is divided into four sections of 2K bytes each, as illustrated in Figure 13–29. Attached to each 2K-byte segment are 128, 21-bit tags. There is a valid bit for each line in the cache. Whenever data are written, they are written to the cache at the same time that they are written to the external bus and memory. This type of operation is known as *write-through*.

The cache is controlled by the CE and WT bits in control register zero (CR0). The function of these two bits is depicted in Table 13–7. To completely disable the cache, both

TABLE 13–6 New 80486 instructions

Instruction	Description
BSWAP	Allows the 4 bytes in a 32-bit register to be reordered from lowest to highest or highest to lowest
XADD	Accomplishes the same thing that BSWAP accomplishes on 16-bit data and also performs addition
CMPXCHG	Reorders 16-bit data and then compares them
INVD	Flushes the internal cache memory
WBINVD	Flushes the internal cache memory after writing dirty lines to the memory system
INVLPG	Invalidates a TLB entry

FIGURE 13–29 The 8K-byte cache on the 80486 microprocessor. (Courtesy of Intel Corporation)

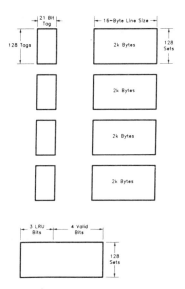

TABLE 13–7 Cache control bit operating modes

WT	CE	Operating Mode
0	0	Cache fills, write-throughs, and invalidates disabled
0	1	Invalid
1	0	Cache fills disabled; write-throughs and invalidates enabled
1	1	Cache fills, write-throughs, and invalidates enabled

WT and CE must be placed at a logic 0, and then the cache is flushed. If not flushed, the cache will still have hits on reads. The same can be accomplished with the software instructions INVD and WBINVD.

13–4 SUMMARY

1. The 80386 microprocessor is an enhanced version of the 8086/8088 microprocessor that includes a memory-management unit that was introduced on the 80286 microprocessor. The 80386 also includes 32-bit extended registers and a 32-bit address and data bus. A scaled-down version of the 80386 with a 16-bit data and 24-bit address bus is available as the 80386SX microprocessor.

2. The 80386 has a physical memory size of 4G bytes that can be addressed as a virtual memory with up to 64T bytes. The 80386 memory is 32 bits in width and is addressable as doublewords, words, or as bytes.

3. When the 80386 is operated in the pipeline mode, it sends the address of the next instruction to the memory system prior to the completion of the execution of the current instruction. This allows the memory system to begin fetching the next instruction before the current is completed reducing the memory speed required in a system.

4. A cache memory system allows data that are frequently read to be accessed in less time because they are stored in a high-speed semiconductor memory. If data are written to memory, the data are also written to the cache so that the most current data are always present in the cache.

5. The I/O structure of the 80386 microprocessor is almost identical to earlier versions of this microprocessor, except that I/O can be inhibited when the 80386 is operated in the protected mode through the I/O bit protection map stored with the TSS.

6. The register set of the 80386 contains extended versions of the registers introduced on the 8086/8088 microprocessor. These registers include: EAX, EBX, ECX, EDX, EBP, ESP, EDI, ESI, EIP, and EFLAGS. In addition to the extended registers, two additional segment registers (FS and GS) are added. Debug registers and control registers are also added to handle system debugging through interrupt vector type number two. The control registers are used during protected mode by the memory-management unit.

7. The instruction set of the 80386 microprocessor is enhanced to include instruction for addressing the 32-bit extended register set. The enhancements to the instruction set also include additional addressing modes that allow any 32-bit extended register to be used to index the memory. Scaling has also been added so that an index register can be multiplied by 1, 2, 4, or 8. New instructions include bit scan, bit test and modify, string moves with sign or zero extend, set byte upon a condition, and double precision shifts.

8. Interrupts, in the 80386, have been expanded to include additional predefined entries in the interrupt vector table. These additional entries are used with the memory-management system.

9. 80386 memory management is similar to the 80286, except that the physical addresses generated by the MMU are 32 bits instead of 24 bits in width. The 80386 MMU is also capable of paging.

10. The 80386 is operated in the 8086 real mode upon a reset where the 80386 appears as a 8086/8088. The real mode allows the microprocessor to address data in the first mega-byte of memory. In the protected mode, the 80386 can address any location in its 4G-byte physical address range.

11. A descriptor is a series of 8 bytes of data that specify how a code or data segment is used by the 80386. The descriptor is selected by a selector that is stored in one of the segment registers. Descriptors are only used in the protected mode of operation.

12. Memory management is accomplished through a series of descriptor tables and descriptor entries in these tables. To facilitate memory management, the 80386 uses three descriptor tables: (1) the global descriptor table (GDT), (2) the local descriptor table (LDT), and (3) the interrupt descriptor table (IDT). The GDT and LDT each hold up to 8K different descriptors, while the IDT holds up to 256 different descriptors. The GDT and LDT are used to hold descriptors that define code and data, while the IDT is used to describe descriptors for the 256 different interrupt types.

13. The TSS (task state segment) contains information about the current task and also the previous task. Appended to the end of the TSS is an I/O privilege map that allows a task to define which I/O devices are available to the task.

14. The memory paging mechanism allows any 4K-byte physical page of the memory to be assigned to any logical address. For example, memory location 00A00000H can be assigned to memory location A0000000H through paging. Page tables are used to reassign logical memory addresses to various physical memory addresses. By using the paging mechanism while operating in the 8086 mode, many images of the 8086 memory can be set up in the 80386 system.

15. The 80486 microprocessor is a highly integrated system containing an enhanced 80386, an 80387 arithmetic coprocessor, and an 8K-byte cache memory system. The enhanced 80386 microprocessor located within the 80486 can execute instructions at approximately twice the speed of the 80386 microprocessor.

16. The 80486 contains six new instructions that are not present in the 80386 or any other earlier version of the 8086 microprocessor. These new instructions include: BSWAP, XADD, CMPXCHG, INVD, WBINVD, and INVLPG.

17. The resident 8K-byte cache is organized in four 2K-byte sections that each contain 128 different 8-byte-long entries. The cache is a write-through cache that writes data both to the cache and the memory whenever a write occurs.

13-5   QUESTIONS AND PROBLEMS

1. The 80386 microprocessor is capable of addressing _____ bytes of physical memory.
2. The 80386 microprocessor is capable of addressing _____ bytes of virtual memory through its memory-management unit.
3. Describe the differences between the two versions of the 80386 microprocessor.
4. Draw the memory map of the 80386 microprocessor when it is operated in
   a. the real mode
   b. the protected mode
5. How much current is available on the various 80386 pin connections? Compare these currents with those available on the 8086/8088 microprocessor.
6. Describe the 80386 memory system and explain the purpose and operation of the bank selection signals.
7. Explain the action of a hardware reset on the address bus connections of the 80386 microprocessor.
8. Explain how pipelining lengthens the access time for many memory references in the 80386 microprocessor.
9. Briefly describe how a cache memory system functions.
10. I/O ports in the 80386 begin at address _____ and extend to address _____ when used with variable I/O instructions such as IN EAX,DX.
11. What I/O ports are used to communicate with the 80387 numeric coprocessor?
12. Contrast the memory and I/O control connections found on the 80386 with those found on the 8086/8088 microprocessor.
13. If the 80386 is to be operated at 20 MHz, what clocking frequency must be applied to the CLK2 input pin connection?
14. What is the purpose of the $\overline{BS16}$ pin connection on the 80386 microprocessor?
15. What two additional segment registers are added to the 80386 microprocessor that are not present on the 8086/8088?
16. List the extended registers found in the 80386 microprocessor.
17. List each 80386 flag bit and describe its purpose.
18. Define the purpose of each 80386 control register.
19. Define the purpose of each 80386 debug register.
20. The debug registers are accessed through which interrupt vector-type number?
21. Describe the operation of the bit scan forward instruction.
22. Describe the operation of the bit test and reset instruction.
23. Describe the operation of the SHRD instruction.
24. Form an instruction that will access data in the FS segment indirectly addressed by the DI register. This instruction should store the number found in register AX into this location in the memory system.
25. What is scaled index addressing?
26. Is the following instruction legal? MOV AX,[EAX + EBX].
27. Explain how the following instructions calculate the memory address:
   a. ADD [EXB + 8*ECX],AL
   b. MOV DATA[EAX + EBX],CX
   c. SUB ECX,DATA
   d. MOV ECX,[EBX]

28. What is the purpose of interrupt type number 7?
29. Which interrupt vector type number occurs whenever a protection violation occurs?
30. What is a double interrupt fault?
31. If an interrupt occurs in the protected mode of operation, what defines the interrupt vectors?
32. What is a descriptor?
33. What is a selector?
34. How does the selector choose the local descriptor table?
35. What register is used to address the global descriptor table?
36. How many global descriptors can be stored in the global descriptor table?
37. Explain how the 80386 can address 64T bytes of memory when the physical memory only contains 4G bytes of memory.
38. What is the difference between a segment descriptor and a system descriptor?
39. What is a task state segment (TSS)?
40. How is the TSS addressed?
41. Describe how the 80386 switches from the real mode to the protected mode of operation.
42. Describe how the 80386 switches from the protected mode to the real mode of operation.
43. How is the paging directory accessed by the 80386 microprocessor?
44. How many bytes are found in a page of memory?
45. Explain how logical memory address D0000000H can be assigned to physical memory address C0000000H with the paging unit of the 80386 microprocessor.
46. Describe the difference between the 80486 microprocessor and the 80386 microprocessor.
47. What is the purpose of the AC flag bit found in the 80486 microprocessor?
48. How many bytes of data or instructions can be stored in the 80486 cache memory?
49. Does the 80486 microprocessor contain any additional registers not found on the 80386 microprocessor. (Ignore the floating-point processor registers.)
50. What is an RISC computer?
51. Explain the term "write-through" as it applies to the cache memory system found within the 80486 microprocessor.
52. Each 80486 cache entry holds _____ bytes of information.
54. The 80486 cache is organized as four banks of _____ K bytes each.
55. Explain what the BSWAP ECX instruction accomplishes in the 80486 microprocessor.

APPENDIX A

The Assembler and Disk Operating System

This appendix is provided so that the use the assembler can be understood and also to show that the DOS (disk operating system) BIOS (binary input/output system) function calls are used from assembly language to control the IBM-PC or its clone. The function calls control everything from reading and writing data to the disk to managing the keyboard and displays. The assembler represented in this text is the Microsoft MASM (Version 5.10) assembler program, but the information provided is valid with most other assemblers that are commonly available.

ASSEMBLER USAGE

The assembler program requires that a symbolic program be first written, using a word processor or the text editor provided with the assembler package. This appendix does not detail the operation and use of the word processor or the editor. Instead, it details how to assemble and link a program written with the word processor or editor. Please refer to the documentation provided with the editor or word processor. If using a word processor, make sure that you generate an ASCII file with the extension .ASM for the source program. This is required for the assembler program to properly locate and assemble the source program. Once the source program is written and stored on the disk, the assembler program is used to assemble the object and optional listing file. If the assembler is invoked (refer to Example A–1), it produces a file with the extension .OBJ and also optionally .LST and a .CRF file. The .OBJ file is the hexadecimal object file, the .LST file is the listing file, and the .CRF file is a cross-reference file. The listing file contains both the source and object versions of the program that is assembled. The cross-reference file lists all labels and pertinent information for cross referencing.

EXAMPLE A–1

```
A>ASM FILE;
```

488

Example A–1 illustrates how to invoke the assembler so that it generates an object program for the assembler language source file FILE.ASM. Do not include the extension on the command line. While the assembler creates the object file FILE.OBJ it lists any errors that might be present on the video display. This example will not generate a listing file. If you need a listing file, the assembler is invoked as in Example A–2. Here the user types the information that is italicized in this example.

EXAMPLE A–2

```
A>MASM

Microsoft (R) Macro Assembler Version 5.10
Copyright (C) Microsoft Corp 1981, 1989. All rights reserved.

Source filename  [.ASM]: FILE
Object filename  [FILE.ASM]: FILE
Source listing  [NUL.LST]: FILE
Cross reference [NUL.CRF]: FILE
```

In Example A–2 MASM is typed at the DOS prompt A>. Notice that the assembler responds and asks first for the name of the source file. Once the name of this file is typed, it asks the name of the object file. Notice that it already suggests that the name is FILE.ASM. If you wish to accept this name, all you need to do is type enter. Optionally you can change the name or type the same name. In all cases notice that no extension is required when the file name is entered. In this example a listing file and a cross-reference file are requested. If these are not needed, type a return as an answer and none will be created.

Once the program is assembled without errors, it must be linked before it can be executed by the computer. The linker converts the object file into an executable file for the computer. The linker is invoked in much the same manner as the assembler by typing the sequence listed in Example A–3. In this example the object file linked is TEST. If more than one object file exists, all are entered and separated by commas on this line. Next the linker asks for the name of the Run File. You may hit the enter key if the suggested name is correct. A .MAP file can be generated that shows the length and placement of the object modules and segments. Also library files may be used, as is the case in this example. The library file contains a grouping of subroutines (procedures) that are used with the object modules. Once a program is assembled and linked, it can be executed by typing the name of the execution file (.EXE) at the DOS prompt. With a little practice, assembling and linking program files will become second nature.

EXAMPLE A–3

```
A>LINK

Microsoft (R) Overlay Linker Version 3.64
Copyright (C) Microsoft Corp 1983-1988. All rights reserved.

Object Modules [.OBJ]: TEST
Run File [TEST.EXE]: TEST
List File [NUL.MAP]: TEST
Libraries [.LIB]: SUBR
```

Assembler Source File Syntax

Before a program can be written using the assembler, a few things about the syntax of the assembler must be known. The assembler allows the user to specify the source program in a few different ways. There are different models of the memory system that are specified with the assembler. These include tiny, small, medium, compact, large, and huge. Table A–1 illustrates each model with a brief description of its meaning. The models are described to the assembler with the .MODEL pseudo-operation. An example is .MODEL SMALL, which informs the assembler that the program uses the small model. Please note that the .MODEL directive is optional and may be eliminated if each segment is described by the user.

When models are used to form a program, certain defaults apply as illustrated in Table A–2. The directive is used to indicate the start of a particular type of segment for the models listed in this table. The directive indicates the name of a segment. If .CODE is placed in a program, it indicates the start of the code segment. Likewise if .DATA is placed in a program, it indicates the start of the data segment. .DATA and .DATA? are both used to indicate that start of data segments where .DATA is used to indicate initialized data such as, DB 100 DUP (2), and .DATA? is used for uninitialized data such as, DB 100 DUP (?). The Name is the name that the assembler assigns to the segment when the label table is displayed in the .LST version of the assembled file. Align indicates that the information is aligned on WORD or PARAgraph boundaries when stored in the memory. Combine indicates the type of segment created, whether PUBLIC and usable by all segments or whether private. The Class indicates the class of the segment whether CODE, DATA, etc. The Group indicates the group type of the segment.

Example A–4 illustrates how a program is set up using the small model. The small model is used for programs that have one DATA segment and one CODE segment. This applies to many programs that are developed. Notice that not only is the program listed,

TABLE A–1   Memory modules for the assembler

Type	Description
Tiny	All data and code fit into one segment. Tiny model programs are written in the .COM file format, which means that a program must be originated to begin at location 100H. This is most often used with small programs.
Small	All data fit into a single 64K segment, and all code fits into another single 64K segment. This allows all data and code to be accessed as near.
Medium	All data fit into a single 64K segment, and all code fits into more than one segment. This allows all data to be accessed as near and code to be accessed as far in multiple segments.
Compact	All code fits into a single 64K segment, and all data fit into more than one segment. Code is near and data are far with the compact model.
Large	Both code and data may be greater than 64K.
Huge	Both code and data may be greater than 64K. Data arrays may be larger than 64K bytes in length.

TABLE A–2 Defaults for the .MODEL directive

Model	Directive	Name	Align	Combine	Class	Group
Small	.CODE	_TEXT	WORD	PUBLIC	'CODE'	
	.DATA	_DATA	WORD	PUBLIC	'DATA'	DGROUP
	.CONST	CONST	WORD	PUBLIC	'CONST'	DGROUP
	.DATA?	_BSS	WORD	PUBLIC	'BSS'	DGROUP
	.STACK	STACK	PARA	STACK	'STACK'	DGROUP
Medium	.CODE	name_TEXT	WORD	PUBLIC	'CODE'	
	.DATA	_DATA	WORD	PUBLIC	'DATA'	DGROUP
	.CONST	CONST	WORD	PUBLIC	'CONST'	DGROUP
	.DATA?	_BSS	WORD	PUBLIC	'BSS'	DGROUP
	.STACK	STACK	PARA	PUBLIC	'STACK'	DGROUP
Compact	.CODE	_TEXT	WORD	PUBLIC	'CODE'	
	.FARDATA	FAR_DATA	PARA	Private	'FAR_DATA'	
	.FARDATA?	FAR_BSS	PARA	Private	'FAR_BSS'	
	.DATA	_DATA	WORD	PUBLIC	'DATA	DGROUP
	.CONST	CONST	WORD	PUBLIC	'CONST'	DGROUP
	.DATA?	_BSS	WORD	PUBLIC	'BSS'	DGROUP
	.STACK	STACK	PARA	PUBLIC	'STACK'	DGROUP
Large or huge	.CODE	name_TEXT	WORD	PUBLIC	'CODE'	
	.FARDATA	FAR_DATA	PARA	Private	'FAR_DATA'	
	.FAR_DATA?	FAR_BSS	PARA	Private	'FAR_BSS'	
	.DATA	_DATA	WORD	PUBLIC	'DATA'	DGROUP
	.CONST	CONST	WORD	PUBLIC	'CONST'	DGROUP
	.DATA?	_BSS	WORD	PUBLIC	'BSS'	DGROUP
	.STACK	STACK	PARA	PUBLIC	'STACK'	DGROUP

but so is all of the information generated by the assembler for this particular program. Here .DATA is used to indicate the beginning of the data segment and .CODE is used to indicate the beginning of the code segment. Also notice that the DS register is loaded by using the group name DGROUP as a segment address.

EXAMPLE A–4

```
Microsoft (R) Assembler Version 5.10              2/10/90 14:34:37

 1                              .MODEL SMALL
 2                              .STACK 100H
 3
 4                              .DATA
 5
 6 0000 0A                      FRED DB                 10
 7 0001 0064[                   DATA1       DB          100 DUB (2)
 8                  02
 9                        ]
10
```

```
11
12                            .CODE
13
14  0000  B8  --- R          BEGIN:      MOV        AX,DGROUP ;setup DS
15  0003  8E D8                          MOV.       DS,AX
16                                         .
17                                         .
18                                         .
19                                       END        BEGIN
```

Symbols-1

Segments and Groups:

Name	Length	Align	Combine	Class
DGROUP....	GROUP			
_DATA.....	0065	WORD	PUBLIC	'DATA'
STACK.....	0100	PARA	STACK	'STACK'
_TEXT.....	0005	WORD	PUBLIC	'CODE'

Symbols:

Name	Type	Value	Attr	
BEGIN....	L NEAR	0000	_TEXT	
DATA1....	L BYTE	0001	_DATA	Length = 0064
FRED....	L BYTE	0000	_DATA	
@CODE.....	TEXT	_TEXT		
@CODESIZE	TEXT	0		
@CPU....	TEXT	010h		
@DATASIZE....	TEXT	0		
@FILENAME....	TEXT	test		
@VERSION....	TEXT	510		

```
16 Source Lines
16 Total Lines
20 Symbols

47468 + 312111 Bytes symbol space free
0 Warning Errors
0 Severe Errors
```

Example A–5 illustrates a program that uses the large model. Notice how it differs from the small model program listed in Example A–4. Models can be very useful in developing software, but are not essential. Programs may also be produced by defining each segment with the SEGMENT pseudo-operation as defined earlier in the text. The use of the MODEL directive is left up to the user of the assembler.

EXAMPLE A–5

Microsoft (R) Assembler Version 5.10   2/10/90 14:39:56

```
                                   .MODEL LARGE

                                   .FARDATA?

0000 0064[                         DATA1     DB   100 DUP (?)
       ??
                          ]
                                   DATA2     DW   100 DUP (?)
       ????
                          ]

                                   .CONST

0000 54 68 69 73 20 69             MES1      DB   'This is a string of data'
     73 20 61 20 73 74
     72 69 6E 67 20 6F
     66 20 64 61 74 61
     2E
0019 54 68 69 73 20 69             MES2      DB   'This is a second string of data'
     73 20 61 20 73 65
     63 6F 6E 64 20 73
     74 72 69 6E 67 20
     6F 66 20 64 61 74
     61 2E

                                   .DATA

0000 0C                            DATA3     DB   12
0001 0200[                         DATA4     DB   200H DUP (1)
       01
                          ]

                                   .CODE

0000                               FUN       PROC
                                             .
                                             .
                                             .
0000 CB                                      RET

0001                               FUN       ENDP

                                             END
```

Segments and Groups:

Name	Length	Align	Combine	Class
DGROUP....	GROUP			
_DATA....	0201	WORD	PUBLIC	'DATA'

```
CONST....               0039      WORD      PUBLIC     'DATA'
FAR_BSS....             012C      PARA      NONE 'FAR_BSS'


TEST_TEXT....           0001      WORD      PUBLIC     'CODE'
```

Symbols:

Name	Type	Value	Attr	Class
DATA1....	L BYTE	0000	FAR_BSS	Length = 0064
DATA2....	L WORD	0064	FAR_BSS	Length = 0064
DATA3....	L BYTE	0000	_DATA	
DATA4....	L BYTE	0001	_DATA	Length = 0200
FUN....	F PROC	0000	TEST_TEXT Length = 0001	
MES1....	L BYTE	0000	CONST	
MES2....	L BYTE	0019	CONST	
@CODE....	TEXT	test_TEXT		
@CODESIZE...	TEXT	1		
@CPU....	TEXT	010h		
@DATASIZE....	TEXT	0		
@FILENAME....	TEXT	test		
@VERSION....	TEXT	510		

```
    28 Source Lines
    28 Total Lines
    25 Symbols

48038 + 3009573 Bytes symbol space free

    0 Warning Errors
    0 Severe Errors
```

The model directive is an aid in program development that is optional. If so desired, the model statement may be eliminated in favor of defining everything in the program with other pseudo-opcodes, as used throughout this text. These pseudo-opcodes include: SEGMENT, ENDS, and ASSUME. The SEGMENT statement is used to indicate the start of a segment, while the ENDS statement indicates the end of a segment. The ASSUME state indicates to the assembler which segments are to function as code, data, extra, and stack segments. Refer to Example A–6 for an illustration of how segments are specified with these statements.

EXAMPLE A–6

```
Microsoft (R) Assembler Version 5.10          2/11/90 21:42:20

    0000                         LIST_SEG   SEGMENT
```

```
0000 0100[                              DATA1      DB     100H DUP (?)
               ??
                      ]

0100 0003                               VARI       DW     3
0102 00000033                           MAKEUP     DD     33H

0106                      LIST_SEG   ENDS

0000                      STACKS     SEGMENT    STACK

0000 0100[                              DW     100H DUP (?)
               ????
                      ]
                                   STACK_TOP EQU   THIS WORD
0200                      STACKS     ENDS
0000                      PROGRAM    SEGMENT

                          ASSUME CS:PROGRAM,DS:LIST_SEG,SS:STACKS

0000                      START    PROC     FAR

0000 B8---R                             MOV    AX,LIST_SEG      ;load DS
0003 8B D0                              MOV    DX,AX
0005 BC 0200 R                          MOV    SP,OFFSET STACK_TOP
                                          .
                                          .
                                          .
0008                      START          ENDP

0008                      PROGRAM        ENDS

                          END            START
```

Symbols-1

Segments and Groups:

Name	Length	Align	Combine	Class
LIST_SEG....	0106	PARA	NONE	
PROGRAM...	0008	PARA	NONE	
STACKS...	0200	PARA	STACK	

Symbols:

Name	Type	Value	Attr
DATA1....	L BYTE	0000	LIST_SEG Length = 0100
MAKEUP...	L DWORD	0102	LIST_SEG
STACK_TOP....	WORD	0200	STACKS
START....	F PROC	0000	PROGRAM Length = 0008

```
VARI....              L WORD     0100        LIST_SEG

@CPU....              TEXT       0101h
@FILENAME...          TEXT       test
@VERSION....          TEXT       510

     32 Source Lines
     32 Total Lines
     13 Symbols

48012 + 311647 Bytes symbol space free

      0 Warning Errors
      0 Severe Errors
```

In this example the SEGMENT and ENDS statements are used to name three segments. One for the program, one for data, and one for stack. STACK must be used after the SEGMENT directive to indicate the STACK segment to the linker. Also notice that the ASSUME statement indicates to the assembler which segment is used for CS, which is used for DS, and which is used for SS.

MACRO Sequences

Macrosequences are used to define commonly used sequences for a program that you do not wish to make into procedures. Each time that a macrosequence is invoked in a program the instructions defined for the macro are placed into the program. Macros are constructed with the MACRO and ENDM statements. MACRO is used to define the name and parameters for the macrosequence and ENDM is used to indicate the end. Example A–7 illustrates a simple macro that is used to sum two 16-bit parameters and leave the sum in the AX register. Notice how the parameters are defined, how the macrosequence is named, and how the sequence is used in the program that follows the definition. The .LALL statement is used to expand the macrosequence each time that it is used in a program. The sequence is indicated by a number to the left of each command that is expanded. If the .LALL statement is replaced with the .SALL statement, the macros are not expanded. Refer to Example A–8 where the same sequence is used without expansion.

EXAMPLE A–7

```
0000                      DATA_SEG SEGMENT

0000 0000                     DATA1   DW    ?
0002 0000                     DATA2   DW    ?
0004 0000                     DATA3   DW    ?
0006 0000                     DATA4   DW    ?
0008 0000                     ANS1    DW    ?
000A 0000                     ANS2    DW    ?

000C                      DATA_SEG   ENDS
```

```
                                    ADDEM      MACRO          A1,A2,A3

                                    PUSH       AX
                                    MOV        AX,A1
                                    ADD        AX,A2
                                    MOV        A3,AX
                                    POP        AX

                                    ENDM

0000                         PROGRAM   SEGMENT

                                    ASSUME     CS:PROGRAM,DS:DATA_SEG

                                    .LALL      ;list macro

                                    START      PROC      FAR

0000 B8---R                                    MOV        AX,DATA_SEG
0003 8E D8                                     MOV        DS,AX

                                    ADDEM      DATA1,DATA2,ANSI1
0005 50                1                       PUSH       AX
0006 A1 0000 R         1                       MOV        AX,DATA1
0009 03 06 0002 R      1                       ADD        AX,DATA2
000D A3 0008 R         1                       MOV        ANS1,AX
0010 58                1                       POP        AX
                                    ADDEM      DATA3,DATA4,ANS2
0011 50                1                       PUSH       AX
0012 A1 0004 R         1                       MOV        AX,DATA3
0015 03 06 0006 R      1                       ADD        AX,DATA4
0019 A3 000A R         1                       MOV        ANS2,AX
001C 58                1                       POP        AX

001D CB                1                       RET

001E                         START             ENDP

001E                 PROGRAM       ENDS

                             END       START
```

EXAMPLE A-8

```
0000                         DATA_SEG     SEGMENT

0000 0000                    DATA1     DW     ?
0002 0000                    DATA2     DW     ?
0004 0000                    DATA3     DW     ?
0006 0000                    DATA4     DW     ?
0008 0000                    ANS1      DW     ?
000A 0000                    ANS2      DW     ?

000C                         DATA_SEG ENDS
```

```
                              ADDEM           MACRO   A1,A2,A3

                                              PUSH    AX
                                              MOV     AX,A1
                                              ADD     AX,A2
                                              MOV     A3,AX
                                              POP     AX

                                              ENDM
0000                          PROGRAM       SEGMENT

                              ASSUME          CS:PROGRAM,DS:DATA_SEG

                              .SALL           ;suppress listing macros

0000                          START           PROC    FAR

000 B8  --- R                                 MOV     AX,DATA_SEG
0003 8E D8                                    MOV     DS,AX

                                              ADDEM   DATA1,DATA2,ANS1
                                              ADDEM   DATA3,DATA4,ANS2

001D CB                                       RET

001E                          START           ENDP

001E                          PROGRAM  ENDS

                                              END     START
```

DOS FUNCTION CALLS

In order to use these calls, place the function call number into register AH and load all
other pertinent information into registers as prescribed in the table. Once this is accomplished, follow with an INT 21H instruction to complete the sequence. Example A–9
illustrates a sequence of instructions that will display an ASCII A on the CRT screen at
the current cursor position. More examples of how to use the DOS function INT 21H are
in the following list and Table A–3.

EXAMPLE A–9

```
0000 B4 06          MOV AH,6
0002 B6 41          MOV DH,'A'
0004 CD 21          INT 21H
```

TABLE A–3 Extended
ASCII codes

Code(s)	Key
03H	Null
0FH	Shift-tab
10H–19H	Alt Q, W, E, R, T, Y, U, I, O, and P
1EH–26H	Alt Z, X, C, V, B, N, and M
3BH–44H	Function keys F1–F10
47H	Home
48H	Up arrow
49H	Page up
4BH	Left arrow
4DH	Right arrow
4FH	End key
50H	Down arrow
51H	Page down
52H	Insert
53H	Delete
54H–5DH	Shift-function keys F1–F10
5EH–67H	Control-function keys F1–F10

*DOS Function
21H Calls*   *Description*

00H   *Terminates a program.* On entry, AH = 00H and CS = the program segment prefix address. On exit, DOS is entered.

01H   *Reads the keyboard.* On entry, AH = 01H and upon exit, AL = the character typed (in ASCII code) on the keyboard. If AL = 00H then the function call must be invoked again to read the extended ASCII character that was typed. Refer to Table A-3, which follows this list, for the extended ASCII coded characters. This call automatically echoes the character typed on the screen.

02H   *Write character to standard output device.* On entry, AH = 02H and the code of the character to be output must be in DL.

03H   *Reads character from standard auxiliary device.* On entry, AH = 02H and upon exit, AL = the character from the auxiliary device.

04H   *Write character to standard auxiliary device.* On entry, AH = 04H and DL = the character to be output to the standard auxiliary device.

05H   *Write character to standard printer device.* On entry, AH = 05H and the character to be printed must be in DL.

DOS Function 21H Calls	Description
06H	*Direct console read/write.* On entry, AH = 06H and DL = 0FFH if this function is to read the console keyboard. If AH = 06H and DL = an ACSII character, this function displays the character on the screen. If a character is read from the keyboard (AH = 06H and DL = 0FFH), the zero flag indicates whether a character was typed. If a zero condition exists, then no character was typed. If the zero flag indicates a not zero condition, then a character was typed that appears in AL. If AL = 00H, then an extended character (see Table A–3) was typed and the function call must be invoked again to retrieve the extended character.
07H	*Direct console input without echo.* Performs the same function as 06H when DL = 0FFH, although DL is not used with function 07H and neither is the zero flag, because this function will not return until the key is actually typed.
08H	*Read standard input device without echo.* Performs the same function as 07H, except it reads the standard input device. This function checks to see whether a control-break was typed and executes an INT 23H if it was typed.
09H	*Display a character string.* On entry, AH = 09H and DS:DX indexes the character string to be displayed. The character string must end with a 24H ($).
0AH	*Buffered keyboard input.* On entry, AH = 0AH and DS:DX indexes the keyboard input buffer. The first byte of the keyboard buffer contains the size of the buffer (up to 255), the second byte is filled with the number of characters typed, and this is followed by the characters typed ending with the carriage return code (0DH). This function continues to read the keyboard until the specified number of characters has been read or until the carriage return (enter) key is typed.
0BH	*Test the status of the standard input device.* On entry, AH = 0BH, and upon exit, AL = the status of the standard input device. If AL = 00H, no character is available, and if AL = 0FFH, then a character is available.
0CH	*Clear keyboard buffer and invoke keyboard function.* On entry, AH = 0CH and AL = 01H, 06H, 07H, or 0AH. The buffer is cleared and then the standard keyboard function in AL is performed.
0DH	*Flushes disk buffers.* Erases all file names currently stored in the disk buffers. This function does not close any files and care should be exercised in its use.
0EH	*Select default disk drive.* On entry, AH = 0EH and DL = the desired drive number. Note that 00H = drive A, 01H = drive B, 02H = drive C, and so forth. Upon return from this function AL indicates the total number of drives present in the system.

DOS Function 21H Calls	*Description*
0FH	*Open file with FCB.* On entry, AH = 0FH and DS:DX is the address of the unopened file control block. (File control blocks (FCB) are only used with early DOS software and should not be used with new programs unless required.) Figure A–1 illustrates the structure of the FCB. To open a file the file must either be present on the disk or must be created with function call 16H. Upon exit, AL = 00H if the file is opened and 0FFH if the file was not found.
10H	*Close file with FCB.* On entry, AH = 10H and DS:DX is the address of the FCB. On exit, if AL = 00H, the file was closed, and if it equals 0FFH, the file was not found.
11H	*Search for first match (FCB).* On entry, AH = 11H and DS:DX is the address of the FCB to be searched for on the disk. Note that wild card characters may be used in the FCB so that this function can be used to search the disk for similar file names or all file names. The ? wildcard is used to indicate any character in the file name section of the FCB. On exit, AL = 0FFH if no match was found.
12H	*Search for next match (FCB).* On entry, AH = 12H and DS:DX is the address of the FCB. On exit, AL = 0FFH if no match is found.
13H	*Delete file (FCB).* On entry, AH = 13H and DS:DX is the address of the FCB. On exit, AL = 00H if the file was deleted and 0FFH if the file was not deleted.
14H	*Sequential read (FCB).* On entry, AH = 14H and DS:DX is the address of an opened FCB. On exit, AL = 00H if the read was successful, 01H if the end of the file was encountered, 02H if the disk

FIGURE A–1 Contents of the file control block (FCB).

Offset	Contents
00H	Drive
01H	8-character filename
09H	3-character file extension
0CH	Current block number
0EH	Record size
10H	File size
14H	Creation date
16H	Reserved space
20H	Current record number
21H	Relative record number

DOS Function 21H Calls	Description
	transfer area was too small, and 03H if the end of the file was found with only a partial reading of the data.
15H	*Sequential write (FCB).* On entry, AH = 15H and DS:DX is the address of the opened FCB. On exit, AL = 00H for a successful write, 01H if the disk is full, and a 02H if the data transfer area was too small.
16H	*Create file (FCB).* On entry, AH = 16H and DS:DX is the address of an unopened FCB. This function both creates a new file on the disk and also opens the file as did function 0FH. On exit, AL = 00H if the file was created and 0FFH if the disk is full.
17H	*Rename a file (FCB).* On entry, AII = 17II and DS:DX is the address of a modified FCB. Refer to Figure A–2 for the modified FCB. On exit, AL = 00H if the file was renamed and 0FFH if it was not.
18H	*Not used.*
19H	*Return current disk drive.* On entry, AH = 19H and on exit, AL = the current disk drive.
1AH	*Set disk transfer area (DTA).* On entry, AH = 1AH and DS:DX is the new DTA. This is normally set up by DOS as 128 bytes at offset 80H in the program prefix. DOS uses the DTA for all disk transfers.
1BH	*Get current drive file allocation table (FAT).* On entry, AH = 1BH and on exit, AL = the number of sectors per cluster, DS:DX = the address of the media-descriptor byte (see Figure A–3), CX = the sector size in bytes, and DX = the number of allocation unit or clusters. DS is changed by this function call, so be certain to save it before using this function.
1CH	*Get disk file allocation table for any drive.* On entry, AH = 1CH and DL = the drive number. On exit, AL = the number of sectors

FIGURE A–2   Contents of the modified file-control block (FCB).

Offset	Content
00H	Drive
01H	8-character filename
09H	3-character extension
0CH	Current block number
0EH	Record Size
10H	File size
14H	Creation date
16H	Second file name

FIGURE A–3 Contents of
the media-descriptor byte.

7	6	5	4	3	2	1	0
?	?	?	.?	?	?	?	?

Bit 0 = 0 if not two-sided
    = 1 if two-sided

Bit 1 = 0 if not eight sectors per track
    = 1 if eight sectors per track

Bit 2 = 0 if nonremovable
    = 1 if removable

DOS Function 21H Calls	Description
	per cluster, DS:BX = the address of the media-descriptor byte, CX = the sector size in bytes, and DX = the number of clusters.
1DH	*Not used.*
1EH	*Not used.*
1FH	*Not used.*
20H	*Not used.*
21H	*Random read using FCB.* On entry, AH = 21H and DS:DX is the address of an opened FCB. On exit, AL = 00H if the read is successful, 01H if the end of the file is reached, 02H if the data is too small, and 03H if the end of the record is reached and not all data are read.
22H	*Random write using FCB.* On entry, AH = 22H and DS:DX is the address of an opened FCB. On exit, AL = 00H if the write is successful, 01H if the disk is full, and 02H if the DTA is too small.
23H	*Return number of records (FCB).* On entry, AH = 23H and DS:DX = the address of an FCB. On exit, the number of records in the file is stored in the random record file of the FCB and AL = 00H if file was found and 0FFH if file was not found.
24H	*Set relative record size (FCB).* On entry, AH = 24H and DS:DX is the address of the file control block. This function sets the record field to the value contained in the current sequential and random record blocks of the FCB.
25H	*Set interrupt vector.* On entry, AH = 25H, AL = the interrupt vector number, and DS:DX is the address of the interrupt subroutine or procedure. Before changing the vector, it is suggested that you get the current vector using function 35H and store it for later so that it can be reset if needed.
26H	*Create new program segment.* On entry, AH = 26H and DX = the segment number or the new prefix. Refer to Figure A–3 for the program segment structure.

DOS Function 21H Calls	Description
27H	*Random file block read (FCB).* On entry, AH = 27H, CX = the number of records to read, and DS:DX is the address of the opened FCB. On exit, CX = the number of records read and AL = 00H if the read was successful, 01H if the end of the file was reached, 02H if the DTA was too small, and 03H if the end of the file was reached with only a partial read.
28H	*Random file block write (FCB).* On entry, AH = 28H, CX = the number of records to be written, and DS:DX is the address of the opened FCB. On exit, CX = the number of records written and AL = 00 if the write was successful, 01H if the disk is full, and 02H if the DTA is too small.
29H	*Parse the command line.* On entry, AH = 29H, AL = the parse mask, DS:SI is the address of the unopened FCB, and DS:DI is the address of the command line to parse. On exit, AL = 00H if no global file name characters are found, 01H if global file name characters are found, and 0FFH if the drive specifier is incorrect, DS:SI = the address of the first character following the file name, and ES:DI is the address of the first byte of the FCB. This function is used only with FCBs.
2AH	*Read system date.* On entry, AH = 2AH and on exit, AL = the day of the week (Sunday = 0 through Saturday which = 6), CX = the year (1980–2099), DH = the month, and DL = the day of the month.
2BH	*Write system date.* On entry, AH = 2BH, CX = year, DH = the month, and DL = the day of the month.
2CH	*Read system time.* On entry, AH = 2CH and on exit, CH = hours (0–23), CL = minutes, DH = seconds, and DL = hundredths of seconds.
2DH	*Write system time.* On entry, AH = 2DH, CH = hours, CL = minutes, DH = seconds, and DL = hundredths of seconds.
2EH	*Disk write verify.* On entry, AH = 2EH and AL = 00H to turn verify off and 01H to turn verify on.
2FH	*Read disk transfer address.* On entry, AH = 2FH and on exit, ES:BX contains the DTA address.
30H	*Read DOS version number.* On entry, AH = 30H and on exit AH = fractional DOS version number and AL = the whole number portion. For example, DOS Version 3.2 would be returned as a 3 in AL and a 2 in AH.
31H	*Terminate and stay resident.* On entry, AH = 31H, AL = the DOS return code, and DX = the number of paragraphs of memory to reserve for the program. A paragraph is 16 bytes of memory.

DOS Function 21H Calls	*Description*
32H	*Not used.*
33H	*Test Control-Break.* On entry, AH = 33H, AL = 00H to request the current status of control-break processing or 01H to change the state, and DL = 01H to turn processing off and 01H to turn processing on. On exit, DL = the state of control-break processing.
34H	*Not used.*
35H	*Read interrupt vector.* On entry, AH = 35H and AL = the interrupt vector number. On exit, ES:BX contains the address of the interrupt service procedure or handler.
36H	*Determine disk-free space.* On entry, AH = 36H and DL = the disk drive number. On exit, AX = 0FFFFH if the disk drive number is invalid or the number of clusters on the media, BX = the number of free clusters, CX = the number of bytes per sector, and DX = the number of cluster on the drive.
37H	*Not used.*
38H	*Return country.* On entry, AH = 38H, AL = 00H for the current country or the country code, BX = a 16-bit country code if required, DS:DX = the address of the data buffer. On exit, AX = error code if the carry flag is set, BX = country code, and DS:DX is the address of the buffer.
39H	*Create subdirectory.* On entry, AH = 39H and DS:DX is the address of the ASCII-Z string that contains the name of the subdirectory. (An ASCII-Z string is a character string that terminates with a NUL (00H). On exit, the carry flag is set if an error occurs.
3AH	*Erase subdirectory.* On entry, AH = 3AH and DS:DX is the address of the ASCII-Z string that contains the name of the subdirectory to remove. On exit, if carry is set, an error occurred preventing the removal of the subdirectory.
3BH	*Change current directory.* On entry, AH = 3BH and DS:DX contains the address of the new subdirectory. On exit, a carry indicates an error.
3CH	*Create a new file.* On entry, AH = 3CH, CX = the attributes of the file to be created, and DS:DX contains the address of the ASCII-Z file name. On exit, carry is set for an error; otherwise, AX = the handle number of the file created. This function also opens the file that it creates. The attributes are as follows and can be used in any combination: 01H = read-only, 02H = hidden file, 04H = system file, 08H = volume label, 10H = subdirectory, and 20H = archive bit set.
3DH	*Open a file.* On entry, AH = 3DH, AL = access code (00H = read only, 01H = write access, and 02H = read/write), and DS:DX

DOS Function 21H Calls	*Description*
	contains the address of the ASCII-Z string file name. On exit, if the carry flag is set, an error occurred; otherwise, AX = the file handle.
3EH	*Close a file.* On entry, AH = 3EH and BX = the file handle, and on exit carry is set if the file cannot be closed.
3FH	*Read from a file.* On entry, AH = 3FH, BX = file handle, CX = the number of bytes to be read, and DS:DX = the address of the data buffer. On exit, if the carry is set, an error has occurred; otherwise, AX = the number of bytes actually read from the file.
40H	*Write to a file.* On entry, AH = 40H, BX = file handle, CX = the number of bytes to be written, and DS:DX is the address of the data to be written. On exit, if carry is set an error occurred; otherwise, AX = the number of bytes actually written.
41H	*Delete a file.* On entry, AH = 41H and DS:DX contains the address of the ASCII-Z string file name to be deleted. On exit, the carry is-set to indicate an error.
42H	*Move file pointer.* On entry, AH = 42H; AL = 00H if the pointer is to be moved from the start of the file, 01H if the pointer is to be moved from the current location, or 02H if the pointer is to be moved from the end of the file; BX = the file handle; and CX and DX are combined for the number of bytes that the pointer is to be moved. Note that CX is the most significant part and DX the least. Upon exit, the carry flag is set for an error; otherwise, AX and DX contain the new pointer location.
43H	*Read/write file attributes.* On entry, AH = 43H, AL = 00H to read the attribute and 01H to write a new attribute, CX = the desired attribute, and DS:DX contains the address of the ASCII-Z string file name. On exit, carry is set for an error; otherwise, CX = the attribute number. Refer to function 3CH for a list of the attribute codes.
44H	*Device I/O control.* On entry, AH = 44H and AL = one of the following:

00H	=	read device status
01H	=	write device status
02H	=	read data from device
03H	=	write data to device
04H	=	read data from disk drive
05H	=	write data to disk drive
06H	=	read input status
07H	=	read output status
08H	=	removable media?

DOS Function 21H Calls	Description
	09H = local or remote device?
	0AH = local or remote handle?
	0BH = change entry count
	0DH = generic driver request
	0EH = return number of logical devices
	0FH = change number of logical devices

Entry parameters use BX as a file handle, CX as the number of bytes, and DS:DX to address a memory buffer or an ASCII-Z string file name. Exit parameters use carry to indicate an error if it is set; otherwise, AX or DX contain parameters.

45H	*Duplicate file handle.* On entry, AH = 45H and BX = the current file handle. On exit, an error is indicated by a carry; otherwise, AX is the new duplicate file handle that points to the same file at thesame position as the current handle.
46H	*Force a duplicate file handle.* On entry, AH = 46H, BX = the current file handle, and CX = the second file handle. On exit, a carry indicates an error. This functions like 45H, except the user selects the file handle number in CX, where function 45H selects the handle for the user.
47H	*Read current directory.* On entry, AH = 47H, DL = the drive number, and DS:SI addresses a 64-byte buffer where the name of the current directory will be stored. On exit, carry indicates an error; otherwise, the location that was addressed by DS:SI contains the name of the current directory.
48H	*Allocate memory.* On entry, AH = 48H and BX = the number of memory paragraphs to allocate. On exit, a carry indicates an error; otherwise, AX addresses the memory allocated. If an error has occurred, BX indicates the largest block of memory available for allocation.
49H	*Release allocated memory.* On entry, AH = 49H and ES = the segment address of the block of memory to release from allocation. On exit, a carry indicates an error.
4AH	*Modify allocated memory.* On entry, AH = 4AH, BX = the new block size, and ES = the segment address of the block. On exit, carry indicates an error. If an error has occurred, then BX contains the size of the largest available block.
4BH	*Load or execute a program.* On entry, AH = 4BH, AL = the function code (00H = load and execute the program and 03H = load the program, but do not execute it.), ES:BX = the address of the parameter block (see Figure A–4), and DS:DX = address of the ACSII-Z string command name. On exit, a carry indicates an error.

FIGURE A–4 The parameter blocks used with function 4BH (EXEC). (a) For function code 00H. (b) For function code 03H.

(a)

Offset	Contents
00H	Environment address (segment)
02H	Command line address (offset)
04H	Command line address (segment)
06H	File control block 1 address (offset)
08H	File control block 1 address (segment)
0AH	File control block 2 address (segment)
0CH	File control block 2 address (offset)

(b)

Offset	Contents
00H	Overlay destination segment address
02H	Relocation factor

DOS Function 21H Calls	Description
4CH	*Terminate a process.* On entry, AH = 4CH and AL = the return status code. This function returns control to DOS and passes the return status code to the DOS ERRORLEVEL batch processing system.
4DH	*Read return code.* On entry, AH = 4DH and on exit, AX = the return code. This function is used to obtain the return status code created by the EXEC function. The return codes are: 01H = normal termination, 01H = control-break termination, 02H = critical device error, and 03H = termination by a INT 31H.
4EH	*Find first matching file.* On entry, AH = 4EH, CX = file attribute used for searching, and DS:DX addresses the ASCII-Z string file name. On exit, carry is set if the file is not found. The file information is found in the DTA, as illustrated in Figure A–5.
4FH	*Find next matching file.* On entry, AH = 4FH and on exit, if carry is set, no additional files have been found. This call also uses the DTA as illustrated in Figure A–5 for passing the parameters.
50H	*Not used.*
51H	*Not used.*
52H	*Not used.*
53H	*Not used.*
54H	*Read disk verify status.* On entry, AH = 54H and on exit, AL = 00H indicates that disk verify is off and AL = 01H indicates that disk verify is on.
55H	*Not used.*

FIGURE A–5 Data transfer
area (DTA) used to find a file.

Offset	Contents
15H	Attributes
16H	Creation time
18H	Creation date
1AH	Low word file size
1CH	High word file size
1EH	Search file name

DOS Function
21H Calls   *Description*

56H   *Rename a file.* On entry, AH = 56H, ES:DI = the address of the
                 ASCII-Z string that contains the new file name, and DS:DX = the
                 address of the ASCII-Z string that contains the old file name. On
                 exit, a carry indicates an error.

57H   *Read/write a file's date and time.* On entry, AH = 57H, AL = the
                 function code (00H = read time and date and 01H = write time
                 and date), BX = the file handle, CX = the new time, and DX =
                 the new date. On exit, a carry indicates an error; otherwise, CX =
                 the time and DX = the date.

58H   *Not used.*

59H   *Get extended error information.* On entry, AH = 59H, and BX = 0
                 for DOS Version 3.X. On exit, AX = the extended error code,
                 BH = the error class, BL = the recommended action, and CH =
                 the locus.

                 Errors found in AX.
                         01H = invalid function number
                         02H = File not found
                         03H = path not found
                         04H = no file handles available
                         05H = access denied
                         06H = insufficient memory
                 Error class found in BH.
                         01H = no resources available
                         02H = temporary error
                         03H = authorization error
                         04H = internal software error
                         05H = hardware error
                         06H = system failure
                         07H = application software error
                         08H = item not found

DOS Function
21H Calls   *Description*

                          09H = invalid format
                          0AH = item locked
                          0BH = media error
                          0CH = item already exists
                          0DH = unknown error
               Recommended action in BL.
                          01H = retry operation
                          02H = delay and retry operation
                          03H = user retry
                          04H = abort processing
                          05H = immediate exit
                          06H = ignore error
                          07H = retry with user intervention
               Locus in CH.
                          01H = unknown source
                          02H = block device error
                          03H = network error
                          04H = serial device error
                          05H = memory error

5AH   *Create unique file name.* On entry, AH = 5AH, CX = the attribute of the new file, and DS:DX = the address of the ASCII-Z file directory path. On exit, a carry indicates an error. The ASCII-Z file directory path must end with a backslash (/) and on exit, the backslash will be followed by the new file name.

5BH   *Create a DOS file.* On entry, AH = 5BH, CX = the attribute of the new file, and DS:DX = the address of the ASCII-Z string that contains the new file name.

5CH   *Lock/unlock contents.* On entry, AH = 5CH, AL = 00H to lock and 01H to unlock, BX = the file handle, CX:DX = the offset address of the locked/unlocked area, and SI:DI = the number of bytes to lock or unlock, beginning at the offset address indicated. On exit, a carry indicates an error.

5DH   *Not used.*

5E00H   *Get name for network.* On entry, AX = 5E00H and DS:DX = the address of the 15-byte ASCII-Z string name buffer. On exit, carry is set for an error; otherwise, CL = the NETBIOS number.

5E02H   *Define network printer.* On entry, AX = 5E02H, BX = the redirection list index, CX = the length of the setup string, and DS:SI =

DOS Function	
21H Calls	*Description*
	the address of the printer setup buffer. On exit, carry is set to indicate an error.
5E03H	*Read network printer setup.* On entry, AX = 5E03H, BX = the redirection list index, and DS:SI = the address of the printer setup buffer. On exit, a carry indicates an error; otherwise, CX = the length of the data, ES:DI = the address of the printer, setup buffer.
5F02H	*Read redirection list entry.* On entry, AX = 5F02H, BX = the redirection list index, DS:DI = the address of a 128-byte local device name buffer, and ES:SI = the address of a 128-byte network device buffer name. On exit, carry indicates an error; otherwise, BH = the device status (bit 0 = 0 if the device is not valid and 1 if the device is valid), BL = the device type, and CX = the stored parameter value.
5F03H	*Redirect a network device.* On entry, AX = 5F03H, BH = the device type (03H = printer and 04H = disk drive), CX = caller number, DS:DI = the address of a 128-byte buffer containing the local device name, and ES:SI the address of a 128-byte buffer containing the network device name. On exit, a carry indicates an error.
62H	*Read program segment prefix.* On entry, AH = 62H and on exit, BX = the address of the program segment prefix. Refer to Figure A–6 for the program segment prefix.

Function usage example number 1 (Example A-10):

Task: Create a file named FRED.TST and store 00H in 300H bytes of this file.

EXAMPLE A–10

```
0000                           DATA_SEG      SEGMENT

0000 0300[                       BUFFER    DB    300H DUP (0)
          00
                                 ]
0300 46 52 45 44 2E 54           FILE_NAME DB    'FRED.TST',0
     53 54 00
0309                           DATA_SEG   ENDS

0000                           PROG_SEG   SEGMENT

                                 ASSUME     CS:PROG_SEG,DS:DATA_SEG

0000                           MODULE     PROC       FAR

                                 ;load DS

0000 B8---R                                MOV   AX,DATA_SEG
0003 8E D8                                 MOV   DS,AX
```

FIGURE A–6 Contents of the program segment prefix (PSP).

Offset	Content
00H	INT 20H
02H	Top of memory
04H	Reserved
05H	Opcode
06H	Number of bytes in segment
0AH	Terminate address (offset)
0CH	Terminate address (segment)
0EH	Control break address (offset)
10H	Control break address (segment)
12H	Critical error address (offset)
14H	Critical error address (segment)
16H	Reserved
2CH	Environment address (segment)
2EH	Reserved
50H	DOS call
52H	Reserved
5CH	File control block 1
6CH	File control block 2
80H	Command line length
81H	Command line

EXAMPLE A–10 (*continued*)

```
                              ;create and open FRED.TST

0005 B4 3C                              MOV   AH,3CH
0007 B9 0000                            MOV   CX,0
000A BA 0300 R                          MOV   DX,OFFSET FILE_NAME
000D CD 21                              INT   21H

                              ;save file handle in BX

000F 8B D8                              MOV   BX,AX

                              ;write file buffer
```

```
0011 B4 40                              MOV    AH,40H
0013 B9 0300                            MOV    CX,300H
0016 BA 0000 R                          MOV    DX,OFFSET BUFFER
0019 CD 21                              INT    21H

                        ;close file

001B B4 3E                              MOV    AH,3EH
001D CD 21                              INT    21H

                        ;return to DOS

001F B4 4C                              MOV    AH,4CH
0021 CD 21                              INT    21H

0023                    MODULE      ENDP
0023                    PROG_SEG    ENDS
                                    END
```

In this example notice that the DS register is first loaded with the location of the data segment (DATA _ SEG). Next the file is created and opened with function call 3CH. Next the BUFFER is written to the disk file. Finally, the file is closed with function call 3EH. No attempt was made to detect errors, but normal practice dictates that errors are tested for and also handled as they appear. Errors that occur with the DISK function calls set the carry flag that could be tested after each INT 21H with a JC to some error handler.

Function usage example 2 (Example A-11):

Task: Develop a procedure that will display the time of day on the CRT screen at the current cursor position.

EXAMPLE A-11

```
0000                    PROG_SEG            SEGMENT

                        ASSUME CS:PROG_SEG

                        PUBLIC DISP_TIME

0000                    DISP_TIME           PROC        FAR

                        ;get time

0000 B4 2C                              MOV         AH,2CH
0002 CD 21                              INT         21H

                        ;convert hours to BCD

0004 8A C5                              MOV         AL,CH
0006 32 E4                              XOR         AH,AH
0008 D4 0A                              AAM

                        ;test for 0 in tens of hours
```

```
000A 0A E4                                      OR        AH,AH
000C 74 09                                      JE        DISP_TIME1

                                ;if 10--23 hours display 10s of hours

000E 50                                         PUSH      AX
000F 8A C4                                       MOV       AL,AH
0011 04 30                                       ADD       AL,'0'
0013 E8 0035 R                                   CALL      DISP_CHAR
0016 58                                          POP       AX

                                ;display units of hours

0017                     DISP_TIME1:

0017 04 30                                       ADD       AL,'0'
0019 E8 0035 R                                   CALL      DISP_CHAR

                                ;display colon

001C B0 3A                                       MOV       AL,':'
001E E8 0035 R                                   CALL      DISP_CHAR

                                ;convert minutes to BCD

0021 8A C1                                       MOV       AL,CL
0023 32 E4                                       XOR       AH,AH
0025 D4 0A                                       AAM

                                ;display tens of minutes

0027 05 3030                                     ADD       AX,'00'
002A 50                                          PUSH      AX
002B 8A C4                                       MOV       AL,AH
002D E8 0035 R                                   CALL      DISP_CHAR
0030 58                                          POP       AX

                                ;display units of minutes

0031 E8 0035 R                                   CALL      DISP_CHAR
0034 CB                                          RET

0035                     DISP_TIME       ENDP

0035                     DISP_CHAR       PROC      NEAR

0035 8A D0                                       MOV       D1,AL
0037 B4 06                                       MOV       AH,6
0039 CD 21                                       INT       21H
003B C3                                          RET

003C                     DISP_CHAR       ENDP

003C                     PROG_SEG        ENDS

                                         ENDS
```

Other BIOS Function Calls

In addition to INT 21H some other interrupts prove useful in controlling the I/O environment of the computer. INT 10H is used to control the video interface. Presented here is a description of the INT 10H functions that apply to many of the common video interfaces in use today. These interfaces include, from the earliest to the latest, CGA (color graphics adapter), EGA (enhanced graphics adapter), VGA (video graphics array), and EVGA (extended video graphics array).

Video Mode Selection. The mode of operation for the video circuit is selected by placing a 00H into register AH, followed by loading one of the codes listed in Table A–4, into register AL, in order to select the mode of operation for the video system. After both registers are loaded, the INT 10H instruction follows. All modes listed are downward compatible, that is, a CGA mode functions on an EGA, VGA, or EVGA video adapter. Example A–12 illustrates how a video mode with a resolution of 640 × 400 is selected so that 256 colors can be displayed using an EVGA adapter.

EXAMPLE A–12

```
0000 B4 00      MOV   AH,0
0002 B0 5E      MOV   AL,5EH
0004 CD 10      INT   10H
```

Cursor Control. The cursor position is controlled with the INT 10H instruction for many of the modes listed in Table A–5. In all cases, AH determines the type of operation performed using the INT 10H instruction. Table A–5 lists many of these functions as they apply mainly to the CGA video adapter.

An example using these functions is the clear screen operation. Refer to Example A–13 for the software required to clear the screen and return to cursor to the upper-left corner of the screen. This functions as the CLS command does in BASIC.

EXAMPLE A–13

```
0000 2A FF      SUB   BH,BH   ;Read display page
0002 B4 08      MOV   AH,08H
0004 CD 10      INT   10H

0006 8A DF      MOV   BL,BH   ;Blank entire screen
0008 8A FC      MOV   BH,AH
000A 2B C9      SUB   CX,CX
000C BA 184F    MOV   DX,184FH
000F B8 0600    MOV   AX,0600H
0012 CD 10      INT   10H

0014 8A FB      MOV   BH,BL   ;Home cursor
0016 2B D2      SUB   DX,DX
0018 B4 02      MOV   AH,02H
001A CD 10      INT   10H
```

TABLE A–4 Video modes

Mode	Type	Columns	Rows	Resolution	Standard	Colors
00H	Text	40	25	320 × 200	CGA	2
00H	Text	40	25	320 × 350	EGA	2
00H	Text	40	25	360 × 400	VGA	2
01H	Text	40	25	320 × 200	CGA	16
01H	Text	40	25	320 × 350	EGA	16
01H	Text	40	25	360 × 400	VGA	16
02H	Text	80	25	640 × 200	CGA	2
02H	Text	80	25	640 × 350	EGA	2
02H	Text	80	25	720 × 400	VGA	2
03H	Text	80	25	640 × 200	CGA	16
03H	Text	80	25	640 × 350	EGA	16
03H	Text	80	25	720 × 400	VGA	16
04H	Gra	40	25	320 × 200	CGA	4
05H	Gra	40	25	320 × 200	CGA	2
06H	Gra	80	25	640 × 200	CGA	2
07H	Text	80	25	720 × 350	EGA	4
07H	Text	80	25	720 × 400	VGA	4
0DH	Gra	40	25	320 × 200	CGA	16
0EH	Gra	80	25	640 × 200	CGA	16
0FH	Gra	80	25	640 × 350	EGA	4
10H	Gra	80	25	640 × 350	EGA	16
11H	Gra	80	30	640 × 480	VGA	2
12H	Gra	80	30	640 × 480	VGA	16
13H	Gra	40	25	320 × 200	VGA	256
54H	Text	132	43	924 × 387	EVGA	16
54H	Text	132	43	1056 × 387	EVGA	16
55H	Text	132	25	924 × 400	EVGA	16
55H	Text	132	25	1056 × 400	EVGA	16
56H	Text	132	43	924 × 387	EVGA	4
56H	Text	132	43	1056 × 387	EVGA	4
57H	Text	132	25	924 × 400	EVGA	4
57H	Text	132	25	1056 × 400	EVGA	4
58H	Gra	100	75	800 × 600	EVGA	16
59H	Gra	100	75	800 × 600	EVGA	2
5EH	Gra	80	25	640 × 400	EVGA	256

Note: gra = graphics; AH = 00H; AL = mode.

TABLE A–5 Cursor control modes

Function	Description	
01H	Sets the cursor type	CH = start line
		CL = end line
02H	Sets cursor position	DH = row
		DL = column
		BH = page number
03H	Read cursor position	BH = page number
		DH = row
		DL = column
		CH = cursor type
		CL = cursor type
05H	Select display page	AL = new page number
06H	Scroll active page up	AH = number of lines blanked at the bottom of the window (0 for entire screen)
		CH = upper-left row
		CL = upper-left column
		DH = lower-right row
		DL = lower-right column
		BH = attribute for blanks
07H	Scroll active page down	AL = number of lines at top of the window
		CH = upper-left row
		CL = upper-left column
		DH = lower-right row
		DL = lower-right column
		BH = attribute for blanks
08H	Read at cursor position	BH = display page number
		AL = character read
		AH = attribute of character
09H	Write at cursor position	BH = display page number
		CX = count of characters
		AL = character to write
		BL = attribute of character
0AH	Write character only	BH = display page number
		CX = count of characters
		AL = character to write
0BH	Set color (CGA)	BH = color ID
		BL = color value
0CH	Write dot (CGA)	DX = row number
		CX = column number
		AL = color value
0DH	Read dot (CGA)	DX = row number
		CX = column number
		AL = value of dot read
0FH ·	Read current video mode	AL = mode currently set
		AH = number of columns
		BH = current display page

Note: ATL = function.

INT 11H

This function is used to determine the type of equipment installed in the system. To use this call, the AX register is first set to an FFFFH and then the INT 11H instruction is executed. In return, INT 11H, provides the information as listed in Figure A–7.

INT 12H

The memory size is determined by using INT 12H. Upon a return from an INT 12H, the AX register indicates how many 1K-byte blocks of memory are currently installed in the computer.

INT 13H

This call controls the 5¼-inch disk drives attached to the system. Table A–6 lists the functions available for controlling the disk drives. The following registers are used during the read, write, and verify functions (AH = 02H, 03H, and 04H): DL = drive number (0–3), DH = head number (0–1), CH = track number (0–39), CL = sector number (1–9), AL = number of sectors (1–9), and ES:BX = the address of the disk data transfer memory buffer. A carry on return indicates that the function failed.

FIGURE A–7 The contents of AX as it indicates the equipment attached to the computer.

15	14	13	12	11	10	9	8	7	6	5	4	3	2	1	0
P1	P0		G	S2	S1	S0	D2	D1							

P1, P0 = number of parallel ports
G = 1 if game I/O attached
S2, S1, S0 = number of serial ports
D2, D1 = number of disk drives

TABLE A–6 INT 13H BIOS function

AH	Description
00H	Reset disk system
01H	Read status into AL
02H	Read desired sectors into memory
03H	Write desired sectors from memory
04H	Verify desired sectors

FIGURE A–8 Memory map of DOS illustrating the first 1M bytes of memory.

FFFFF

A0000

9FFFF

00000

Read-only memory system

Transient program area

DOS System Memory Map

Refer to Figure A–8 for a map of the first 1M byte of memory. In 80286-, 80386-, and 80486-based machines the memory can extend above this 1M-byte boundary to form *extended memory*. Extended memory begins at address 100000H and continues to memory location FFFFFFH on the 80286 microprocessor (16M bytes) and to location FFFFFFFFH on the 80386 and 80486 microprocessors (4G bytes).

DOS Low Memory Assignments

Table A–7 illustrates the low memory assignments (00000H–005FFH) for the DOS-based microprocessor. Location 00400H–004EFH is the BIOS data area. BIOS is the binary I/O system that is stored on EPROMs located at and above memory addresses C0000H. The exact location(s) of the BIOS EPROMs is (are) determined by the hardware configuration of your system.

TABLE A-7 Low memory assignments

Addresses	Purpose
00000–002FF	System interrupt vectors
00300–003FF	System interrupt vectors, power on, and bootstrap area
00400–00407	COM1–COM4 I/O port base addresses
00408–0040F	LPT1–LPT4 I/O port base addresses
00410–00411	Equipment flag word, returned in AX by an INT 11H

Bits	Purpose
15–14	Number of printers (LPT1–LPT4)
13	Internal MODEM installed
12	Joystick installed
11–9	Number of communications ports (COM1–COM4)
8	Unused
7–6	Number of disk drives
5–4	Initial video mode (01 = 40 × 25 black and white using color card, 10 = 80 × 25 black and white using color card, 11 = monochrome card)
3–2	Unused
1	Math coprocessor installed
0	IPL disk installed

Addresses	Purpose
00412	Reserved
00413–00414	Memory size in K bytes (0–640)
00415–00416	Reserved
00417	Keyboard control

Bits	Purpose
7	Insert locked
6	Caps locked
5	Numbers locked
4	Scroll locked
3	Alternate key pressed
2	Control key pressed
1	Left shift key pressed
0	Right shift keypressed

Addresses	Purpose
00418	Keyboard control

Bits	Purpose
7	Insert key pressed
6	Caps lock key pressed
5	Numbers lock key pressed
4	Scroll lock key pressed
3	Pause locked

Addresses	Purpose
	2 System request key pressed
	1 Left alternate key pressed
	0 Right control key pressed
00419	Alternate keyboard entry
0041A–0041B	Keyboard buffer header pointer
0041C–0041D	Keyboard buffer tail pointer
0041E–0043D	32-byte keyboard buffer
0043E–00448	Disk drive data area
00449–00466	Video control data area one
00467–0046B	Reserved
0046C–0046F	Timer counter
00470	Timer overflow
00471	Break key state
00472–00473	Reset flag
00474–00477	Hard disk drive data area
00478–0047B	LPT1–LPT4 timeout area
0047C–0047F	COM1–COM4 timeout area
00480–00481	Keyboard buffer start offset pointer
00482–00483	Keyboard buffer end offset pointer
00484–0048A	Video control data area two
0048B–00495	Hard drive control area
00496	Keyboard mode, state, and type flag
00497	Keyboard LED flags
00498–00499	Offset address to user wait complete flag
0049A–0049B	Segment address to user wait complete flag
0049C–0049D	User wait count (low word)
0049E–0049F	User wait count (high word)
004A0	Wait active flag
004A1–004A7	Reserved
004A8–004AB	Pointer to video parameters
004AC–004EF	Reserved
004F0–004FF	Applications program communications area
00500	Print screen status
00504	Single drive mode status
00510–00521	Used by BASIC
00522–0052F	Used by DOS for disk initialization
00530–00533	Used by MODE command
00534–005FF	Reserved

APPENDIX B

Instruction Set Summary

The instruction set summary, which follows this introductory material, contains complete information on the 8086, 8088, 80286, 80386, and 80486 microprocessor's instructions. Note that the numeric coprocessor instructions for the 80486 are covered in the chapter that deals with the 8087 family of numeric coprocessor. Each entry in the listing indicates the mnemonic of the instruction and a brief statement that explains what the instruction accomplishes. This is followed by the machine language coding for the instruction containing the opcode, displacement (*Disp*), and data (*Data*). Note that not all instructions contain a displacement and data. Listed next to the machine language version of the instruction are the flag bits and any changes that may occur for a given instruction. In this listing a blank indicates that a flag does not change, a ? indicates it does change, but the outcome is unpredictable, a * indicates it changes with a predictable outcome, and a 1 or 0 may appear to indicate that the flag is set or cleared.

Following are tables that list the function of codes that appear in the machine language forms of the instructions. These appears as oo for the modifier, rrr as a register, mmm as the register/memory option, and various other codes that are listed and explained. The letter w is used to indicate a word if it is a 1 and a byte if it is 0. The letter d indicates the direction and if a 1, a memory to register transfer occurs. The s bit indicates 8 bits of sign-extended immediate data if set and 16 bits if cleared. Table B–1 lists the modifier field found in the second or third byte of the instructions.

Table B–2 lists the memory-addressing modes available with the register/memory field as encoded in the instruction summary with an mmm. This table applies to all versions of the microprocessor.

Table B–3 lists the register options (rrr) when encoded for either 8- or 16-bit normal registers. This table also illustrates the 32-bit registers defined for the 80386 and 80486 microprocessors. Table B–4 lists rrr when used to specify a segment register.

When the 80386 and 80486 microprocessors are used, some of the definitions provided in the prior tables will change. Refer to Tables B–5 and B–6 for these changes as they apply to the 80386 microprocessor.

TABLE B–1 The modifier bits coded oo in the instruction summary

oo	Function
00	If mmm = 110, then a displacement follows, and if mmm is not 110, no displacement is used.
01	An 8-bit signed displacement
10	A 16-bit displacement
11	mmm specifies a register rather than a memory-addressing mode as contained in Table B–2

TABLE B–2 Register/memory field (mmm) description

mmm	Function
000	DS:[BX + SI + disp]
001	DS:[BX + DI + disp]
010	SS:[BP + SI + disp]
011	SS:[BP + SI + disp]
100	DS:[SI + disp]
101	DS:[DI + disp]
110	SS:[BP + disp]
111	DS:[BX + disp]

TABLE B–3 Register field options (rrr)

rrr	w = 0	w = 1	reg32
000	AL	AX	EAX
001	CL	CX	ECX
010	DL	DX	EDX
011	BL	BX	EBX
100	AH	SP	ESP
101	CH	BP	EBP
110	DH	SI	ESI
111	BH	DI	EDI

TABLE B–4 Register field segment register (rrr)

rrr	Register
000	ES
001	CS
010	SS
011	DS

TABLE B–5 Index registers as specified with rrr in the instruction listing for certain instructions

rrr	Index Register
000	EAX
001	ECX
010	EDX
011	EBX
100	No index
101	EBP
110	ESI
111	EDI

TABLE B–6 Possible 80386 and 80486 combinations for the oo rrr mmm fields as listed in the instruction summary using the 32-bit addressing mode

oo	mmm	rrr	Function
00	000	—	DS:[EAX]
00	001	—	DS:[ECX]
00	010	—	DS:[EDX]
00	011	—	DS:[EBX]
00	100	000	DS:[EAX + (scale*index)]
00	100	001	DS:[ECX + (scale*index)]
00	100	010	DS:[EDX + (scale*index)]
00	100	011	DS:[EBX + (scale*index)]
00	100	100	SS:[ESP + (scale*index)]
00	100	101	DS:[disp32 + (scale*index)]
00	100	110	DS:[ESI + (scale*index)]
00	100	111	DS:[EDI + (scale*index)]
00	101	—	DS:disp32
00	110	—	DS:[ESI]
00	111	—	DS:[EDI]
01	000	—	DS:[EAX + disp8]
01	001	—	DS:[ECX + disp8]
01	010	—	DS:[EDX + disp8]
01	011	—	DS:[EBX + disp8]
01	100	000	DS:[EAX + (scale*index) + disp8]
01	100	001	DS:[ECX + (scale*index) + disp8]
01	100	010	DS:[EDX + (scale*index) + disp8]
01	100	011	DS:[EBX + (scale*index) + disp8]
01	100	100	SS:[ESP + (scale*index) + disp8]
01	100	101	SS:[EBP + (scale*index) + disp8]

TABLE B–6 *continued*

oo	mmm	rrr	Function
01	100	110	DS:[ESI + (scale*index) + disp8]
01	100	111	DS:[EDI + (scale*index) + disp8]
01	101	—	SS:[EBP + disp8]
01	110	—	DS:[ESI + disp8]
01	111	—	DS:[EDI + disp8]
10	000	—	DS:[EAX + disp32]
10	001	—	DS:[ECX + disp32]
10	010	—	DS:[EDX + disp32]
10	011	—	DS:[EBX + disp32]
10	100	000	DS:[EAX + (scale*index) + disp32]
10	100	001	DS:[ECX + (scale*index) + disp32]
10	100	010	DS:[EDX + (scale*index) + disp32]
10	100	011	DS:[EBX + (scale*index) + disp32]
10	100	100	SS:[ESP + (scale*index) + disp32]
10	100	101	SS:[EBP + (scale*index) + disp32]
10	100	110	DS:[ESI + (scale*index) + disp32]
10	100	111	DS:[EDI + (scale*index) + disp32]
10	101	—	SS:[EBP + disp32]
10	110	—	DS:[ESI + disp32]
10	111	—	DS:[EDI + disp32]

Note: disp8 = 8-bit displacement and disp32 = 32-bit displacement.

Table B–7 illustrated the effective address calculations that apply only to the 8086/8088 microprocessors. These are used as indicated in the examples given with each addressing mode. These times do not apply to the 80286, 80386, and 80486 microprocessors.

The instruction set summary in the following section lists all of the 8086–80486 instructions in machine code form with examples. It also illustrates the effect of each instruction on the flag bits. In this list a * is used to indicate a predictable change in a flag bit and a ? indicates an unpredictable change. If a blank column appears under a flag bit, then the flag bit remains unchanged by the instruction. Missing from the table are the segment override prefixes CS (2EH), SS (36H), DS (3EH), ES (26H), FS (64H), and GS(65H). These prefixes are one byte in length as listed in the prior sentence and are placed in the memory before an instruction that they are used with.

The D-bit in the code segment descriptor indicates the default size of the operand and the address for 80386 and 80486 instructions. If D = 1, then all addresses and operands are 32 bits, and if D is a zero, all addresses and operands are 16 bits. In the real mode the D-bit is set to a zero by the 80386 and 80486 so that operands and addresses are 16 bits.

TABLE B–7   Effective address calculations for the 8086 and 8088 microprocessors

Type	Clocks	Example
Base or index	5	MOV CL,[DI]
Displacement	6	MOV AL,DATA
Base plus index [BP + DI] or [BX + SI]	7	MOV BL,[BP + DI]
Base plus index [BP + SI = or [BX + DI]	8	MOV CL,[BP + SI]
Displacement plus base or index	9	MOV DH,[DI + 20]
Base plus index plus displacement [BP + DI + disp] or [BX + SI + disp]	11	MOV CX,DATA[BX + SI]
Base plus index plus displacement [BP + SI + disp] or [BX + DI + disp]	12	MOV CX,[BX + DI + 2]
Segment override	ea + 2	MOV AL,ES:DATA

The address-size prefix (67H) must be placed before instructions in the 80386 and 80486 only, to change the default address size as selected by the D-bit. For example, the MOV AX,[ECX] instruction must have the address-size prefix placed before it in machine code only if the default size is 16 bits. If the default size is 32 bits, then the address prefix is not needed with this instruction. The operand-size prefix (66H) functions in much the same manner as the address-size prefix. In the previous example, the operand size is 16 bits. If the D-bit selects 32 bit operands and addresses, this instruction requires the operand-size prefix to change the operand size from 32 bits to 16 bits for this instruction. In many systems, the D-bit is cleared so that the operand size is 16 bits. If 32 bit addresses or operands are required, then the instruction is prefixed.

INSTRUCTION SET SUMMARY

AAA	ASCII adjust for addition		

00110111		O D I T S Z A P C ? ? ? * ? *	

Examples		Clocks	
AAM	8086	8	
	8088	8	
	80286	3	
	80386	4	
	80486	3	

AAD	ASCII adjust before division		

11010101 00001010		O D I T S Z A P C ? * * ? * ?	

Examples		Clocks	
AAD	8086	60	
	8088	60	
	80286	14	
	80386	19	
	80486	14	

AAM	ASCII adjust after multiplication		

11000100 00001010		O D I T S Z A P C ? * * ? * ?	

Examples		Clocks	

AAM		8086	83
		8088	83
		80286	16
		80386	17
		80486	15

AAS	ASCII adjust after subtraction		

00111111		O D I T S Z A P C ? ? ? ★ ? ★	
Examples		Clocks	
AAS		8086	8
		8088	8
		80286	3
		80386	4
		80486	3

ADC	Add with carry		

000100dw	oorrmmm disp	O D I T S Z A P C ★ ★ ★ ★ ★	
	Examples	Clocks	
ADC reg, reg	ADC AX,BX	8086	3
	ADC DI,SI	8088	3
	ADC AL,CL	80286	2
	ADC BL,DL	80386	2
	ADC EAX,EBX	80486	1
ADC mem,reg	ADC DATA,AL	8086	16+ea
	ADC LIST,SI	8088	b=16+ea w=24+ea
	ADC DATA[DI],CL	80286	7

	ADC NUMB,BX	80386	7
	ADC [DI+3],DL	80486	3
ADC reg,mem	ADC AX,DATA	8086	9+ea
	ADC DI,DATA [SI]	8088	b= 9+ea w=13+ea
	ADC AL,[SI+2]	80286	7
	ADC BL,[BX+SI]	80386	6
		80486	2

100000sw   oo010mmm   disp   data

	Examples		Clocks
ADC reg,imm	ADC BX,3	8086	4
	ADC DI,1AH	8088	4
	ADC DL,34	80286	3
	ADC BL,'L'	80386	3
		80486	1
ADC mem,imm	ADC DATA,33	8086	17+ea
	ADC LIST,'A'	8088	b=17+ea w=23+ea
	ADC DATA[DI],1	80286	7
		80386	7
		80486	3

0001010w   data

	Examples		Clocks
ADC acc,imm	ADC AX,3	8086	4
	ADC AH,1AH	8088	4
	ADC AL,34	80286	3

		80386	2
		80486	1

ADD	Add		

000000dw	oorrrmmm disp		O D I T S Z A P C
			* * * * * *

	Examples		Clocks
ADD reg,reg	ADD CX,BX	8086	3
	ADD RP,SI	8088	3
	ADD BH,CL	80286	2
	ADD BL,AL	80386	2
		80486	1
ADD mem,reg	ADD NUMB,DL	8086	16+ea
	ADD LIST,SP	8088	b=16+ea w=24+ea
	ADD DATA[BX],CH	80286	7
	ADD [SI+9],DL	80386	7
		80486	3
ADD reg,mem	ADD CX,DATA_A4	8086	9+ea
	ADD DI,DATA[BX]	8088	b= 9+ea w=13+ea
	ADD AH,[SI+20H]	80286	7
	ADD CL,[BX+DI]	80386	6
		80486	2

100000sw	oo000mmm disp data		

	Examples		Clocks
ADD reg,imm	ADD BP,3	8086	4
	ADD SI,1AH	8088	4

	ADD DH,34H	80286	3
	ADC CL,'R'	80386	2
		80486	1
ADD mem,imm	ADD DATA,33ADH	8086	17+ea
	ADD LIST,123	8088	b=17+ea w+23+ea
	ADD DATA[BX],1	80286	7
		80386	7
		80486	3

0000010w   data

		Examples		Clocks
ADD acc,imm	ADD AX,3	8086	4
	ADD AH,1AH	8088	4
	ADD AL,34	80286	3
		80386	2
		80486	1

AND	Logical AND

001000dw oorrrmmm disp

```
O D I T S Z A P C
0       * * ? * 0
```

		Examples		Clocks
AND reg,reg	AND CX,BX	8086	3
	AND BP,SI	8088	3
	AND BH,CL	80286	2
	AND BL,AL	80386	2
		80486	1
AND mem,reg	AND BIT,DL	8086	16+ea

	Examples		Clocks
	AND LIST3,BP	8088	b=16+ea w=24+ea
	AND DATA[BX],CH	80286	7
	AND [SI+10H],DL	80386	7
		80486	3
AND reg,mem	AND CX,DATA_A4	8086	9+ea
	AND SI,DATA[BX]	8088	b= 9+ea w=13+ea
	AND AL,[SI+20]	80286	7
	AND DL,[BP+DI]	80386	6
		80486	2

100000sw oo100mmm disp data

	Examples		Clocks
AND reg,imm	AND BP,1	8086	4
	AND SI,10H	8088	4
	AND DH,2	80286	3
	AND CL,8	80386	2
	AND CL,8	80486	1
AND mem,imm	AND DATA,0002H	8086	17+ea
	AND LIST,4	8088	b=17+ea w=23+ea
	AND DATA [BX],1	80286	7
		80386	7
		80486	3

0100010w data

	Examples		Clocks
AND acc,imm	AND AX,40H	8086	4

	AND AH,10H	8088	4
	AND AL,4	80286	3
		80386	2
		80486	1

ARPL	Adjust requested privilege level		

01100011 oorrrmmm disp   O D I T S Z A P C
                                                                       *

	Examples		Clocks
ARPLreg,reg	ARPL AX,BX	8086	—
	ARPL BX,SI	8088	—
	ARPL CX,DX	80286	10
	ARPL BX,AX	80386	20
		80486	9
ARPLmem,reg	ARPL NUMB,AX	8086	—
	ARPL LIST,SP	8088	—
		80286	11
		80386	21
		80486	9

BOUND	Check array bounds		

01100010 oorrrmmm disp   O D I T S Z A P C

	Examples		Clocks
BOUND reg,mem	BOUND DI,DATA	8086	—
	BOUND AX,[DI]	8088	—
		80286	13
		80386	10

		80486	7

BSF — Bit scan forward

00001111	10111100	oorrmmm	(di = 0, 2, or 4)

```
O D I T S Z A P C
              *
```

Examples			Clocks
BSF reg,reg	BSF CX,BX	8086	—
	BSF BX,SI	8088	—
	BSF EBX,EAX	80286	—
	BSF ECX,EDX	80386	10+3n
		80486	6-42
BSF REG,MEM	BSF DX,DATA	8086	—
	BSF BP,LISTG	8088	—
	BSF DATA,ECX	80286	—
	BSF [SI+10H],EAX	80386	10+3n
		80486	7-43

BSR — Bit scan reverse

00001111	10111101	oorrmmm	(di = 0, 2, or 4)

```
O D I T S Z A P C
              *
```

Examples			Clocks
BSR reg,reg	BSR AX,BX	8086	—
	BSR BP,DI	8088	—
	BSR EAX,ECX	80286	—
	BSR EBX,EDX	80386	10+3n

		80486	6-103
BSR REG,MEM	BSR BX,NUMBER	8086	—
	BSR CX,DATA	8088	—
	BSR DATA,EDX	80286	—
	BSR [SI+10],EDX	80386	10+3n
		80486	7-104

BSWAP	Byte swap		

```
00001111   11001rrr
```

O D I T S Z A P C

	Examples		Clocks
BSWAP reg	BSWAP EAX	8086	—
		8088	—
		80286	—
		80386	—
		80486	1

BT	Bit test		

```
00001111   10111010   oo100mmm   (di = 0, 2, or 4) da
```

O D I T S Z A P C
                                                                                  *

	Examples		Clocks
BT reg,imm8	BT AX,2	8086	—
	BT CX,4	8088	—
	BT BP,10H	80286	—
	BT CX,8	80386	3

		Examples		Clocks
	BT	AX,1	80486	3
BT mem,imm8	BT	DATA,2	8086	
	BT	LIST,8	8088	—
			80286	—
			80386	6
			80486	3

```
00001111   10100011   disp
```

```
                                                    O D I T S Z A P C
                                                                    *
```

		Examples		Clocks
BT reg,reg	BT	AX,CX	8086	—
	BT	CX,DX	8088	—
	BT	BP,AX	80286	—
	BT	SI,CX	80386	3
	BT	CX,BP	80486	3
BT mem,reg	BT	DATA,AX	8086	—
	BT	LIST,DX	8088	—
			80286	—
			80386	12
			80486	8

BTC		Bit test and complement

```
00001111   10111010   oo111mmm   disp
```

```
                                                    O D I T S Z A P C
                                                                    *
```

	Examples		Clocks

BTCreg,imm8	BTC AX,2	8086	—
	BTC CX,4	8088	—
	BTC BP,10H	80286	—
	BTC CX,8	80386	6
		80486	6
BTCmem,imm8	BTC DATA,2	8086	—
	BTC LIST,8	8088	—
	BTC DATA[DI],2	80286	—
		80386	8
		80486	8

```
00001111   10111011   disp
```

```
                                          O  D  I  T  S  Z  A  P  C
                                                                  *
```

	Examples		Clocks
BTCreg,reg	BTC DX,CX	8086	—
	BTC CX,BX	8088	—
	BTC BP,SI	80286	—
	BTC CX,DI	80386	6
		80486	3
BTCmem,reg	BTC DATA,CX	8086	—
	BTC LIST,DI	8088	—
	BTC DATA[DI],BP	80286	—
		80386	13
		80486	13

BTR	Bit test and reset

```
00001111   10111010   oo110mmm   disp   data
```

```
                                                    O D I T S Z A P C
                                                                    *
```

	Examples		Clocks
BTRreg,imm8	BTR AX,2	8086	—
	BTR CX,4	8088	—
	BTR BP,10H	80286	—
	BTR SI,9	80386	6
		80486	6
BTRmem,imm8	BTR DATA,2	8086	—
	BTR LIST,8	8088	—
		80286	—
		80386	8
		80486	8

```
00001111    10110011    disp
```

```
                                                    O D I T S Z A P C
                                                                    *
```

	Examples		Clocks
BTRreg,reg	BTR DX,CX	8086	—
	BTR CX,BX	8088	—
	BTR BP,SI	80286	—
	BTR CX,DI	80386	6
		80486	3
BTRmem,reg	BTR DATA,CX	8086	—
	BTR LIST,DI	8088	—
	BTR DATA[DI],BP	80286	—

		80386	13
		80486	13

BTS	Bit test and set		

```
00001111   10111010   oo101mmm   disp   data
```

```
                                            O D I T S Z A P C
                                                            *
```

	Examples	Clocks	
BTSreg,imm8	BTS AX,2	8086	—
	BTS CX,4	8088	—
	BTS BP,10H	80286	—
	BTS DI,44H	80386	6
		80486	6
BTSmem,imm8	BTS DATA,2	8086	—
	BTS LIST,8	8088	—
		80286	—
		80386	8
		80486	8

```
00001111   10101011   disp
```

	Examples	Clocks	
BTSreg,reg	BTS DX,CX	8086	—
	BTS CX,BX	8088	—
	BTS BP,SI	80286	—
	BTS SI,BP	80386	6

		80486	6
BTSmem,reg	BTS DATA,CX	8086	—
	BTS LIST,DI	8088	—
	BTS DATA[DI],BP	80286	—
		80386	13
		80486	13

CALL	Call procedure (subroutine)		

11101000 disp			O D I T S Z A P C

	Examples		Clocks
CALL label	CALL FOR_FUN	8086	19
(near)	CALL HOME	8088	23
	CALL ET	80286	7+z
	CALL WAITING	80386	7+z
		80486	3

10011010 disp			

	Examples		Clocks
CALL label	CALL FAR PTR DATE	8086	28
(far)	CALL WHAT	8088	36
	CALL WHERE	80286	13+z
	CALL PARSE	80386	17+z
		80486	3

11111111 oorrrmmm			

	Examples		Clocks
CALL reg	CALL AX	8086	16

	CALL BX	8088	20
	CALL CX	80286	7+z
	CALL DX	80386	7+z
		80486	5
CALL mem	CALL ADDRESS	8086	21+ea
	CALL [DI]	8088	29+ea
		80286	11+z
		80386	10+z
		80486	5

11111111   oo011mmm

	Examples		Clocks
CALL mem	CALL FAR_LIST[SI]	8086	37+ea
		8088	53+ea
		80286	16+z
		80386	22+z
		80486	5

CBW	Convert byte to word		

10011000   O D I T S Z A P C

	Examples		Clocks
CBW		8086	2
		8088	2
		80286	2
		80386	3
		80486	3

CDQ	Convert doubleword to quadword

10011001	O D I T S Z A P C

Examples		Clocks
CDQ	8086	—
	8088	—
	80286	—
	80386	2
	80486	2

CLC	Clear carry flag

11111000	O D I T S Z A P C
	0

Examples		Clocks
CLC	8086	2
	8088	2
	80286	2
	80386	2
	80486	2

CLD	Clear direction flag

11111100	O D I T S Z A P C
	0

Examples		Clocks
CLD	8086	2
	8088	2
	80286	2
	80386	2

		80486	2

CLI — Clear interrupt flag

11111010		O D I T S Z A P C
		0

	Examples		Clocks
CLI		8086	2
		8088	2
		80286	3
		80386	3
		80486	5

CLTS — Clear task switched flag

00001111	00000110	O D I T S Z A P C

	Examples		Clocks
CLTS		8086	—
		8088	—
		80286	2
		80386	5
		80486	7

CMC — Complement carry flag

11110101		O D I T S Z A P C
		*

	Examples		Clocks
CMC		8086	2
		8088	2

		80286	2
		80306	2
		80486	2

CMP		Compare operands	

001110dw oorrrmmm disp

```
O  D  I  T  S  Z  A  P  C
*           *  *  *  *  *
```

	Examples		Clocks
CMP reg,reg	CMP AX,BX	8086	3
	CMP DI,SI	8088	3
	CMP AL,CL	80286	2
	CMP BL,DL	80386	2
		80486	1
CMP mem,reg	CMP DATA,AL	8086	9+ea
	CMP LIST,SI	8088	b=9+ea w=13+ea
	CMP DATA[DI],CL	80286	7
	CMP [DI+3],DL	80386	5
		80486	2
CMP reg,mem	CMP AX,DATA	8086	9+ea
	CMP DI,DATA[SI]	8088	b=9+ea w=13+ea
	CMP AL,[SI+2]	80286	6
	CMP BL,[BX+SI]	80386	6
		80486	2

100000sw   oo111mmm   disp   data

	Examples		Clocks
CMP reg,imm	CMP BX,3	8086	4

	CMP DI,1AH	8088	4
	CMP DL,34	80286	3
	CMP BL,'C'	80386	2
		80486	1
CMP mem,imm	CMP DATA,33	8086	10+ea
	CMP LIST,'A'	8088	b=10+ea w=14+ea
	CMP DATA[DI],1	80286	6
		80386	5
		80486	2

0011110w   data

	Examples		Clocks
CMP acc,imm	CMP AX,3	8086	4
	CMP AH,1AH	8088	4
	CMP AL,34	80286	3
		80386	2
		80486	1

CMPS	Compare string		

	Examples	Clocks	
CMPSB	CMPSB	8086	22
CMPSW	REPE CMPSD	8088	b=22 w=30
CMPSD	CMPSW	80286	8
		80386	10
		80486	8

CMPXCHG	Compare and exchange		

00001111 1010011w 11rrrrrr		O D T T S X A P C * * * * * *	

	Examples	Clocks	
CMPXCHG	CMPXCHG EAX,EBX	8086	—
reg,reg		8088	—
		80286	—
		80386	—
		80486	6

00001111 1010011w oorrrmmm			

	Examples	Clocks	
CMPXCHG	CMPXCHG DATA,EAX	8086	—
mem,reg		8088	—
		80286	—
		80386	—
		80486	7

CWD	Convert word to doubleword		

10011001		O D I T S Z A P C	

	Examples	Clocks	
CWD		8086	5
		8088	5
		80286	2
		80386	2

CWDE	Convert word to extended doubleword		

10011000		O D I T S Z A P C	

Examples		Clocks	
CWDE	8086	—	
	8088	—	
	80286	—	
	80386	3	
	80486	3	

DAA	Decimal adjust after addition		

00100111		O D I T S Z A P C ? * * * * *	

Examples		Clocks	
DAA	8086	4	
	8088	4	
	80286	3	
	80386	4	
	80486	2	

DAS	Decimal adjust after subtraction		

00101111		O D I T S Z A P C ? * * * * *	

Examples		Clocks	
DAS	8086	4	
	8088	4	
	80286	3	

		80386	4
		80486	2

DEC	Decrement		

1111111w	oo001mmm disp		O D I T S Z A P C * * * * *

	Examples		Clocks
DEC reg8	DEC BL	8086	3
	DEC AL	8088	3
	DEC DH	80286	2
	DEC CL	80386	2
	DEC CH	80486	1
DEC mem	DEC DATA	8086	15+ea
	DEC WORD PTR [DI]	8088	b=15+ea w=23+ea
		80286	7
		80386	6
		80486	3

01001rrr			

	Examples		Clocks
DEC reg16	DEC AX	8086	3
DEC reg32	DEC BP	8088	3
	DEC EAX	80286	2
	DEC EBX	80386	2
	DEC ECX	80486	1

DIV	Unsigned division		

1111011w oo110mmm disp			O D I T S Z A P C ? ? ? ? ? ?	
	Examples		Clocks	
DIV reg	DIV BL	8086	b=90 w=162	
	DIV CX	8088	b=90 w=162	
	DIV ECX	80286	b=14 w=22	
		80386	b=14 w=22 d=38	
		80486	b=16 w=24 d=40	
DIV mem	DIV DATA	8086	b=96 w=168	
	DIV WORD PTR [DI]	8088	b=96 w=176	
		80286	b=17 w=25	
		80386	b=17 w=25 d=41	
		80486	b=16 w=24 d=40	

ENTER	Make a stack frame			
11001000 data			O D I T S Z A P C	
	Examples		Clocks	
ENTER imm16,0	ENTER 4,0	8086	—	
	ENTER 100,0	8088	—	
		80286	11	
		80386	10	
		80486	14	
ENTER imm16,1	ENTER 8,1	8086	—	
	ENTER 0,1	8088	—	
		80286	15	
		80386	12	
		80486	17	

ENTER imm16,imm8	ENTER 2,5	8086	—
		8088	—
		80286	12+4(n-1)
		80386	15+4(n-1)
		80486	17+41

ESC	Escape		

	Examples		Clocks
ESC imm,reg	ESC 5,al	8086	2
		8088	2
		80286	9-20
		80386	Variable
		80486	Variable
ESC imm,mem	ESC 2,[BP]	8086	8+ea
		8088	b=8+ea w=12+ea
		80286	9-20
		80386	Variable
		80486	Variable

HLT	Halt		

11110100			O D I T S Z A P C

	Examples		Clocks
HLT		8086	2
		8088	2
		80286	2

		80386	5
		80486	4

IDIV	Signed division		

1111011w oo111mmm disp			O D I T S Z A P C ? ? ? ? ?

	Examples		Clocks
IDIV reg	IDIV BL	8086	b=112 w=184
	IDIV CX	8088	b=112 w=184
	IDIV ECX	80286	b= 17 w=25
		80386	b= 19 w=27 d=43
		80486	b= 19 w=27 d=43
IDIV mem	IDIV DATA	8086	b=118 w=190
	IDIV LIST [DI]	8088	b=118 w=194
		80286	b= 20 w=28
		80386	b= 22 w=30 d=46
		80486	b= 20 w=28 d=44

IMUL	Signed multiplication		

1111011w oo101mmm disp			O D I T S Z A P C * ? ? ? ? *

	Examples		Clocks
IMUL reg	IMUL BL	8086	b= 98 w=154
	IMUL CX	8088	b= 98 w=154
	IMUL ECX	80286	b= 13 w=21
		80386	b= 14 w=22 d=38
		80486	b= 18 w=26 d=42
IMUL mem	IMUL DATA	8086	b=104 w=160

	IMUL NUMBER[SI]	8088	b=104 w=164
		80286	b= 16 w=24
		80386	b= 17 w=25 d=41
		80486	b= 18 w=26 d=42

011010sl   oorrrmmm   disp   data

	Examples	Clocks	
IMUL reg,imm	IMUL CX,16	8086	–
	IMUL DX,100	8088	–
	IMUL EAX,20	80286	21
		80386	w= 22 d=38
		80486	w= 22 d=38
IMUL reg,reg,imm	IMUL DX,AX,2	8086	–
		8088	–
		80286	21
		80386	w= 22 d=38
		80486	w= 25 d=38
IMUL reg,mem,imm	IMUL DX,DD,2	8086	–
		8088	–
		80286	24
		80386	w= 22 d=38
		80486	w= 25 d=41

00001111 10101111 oorrrmmm   disp

	Examples	Clocks	
IMUL reg,reg	IMUL CX,DX	8086	–

	IMUL DX,CX	8088	—
	IMUL BP,SI	80286	—
		80386	w=22 d=38
		80486	w=22 d=38
IMUL reg,mem	IMUL CX,[DI]	8086	—
	IMUL EDX,[SI]	80,88	—
		80286	—
		80386	w=22 d=38
		80486	w=25 d=41

IN	Input from port

1110010w data	O D I T S Z A P C

	Examples	Clocks	
IN acc,imm	IN AL,12H	8086	10
	IN AX,34H	8088	b=10 w=14
		80286	5
		80386	12
		80486	9

1110110w

	Examples	Clocks	
IN acc,DX	IN AL,DX	8086	8
	IN AX,DX	8088	b=8 w=12
		80286	5
		80386	13
		80486	8

INC	Increment		

1111111w oo000mmm disp		O D I T S Z A P C * * * * *	
	Examples		Clocks
INC reg8	INC BL	8086	3
	INC AL	8088	3
	INC DH	80286	2
	INC CL	80386	2
		80486	1
INC mem	INC DATA	8086	15+ea
	INC WORD PTR [DI]	8088	b=15+ea w=23+ea
		80286	7
		80386	6
		80486	3

01000rrr			
	Examples		Clocks
INC reg16	INC AX	8086	3
INC reg32	INC BP	8088	3
	INC EAX	80286	2
	INC ECX	80386	2
		80486	1

INS	Input from port to string		

0110110w		O D I T S Z A P C	
	Examples		Clocks

INSB	INSB	8086	—
INSW	INSW	8088	—
INSD	INSD	80286	5
	REP INSB	80386	15
		80486	10

INT	Interrupt		

11001101 data		ODITSZAPC 0 0	

	Examples	Clocks	
INT imm8	INT 21H	8086	51
	INT 20H	8088	71
	INT 10H	80286	23
		80386	37
		80486	30

11001100			

	Examples	Clocks	
INT 3		8086	52
		8088	72
		80286	23
		80386	33
		80486	26

INTO	Interrupt on overflow		

11001110		ODITSZAPC * *	

Examples		Clocks	
INTO		8086	53
		8088	73
		80286	24
		80386	35
		80486	28

INVD	Invalid data cache

00001111 00001000	O D I T S Z A P C

Examples		Clocks	
INVD		8086	—
		8088	—
		80286	—
		80386	—
		80486	4

INVLPG	Invalid TLB entry

00001111 00000001 oo111mmm	O D I T S Z A P C

Examples		Clocks	
INVLPG	INVLPG DATA	8086	—
mem		8088	—
		80286	—
		80386	—
		80486	12

IRET	Interrupt return

11001101 data	O D I T S Z A P C
	* * * * * * * * *

	Examples		Clocks
IRET	IRET	8086	32
IRETD	IRETD	8088	44
	IRET 10H	80286	17
		80386	22
		80486	15

Jconditional Conditional jump

0111cond disp			O D I T S Z A P C

	Examples		Clocks
Jcond label	JB BELOW	8086	16/4
	JG GREATER	8088	16/4
	JE EQUAL	80286	7/3
		80386	7/3
		80486	3/1

00001111 1000cond disp			

	Examples		Clocks
Jcond label	JNE NOT_EQUAL	8086	—
	JS POSITIVE	8088	—
		80286	—
		80386	7/3
		80486	3/1

Condition		Flags	

Codes	MNemonic	Tested	Description
0000	JO	O=1	Jump if overflow
0001	JNO	O=0	Jump if no overflow
0010	JB/JNAE	C=1	Jump if below
0011	JAE/JNB	C=0	Jump if above or equal
0100	JE/JZ	Z=1	Jump if equal
0101	JNE/JNZ	Z=0	Jump if not equal
0110	JBE/JNA	C=1+Z=1	Jump if below or equal
0111	JA/JNBE	C=0•Z=0	Jump if above
1000	JS	S=1	Jump if sign
1001	JNS	S=0	Jump if no sign
1010	JP/JPE	P=1	Jump if parity
1011	JNP/JPO	P=0	Jump if no parity
1100	JL/JNGE	S•O	Jump if less
1101	JGE/JNL	S=O	Jump if greater/equal
1110	JLE/JNG	Z=1+S•0	Jump if less/equal
1111	JG/JNLE	Z=0+S=0	Jump if greater

JCXZ/JECXZ Jump if CX/ECX equals zero

11100011			O D I T S Z A P C

Examples				Clocks
JCXZ label	JCXZ LOTSA		8086	18/6
JECXZ label	JECXZ NEXT		8088	18/6
			80286	8/4
			80386	9/5
			80486	8/5

JMP	Unconditional Jump

11101011	disp		O D I T S Z A P C

	Examples		Clocks
JMP label	JMP SHORT UP	8086	15
(short)	JMP SHORT STEP	8088	15
		80286	7
		80386	7
		80486	3

11101001	disp

	Examples		Clocks
JMP label	JMP .OVER	8086	15
(near)		8088	15
		80286	7
		80386	7
		80486	3

11101010	disp

	Examples		Clocks
JMP label	JMP THREE	8086	15
(far)	JMP FAR PTR HOP	8088	15¯
		80286	11
		80386	12
		80486	17

11111111   oo100mmm

	Examples		Clocks
JMP reg	JMP AX	8086	11
	JMP EAX	8088	11
		80286	7
		80386	7
		80486	3
JMP mem	JMP WORD PTR [BX]	8086	18+ea
	JMP TABLE [SI]	8088	18+ea
		80286	11
		80386	10
		80486	5

11111111   oo101mmm

	Examples		Clocks
JMP mem	JMP FWORD PTR [DI]	8086	24+ea
	JMP WAYOFF	8088	24+ea
		80286	15
		80386	12
		80486	13

LAHF	Load AH from flags		

10011111   O D I T S Z A P C

	Examples		Clocks
LAHF	LAHF	8086	4

		8088	4
		80286	2
		80386	2
		80486	3

LAR	Load access rights		

00001111 00000010 00rrrmmm disp			O D I T S Z A P C *

	Examples		Clocks
LAR reg,reg	LAR AX,BX	8086	—
	LAR EAX,EBX	8088	—
		80286	14
		80386	15
		80486	11
LAR reg,mem	LAR CX,DATA	8086	—
	LAR EDX,LIST	8088	—
		80286	16
		80386	16
		80486	11

LDS	Load far pointer		

11000101 oorrrmmm			O D I T S Z A P C

	Examples		Clocks
LDS reg,mem	LDS DI,PNTR	8086	16+ea
		8088	24+ea
		80286	7
		80386	7

		80486	6
LES	Load far pointer		

11000100	oorrmmm		O D I T S Z A P C

	Examples		Clocks
LES reg,mem	LES BP,WELCOME	8086	16+ea
		8088	24+ea
		80286	7
		80386	7
		80486	6

LFS	Load far pointer		

00001111 10110100	oorrmmm disp		O D I T S Z A P C

	Examples		Clocks
LFS reg,mem	LFS EDI,POINT	8086	—
		8088	—
		80286	—
		80386	7
		80486	6

LGS	Load far pointer		

00001111 10110101 oorrmmm disp			O D I T S Z A P C

	Examples		Clocks
LGS reg,mem	LGS DI,GREAT	8086	—
		8088	—

		80286	—
		80386	7
		80486	6

LSS	Load far pointer		

00001111 10110010 oorrrmmm disp		O D I T S Z A P C	

	Examples		Clocks
LSS reg,mem	LSS SI,GREAT	8086	—
		8088	—
		80286	—
		80386	7
		80486	6

LEA	Load effective address		

10001101 oorrrmmm disp		O D I T S Z A P C	

	Examples		Clocks
LEA reg,mem	LEA DI,DATA	8086	2+ea
		8088	2+ea
		80286	3
		80386	2
		80486	1-2

LEAVE	Procedure exit		

11001001		O D I T S Z A P C	

	Examples		Clocks
LEAVE		8086	—

8088	—
80286	5
80386	4
80486	5

LGDT	Load descriptor table

00001111	00000001	oo010mmm	disp	O D I T S Z A P C

	Examples		Clocks
LGDT mem64	LGDT DESCRIPT	8086	—
		8088	—
		80286	11
		80386	11
		80486	11

LIDT	Load far pointer

00001111	00000001	oo011mmm	disp	O D I T S Z A P C

	Examples		Clocks
LIDT mem64	LIDT DESCRIPT	8086	—
		8088	—
		80286	12
		80386	11
		80486	11

LLDT	Load far pointer

00001111	00000000	oo010mmm	disp	O D I T S Z A P C

	Examples	Clocks	
LLDT reg	LLDT AX	8086	—
		8088	—
		80286	17
		80386	20
		80486	11
LLDT mem	LLDT SELECT	8086	—
		8088	—
		80286	19
		80386	24
		80486	11

LMSW	Load machine status word		

00001111	00000001	oo110mmm disp	O D I T S Z A P C

	Examples	Clocks	
LMSW reg	LMSW AX	8086	—
		8088	—
		80286	3
		80386	10
		80486	2
LMSW mem	LMSW STATUS	8086	—
		8088	—
		80286	6
		80386	13
		80486	3

LOCK	Lock the bus		

11110000			O D I T S Z A P C
	Examples		Clocks
LOCK inst	LOCK XCHG AX,BX	8086	2
		8088	2
		80286	0
		80386	0
		80486	1

LODS	Load string operand

1010110w			O D I T S Z A P C
	Examples		Clocks
LODSB	LODSB	8086	12
LODSW	LODSW	8088	b=12 w=16
LODSD	LODSD	80286	5
		80386	5
		80486	5

LOOP	Loop until CX = 0

11100010	disp		O D I T S Z A P C
	Examples		Clocks
LOOP label	LOOP AGAIN	8086	17/5
		8088	17/5
		80286	8/4
		80386	11
		80486	7/6

LOOPE	Loop while equal		

11100001	disp		O D I T S Z A P C
	Examples		Clocks
LOOPE label	LOOPE BACK	8086	18/6
LOOPZ label	LOOPZ BACK	8088	18/6
		80286	8/4
		80386	11
		80486	9/6

LOOPNE	Loop while not equal		

11100000 disp			O D I T S Z A P C
	Examples		Clocks
LOOPNE label	LOOPNE REPEAT	8086	19/5
LOOPNZ label	LOOPNZ REPEAT	8088	19/5
		80286	8/4
		80386	11
		80486	9/6

LSL	Load segment limit		

00001111 00000011 oorrmmm disp			O D I T S Z A P C *
	Examples		Clocks
LSL reg,reg	LSL AX,BX	8086	—
	LSL EAX,EBX	8088	—
		80286	14
		80386	25

		80486	10
LSL reg,mem	LSL AX,LIMIT	8086	—
	LSL EAX, NUMB	8088	—
		80286	16
		80386	26
		80486	10

LTR	Load task register

00001111 00000000 oo001mmm disp		O D I T S Z A P C

	Examples		Clocks
LTR reg	LSL AX	8086	—
		8088	—
		80286	17
		80386	23
		80486	20
LTR mem	LTR TASK	8086	—
		8088	—
		80286	19
		80386	27
		80486	20

MOV	Move data

100010dw oorrrmm		O D I T S Z A P C

	Examples	Clocks	
MOV reg,reg	MOV CL,BL	8086	2
	MOV BX,DI	8088	2
		80286	2
		80386	2
		80486	1
MOV mem,reg	MOV DATA,DL	8086	9+ea
	MOV DATA1,BX	8088	b= 9+ea w=13+ea
		80286	3
		80386	2
		80486	1
MOV reg,mem	MOV CH,READ	8086	8+ea
	MOV BP,BEETS	8088	b= 8+ea w=12+ea
		80286	5
		80386	4
		80486	1

1100011w	oo000mmm disp data

	Examples	Clocks	
MOV mem,imm.	MOV DATA,12H	8086	10+ea
	MOV LIST,3A33H	8088	b=10+ea w=14+ea
		80286	3
		80386	2

		80486	1

	Examples		Clocks
MOV reg,imm	MOV DL,22H	8086	4
	MOV DX,2222H	8088	4
	MOV DI,OFFSET GO	80286	2
		80386	2
		80486	1

101000dw   disp

	Examples		Clocks
MOV mem,acc	MOV DATA,AL	8086	10
	MOV LIST,AX	8088	b=10 w=14
		80286	3
		80386	2
		80486	'1
MOV acc,mem	MOV AL,LIST	8086	10
	MOV AX,NUMBER	8088	b=10 w=14
		80286	5
		80386	4
		80486	1

```
100011d0   oosssmmm   disp
```

	Examples		Clocks
MOV seg,reg	MOV DS,AX	8086	2
		8088	2
		80286	2
		80386	2
		80486	1
MOV seg,mem	MOV ES,SEGS	8086	8+ea
		8088	b=8+ea w=12+ea
		80286	5
		80386	5
		80486	1
MOV reg,seg	MOV AX,SS	8086	2
		8088	2
		80286	2
		80386	2
		80486	1
MOV mem,seg	MOV LOCAL,SS	8086	9+ea
		8088	b=9+ea w=13+ea
		80286	3
		80386	2
		80486	1

```
00001111    001000d0    11rrrmmm
```

	Examples	Clocks	
MOV reg,cr	MOV EAX,CRO	8086	—
		8088	—
		80286	—
		80386	6
		80486	4
MOV cr,reg	MOV CR2,EBX	8086	—
		8088	—
		80286	—
		80386	4-10
		80486	4

```
00001111    001000d1    11rrrmmm
```

	Examples	Clocks	
MOV reg,dr	MOV EBX,DR6	8086	—
		8088	—
		80286	—
		80386	14-22
		80486	10
MOV dr,reg	MOV DR2,EAX	8086	—
		8088	—
		80286	—
		80386	16-22
		80486	11

```
00001111  001001d0  11rrrmmm
```

	Examples		Clocks
MOV reg,tr	MOV EAX,TR7	8086	—
		8088	—
		80286	—
		80386	12
		80486	3-4
MOV tr,reg	MOV TR6,EBX	8086	—
		8088	—
		80286	—
		80386	12
		80486	4-6

MOVS	Move string data

```
1010010w
```
O D I T S Z A P C

	Examples		Clocks
MOVSB	REP MOVSW	8086	18
MOVSW	REP MOVSD	8088	b=18 w=26
MOVSD	MOVSB	80286	5
		80386	7
		80486	7

MOVSX	Move with sign extend

```
00001111  1011111w  oorrrmmm  disp
```
O D I T S Z A P C

	Examples		Clocks

MOVSX rg,rg	MOSSX BX,AL	8086	—
	MOVSX EAX,BX	8088	—
		80286	—
		80386	3
		80486	3
MOVSX rg,me	MOV CX,MEMORY	8086	—
	MOV EAX,DATA	8088	—
		80286	—
		80386	6
		80486	3

MUL	Unsigned multiplication

```
1111011w  oorrrmmm  disp                          O D I T S Z A P C
                                                  *       ? ? ? ? *
```

	Examples		Clocks
MUL reg	MUL BL	8086	b=77 w=118
	MUL BX	8088	b=77 w=143
	MUL EBX	80286	b=13 w=21
		80386	b=14 w=22 d=38
		80486	b=18 w=26 d=42
MUL mem	MUL DATA	8086	b=83 w=139
		8088	b=83 w=143
		80286	b=16 w=24
		80386	b=17 w=25 d=41
		80486	b=18 w=26 d=42

NEG	Negate

| 1111011w | oo011mmm | disp | O D I T S Z A P C
*   * * * * * |

	Examples	Clocks	
NEG reg	NEG BL	8086	3
	NEG CX	8088	3
	NEG EAX	80286	2
		80386	2
		80486	1
NEG mem	NEG DATA	8086	16+ea
		8088	b=16+ea w=24+ea
		80286	7
		80386	6
		80486	3

| NOP | No operation |

| 10010000 | O D I T S Z A P C |

	Examples	Clocks	
NOP	NOP	8086	3
		8088	3
		80286	3
		80386	3
		80486	3

| NOT | One's complement |

| 1111011w | oo010mmm | disp | O D I T S Z A P C |

	Examples	Clocks	
NOT reg	NOT CL	8086	3

	NOT BX	8088	3
	NOT ECX	80286	2
		80386	2
		80486	1
NOT mem	NOT DATA	8086	16+ea
		8088	b=16+ea w=24+ea
		80286	7
		80386	6
		80486	3

OR	Inclusive OR		

000010dw	oorrrmmm disp	O D I T S Z A P C 0 * * ? ^ 0	
	Examples		Clocks
OR reg,reg	OR CL,BL	8086	3
	OR BX,SI	8088	3
		80286	2
		80386	2
		80486	1
OR mem, reg	OR DATA1,DL	8086	16+ea
	OR LISTX1,BX	8088	b=16+ea w=24+ea
		80286	7
		80386	7
		80486	3
OR reg,mem	OR CH,READ_DATA	8086	9+ea
	OR BP,WATTS	8088	b= 9+ea w=13+ea
		80286	7

		80386	6
		80486	2

100000sw	oo001mmm	disp	data		

	Examples		Clocks
OR reg,imm	OR CL,3	8086	4
	OR DX,44H	8088	4
		80286	3
		80386	2
		80486	1
OR mem,imm	OR DATA,2222H	8086	17+ea
		8088	b=17+ea w=25+ea
		80286	7
		80386	7
		80486	3

	Examples		Clocks
OR acc,imm	OR AL,3	8086	4
	OR AX,44H	8088	4
		80286	3
		80386	2
		80486	1

OUT	Output data to port		

1110011w	data		O D I T S Z A P C

	Examples		Clocks
OUT imm,acc	OUT 10H,AL	8086	10
	OUT 20H,AX	8088	14
		80286	3
		80386	10
		80486	10

1110111w

	Examples		Clocks
OUT DX,acc	OUT DX,AL	8086	8
	OUT DX,AX	8088	12
		80286	3
		80386	11
		80486	10

OUTS	Output string data to port

0110111w   O D I T S Z A P C

	Examples		Clocks
OUTSB	REP OUTSB	8086	—
OUTSW		8088	—
OUTSD		80286	5
		80386	14
		80486	10

POP	Pop data from stack

01011rrr   O D I T S Z A P C

	Examples	Clocks	
POP reg	POP AX	8086	8
	POP EBX	8088	12
		80286	5
		80386	4
		80486	1

10001111   oo000mmm   disp

	Examples	Clocks	
POP mem	POP DATA	8086	17+ea
		8088	25+ea
		80286	5
		80386	5
		80486	4

00sss111

	Examples	Clocks	
POP seg	POP ES	8086	8
		8088	12
		80286	5
		80386	7
		80486	3

00001111   10sss001

Examples   Clocks

POP seg	POP FS	8086	—
	POP GS	8088	—
		80286	—
		80386	7
		80486	3

POPA/PAPAD	Pop all

01100001			O D I T S Z A P C
	Examples		Clocks
POPA	POPA	8086	—
POPAD	POPAD	8088	—
		80286	19
		80386	24
		80486	9

POPF/POPFD	Pop flags

10011101			O D I T S Z A P C
			* * * * * * * * *
	Examples		Clocks
POPF	POPF	8086	8
POPFD	POPFD	8088	12
		80286	5
		80386	5
		80486	6

PUSH	Push data onto stack

01010 rrr	O D I T S Z A P C

	Examples	Clocks	
PUSH reg	PUSH DX	8086	11
	PUSH ECX	8088	15
		80286	3
		80386	2
		80486	1

11111111   oo110mmm   disp

	Examples	Clocks	
PUSH mem	PUSH COUNT	8086	16+ea
		8088	24+ea
		80286	5
		80386	5
		80486	4

00sss110

	Examples	Clocks	
PUSH seg	PUSH DS	8086	10
		8088	14
		80286	3
		80386	2
		80486	3

00001111   10sss000

Examples		Clocks

PUSH seg	PUSH FS	8086	—
	PUSH GS	8088	—
		80286	—
		80386	2
		80486	3

| 011010s0 | data | | |

	Examples		Clocks
PUSH imm	PUSH 2000H	8086	—
		8088	—
		80286	3
		80386	2
		80486	1

| PUSHA/PUSHAD | Push all | | |

| 01100000 | | | O D I T S Z A P C |

	Examples		Clocks
PUSHA	PUSHA	8086	—
PUSHAD		8088	—
		80286	17
		80386	18
		80486	11

| PUSHF/PUSHFD | Push flags | | |

| 10011100 | | | O D I T S Z A P C |

	Examples	Clocks	
PUSHF	PUSHF	8086	10
PUSHFD		8088	14
		80286	3
		80386	4
		80486	3

RCL/RCR/ROL/ROR   Rotate

1101000w	ooTTTmmm disp		O D I T S Z A P C * *

TTT = 000 = ROL
TTT = 001 = ROR
TTT = 010 = RCL
TTT = 011 = RCR

	Examples	Clocks	
ROL reg,1	ROR AL,1	8086	2
ROR reg,1	ROL AX,1	8088	2
		80286	2
		80386	3
		80486	3
RCL reg,1	RCL DL,1	8086	2
RCR reg,1	RCR CX,1	8088	2
		80286	2
		80386	9
		80486	3
ROL mem,1	ROL DATA,1	8086	15+ea
ROR mem,1	ROR LIST,1	8088	23+ea
		80286	7
		80386	7

		80486	4
RCL mem,1	RCL NUMBER,1	8086	15+ea
RCR mem,1	RCR DAIRY,1	8088	23+ea
		80286	7
		80386	10
		80486	4

1101001w   ooTTTmmm   disp

	Examples		Clocks
ROL reg,CL	ROL DX,CL	8086	8+4n
ROR reg,CL	ROR BX,CL	8088	8+4n
		80286	5+n
		80386	3
		80486	3
RCL reg,CL	RCL DL,CL	8086	8+4n
RCR reg,CL	RCR CX,CL	8088	8+4n
		80286·	5+n
		80386	9
		80486	8
ROL mem,CL	ROL DATA,CL	8086	20+ea+4n
ROR mem,CL	ROR LIST,CL	8088	28+ea+4n
		80286	8+n
		80386	7
		80486	4
RCL mem,CL	RCL NUMBER,CL	8086	20+ea+4n
RCR mem,CL	RCR SHOES,CL	8088	28+ea+4n
		80286	8+n

		80386	10
		80486	9

1100000w	ooTTTmmm disp data		
	Examples		Clocks
ROL reg,imm	ROL DX,6	8086	—
ROR reg,imm	ROR BX,12	8088	—
		80286	5+n
		80386	3
		80486	2
RCL reg,imm	RCL DL,3	8086	—
RCR reg.imm	RCR CX,4	8088	—
		80286	5+n
		80386	9
		80486	8
ROL mem,imm	ROL NUMBER,9	8086	—
ROR mem,imm	ROR,SHOES,2	8088	—
		80286	8+n
		80386	7
		80486	4
RCL mem,imm	RCL NUMBER,6	8086	—
RCR mem,imm	RCR MOOSE,3	8088	—
		80286	8+n
		80386	10
		80486	9
REP	Repeat prefix		

11110010 1010010w			O D I T S Z A P C
	Examples		Clocks
REP MOVS	REP MOVSB	8086	9+17n
	REP MOVSW	8088	b=9+17n w=9+25n
		80286	5+4n
		80386	8+4n
		80486	12+3n

11110010 1010101w

	Examples		Clocks
REP STOS	REP STOSB	8086	9+10n
	REP STOSW	8088	b=9+10n w=9+14n
		80286	4+3n
		80386	5+5n
		80486	7+4n

11110010 0110110w

	Examples		Clocks
REP INS	REP INSB	8086	—
	REP INSW	8088	—
		80286	5+4n
		80386	13+6n
		80486	16+8n

11110010   0110111w

	Examples		Clocks
REP OUTS	REP OUTSB	8086	—
	REP OUTSW	8088	—
		80286	5+4n
		80386	12+5n
		80486	17+5n

REPE/REPNE	Repeat conditional

11110011	1010011w		O D I T S Z A P C
			*

	Examples		Clocks
REPE CMPS	REPE CMPSB	8086	9+22n
	REPE CMPSW	8088	b=9+22n w=9+30n
		80286	5+9n
		80386	5+9n
		80486	7+7n

11110011 1010111w

	Examples		Clocks
REPE SCAS	REPE SCASB	8086	9+15n
	REPE SCASW	8088	b=9+15n w=9+19n
		80286	5+8n
		80386	5+8n
		80486	7+5n

11110010 1010011w

	Examples		Clocks
REPNE CMPS	REPNE CMPSB	8086	9+22n
	REPNE CMPSW	8088	b=9+22n w=9+30n
		80286	5+9n
		80386	5+9n
		80486	7+7n

11110010	1010111w

	Examples		Clocks
REPNE SCAS	REPNE SCASB	8086	9+15n
	REPNE SCASW	8088	b=9+15n w=9+19n
		80286	5+8n
		80386	5+8n
		80486	7+5n

RET	Return

11000011	O D I T S Z A P C

	Examples		Clocks
RET		8086	16
(near)		8088	20
		80286	11
		80386	10
		80486	5

11000010

	Examples	Clocks	
RET imm	RET 4	8086	20
		8088	24
(near)		80286	11
		80386	10
		80486	5

11001011

	Examples	Clocks	
RET		8086	26
		8088	34
(far)		80286	15
		80386	18
		80486	13

11001010

	Examples	Clocks	
RET imm	RET 100	8086	25
		8088	33
(far)		80286	15
		80386	18
		80486	14

SAHF	Store AH in flags	

		O D I T S Z A P C
10011110		* * * * *

	Examples	Clocks

SAHF		8086	4
		8088	4
		80286	2
		80386	3
		80486	2

SAL/SAR/SHL/SHR Shift

1101000w	ooTTTmmm	disp		O D I T S Z A P C
				* * * ? * *

```
TTT = 100 = SHL/SAL
TTT = 101 = SHR
TTT = 111 = SAR
```

	Examples	Clocks	
SAL reg,1	SAL DL,1	8086	2
SHL reg,1	SHL CX,1	8088	2
SHR reg,1	SHR BP,1	80286	2
SAR reg,1	SAR SI,1	80386	3
		80486	3
SAL mem,1	SAL NUMBER,1	8086	15+ea
SHL mem,1	SHL DAIRY,1	8088	b=15+ea w=23+ea
SHR mem,1	SHR MASK,1	80286	7
SAR mem,1	SAR FROG,1	80386	7
		80486	4

1101001w	ooTTTmmm	disp	

	Examples	Clocks	
SAL reg,CL	SAL DL,CL	8086	8+4n
SHL reg,CL	SHL CX,CL	8088	8+4n

SHR reg,CL	SHR BX,CL	80286	5+n
SAR reg,CL	SAR DX,CL	80386	3
		80486	3
SAL mem,CL	SAL NUMBER,CL	8086	20+ea+4n
SHL mem,CL	SHL SHOES,CL	8088	28+ea+4n
SHR mem,CL	SHR BOOTS,CL	80286	8+n
SHR mem,CL	SAR NICE,CL	80386	7
		80486	4

1100000w	ooTTTmmm disp data		
	Examples		Clocks
SAL reg,imm	SAL DL,3	8086	—
SHL reg,imm	SHL CX,4	8088	—
SHR reg,imm	SHR AX,3	80286	5+n
SAR reg,imm	SAR BL,2	80386	3
		80486	2
SAL mem,imm	SAL NUMBER,6	8086	—
SHL mem,imm	SHL MOOSE,3	8088	—
SHR mem,imm	SHR DATA,15	80286	8+n
SAR mem,imm	SAR WATER,2	80386	7
		80486	4

SBB	Subtract with borrow		
000110dw	oorrrmmm disp		O D I T S Z A P C * * * * * *
	Examples		Clocks

SBB reg,reg	SBB BL,CL	8086	3
	SBB CX,DX	8088	3
		80286	2
		80386	3
		80486	1
SBB mem,reg	SBB DATA,DL	8086	16+ea
	SBB LIST,CX	8088	b=16+ea w=24+ea
		80286	7
		80386	6
		80486	3
SBB reg,mem	SBB DL,DATA	8086	9+ea
	SBB CX,LIST	8088	b= 9+ea w=13+ea
		80286	7
		80386	7
		80486	2

100000sw   oo011mmm   disp   data

	Examples		Clocks
SBB reg,imm	SBB DH,3	8086	4
	SBB DX,33H	8088	4
		80286	3
		80386	2
		80486	1
SBB mem,imm	SBB DATA,4AH	8086	17+ea
		8088	b=17+ea w=25+ea
		80286	7
		80386	7

		80486	3

0001110w	data		

	Examples	Clocks	
SBB acc,imm	SBB AL,33H	8086	4
	SBB AX,42H	8088	4
		80286	3
		80386	2
		80486	1

SCAS	Scan string		

1010111w		O D I T S Z A P C
		* * * * * *

	Examples	Clocks	
SCASB	REPE SCASB	8086	15
SCASW	REPNE SCASW	8088	b=15 w=19
SCASD		80286	7
		80386	7
		80486	6

SET	Set conditional		

00001111 1001cond oo000mmm		O D I T S Z A P C

	Examples	Clocks	
SET cd,reg8	SETA BL	8086	—
	SETZ DH	8088	—
		80286	—

		80386	4
		80486	3
SET cd,mem8	SETB DATA	8086	–
	SETS FLAG	8088	–
		80286	–
		80386	5
		80486	3

Condition Codes	Mnemonic	Flags Tested	Description
0000	SETO	O=1	Set if overflow
0001	SETNO	O=0	Set if no overflow
0010	SETB/SETNAE	C=1	Set if below
0011	SETAE/SETNB	C=0	Set if above or equal
0100	SETE/SETZ	Z=1	Set if equal
0101	SETNE/SETNZ	Z=0	Set if not equal
0110	SETBE/SETNA	C=1+Z=1	Set if below or equal
0111	SETA/SETNBE	C=0•Z=0	Set if above
1000	SETS	S=1	Set if sign
1001	SETNS	S=0	Set if no sign
1010	SETP/SETPE	P=1	Set if parity
1011	SETNP/SETPO	P=0	Set if no parity
1100	SETL/SETNGE	S•O	Set if less
1101	SETGE/SETNL	S=0	Set if greater/equal
1110	SETLE/SETNG	Z=1+S•O	Set if less/equal
1111	SETG/SETNLE	Z=0+S=0	Set if greater

SGDT/SIDT/SLDT Store descriptor table

00001111 00000001 oo000mmm disp			O D I T S Z A P C

	Examples		Clocks
SGDT mem	SGDT MEMORY	8086	—
		8088	—
		80286	11
		80386	9
		80486	10

00001111 00000001 oo001mmm disp			

	Examples		Clocks
SIDT mem	SIDT MEMORY	8086	—
		8088	—
		80286	12
		80386	9
		80486	10

00001111 00000000 oo000mmm disp			

	Examples		Clocks
SLDT reg	SLDT CX	8086	—
		8088	—
		80286	2
		80386	2
		80486	2
SLDT mem	SLDT SAVE_IT	8086	—

		8088	—
		80286	3
		80386	2
		80486	3

SHLD/SHRD	Double precision shift

```
00001111    10100100    oorrrmmm

disp        data
```

```
O  D  I  T  S  Z  A  P  C
?           *  *  ?  *  *
```

	Examples		Clocks
SHLD	SHLD AX,CX,10	8086	—
reg,reg,imm		8088	—
		80286	—
		80386	3
		80486	2
SHLD	SHLD DATA,DX,3	8086	—
mem,reg,imm		8088	—
		80286	—
		80386	7
		80486	3

```
00001111    10101100    oorrrmmm    disp    data
```

	Examples		Clocks
SHRD	SHRD CX,DX,4	8086	—
reg,reg,imm		8088	—
		80286	—
		80386	3
		80486	2

SHRD	SHRD DATA,CX,10	8086	—
		8088	—
mem,reg,imm		80286	—
		80386	7
		80486	3

0000111 10100101 oorrrmmm disp

	Examples		Clocks
SHLD	SHLD AX,BX,CL	8086	—
		8088	—
reg,reg,CL		80286	—
		80386	3
		80486	3
SHLD	SHLD DATA,AX,CL	8086	—
		8088	—
mem,reg,CL		80286	—
		80386	7
		80486	4

00001111 10101101 oorrrmmm disp

	Examples		Clocks
SHRD	SHRD SI,DX,CL	8086	—
		8088	—
reg,reg,CL		80286	—
		80386	3
		80486	3

SHRD	SHRD DATE,DX,CL	8086	—
mem,reg,CL		8088	—
		80286	—
		80386	7
		80486	4

SMSW	Store machine status word		

00001111 00000001 oo100mmm disp		O D I T S Z A P C	
	Examples	Clocks	
SMSW reg	SMSW DI	8086	—
		8088	—
		80286	2
		80386	10
		80486	2
SMSW mem	SMSW PLACE	8086	—
		8088	—
		80286	3
		80386	3
		80486	3

STC	Set carry flag		

11111001		O D I T S Z A P C	
	Examples	Clocks	
STC		8086	2
		8088	2

	80286	2
	80386	2
	80486	2

STD	Set direction flag	

11111101		O D I T S Z A P C 1

	Examples		Clocks
STD		8086	2
		8088	2
		80286	2
		80386	2
		80486	2

STI	Set interrupt flag	

11111011		O D I T S Z A P C 1

	Examples		Clocks
STI		8086	2
		8088	2
		80286	2
		80386	3
		80486	5

STOS	Store string data	

1010101w		O D I T S Z A P C

	Examples	Clocks	
STOSB	REP STOSB	8086	11
STOSW		8088	b=11 w=15
STOSD		80286	3
		80386	4
		80486	5

STR	Store task register

00001111 00000000 oo001rrr	O D I T S Z A P C

	Examples	Clocks	
STR reg	STR DX	8086	—
		8088	—
		80286	2
		80386	2
		80486	2
STR mem	STR SAFE_PLACE	8086	—
		8088	—
		80286	3
		80386	2
		80486	3

SUB	Subtract

001010dw oorrrmmm disp	O D I T S Z A P C * * * * * *

	Examples	Clocks	
SUB reg,reg	SUB BL,CL	8086	3

	SUB CX,DX	8088	3
		80286	2
		80386	2
		80486	1
SUB mem,reg	SUB DATA,DL	8086	16+ea
	SUB LIST,CX	8088	b=16+ea w=24+ea
		80286	7
		80386	6
		80486	3
SUB reg,mem	SUB DL,DATA	8086	9+ea
	SUB CX,LIST	8088	b= 9+ea w=13+ea
		80286	7
		80386	7
		80486	2

100000sw   oo101mmm   disp   data

	Examples		Clocks
SUB reg,imm	SUB DH,3	8086	4
	SUB DX,33H	8088	4
		80286	3
		80386	2
		80486	1
SUB mem,imm	SUB DATA,4AH	8086	17+ea
		8088	b=17+ea w=25+ea
		80286	7
		80386	7

		80486	3
0010110w data			

	Examples	Clocks	
SUB acc,imm	SUB AL,33H	8086	4
	SUB AX,42H	8088	4
		80286	3
		80386	2
		80486	1
TEST	Logical compare		

1000011w	oorrmmm disp	O D I T S Z A P C 0 * * ? * 0	

	Examples	Clocks	
TEST	TEST BL,CL	8086	3
reg,reg	TEST CX,DX	8088	3
		80286	2
		80386	2
		80486	1
TEST	TEST DATA,DL	8086	9+ea
mem,reg	TEST LIST,CX	8088	b=9+ea w=13+ea
reg,mem	TEST AX,GOOD	80286	6
		80386	5
		80486	2
1111011w	oo000mmm disp data		

	Examples		Clocks
TEST	TEST DL,1	8086	5
reg,imm	TEST CX,10H	8088	5
		80286	3
		80386	2
		80486	1
TEST	TEST DATA,100H	8086	11+ea
mem,imm		8088	11+ea
		80286	6
		80386	5
		80486	2

1010100w   data

	Examples		Clocks
TEST	TEST AL,2	8086	4
acc,imm	TEST AX,64	8088	4
		80286	3
		80386	2
		80486	1

VERR/VERW   Verify read or write

00001111   00000000   oo100mmm   disp   O D I T S Z A P C
                                              *

	Examples		Clocks
VERR reg	VERR BX	8086	—
		8088	—
		80286	14

		80386	10
		80486	11
VERR mem	VERR DATA	8086	—
		8088	—
		80286	16
		80386	11
		80486	11

00001111   00000000   oo101mmm   disp

	Examples		Clocks
VERW reg	VERW CX	8086	—
		8088	—
		80286	14
		80386	15
		80486	11
VERW mem	TEST DATA,100H	8086	—
		8088	—
		80286	16
		80386	16
		80486	11

WAIT	Wait for test pin

10011011   O D I T S Z A P C

	Examples		Clocks
WAIT		8086	4

	8088	4
	80286	3
	80386	6
	80486	6

WBINVD	Write back and invalidate data cache

00001111 00001001   O D I T S Z A P C

	Examples		Clocks
WBINVD		8086	—
		8088	—
		80286	—
		80386	—
		80486	5

XADD	Exchange and add

00001111 1100000w 11rrrrrr
```
                                                         O D I T S Z A P C
                                                         *       * * * * *
```

	Examples		Clocks
XADD	XADD EAX,EBX	8086	—
reg,reg		8088	—
		80286	—
		80386	—
		80486	3

00001111 1100000w   oorrrmmm

	Examples		Clocks

XADD	XADD DATA,EAX	8086	—
mem,reg		8088	—
		80286	—
		80386	—
		80486	4

XCHG	Exchange data		

1000011w	oorrrmmm disp		O D I T S Z A P C
	Examples		Clocks
XCHG	XCHG CL,BL	8086	4
reg,reg	XCHG DX,CX	8088	4
		80286	3
		80386	3
		80486	3
XCHG	XCHG CL,DATA	8086	17+ea
reg,mem	XCHG DATA,CL	8088	b=17+ea w=25+ea
mem,reg		80286	5
		80386	5
		80486	5

10010rrr			
	Examples		Clocks
XCHG	XCHG AX,CX	8086	3
reg,acc	XCHG BX,AX	8088	3
acc,reg		80286	3

		80386	3
		80486	3

XLAT	Translate		

11010111			O D I T S Z A P C

	Examples		Clocks
XLAT		8086	11
		8088	11
		80286	5
		80386	5
		80486	4

XOR	Exclusive OR		

001100dw	oorrmmm disp		O D I T S Z A P C 0 * * ? * 0

	Examples		Clocks
XOR reg,reg	XOR BL,CL	8086	3
	XOR CX,DX	8088	3
		80286	2
		80386	2
		80486	1
XOR mem,reg	XOR DATA,DL	8086	16+ea
	XOR LIST,CX	8088	b=16+ea w=24+ea
		80286	7
		80386	6
		80486	3

XOR reg,mem	XOR DL,DATA	8086	9+ea
	XOR CX,LIST	8088	b= 9+ea w=13+ea
		80286	7
		80386	7
		80386	2

100000sw   oo110mmm   disp   data

	Examples		Clocks
XOR reg,imm	XOR DH,3	8086	4
	XOR DX,33H	8088	4
		80286	3
		80386	2
		80486	1
XOR mem,imm	XOR DATA,4AH	8086	17+ea
		8088	b=17+ea w=25+ea
		80286	7
		80386	7
		80486	3

0011010w   data

	Examples		Clocks
XOR acc,imm	XOR AL,33H	8086	4
	XOR AX,42H	8088	4
		80286	3
		80386	2
		80486	1

APPENDIX C

Flag Bit Changes

(Only instructions that actually change the flags are listed)

Instruction	O	D	I	T	S	Z	A	P	C
Flags									
AAA	?				?	?	*	?	*
AAD	?				*	*	?	*	?
AAM	?				*	*	?	*	?
AAS	?				?	?	*	?	*
ADC	*				*	*	*	*	*
ADD	*				*	*	*	*	*
AND	0				*	*	?	*	0
ARPL						*			
BSF						*			
BSR						*			
BT									*
BTC									*
BTR									*
BTS									*
CLC									0
CLD		0							
CLI			0						
CMC									*
CMP	*				*	*	*	*	*
CMPXCHG	*				*	*	*	*	*
DAA	?				*	*ₗ	*	*	*
DAS	?				*	*	*	*	*
DEC	*				*	*	*	*	
DIV	?				?	?	?	?	?
IDIV	?				?	?	?	?	?
IMUL	*				?	?	?	?	*
INC	*				*	*	*	*	
INT			0	0					
INTO				*	*				
IRET	*	*	*	*	*	*	*	*	*
LAR						*			
LSL						*			

Instruction	Flags								
MUL	*				?	?	?	?	*
NEG	*				*	*	*	*	*
OR	0				*	*	?	*	0
POPF/POPFD	*	*	*	*	*	*	*	*	*
RCL/RCR	*								*
ROL/ROR	*								*
SAHF					*	*	*	*	*
SAL/SAR	*				*	*	?	*	*
SHL/SHR	*				*	*	?	*	*
SBB	*				*	*	*	*	*
SCAS	*				*	*	*	*	*
SHLD/SHRD	?				*	*	?	*	*
STC									1
STD		1							
STI			1						
SUB	*				*	*	*	*	*
TEST	0				*	*	?	*	0
VERR/VERW						*			
XADD	*				*	*	*	*	*
XOR	0				*	*	?	*	0

APPENDIX D

The 8- and 16-bit Personal Computer Buses

This appendix defines the buses of common personal computers. The buses illustrated are for the 8-bit XT-style computer and the 16-bit AT-style computer. Figure D–1 illustrates the 8-bit bus version and Figure D–2 illustrates the 16-bit bus version. Notice that the top portion of the AT connector is identical to the XT connector. This allows 8-bit bus cards to fit into the 16-bit bus connector.

FIGURE D–1 The 8-bit XT-style edge connector.

Rear of computer

	B	A	
GND	B1	A1	IO CHCK
RESET DRV	B2	A2	SD7
+5VDC	B3	A3	SD6
IRQ9	B4	A4	SD5
-5VDC	B5	A5	SD4
DRQ2	B6	A6	SD3
-12VDC	B7	A7	SD2
OWS	B8	A8	SD1
+12VDC	B9	A9	SD0
GND	B10	A10	IO CHRDY
SMEMW	B11	A11	AEN
SMEMR	B12	A12	SA19
IOW	B13	A13	SA18
IOR	B14	A14	SA17
DACK3	B15	A15	SA16
DRQ3	B16	A16	SA15
DACK1	B17	A17	SA14
DRQ1	B18	A18	SA13
REFRESH	B19	A19	SA12
CLK	B20	A20	SA11
IRQ7	B21	A21	SA10
IRQ6	B22	A22	SA9
IRQ5	B23	A23	SA8
IRQ4	B24	A24	SA7
IRQ3	B25	A25	SA6
DACK2	B26	A26	SA5
T/C	B27	A27	SA4
BALE	B28	A28	SA3
+5VDC	B29	A29	SA2
OSC	B30	A30	SA1
GND	B31	A31	SA0

Component side edge connector

FIGURE D–2 The 16-bit
AT-style bus connector.

Rear of computer

GND	B1	A1	IO CHCK
RESET DRV	B2	A2	SD7
+5VDC	B3	A3	SD6
IRQ9	B4	A4	SD5
-5VDC	B5	A5	SD4
DRQ2	B6	A6	SD3
-12VDC	B7	A7	SD2
OWS	B8	A8	SD1
+12VDC	B9	A9	SD0
GND	B10	A10	IO CHRDY
SMEMW	B11	A11	AEN
SMEMR	B12	A12	SA19
IOW	B13	A13	SA18
IOR	B14	A14	SA17
DACK3	B15	A15	SA16
DRQ3	B16	A16	SA15
DACK1	B17	A17	SA14
DRQ1	B18	A18	SA13
REFRESH	B19	A19	SA12
CLK	B20	A20	SA11
IRQ7	B21	A21	SA10
IRQ6	B22	A22	SA9
IRQ5	B23	A23	SA8
IRQ4	B24	A24	SA7
IRQ3	B25	A25	SA6
DACK2	B26	A26	SA5
T/C	B27	A27	SA4
BALE	B28	A28	SA3
+5VDC	B29	A29	SA2
OSC	B30	A30	SA1
GND	B31	A31	SA0

MEMCS16	D1	C1	SBHE
IOCS16	D2	C2	LA23
IRQ10	D3	C3	LA22
IRQ11	D4	C4	LA21
IRQ12	D5	C5	LA20
IRQ15	D6	C6	LA19
IRQ14	D7	C7	LA18
DACK0	D8	C8	LA17
DRQ0	D9	C9	MEMR
DACK5	D10	C10	MEMW
DRQ5	D11	C11	SD08
DACK6	D12	C12	SD09
DRQ6	D13	C13	SD10
DACK7	D14	C14	SD11
DRQ7	D15	C15	SD12
+5VDC	D16	C16	SD13
MASTER	D17	C17	SD14
GND	D18	C18	SD15

Component side edge connector

APPENDIX E

Programmable Logic Devices

The PAL *(programmable array logic)*, PLA *(programmable logic array)*, or GAL *(generic array logic)* decoder is available in many different versions for use as decoders and other circuit elements. The PAL, PLA, and GAL look exactly like a PROM decoder in a system because they require no additional circuitry to implement as the PROM decoder. The difference is the way that the decoder is internally constructed.

Figure E–1 illustrates the internal structure of a PAL10L8 device. The PAL is programmed by burning fuses just as the PROM is programmed. PALs contain logic gates that can be wired to perform functions. Many PAL circuits also contain flip-flops and many other digital circuits that allow complex functions to be programmed into the PAL. PALs are often called *glue* because they connect microprocessors, memory, and other circuits together without the use of any additional logic gates or circuits.

The PAL illustrated in Figure E–1 has 10 input pins and 8 output pins. Each input pin has its true and inverted form that can be connected to any output. For example, if you look closely at input I1 you will notice that there are two outputs from the buffer. One output is in true form and the other is inverted. A close look at output $\overline{I1}$ will show an X connection to one input of the NOR gate connected to pin 19 or O1. The other pin on the NOR gate is connected to three places: I2, I4, and I5. These three connections are wire-anded together so that they form an AND gate. The output function found on O1 is $\overline{I1}$ + I2 · I4 · I5. None of the other outputs are wired in this illustration.

Programming any PAL is accomplished through software rather than through the logic diagram illustrated in Figure 7–10 (a). This is fortunate because the logic circuit, for some advanced PAL circuits, contains many logic gates. Example E–1 illustrates the software required to program the 10L8 illustrated in Figure E–1. Notice that this is a very short program that is easy to understand. This listing is produced with any word processor. The output of the word processor must be set to produce a clean ASCII file. A *clean ASCII file* is one that doesn't contain control characters.

Example E–1 illustrates the exact steps required to set up a file that is used to program the PAL. Notice that the first six instructions set up information that identifies the project and author's name. These steps must be included in the file. The CHIP statement

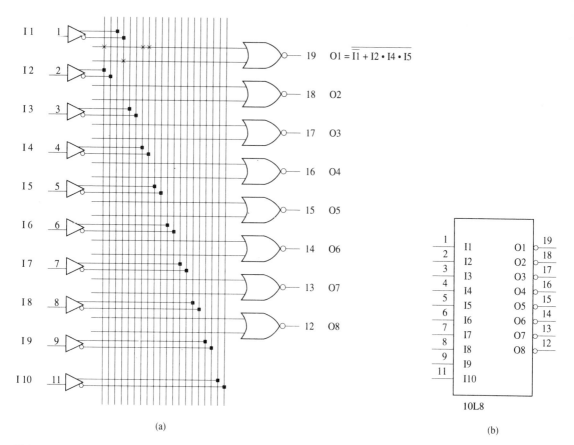

FIGURE E–1   The internal structure of the PAL10L8 (a) showing O1 programmed as an AND–NOR gate with the logic function illustrated. The pinout (b) of the PAL10L8.

identifies the name of the circuit (gates), which can be anything, and the PAL type. Next the pins are defined with any name that the author desires. Finally, the equations for the PAL are entered. Note that the / is used to indicate inversion, an * is used for AND, and a + is used to indicate OR. So the equation illustrated, /O1 = /I1 + I2 * I4 * I5, matches the equation in Figure E–1. The equation also can be entered as O1 = /(/I1 + I2 * I4 * I5).

EXAMPLE E–1

```
TITLE       Example
PATTERN     Test
REVISION    A
AUTHOR      BARRY BREY
COMPANY     DeVRY
DATE        7/7/90
CHIP Gates PAL10L8

;PINS       1  2  3  4  5  6  7  8  9 10
            I1 I2 I3 I4 I5 I6 I7 I8 I9 GND
```

```
;PINS        11 12 13 14 15 16 17 18 19 20
             I10 08 07 06 05 04 03 02 01 VCC

EQUATIONS
/01 = /I1+I2*I4*I5
```

E–1 USING THE PAL TO INTERFACE MEMORY

The PAL is a useful tool when interfacing memory to a system. Once the design is accomplished, using the same techniques as for a decoder or a PROM, the logic equations are formed and written in the programming file.

Suppose that a memory system for the 8088 is designed so that it contains a 32K × 8 EPROM at locations F8000H–FFFFFH, and two 32K × 8 RAMs at locations 00000H–07FFFH and 08000–0FFFFH. This design would require two decoders to implement. If a PAL is used it is implemented with a single PAL.

Example E–2 illustrates the program required for programming the PAL10L8 to function as memory selection logic for this memory system. Notice that input pins have been labels A19, A18, A17, A16, A15, and IOM. These are the signals from the microprocessor required to decode these three memory areas. The outputs have been labeled ROM, RAM1, and RAM2.

EXAMPLE E–2

```
TITLE       Decoder
PATTERN     Test
REVISION    A
AUTHOR      BARRY BREY
COMPANY     DeVRY
DATE        7/7/90
CHIP Decode PAL10L8

;PINS        1   2   3   4   5   6   7  8  9  10
             A19 A18 A17 A16 A15 IOM NC NC NC GND

;PINS        11 12   13    14    15 16 17 18 19 20
             NC ROM RAM1 RAM2 NC NC NC NC NC VCC

EQUATIONS
/ROM  = A19*A18*A17*A16*A15*/IOM
/RAM1 = /A19*/A18*/A17*/A16*/A15*/IOM
/RAM2 = /A19*/A18*/A17*/A16*A15*/IOM
```

The program illustrates that ROM is an active low output (/ROM). The equation for the ROM output shows that address connections A19–A15 must all be logic 1s for /ROM to become a logic 0. This comes from the address range of F8000H–FFFFFH for the ROM. Notice that the first five bits must be logic 1s to select the ROM for this section of the memory. In addition, the IOM (IO/$\overline{\text{M}}$) signal must also be a logic 0. The remaining outputs are arrived at in exactly the same manner.

Using the same methodology and programming techniques, other decoders can be designed. In order to program the PAL a PAL programmer is purchased. Software that interprets the PAL programs is also needed to program the PAL. One source of such a programmer and for programming software is Advanced Micro Devices, Inc. (AMD), which also manufactures the PALS. The examples in this appendix follow the software guidelines provided by AMD. They assume that the PALASM (PAL assembler) program from AMD is used for programming the PAL device.

APPENDIX F

Answers to Selected Odd-Numbered Questions

Chapter 1

1. The early 4-bit microprocessors were very limited because of their speed, memory size, and instruction sets.
3. The 8-bit microprocessors were improved by adding instructions to their instruction sets and increasing their speed and memory.
5. 1M bytes or 512K words.
7. The BIU is the *bus interface unit,* and its purpose is to transfer data between the 8086/8088 and the system memory and I/O.
9. 6 and 4.
11. 1M.
13. 2.
15. The logical memory is arranged in bytes and numbered from location 00000H to location FFFFFH. The physical memory is arranged in two banks of bytes with the high bank containing all the odd-numbered memory locations and the low bank containing all the even-numbered memory locations.
17. AH, AL, BH, BL, CH, CL, DH, and DL.
19. CX is called the count because, for certain instructions, it contains the count of repeated operations.
21. IP (instruction pointer) is used along with the CS (code segment) register to address instructions in the program. SP (stack pointer) is used along with the SS (stack segment) register to address the LIFO stack memory for PUSH, POP, CALL, and RET instructions. BP (base pointer) is used along with the SS register to address data in the stack segment. DI (destination index) is used with the DS (data segment) register to address memory data or the ES (extra segment) register to address memory data for string operations. SI (source index) is used along with the DS register to address data for memory or string operations.
23. Memory segments may overlap on 16-byte boundaries. A 16-byte boundary is often called a *paragraph*.
25. 12340H + 0100H = 12440H.

27. Data and extra.
29. Z (zero flag) indicates that the result of an arithmetic or logic operation is 0. S (sign flag) indicates the arithmetic sign of the result of an arithmetic or logic operation. P (parity flag) indicates the parity of the result of an arithmetic or logic operation. C (carry flag) indicates a carry or a borrow after an arithmetic operation and is cleared by a logic operation. A (auxiliary flag) indicates a carry or borrow from bit position 3 to 4 after an arithmetic operation and is cleared by logic operations.
31. An overflow occurs when the signed result of an addition or subtraction is too large to be contained in the destination register or memory location.
33. True.
35. 04000H = 34H, 04001H = 12H, 04002H = 00H, and 04003H = 10H.

Chapter 2

1. (a) Copies the contents of BX into AX. (b) Copies the contents of AX into BX. (c) Copies the contents of CH into BL. (d) Copies the contents of DI into SP. (e) Copies the contents of AX into CS (this instruction is illegal, but it will function).
3. AX, BX, CX, DX, SP, BP, DI, SI, CS, DS, SS, and ES.
5. You may not move a 16-bit register into an 8-bit register.
7. You may not move anything into the CS (code segment) register.
9. A MOV AL, address instruction.
11. Brackets [] indicate that a pointer or index register is used to address data in the memory. The contents of the register indicated in the [] holds the offset address of the data.
13. Memory-to-memory moves are not allowed.
15. (a) 21100H. (b) 10100H. (c) 21000H.
17. (a) 11750H. (b) 11950H. (c) 11700H.
19. Short (within + 127 – – 128), near (within the code segment), and far (anywhere in the memory).
21. (a) Short. (b) Long. (c) Short. (d) Direct.
23. JMP [DI] if DI = TABLE.
25. The PUSH [DI] instruction pushes the 16-bit word addressed by the DI register from the memory to the stack.

Chapter 3

1. Opcode.
3. The type of addressing used with the instruction such as: register, 8-bit displacement, 16-bit displacement, and no displacement.
5. [BX + DI].
7. MOV AX,[BX].
9. 8B3702
11. 16-bit move immediate with a 16-bit displacement.
13. Code segment register (CS).
15. 01FFFH = BH, and 01FFEH = BL.
17. SP = 0000H, and SS = 0220H.

19. The only difference is the amount of time required by the 8086/8088 to execute these instructions. The LEA instruction requires more time to execute than the MOV.

21. The contents of memory location DATA and DATA + 1 are loaded into BX, and the contents of DATA + 2 and DATA + 3 are loaded into DS.

23. See Example F–1.

EXAMPLE F–1

```
MOV BX,DATA
MOV DS,BX
MOV SI,BX
```

25. STD sets the direction flag, and CLD clears it.

27. The LODSB instruction will load the AL register with the byte of data stored at the memory location addressed by the SI register within the data segment. After the load, the contents of SI are incremented by a 1.

29. The REP prefix causes a string operation to be repeated CX number of times.

31. See Example F–2.

EXAMPLE F–2

```
MOV CX,12
MOV DI,OFFSET DEST
MOV SI,OFFSET SOURCE
CLD
REP MOVSB
```

33. Not normally, because they are designed to be used when 8085 software is converted to 8086/8088 software.

35. The contents of I/O port address 12H are copied into the accumulator.

37. MOV AH,ES:[BX].

39. DB defines a byte or bytes of memory, DW defines a word or words of memory, and DD defines a doubleword or doublewords of memory.

41. The EQU (equate) directive equates a label to a value or to another label.

43. PROC and ENDP.

45. In a system that uses PC-DOS, the INT 20H instruction terminates execution of a program and returns control to the operating system.

Chapter 4

1. (a) ADD AX,BX. (b) ADD AL,12H. (c) ADD BP,DI. (d) ADD CX,22H. (e) ADD AL,[SI]. (f) ADD CL,[BX + 2]. (g) ADD FROG,CX.

3. Not directly; the only instructions that allow any segment register to be used are MOV, PUSH, and POP.

5. See Example F–3.

EXAMPLE F-3

```
ADD  AL,BL
ADD  AL,CL
ADD  AL,DL
ADD  AL,AH
MOV  DH,AL
```

7. ADC BC,BX.
9. The assembler doesn't know where the byte or word in memory is incremented.
11. Difference = 81H, C = 0, A = 0, P = 1, O = 0, S = 1, and Z = 0.
13. DEC BL.
15. The only difference between a subtract and a compare is that the difference is lost in a compare and only the flag bits change to reflect the value of the difference.
17. The most significant portion of the product is found in DX, and the least significant portion is found in AX.
19. The MUL instruction multiplies unsigned numbers, and the IMUL instruction multiplies signed numbers.
21. AL.
23. Division by a 0 and an overflow.
25. AX.
27. DAA, DAS, AAM, and AAD.
29. AAM is used after two unpacked BCD numbers are multiplied to give the correct BCD product in AX.
31. (a) AND BX,DX. (b) AND DH,OEAH. (c) AND DI,BP. (d) AND AX,1122H. (e) AND [BP],CX. (f) AND DX,[SI − 4]. (g) AND WHAT,AL.
33. (a) OR AH,BL. (b) OR CX,88H. (c) OR SI,DX. (d) OR BP,1122H. (e) OR [BX],CX. (f) OR AL,[BP+40]. (g) OR WHEN,AH.
35. (a) XOR AH,BH. (b) XOR CL,99H. (c) XOR DX,DI. (d) XOR SP,0A122H. (e) XOR [BX],DX. (f) XOR DX,[BP+30]. (g) XOR WELL,DI.
37. Both instructions perform the AND operation except that the logical product is lost with the TEST instruction. TEST modifies the flag bits to reflect the logical product.
39. (a) SHR DI. (b) SHL AL. (c) ROL SI. (d) RCR DX. (e) SAR DH.
41. The extra segment (ES).
43. The REPE instruction repeats a string operation as long as the zero flag bit indicates an equal condition.
45. The CMPSB instruction compares the bytes of data stored at the address pointed to by DI in the extra segment with the data stored in the location addressed by SI in the data segment. After the comparison, the contents of both DI and SI are incremented by a 1.

Chapter 5

1. A short jump goes between +127 bytes from the next opcode and −128 bytes from the next opcode.
3. The far jump or, as it is called, the intersegment jump.
5. (a) Near. (b) Far. (c) Far. (d) Near. (e) Far. (f) Near.
7. The far jump changes both the CS and IP registers.

9. The JMP DI instruction jumps to the address stored in DI, and the JMP [DI] instruction jumps to the address stored in the memory location addressed by DI.

11. Short.

13. JO will jump to the label only if the overflag is set.

15. The JCXZ instruction jumps if the CX register is equal to a 0000H.

17. The LOOPE instruction decrements the contents of CX each time it is encountered. If CX is not a zero and the zero flag bit indicates an equal condition, then a jump to the label occurs.

19. See Example F–4.

EXAMPLE F–4

```
CMP CX,0400H
JA   NEXT
```

21. A far CALL pushes the contents of the CS and IP registers onto the stack and then jumps to the new offset and segment address stored in the memory following the CALL opcode.

23. RET.

25. PROC.

27. The RET 6 instruction POPs either IP from the stack or IP and CS, depending on whether it is near or far. After the POP or POPs, a 6 is added to the contents of the SP register.

29. See Example F–5.

EXAMPLE F–5

```
PROG     NEAR PROC
         MOV  AX,DI
         MUL  SI
         PUSH SI
         MOV  SI,100H
         DIV  SI
         POP  SI
         RET
PROG     ENDP
```

31. INT, INT3, or INTO.

33. Interrupt vector 0 is used by the divide instruction for a divide-by-0 or an overflow.

35. The INT 40H instruction calls the interrupt service procedure whose address is stored at memory location 100H–103H.

37. An overflow condition (0 = 1).

39. The WAIT instruction.

41. The OBJ file is generated by the assembler from the source file.

43. An assembly language file is first assembled by the assembler and then linked by the linker to create an execution file.

45. SEGMENT identifies the start of a segment.

47. ENDS.

49. The return address is set up by pushing DS onto the stack followed by a 0.
51. The PUBLIC statement creates a module that can be added to any other module when linking a program.
53. It connects library modules and program modules into one execution file.

Chapter 6

1. The differences are: 8-bit data bus on the 8088 versus a 16-bit data bus on the 8086; IO/$\overline{\text{M}}$ on the 8088 versus M/$\overline{\text{IO}}$ on the 8086; and $\overline{\text{BHE}}$ on the 8086 versus no $\overline{\text{BHE}}$ on the 8088.
3. (a) 1. (b) 10. (c) 10. (d) 10.
5. S_3 and S_4 indicate what segment is used for the current bus cycle.
7. The WAIT instruction performs no operation if the $\overline{\text{TEST}}$ pin is a logic 0 and waits if $\overline{\text{TEST}}$ is a logic 1.
9. Maximum mode.
11. Never.
13. The address, data, and control buses all go to their high-impedance states. After this, the HLDA pin becomes a logic 1.
15. The $\overline{\text{LOCK}}$ pin (found in maximum mode only) becomes a logic 0 for the duration of an instruction that is prefixed with LOCK.
17. Clock generation, RESET synchronization, and READY synchronization.
19. The timing signal is applied to the external frequency input (EFI).
21. Zero.
23. A_7-A_0 and $A_{19}-A_{16}$.
25. $\overline{\text{BHE}}$ selects the odd bank (high bank) of memory.
27. DT/$\overline{\text{R}}$.
29. 1 µs.
31. 5 MIPS maximum burst.
33. 460 ns.
35. Wait.
37. $\overline{\text{AEN}}$ = 0, and RDY$_1$ = 1.
39. It generates the system control signals for the memory and the I/O.

Chapter 7

1. Address pins, input/output or output pins, and selection pins.
3. (a) 2048, 4-bit numbers. (b) 1024, 1-bit numbers. (c) 4096, 8-bit numbers. (d) 16,384, 1-bit numbers. (e) 65,536, 4-bit numbers.
5. The $\overline{\text{OE}}$ pin turns on the output buffers of a ROM or a RAM for reading memory data.
7. (a) 1K × 8. (b) 2K × 8. (c) 4K × 8. (d) 8K × 8. (e) 8K × 8.
9. Static random access memory.
11. 250 ns.
13. The 16-bit memory address is forced into the address pins 8 bits at a time.
15. 2–4 ms.
19. All 8 output pins are at a logic 1 level.
23. The PROM address decoder is found because it reduces the component count, which often reduces the cost and always reduces the size of a system.

25. See Table F–1.
31. Odd parity is generated with a parity generator and stored in an extra bit of the memory. It is checked when read from the memory by a parity checker. Note that the EVEN output of the parity generator is used to generate odd parity.
33. SEF indicates a single-bit error.
35. The 8086 data bus is 16 bits wide, and the 8088 data bus is 8 bits wide.
37. Separate decoders for each memory bank or separate write strobes for each memory bank.
39. Even or low bank.
43. DRAM can be refreshed while other sections of the memory are read or written.
45. CA_7–CA_0 and MA_7–MA_0.
47. The 8086/8088 $\overline{WR}$ signal.

Chapter 8

1. Data flow from the I/O device to the microprocessor for an IN and from the microprocessor to the I/O device for an OUT.
3. In register DX.
5. Isolated I/O is a separate map of 64K different I/O devices accessed by an IN or an OUT instruction. Memory-mapped I/O uses any memory reference instruction to access the I/O devices that are treated as memory locations.
7. The basic output interface is a decoder that selects and applies a clock pulse to the clock input of a latch. The latch captures the contents of either AL or AX and holds it for the external system.
9. The main difference is the selection signal $\overline{IO}/M$ on the 8088 and $M/\overline{IO}$ on the 8086.
15. Generally, this reduces the need for more than one I/O port decoder.
17. The $\overline{BHE}$ and A_0 signals select 8-bit banks of memory that don't exist for a 16-bit I/O operation.
21. Group A $= PA_7 - PA_0$ and $PC_7 - PC_4$. Group B $= PB_7 - PB_0$ and $PC_3 - PC_0$.
25. Basic I/O, strobed I/O, and bidirectional I/O.

TABLE F–1 PROM programming bit pattern for address range 3C000H–3FFFFH

| | | | | Inputs | | | | | | | | | Outputs | | | | |
$\overline{G}$	A_8	A_7	A_6	A_5	A_4	A_3	A_2	A_1	A_0	O_0	O_1	O_2	O_3	O_4	O_5	O_6	O_7
0	0	0	1	1	1	1	0	0	0	0	1	1	1	1	1	1	1
0	0	0	1	1	1	1	0	0	1	1	0	1	1	1	1	1	1
0	0	0	1	1	1	1	0	1	0	1	1	0	1	1	1	1	1
0	0	0	1	1	1	1	0	1	1	1	1	1	0	1	1	1	1
0	0	0	1	1	1	1	1	0	0	1	1	1	1	0	1	1	1
0	0	0	1	1	1	1	1	0	1	1	1	1	1	1	0	1	1
0	0	0	1	1	1	1	1	1	0	1	1	1	1	1	1	0	1
0	0	0	1	1	1	1	1	1	1	1	1	1	1	1	1	1	0

27. The $\overline{\text{STB}}$ signal strobes data into an internal latch where it is held until the microprocessor removes it.
29. See Example F–6.

EXAMPLE F–6

```
MOV     AL,00001111B    ;select bit seven for set
OUT     CONTROL,AL
```

31. Output buffer fill ($\overline{\text{OBF}}$) is cleared by an output to the port and set when the data are strobed from the port with $\overline{\text{STB}}$.
33. Group A.
35. The PCLK output of the 8284A clock generator chip.
37. See Example F–7.
39. See Example F–8.

EXAMPLE F–7

```
MOV     AL,00111110B    ;set clock divider to 30
OUT     CONTROL,AL
```

EXAMPLE F–8

```
;
;this procedure assumes the data to be looked up is in
;the AL register.  Upon return AL holds the ASCII code.
;
LOOKUP      PROC    NEAR
            MOV     BX,OFFSET TABLE     ;address table
            XLAT                        ;lookup ASCII code
            RET
LOOKUP      ENDP
```

41. 10 MHz.
43. See Example F–9.

EXAMPLE F–9

```
;procedure that will cause timer 2 of figure D-9 to generate a
;KHz squarewave with a 2.5 MHz clock.
;
TIMER_2     PROC    NEAR
            MOV     AL,10110110B        ;select timer 2
            OUT     83H,AL
            MOV     AL,0C4H             ;count = 2500
```

```
                    OUT       82H,AL
                    MOV       AL,09H
                    OUT       82H,AL
                    RET
TIMER_2     ENDP
```

45. Least significant byte must be first.
47. Mode 2.
49. Backwards.
51. See Example F–10.
53. The baud rate is the number of bits transmitted or received per second. These bits include data, parity, start, and stop.
55. The 8251A is reset by sending its command port a series of three logic 0s followed by a 04H.

EXAMPLE F–10

```
;
;procedure that programs the 8251A for 6 data bits,
;even parity, 1 stop bit, and a baud rate divider of 1.
;
USART   PROC          NEAR
                MOV       AL,0        ;reset 8251A
                OUT       21H,AL
                OUT       21H,AL
                OUT       21H,AL
                MOV       AL,4
                OUT       21H,AL
                MOV       AL,01110101B
                RET
USART   ENDP
```


Chapter 9

1. An interrupt interrupts the program that is currently executed by the 8086/8088.
3. An interrupt calls an interrupt service procedure.
5. NMI, INTR, and $\overline{\text{INTA}}$.
7. An interrupt vector is a 32-bit number that contains the address of the interrupt service procedure.
9. 256.
11. A type 0 interrupt occurs whenever a division by zero is attempted or whenever the quotient is too large.
13. 110H–113H.
15. (1) Flags are pushed onto the stack. (2) I and F are cleared to 0. (3) CS and IP are pushed onto the stack. (4) The interrupt vector is fetched from memory and placed into CS and IP.

17. I is set and cleared with the STI and CLI instructions.
19. T is set and cleared with the STD and CLD instructions.
21. $\overline{\text{INTA}}$ is never active for an NMI interrupt input.
23. Positive-edge sensitive.
25. An FIFO is a memory that stores data on a first-in, first-out basis.
27. If the data bus is pulled up to a logic 1 whenever an interrupt acknowledge occurs, the contents of the data bus are an FFH.
29. It must be polled because any interrupt request signal causes the same type of interrupt. Polling determines exactly which interrupt output of the 8255A caused the interrupt.
31. The 8259A is a programmable interrupt controller (PIC).
33. An output that controls the data bus transceivers.
35. The slave INTR output is connected to one of the master's IR inputs.
37. Operation command word.
39. T_7-T_3 of ICW_2.
41. OCW_1 both sets and clears the interrupt masks if written or reads the interrupt masks if read.
43. The nonspecific end-of-interrupt command causes whichever interrupt that was accepted to be cleared or ended.
45. The IRR indicates which interrupt requests are pending.

Chapter 10

1. DMA transfer is used to transfer data at higher speeds than possible with software—up to 10M bytes per second with modern memory components.
3. The speed of the DMA transfer is mainly limited by the speed of the system memory.
5. The HLDA acknowledge signal indicates that the 8086/8088 is in the hold condition with its address, data, and control buses at their high-impedance states.
7. This circuit synchronizes the HOLD input to the 8086/8088 microprocessor.
9. Memory, I/O device.
11. These three signals cannot be used for a DMA transfer because it is impossible to do a memory read at the same time as an I/O write occurs or a memory write at the same time that an I/O read occurs.
13. The 74LS247 is a quad, 2-line to 1-line multiplexer. When B is high for an I/O operation, the $\overline{\text{RD}}$ and $\overline{\text{WR}}$ signals are steered through to the $\overline{\text{IOR}}$ and $\overline{\text{IOW}}$ output pins. When B is low for a memory operation, the $\overline{\text{RD}}$ and $\overline{\text{WR}}$ signals are steered to the $\overline{\text{MEMW}}$ output pins. During a hold, HLDA is a logic 1, which disables the output pins of this multiplexer.
15. 4.
17. The DREQ pins request DMA channel attention.
19. 1.
21. Bit 0 enables or disables memory-to-memory transfers, bit 1 causes the address in channel 0 to be held constant, bit 2 enables or disables the controller, bit 3 selects normal or compressed timing, bit 4 selects fixed or rotating priority, bit 5 selects late or extended write, bit 6 sets the activity level of the DREQ pins, and bit 7 selects the activity level of the DACK outputs.

23. Used to request a software DMA action.
25. Disabled.
27. After the F/L flip-flop is cleared, the least significant portion of the count followed by the most significant part of the count is programmed. After the count is programmed, the DMA address is programmed least significant portion first.
29. See Example F–11.
31. Source, destination.
33. Channel 0.

EXAMPLE F–11

```
;
;procedure that programs DMA channel 2 for an address
;of 2345H and a count of 123H.
;

PROG          PROC    NEAR
              OUT     1 CH,AL            ;clear F/L
              MOV     AL,45H             ;program DMA address
              OUT     14H,AL
              MOV     AL,23H
              OUT     14H,AL
              MOV     AL,22H             ;program count
              OUT     15H,AL
              RET
PROG          ENDP
```

35. DACK.

Chapter 11

1. Integer, real, and BCD.
3. A BCD number is stored in 10 bytes of memory. The most significant byte contains the sign of the number, and the remaining 9 bytes contain 18 packed BCD digits.
5. (a) 01000001 11100010 00000000 00000000. (b) 01000100 00011100 00000000 00000000. (c) 10111111 00100000 00000000 00000000. (d) 00000000 00000000 00000000 00000000. (e) 11000100 01111011 11100000 00000000.
7. Memory-read and memory-write operations.
9. This input connects the 8087 to the 8086/8088.
11. 68.
13. Whenever a comparison operation is used.
15. Disable.
17. The chop mode of rounding removes the fractional portion of a mixed number without affecting the integer portion.
19. Escape.
21. The top of the stack is copied into the short floating-point form stored at memory location DATA.

23. FADD ST,ST(3).
25. Stores the 10-byte-long BCD number, copied from the top of the stack, into the memory location DATA.
27. FTST subtracts a 0 from the number at the top of the stack and indicates a few conditions while FXAM examines the number at the top of the stack and gives complete information about it.
29. FLDPI.
31. The FSAVE instruction stores the contents of all the internal registers in the memory.
33. See Example F–12.
35. See Example F–13.

EXAMPLE F–12

```
;
;procedure that finds the area of a rectangle
;
AREA          PROC          NEAR
              FLD           L
              FLD           W
              FMULP         ST,ST(1)
              FSTP          A
              RET
AREA          ENDP
```

EXAMPLE F–13

```
;
;procedure that finds the square roots of the integers
;2 through 10 and stores them in memory as short floating
;point number at memory locations through TABLE through
;TABLE+8
;
TWO           DW      ?
TABLE   DD    10      (DUP) (?)
;
ROOT          PROC    NEAR
              MOV     BX,OFFSET TABLE     ;address TABLE
              MOV     CX,9                ;load count
              MOV     TWO,2               ;save a 2
AGAIN:  FILD          TWO                 ;find a square root
              FSQRT
              FSTP    DWORD PTR[BX]       ;save result and POP
              ADD     BX,4                ;modify pointer
              INC     TWO                 ;generate next integer
              LOOP    AGAIN
              RET
ROOT          ENDP
```

Chapter 12

1. The main difference is some additional reserved software interrupt vectors on the 80186/80188 that are not present in the 8086/8088.
3. A leadless chip carrier (LCC).
5. If the $\overline{RD/QSMD}$ pin is grounded, the queue status becomes available on the ALE and $\overline{WR}$ pins.
7. 4.
9. The amount of memory access time provided by the microprocessor determines the type of memory selected.
11. IMUL immediate differs because it has three operands: the destination, the immediate byte or word, and the source. The source register or memory location data and immediate byte are multiplied and the 16-bit product is stored in the destination register.
13. The INSB inputs byte data to the AL register from the memory address located by the SI register in the data segment. After the data are input, the contents of SI are incremented by a 1.
15. A BOUND interrupt occurs if the number in DI is not greater than the number stored in memory location NUMBER or less than the number stored in memory location NUMBER + 2.
17. See Example F–14.

EXAMPLE F–14

```
MOD        PROC     NEAR
           MOV      AX,0100000100000000B     ;setup new address
           MOV      DX,OFFFEH                ;address current
                                             ;relocation reg
           OUT      DX,AX                    ;change location
           RET
MOD        ENDP
```

19. Five interrupt inputs are present: INT_0–INT_4 and NMI.
21. The interrupt control register selects priority level. In master-mode operation, the interrupt control register also selects special nested mode, cascade mode, and level-trigger mode.
23. The difference is that, when the interrupt poll register is read, the interrupt is acknowledged, and when the interrupt poll status register is read, no interrupt acknowledge occurs.
25. This register specifies the five most significant bits of the interrupt type number.
27. Timers 0 and 1.
29. If both maximum-count registers are used, the counter counts to the maximum in max-count register A and then to the maximum in max-count register B. This is repeated until the timer is reprogrammed.
31. The P bit selects whether the clock source for timer 0 or timer 1 is external, internal at ¼ of the system of the system clock, or the output of timer 2.

33. The timer output pins generate either square waves or pulses.
35. Two channels.
37. The SR/$\overline{\text{STOP}}$ bit starts and stops DMA transfers.
39. Seven.
41. 00000H.
43. 0 and 3.
45. If EX is a logic 0, pins $\overline{\text{PCS}}_5$ and $\overline{\text{PCS}}_6$ are used as latched address bits A_0 and A_1.
47. 1G bytes of memory.
49. Descriptors define the use of the virtual memory space.
51. 16 MHz.

Chapter 13

1. 4G bytes.
3. The 80386DX contains a full 32-bit address and data bus. The 80386SX contains a 24-bit address bus and a 16-bit data bus.
5. The 80386 has increased drive on its output connections when compared to the 8086/8088.
7. The address bus becomes a FFFFFFF0H after a hardware reset. The most significant pins remain high until a far jump or far call instruction is encountered.
9. A cache memory stores all information as it is read from the memory. If a location is read a second time, the microprocessor reads the data from the cache. This increases system speed because the cache memory is constructed with high-speed static RAM.
11. 800000F8H to 800000FFH.
13. 40 MHz.
15. FS and GS.
19. DR0–DR3 are used to hold linear breakpoint addresses. DR6 is the debug status register. DR7 is the debug control register.
21. The BSF instruction scans a word or doubleword for the first one bit. The number of the first one bit is stored in the destination register.
23. The SHRD instruction shifts a word or doubleword right from one register to another.
25. Scaled index addressing allows a scaling factor of 1, 2, 4, or 8, to be used as a multipler for an 80386 index register.
27. (a) EBX is added to eight times ECX. (b) EAX is added to EBX. (c) DATA is the address. (d) EBX is the address.
29. Exception 13.
31. The interrupt descriptor table.
33. A selector addresses a descriptor in either the local or global descriptor table. It also specifies the requested privlege level.
35. The global descriptor table register
37. It addresses this amount of virtual memory because 16K different descriptors are stored in two descriptor tables. Each descriptor defines a 4G bytes section of the memory. 16K times 4G is 64T bytes of memory.
39. The TSS contains the state of the system.
41. The switch is made after the IDT and GDT registers are loaded and descriptors are placed in these tables. The switch itself is accomplished by setting the PE bit of CR0.

43. Paging is accessed by setting the PE bit in CR0.
45. The paging table is used in reassigning the linear address (D0000000H) to the physical address (C0000000H).
47. The AC flag is set if an attempt is made to address a word on an odd memory boundary or a doubleword on a non-doubleword boundary.
49. No.
51. When data are written to memory, it is written to memory and to the cache.
53. 2K.

INDEX

632